MAN

MONEY

&

MEDICINE

AN AMERICAN

MIGRATORY ECOLOGICAL
&
ECONOMIC HISTORY

Ralph John DiLibero, MD

2017
ISBN-10
0--9815969-8-3
ISBN-13
978-0-9815969-8-3

Printed and bound in Canada

Dedication:

To
Heidi

At the relatively innocent and perhaps naïve age of 14, my daughter Heidi requested parental assistance to compose a dull and tedious 300-word high school homework assignment, a single page paragraph to answer the question, "What is Medicare?". Man, Money and Medicine ultimately launched as an unintended consequence, a paternal penalty resulting from a loving father's quick, trite and off-the-cuff response to his daughter's query. I was driven by torment to deliver more exacting additional explanations, all fostered by my daughter's continued and unrelenting successive queries concerning my overly simplistic answer to the homework question. What was my now historic initial floweret-like response? -- "Medicare is just one result of a continual dynamic migratory economic force in America that defines and redefines capitalistic production and value in terms of evolving societal norms for health and the art of living."

Disclaimer -- Renunciation

Introductions

MAN

"Two different sets of philosophers have attempted to teach us this hardest of all the lessons of morality. One set have laboured to increase our sensibility to the interests of others; another, to diminish that to our own. The first would have us feel for others as we naturally feel for ourselves. The second would have us feel for ourselves as we naturally feel for others. Both, perhaps, have carried their doctrines a good deal beyond the just standard of nature and propriety.....There is, however, one virtue of which the general rules determine with the greatest exactness every external action which it requires. This virtue is justice.....(Virtue is more to be feared than vice, because its excesses are not subject to the regulation of conscience.).....The rules of justice are accurate in the highest degree, and admit of no exceptions or modifications, but such as may be ascertained as accurately as the rules themselves, and which generally, indeed, flow from the very same principles with them......When the happiness or misery of others depends in any respect upon our conduct, we dare not, as self-love might suggest to us, prefer the interest of one to that of many."

--- "The Theory of Moral Sentiments"   Adam Smith (1723 --1790)

However, multiple documented eons of historical evidence and data concerning the well-contemplated devious and destructive actions of Man give little support to the supposed "Ideal Interests of Man"; and societal definitions of "Justice" tend to vary along with the indiscriminate prevailing winds of time that blow ever-evolving mythological standards. Economist T. R. Malthus (1776–1834) predicted future dismal consequential relationships between Man's ever-increasing biomass and the required cost of welfare to sustain the voracious diet of such a population. Industrialization brought up the moral/ethical/survival conflicts between Man's dependence upon versus Man's depletion of his global environment. The mores and ethics of Man continue to follow a migratory economic course determined by Man's evolving economics and politics, while recidivistically differing and contradicting themselves at any particular chosen point in time during Man's acknowledged ephemeral existence on planet earth.....

MONEY AND MEDICINE

Money and Medicine comprise common interchangeable commodities that define, visualize and express a metaphorical difficult-to-balance scale that continually is labored upon to weigh a capriciously perceived "worth" of Man. The "fiscal wealth" of Man vies against the "physical/mental wealth" of Man for his "joie de vivre" and "art of living" – while also providing an unending contest for an ultimate worldly prize -- Man's combined wealth -- whimsically determined by a wrestling match between Man's migratory economics and Man's health.   The selfish addicting natures of Man's desires and wants conspire to claim, guard and hoard all of Mother Earth's cookies and pleasures, but the intellect of Man sadly recognizes that all those possessions can never be for a creature such as Man.....

During most of the 19th Century in America, a cooperative or collaborative effort from varied economically migrating groups of early and naïve healthkeepers accomplished a somewhat primitive data-based and surely technological-lacking, yet still inspiring form of **Healthcare Reform**, a satisfactory Healthcare Delivery mechanism for the growing population of the USA at that time: The Clergy took on the serious responsibility for treating mental health and the associated illness as well as accomplishing mental health rehabilitation. Midwives routinely delivered babies at home with lower infection rates than identical deliveries performed in hospitals. Barbers performed the suturing of lacerations and hung red, white and Solferino blue-purple bloody bandages to dry on a pole outside their shops -- the barber pole. The traumatic injuries incurred from and treated in military battle trained the very best surgeons. The highly respected Apothecary took a medical history, prescribed a course of medical treatment, and then formulated-prepared and sold-dispensed material medica (drugs) to the many types of "doctor" healthkeepers and also directly to the general populace. Immigrant groups settled in housing project-sections and organized "Lodges" for social services and healthcare delivery to their constituents. Silver-tongued Snake Oil Salesmen abounded in traveling and migrating Medicine shows, hocking a multitude of "OTC" or "over the counter" cure-all elixir remedies, none of which were derived from the traditional cure-all, the ancient Chinese water snake. Hospitals were feared by many, as places where people went to die. The Biblical meaning of "physician" included the concept of "teacher" and academic-oriented physicians of the day predominantly took on a truly professorial role rather than a direct hands-on healer or medical practitioner assignment. The healthcare delivery tasks of an overly-demanded country doctor were continually expanding and the good doctor often took on an apprentice or two to help with and eventually take over all his former "doctors' duties" upon his retirement, which usually coincided with the day of his death. The many correspondent, apprentice and formal academic schools for training a medical doctor or practicing physician varied greatly in their medical philosophy, methodology and efficacy. There was no real opportunity to compile substantial wealth-Money through the hands-on practice of general Medicine. One thing was for sure and painfully obvious -- there existed a continually expanding vital need within a demographically divergent and growing populace for all varied types of practicing healthcare professionals, healthkeepers – all generally termed and greatly respected within the American society of that century as "doctors".

The 20th Century in America told a remarkable tale of healthkeeper and healthcare delivery condensations and federally enforced economic migrations – the all too many unique and anachronous American trial and error experiments with **Healthcare Reform**: Changing cultural and economic values mixed with ever-expanding technological knowledge to create positive yet severely disruptive evolutionary forces that demanded the course of healthcare delivery adapt to, or else falter in the United States. The role of an expanding hospital system evolved to treatment centers for all types of maladies. At the brink of **Healthcare Reforms**, healthcare providers and recipients economically and physically migrated in varied dynamic-advantaged directions, all pursuing what they felt to be economically and functionally best for themselves and their families. Restrictive federal governmental policies created an economic and cultural barrier to **Healthcare Reform** by discouraging the advancement of and eliminating many of those former 19th Century diverse economically and functionally driven migrations for healthcare delivery. An opportunistic window of opportunity opened for wealth-Money to be gleaned through the hands-on practice of general Medicine, but much more Money could be earned by those possessing the entrepreneurial and economic interest to organize and administrate that practice of Medicine. The American populace stood on the high cliff edges of a great battlefield valley from which they continually witnessed opposing governmental forces do battle in a **hundred-year Healthcare Reform war** against and in face of an uncontrolled chain-reactive explosion of technology, public knowledge and proven specialized training and outcomes.

The 21st Century brought back to American healthcare delivery the former cooperative or collaborative expansion effort for **Healthcare Reform** that once existed in the heart of Man and in the migratory economics of Money that had been in place during the 19th Century: Those varied but not forgotten interest groups, all types of healthkeepers, became exquisitely trained 21st Century specialized professionals, all working to accomplish their time-honored healing task and duty, utilizing and providing high-tech primary care healthcare delivery through a new but actually old recycled mechanism for Healthcare Delivery. The four-year standardized formal academic schools for training a medical doctor or practicing physician were transformed into two and three year clinical-apprentice programs from enrollment day one. There was once again no real opportunity to compile substantial wealth-Money solely through the hands-on practice of general Medicine. Migratory economic forces, Men, Money and Medicine, sub-divided hospitals into more efficient individualized centers for specific types, acuities and intensities of disease processes. Diverse and quality-driven cost-effective mechanisms evolved to more than satisfy the medically necessary needs for a well-informed migrating public in the USA, then transformed into migratory marketable commodities for assisting growing the new national migratory economies on a global scale.

Hoarding versus spending Money in the quest of the ultimate human desire for health/wealth and longevity above all else resulted in a never-ending contest between individuals versus society, a continual compromising battle for Man.

"Medicare is just one result of a continual dynamic migratory economic force in America that defines and redefines capitalistic production and value in terms of evolving societal norms for health and the art of living."

The expected and rational goal or end-game of **Healthcare Reform** is to enhance one's abilities – that prized ability to enjoy an increased longevity and that health-necessary enablement ability to strive for and pursue happiness. As such, **Healthcare Reform** enjoys an intimate relationship with economics and shares a long history of reforms associated with economic changes and preferences driven by Man, Money and Medicine. Through that exciting and intertwining complex history, a simple story becomes unraveled and revealed – **The Migratory Economics of Healthcare Reform – Man, Money and Medicine.**

MAN

THE DYNAMIC SOCIETAL ECOLO-NOMIC EVOLUTION MECHANISM

DRIVING

THE MYTHS AND MORES OF MAN

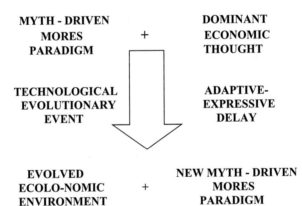

MYTH - DRIVEN MORES PARADIGM	+	DOMINANT ECONOMIC THOUGHT
TECHNOLOGICAL EVOLUTIONARY EVENT		ADAPTIVE- EXPRESSIVE DELAY
EVOLVED ECOLO-NOMIC ENVIRONMENT	+	NEW MYTH - DRIVEN MORES PARADIGM

MONEY

THE DYNAMIC SOCIETAL ECOLO-NOMIC EVOLUTION MECHANISM

DRIVING

ECONOMIC EQUILIBRIUM THEORY PARADIGMS

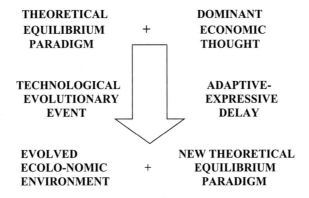

THEORETICAL EQUILIBRIUM PARADIGM	+	DOMINANT ECONOMIC THOUGHT
TECHNOLOGICAL EVOLUTIONARY EVENT		ADAPTIVE-EXPRESSIVE DELAY
EVOLVED ECOLO-NOMIC ENVIRONMENT	+	NEW THEORETICAL EQUILIBRIUM PARADIGM

MEDICINE

THE DYNAMIC SOCIETAL ECOLO-NOMIC EVOLUTION MECHANISM

DRIVING

HEALTHCARE REFORM

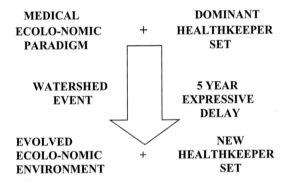

MEDICAL ECOLO-NOMIC PARADIGM	+	DOMINANT HEALTHKEEPER SET
WATERSHED EVENT		5 YEAR EXPRESSIVE DELAY
EVOLVED ECOLO-NOMIC ENVIRONMENT	+	NEW HEALTHKEEPER SET

EVOLUTIONARY HEALTHCARE -- REFORMING WATERSHED EVENTS

1910 -- FLEXNER REPORT
1945 -- EMPLOYEE BENEFIT INSURANCE
1965 -- MEDICARE -- MEDICAID
1985 -- DIAGNOSTIC RELATED GROUPS
2005 -- GLOBALIZATION
2025 -- NANO-HISTONE CODES

ECOLO-NOMIC PARADIGMS
OF
HEALTHKEEPER SETS
EVOLVING
HEALTHCARE REFORM

1906 ➔ (1910-1950)
- First half 20th Century ecolo-nomics
IATROGENIC ERA
PHYSICIAN DRIVEN

1945 ➔ (1950-1970)
- 1st overlapping ecolo-nomic generation
GOLDEN ERA
QUALITY DRIVEN

1965 ➔ (1970-1990)
- 2nd overlapping ecolo-nomic generation
ENTITLEMENT ERA
ACCESS DRIVEN

1985 ➔ (1990-2010)
- 3rd overlapping ecolo-nomic generation
EQUALIZATION ERA
COST DRIVEN

2005 ➔ (2010-2030)
- Universal Healthcare Delivery ecolo-nomics
ENLIGHTENMENT ERA
PATIENT DRIVEN

2025 ➔ (2030-2050)
- 21st Century nano-histone ecolo-nomics
GTO ERA
TECHNOLOGY DRIVEN

MIGRATORY ECONOMIC FACTORS & PATTERNS EVOLVING MAN, MONEY & MEDICINE

PART ONE

THE HISTORIC AND PERSISTENT INTERLINKING FORCES DRIVING MAN, MONEY, AND MEDICINE

Human independent cognitive reasoning encourages Man to know that he knows, but a unique human instinct drives Man to discover that which he does not know and more, that which he may never know.

-- Ralzak

A moment for pause and perspective CONCERNING MAN:

No one, no person, not anyone and nobody can ever get to live on forever. No complex biological organism currently alive is individually immortal. Life ends when cellular telomeres, disposable buffers at each end of a chromatid, eventually disintegrate. Individual cells of an organism do attempt to rejuvenate themselves by breaking down or dis-assembling various sub-cellular components and then engulfing them in a process known as autophagy, but this limited life preserver has no long lasting permanent consequence for the entire organism – alas, the telomeres do ultimately fail to respond and the hopeful re-digestive process regresses to apoptosis. Whether or not Man persists in recidivistic endeavors that devise methodology for continued repeated replacement of telomere defective parts, either by utilizing natural biological systems or by a re-stringing of chromatids through highly technological and mechanical man-made genetic manipulation, matters not; all such diligent and exhaustive efforts miserably fail practical consequence. All of those futile attempts to sustainably prolong a natural life span ultimately become ineffective. Unless eliminated by excision, radiation, chemicals, physio-electric shock or specific DNA-directed antibodies, cancer cells persist in multiplying until they kill their host organism; a cancer cell defies all prescribed rules and contrives to wildly multiply, to continually reproduce out of control, and to affect the further detriment of dear and essential life-sustaining cells, thus sentencing its host life-form to a brief prison sentence on death row.

With or without human acceptance or acknowledgement, biologic cell death is reliably proven inevitable. If Man is fortunate enough to live a life free of all possible ailments as well as all detrimental environmental exposures and influences, then Man might hopefully expect to live relatively long and attain a ripe old average age of 120 years before succumbing to the inevitable Hayflick limit, that point representing irreplaceable loss of functional telomeres and the assured finality of terminal cellular apoptosis, because biological cells simply give up, quit their existence by relentlessly refusing to divide. Expressed first by an ancient mythological Babylonian character in the Epic of Gilgamesh, "The gods endowed Man with what they could never possess -- Death. Life is for the gods alone, their most precious personal property." No treasure of Mankind has ever been greater than his limited treasure of time. Yet hoping to invalidate the inevitable conclusions of Gilgamesh, today there are highly technological researchers diligently working in the field of tissue engineering for "age repair" – tinkering with nano-techniques to manipulate telomere lengthening machinery – all to no avail.

Genetic factors have molded the evolutionary construction of modern Man; and Man can trace his DNA back in time: Modern Man's oldest direct genetic ancestors, the first of the *Homo sapiens*, once lived and prospered throughout the African continent some 150 thousand years ago. All of us alive and living here on planet earth today, all the world's peoples, can trace a common cytoplasmic genetic origin to one woman who lived in what is now Northern Africa about 100 thousand years ago. Modern Man can also trace his nuclear DNA origin to one single documented man whose *Homo sapient* genetics had further evolved-adapted beyond Man's original cytoplasmic ancestry over a period of 40 thousand years. This particular 60-thousand-year old ancient gentleman also resided in the same general region of Northern Africa as his and modern Man's ancestral 100-thousand-year-old relative. Man's thusly evolved genetics have been documented to possess immense creativity and powers of imagination within the same sized cranium, while also continually expressing, debating and doubting the source and meaning of his independent cognitive reasoning. Man has accomplished all of this marvelous brain power of independent thought through a neuro-synaptical weaving that only utilizes an approximate average 10% of his potential cerebral capability.

This genetic adaptation to cognitive reasoning posed an immediate threat that could have potentially justified and then accomplished Man's self-annihilation. If death was reasoned inevitable for all Mankind, then a purpose had to be contemplated for living. Fortunately, the cleverly protective imaginative mind of Man simultaneously developed the ultimate coping mechanism -- the marvelous blind belief and ultimate servitude to the "Rule of Myth". Man is best united by a commonly shared myth; and myths have also unfortunately granted Man the guts, justifiable action and "reason" to do evil. Man's myths have resulted in artificially contrived: spiritual, religious, tribal, societal, political, military, national, or global, as well as economic entities -- firms and corporations. All myths endow Man with "rights" and "privileges", a mythical set of inalienable yet prejudicial permissions for his particular strange and temporary habit of existence, differing in scope, amount and duration during any particular point or paradigm on a time continuum of his evolutionary and migratory economic development. Myths, intertwined with prejudicial sets of "chosen facts", when added to an infinite range of imagination, have randomly unified and disenfranchised groupings of Man. Myths justified Man's way of life changing to the Agricultural Revolution around 1200 BC; newly evolved myths allowed him to cope with the sequential Scientific-Industrial revolutions to follow from about the 1600's to the Technological revolutions of today; and newer myths will certainly guide and direct him beyond into the future, when he will eventually seek a universal commonality and unity to end his bickering diversities.

Despite some crossbreeding in migratory conquered land masses and the resultant accumulation of some Neanderthal genes into the Cro-Magnon gene pool, the eventually evolved physiological functions of the adapted Cro-Magnon brain predominated, while the more primitive instinctive survival traits typical of the Neanderthal's mental function gradually disappeared. Survival proved to be the greatest force for the ultimate culling of Man's genetics. For Man living in the here and now, the world dwellers of today, not so very much has significantly changed in functioning cerebral biological systems or in mental evolution from that very ancient time of 60 thousand years ago till now, right now, right here -- today. All of Mankind shares a common 99.9% of that same nuclear DNA first inherited over 60 thousand years ago. Man's DNA contains over 10 Million Single Nuclear Polymorphisms (SNP) with each and every gene possessing well over 1000 SNP. Earth's most recent Ice Age re-adapted only 0.1% of ancient Man's DNA and randomly re-combined his SNP in various forms to add a temporary paradigm of slight competitive adaptive advantage for an ancient Man who was once forced by Mother Nature to live and further adapt in Ice Age silos of civilization. Those slight adaptive advantages, mainly survival adaptations in the form of physical health/wealth, continually fostered a perhaps insane desire for Man to be the unquestioned and unopposed permanent king of the evolutionary hill. The adaptations naturally enhanced Man's ability to attain fiscal Money/wealth at the expense of his fellow Man. However, although the bell curve depicting the range of Man's intellect has significantly extended on both ends since 60,000 BC, there has been an overall shift of the mean and median portion of the bell back to the left of center. From that ancient point in time to the present, Man has thusly progressively culled his species: The average Man of today is less clever, less dexterous, less agile, and has a slightly decreased cranial brain capacity. If the average modern Man had to resort to hunter-gathering today, he would be disadvantaged in comparison to his average ancient ancestor.

Geographical landmarks on Mankind's planet have shifted over earth-time. Beyond the migratory action of rotating titanic plates about the crust of his earth, huge water masses, oceans are independently rising and Man's land masses reveal great green valleys and craggy steep canyons where massive torrents in overflowing rivers once tumbled along their merry way. Man's present-day arid barren dry deserts were once magnificent green-forested lands. During the past sixty thousand years, the climate on planet earth drastically changed to first form an ancient ice age that separated the migratory patterns of primitive Mankind out into civilization silos, eliminating Mankind's migratory interactive networking which was previously fostered by former multitudes of diverse natural migrations. That extreme cold and ice era further fostered Mankind's prolonged geographic isolation and health survival odds. Those climate-change civilization silos allowed plagues and diseases to run their local horrific course and never spread to become world-wide threats. This long-lasting climatic-induced separation also permitted independent dynamically competing minor evolutionary adaptive advantages to be realized within Mankind's geographic silos, to selectively produce various slight adaptive genetic admixtures that resulted in such phenotypes as vaguely organized skin and facial characteristics, the quite inappropriately so-called purity divisions or mythical imaginary "races" of Mankind. Those vague and evolutionary disappearing phenotypes make up the tiniest fraction of Man's total genepool, just a drop in the bucket that hardly even begins to define the human experience. Moreover, there is absolutely no ideal or true adaptive genetic set; we humans on planet earth really are all of a recombinant and varied genetic mixture of Man. According to Italian-American geneticist Luigi Luca Cavalli-Sforza, a European ancestry encompasses a genetic pool composed of 2/3 Asian and 1/3 African genes. Painfully obvious and enlightening to anyone seriously willing to contemplate evolutionary-anthropological trends on planet earth, today modern Man lives in the cyclic age of a great ice melt, highlighted by shifting natural and induced migratory economic resources that continually force global human population migrations and global interactive genetic integrations. These continuous and ongoing active re-mixings of Mankind's slight genetic variations through his repeated economic migrations will eventually produce a blending of his varied and diverse racial and ethnic characteristics that will result in a return to

Man's former common phenotype, a blended visible commonality for all of Mankind to share and equally enjoy.

Gazing upwards to the tall grandiose mountains of planet earth, the angular orientations of volcanic iron deposits from ancient, selectively-dated volcanos paint and portray a time-sequenced picture of continually shifting magnetic poles throughout a timeline on the planet of Man. Earth's magnetic poles shift from north to south and vice versa as the magna in the center of Man's dear planet rotates at random intervals, some intervals being somewhat shy of 20 thousand years or so. During the approximate 300 earth years that are necessary to complete one of these magnetic rotatory switches, Man's atmosphere becomes unstable, and Man's great hoodwinking sun plays innumerable climate changing tricks with and all about Man's dear planet. Nothing in the least subtle from Mother Nature and totally beyond the control of Mankind, all life forms are ultimately and adversely affected by this gradual yet direly painful process.

Since all complex living life-forms must eventually die, Man might nonchalantly sing, as in the musical "Cabaret", "Start by admitting that from cradle to tomb, it ain't so long a stay". For that brief stay on planet earth, youth in America is usually a wonderful and enjoyable experience, but a decreased quality of life resulting from poor health can rapidly and severely cut through all that joy and especially Man's potential privilege of living to a ripe old age, slash through the happiness like a sharp fine hot wire slicing through butter; so Man hopefully strives to accomplish a most healthful, pleasurable and productive lifetime for as long as he is physically and mentally able, and then Man can at least live to angrily proclaim and shout, "Rage, rage against the dying of the light" (Dylan Thomas). Obvious essential prerequisites to accomplish those ephemeral lifetime "art of living" goals for Man are continued and sustainable good health and politico-economic stability. Three root requirements have always gone hand-in-hand – Man, Money, and Medicine.

Primitive Man chose a consistent path not taken by other living beasts, an evolving Migratory Economic path to sustain his health and economic stability, which always traveled together, like Money and Medicine, continually linked in various strange arrays of paradigm partnerships. The *Homo sapiens* species economically adapted to its long period of infancy, childhood and then onto final physiological maturity. The young and immature could not survive on their own. Therefore, compassion for health, healthcare and wellbeing within a family structure stood as essential ingredients for Mankind's historical evolutionary survival. Although forever claiming to be unique, there are many ways to view that particular marvelous beast called Man, including: "Man is a beast that knows that he is a beast" – Gene Roddenberry; or "A beast does not know that he is a beast, and the nearer Man gets to being a beast the less he knows it." -- George MacDonald.

The title of "beast" is disturbing to the mythology engrained into Man's psyche; Man rejects viewing himself as "beast" and favors a myth of goodness expressed as "humanity". Still, primitive primal drives yearning for human conflict, wealth and wellbeing continually express themselves in categorical terms tempered by Man, Money, and Medicine. Evolution among Man's myriads of myths, recidivist offenders to the primitive psyche, construct and destruct the various ideologies of Mankind, clustering Man into semi-sustainable quasi-organized progressive groupings of societies, kingdoms, nations, and global alliances. However, perhaps Man's "inhumanity" to Man is also just a myth that believes "humanity" consists of loving and constructive traits rather than imperialistic, warlike destructive traits that have historically permitted Man to hunt, kill and dominate himself as lord and master over planet earth's entire animal kingdom for over 150,000 years. Guilty as charged -- Man had evolved an intellectual ability for credible means, a pre-meditated mindset for opportunistic jeopardy, and a motive of greed for probable cause to enact the habitual crimes of altering his ecologic and economic environment just to suit his fancy. Man continues to play the ecologically treacherous games of "top of the mound", "king of the hill", and now "master of the universe". Man's "humanity" confined conquered groups of his fellow Man to slavery and often extinction, much like the fate of any plant or animal life form that might have in any way threatened his presence. Domestication of animals and of his fellow Man often involved castration and bondage – such may be the true nature of Man's "humanity".

The virtuous ideal or vision and drive/directive for modern Man living in an advanced industrialized society portends to be the achievement of a long and healthy life filled with "good" and "important" accomplishments for his fellow Man. These would include love/caring with respect for an equal equivalency role extended to all humans inhabiting planet earth. If such a drive/directed existed or had been practiced by primitive Man, he would never have evolved to walk the surface of earth today; he would have most likely vanished into extinction. The prime directives for primitive Man were driven to enhance his survival among the many animal beasts and resulted in an intellectual culling of the human species to favor those best adapted to succeed in such dire competition. The sport activities of modern Man honor that ancient tradition. Tribal territorial boundaries were defended to the point of death in order to assure adequate range for food supplies, clothing and shelter for each individual tribe. The "weak" or unfavorably adapted for primitive survival were culled in favor of the more aggressive genetic stock. During an epoch in time consisting of hundreds of thousands of years, Man's intellectual development yielded a clear and functional dynamic competitive advantage over species who were less inventive and over those of the human species who were less aggressive. Primal drives/directives, no matter how confused, denied or intellectually suppressed by various ego defense mechanisms, never seem to disappear.

Pre "civilized" Man lived as a nomadic hunter-gatherer in mobile groups of about two dozen to a clan. His migratory economic system functioned well and remained quite simple. During that primitive pre-civilization era, Mankind shared just about everything; that sharing occurred immediately and for the most part remained fairly equal. People living at that time and in those circumstances did not engage in significant long term hoarding or collecting of valued private property, because there was really no place to store and safely transport such merchandise. This primitively eloquent but risky way of life eventually gave way to Man living in larger groupings at permanent locations and abundantly cultivating his necessary sustenance from the land. The development of agriculture provided Man with a more reliable and stable guarantee for health and economic existence, but all social evolution comes with a price. That guaranteed safer existence substantially fostered Man's manipulative abilities for the attainment of an art of living, but Man's ability to manipulate his environment came with a codicil -- the price/motive, opportunity and ability for Man to Manipulate his fellow Man.

Hunter–Gathering was entrepreneurial, exciting, risky, and required a sharp mind, dexterity and agility; Agricultural pursuits were laborious, lethargic, filled with ennui to the point of depression, but routine, dependable and requiring compliance, obedience, and complacency. The tradeoff enabled a sustainable fat belly and no stress that would have resulted from fear of safety and survival. Therefore, the masses of Man chose agriculture at that paradigm in time. Through the same logical reasoning process, if given the opportunity of total equality, Man would choose a satiated welfare state of existence today. Therefore, the tittering of welfare is critical.

For Man to be civilized, he had to curb his primal "humanity" drives, which has led to a myriad of unintended consequences..... The end of Man's migratory life style as a nomadic hunter-gatherer signaled the anthropologic conception of ownership, nurtured a pregnancy of private property desire, and then gave birth to migratory evolutionary economic factors and forces that would henceforth continually plague the political-social structure of Mankind. No longer having to consume his total mental concentration on the day-long hunt and search for his next meal, leisure time allowed the individual philosophical awareness plight of Mankind to become increasingly more acute and painfully obvious. Blessed or perhaps cursed with an increased time interval within each day to ponder in questionably mysterious but definably rational cognitive awareness, the realization of Man's mortality became a matter of his increasing concern. Fear, fear of death and fear of prematurely ending his life tortured Man's independent cognitive rationality. Man desperately needed mental health help, thus powerful ego defenses came into sharper play to save the day. Mankind pondered further to produce or mythically manufacture plausible or possibly believable reasons for Man's -- so very much in his face -- ultimately short and fragile human form of mortal existence. Man hoped, wished and prayed that perhaps he could become immortal or at least be immortalized in some way, such as through an after-life existence provided by the celebrity of infamy, religious or mythical ideologies, renown fame, family fortune or family heirs. Then again, perhaps he could just simply slip on by, live for the day, sing along, be jolly and self-indulgent while simply forgetting about that ever-pressing immortality thing on his conscience. Perhaps he could finally intellectually accept his personal curse of mortality as Man and the ephemeral existence of all Mankind. The more that he pondered the subject of his mortality, the more he felt the need to ponder further. Those aforementioned ephemeral lifetime "art of living" goals along with sustainable good health and politico-economic stability offered reasons to appreciate and enjoy his existence as a newly "civilized" Man. Healthcare significantly enhanced his ability to enjoy a greater longevity and provided the opportunity for additional devoted time to strive for personal prosperity and the pursuit of happiness. Good health permitted such action, and through action Man could now attain an increased state of wealth/health. There again stood that intimate association of health with economics – Man, Money and Medicine.

Aside from Man's apparently unconscionable ability to give up his greed for personal property, going back to that freedom-filled hunter-gatherer way of life would require a constant alertness and willingness to preserve such a way of life. Man found it so much easier and convenient not to try, to simply adapt to a lowered stress environment of economic slavery even when it meant working in the fields for hours on end, then continually expanding field and family size in a cyclic need for continuing to increase the food supply for his increased population. More and more production was demanded from those newly cleared and planted lands. The culling effect of repetitious warfare served as an unfortunate practical mechanism to slow down that cyclic process and maintain Man's sustained miserable hierarchical indebtedness to the land. A less stressful life with an overall lowered set of expectations, lowered communal standard of living, compliance with kingly or governmental laws from above, and progressive loss of personal freedom all added to the envisioned sustainability of social stratification preferences that were not to be questioned. Man's vulgar humanity primarily demanded that he do that which was necessary for his survival and not much more; Man's overwhelming powerful secondary humanistic greed and avarice erupted into overconsumption, hoarding and environmental destruction, but also laid a foundation for capitalism. The intellectually entrepreneurial and those of Man that were consumed by wanderlust remained as outliers while totalitarian or religious theocracies successfully spun compliance and obedience myths concerning governmental acceptance and privilege, hypnotically convincing the masses of Man to abandon hope of personal freedom, to be unquestionably governed and to lead earthly lives of personal sacrifice.

The new and evolved economics of Man's "Civilization", however, also equaled an unequal sharing of competitively attained wealth. The necessary stratification of Mankind's labor for economic efficiency and mutual productive gain contributed to inforce his greed and eventual disproportionate stratification of wealth distribution. Such an inherent unsharring migratory economic functional pattern was and is within the nature of being a member of a "civilized" human society. Exploitable relationships naturally became exploited. Some of Mankind, often by hook or by crook, became able to cultivate and harvest more than others. These individuals hoarded their product and at first bartered for other types of personal property; but eventually they bartered their surplus product for the labor of others to produce even more product for themselves, providing an increased surplus product which promoted an opportunity to barter on further. This widening unequal distribution of and non-sharing of the products derived from every Man's labor inevitably led to temporal societal divisions, divisive separations into "have and have-nots" as well as prejudicial human worth categories such as "richer or poorer". According to Polish macroeconomist Michael Kalecki's theory of economic dynamics, there are opposing and different dynamic competitive advantages at work or play in considering the evolution of wealth and income disparity that could be cleverly summed up as, "the capitalists earn what they spend"....."the workers spend what they earn".

General acceptance of "assigned" societal strata levels became a permanent and eventually generational life style. Various sub-strata segregation and subjugation evolved, and the further downtrodden eventually accepted their societal existence as a natural and generational way of life. At this point in ancient migratory economic evolution, all the poorer individuals could possibly have easily departed from the growing agrarian society, simply walked away from their stratified settlement life and returned to the life style of hunter-gatherers; but the ostensible risk to life and limb inherent in such cultural devolution portrayed Man's economic survival fate to be clearly much worse than living in the assured and quasi-protected yet guaranteed life of continued indebtedness to his fellow Man. Most of Mankind refused to part; by their own free will, they chose to stay. Man has always been an economic slave to his societal norms and mores. His supposed "rational" cognitive reasoning has always been set and readjusted as a function of his response to various self-created mythological forces, the powerful and believable forces generated by a changing ecological and economic environment. For the overwhelming majority of the great masses of Mankind, near starvation was and still is ultimately more economically acceptable than a reasonable likelihood risk of total starvation.

The masses of Man were and are overly anxious to be led: Consider that a hypnotist performing on stage is so easily able to pick and choose dozens of eager volunteers out of just about any audience, people ready and willing be hypnotized, anxious to be embarrassed to the point of crawling on all fours and clucking like a chicken. As is well documented in psychological studies, an overt lie repeated over and over again often enough has the very probable potential to become a great big believable and unquestioned fact. Therefore, Mankind's political inference of cognitive dissonance becomes not so difficult to comprehend. Despotic rule by Man often utilized the hypnotic effect of theologies or actual drugs to achieve appalling human consequences. Brittan imported opium to China to exert hypnotic control over their distant colony; and with rum for barter, New World Colonists purchased the fiscal saviors of the Jamestown Colony in 1619 -- black slaves purchased from black African tribes to work in sugar, cotton and tobacco fields -- and then to be controlled with the rum that the slaves themselves produced along with added cocaine and a constant repetitive demeaning ridicule. Alcohol mixed with constant harassing control along with the known sequela of a Stockholm-like syndrome fostered a sustainable generational transfixed mesmerized state for downtrodden residents in Ghettos, Slave Quarters and Reservations – a hypnotic belief that continually shouted into their ears, a great made-believable lie that there could never be an escape from their situational immorally wicked depravity. Thus, the beast known as Man ignominiously achieved a state of despicable generational acceptance for his fellow Man on opposite sides of planet earth. The monitory profitable proceeds from the infamous "southern" slave-trade triangle eventually found their way to fund the construction of the many magnificent mansions along the cliffs at Newport, Rhode Island.

Once drugged politically or chemically and content to envision a foreseeable future that provided for sustainable food and shelter, those masses of Man drifted into that lowered-expectation dynamic complacency that was passed down to for generations to come. A migratory economic welfare state likewise tends to perpetuate itself on a generational basis like a Benoit Mandelbrot fractal expansion. However, the exquisite hidden beauty of a fractal expansion lies in the outlier exception that fails all congruence testing. Interestingly, the obvious potential of great masses of Man as a united body did not and do not determine the course of Mankind's cultural evolution or patterns of migratory economic migrations. Rather, an outlier like the fractal expansion outlier that terribly fails all congruence testing, a singularly and uniquely human type of intellectual greed, a powerful human instinct, persists and prevails in a small percentage of the *Homo sapiens* genotype; and that special grouping of individuals sets the multitude of pathways for the great masses to eventually follow. Mankind's inborn cathexis to travel, wander, explore and discover continually and persistently expresses itself as "wanderlust". The gut-wrenching insatiable human emotional desire for wanderlust must be continually replenished, nourished and fed over and over again. This irascible, irresistible and unquenchable primitive urge to escape from the order of any fixed society has not only allowed but forcefully demanded Mankind to populate the entire world. Wanderlust will project Man into the exploration of the entire universe. **Human independent cognitive reasoning encourages Man to know that he knows, but a unique human instinct drives Man to discover that which he does not know and more, that which he may never know (Ralzak).**

At the start of a long distance foot race, all of Mankind's contestants initially line up equally and evenly; but long before the finish line at the end of the course, there is a great distribution inequality gap for success, with substantial spaces stretching out from Mankind's fastest winners to Mankind's slowest losers. All of Mankind may be initially created equal in spirit, but Man's individual genetics develop Man to become unequal to his fellow Man in so many ways. For the masses of students lining up to enter college on equal and even footing, so goes their natural course and income inequality gapping for long term financial success. The true entrancing beauty of it all is that throughout Mankind, all strata are indeed wonderfully different and equally worthwhile in spite of any income gap differences. Much like wanderlust, entrepreneurial determinism acts as an agent of Man's individual genetic factors rather than Man's societal genetic factors. Some of Mankind do indeed possess a gut-wrenching genetic desire to continue to strive, to repeatedly battle, to fight to win in the face of persistent set-backs and losses, while others, be it by choice or circumstance, do not. What does not kill makes some stronger and others weaker.

For those "wanderlusting" entrepreneurial within Mankind: The pleasure in the process of attaining an award is greater than the pleasure in having the award. The game of winning is more inspiring than the game having been won. The greatest adventure is in getting there, not in having arrived. Personal greed is best fed by the task of successful attainment and not in what has been attained. Creation within innovation, the spewing of disruptive technologies, becomes the ultimate reward of success within a lifetime. The establishment of a higher plateau for the start of a future genetic generation's entrepreneurial climb up that mountain of success becomes the dream or goal of the entrepreneurial Man.

Meanwhile back on the agrarian societal farm, another primitive human greed, greed and lust for power and control, also traditionally shouted to be heard by the herd of Man. Migratory ecology and economics demanded then called for a culling of the mass herd of populous through hegemony and resultant economic slavery. Physically enforced human labor became a productive migratory economic enterprise. Higher per capita increases for some and demeaning low income inequalities for the masses evolved to persist among all the new agrarian society residents. Before long, one percent of the rustic agricultural population owned and controlled greater than fifty percent of the available farm-country property. Those relatively few top richest individuals at the permanent agrarian settlements envisioned themselves as permanent superiors, while the remaining pastoral residents in cultivated lands adapted to and accepted their role as inferiors, along with lowered expectations for horizons of future personal and generational economic advancement. Generational affluence of the few led to an elite status of family nobility, and the accumulated wealth of that nobility naturally had to be protected from the threat of the jealous peasantry. There was no end to the personal property greed of nobility. A collection of wealth led to a collection of all types of art along with a separate and unique "artful" style of living reserved for only those relatively few, the elitist families. The "haves" had Money (gold) and the "have nots" had not that personal fiscal wealth – Money equivalent to a set gold commodity. The evolved "Kings" insisted that their personal property (gold) should forever remain in their possession as if issued by an order from a heavenly God. Thereby, the Kings and the otherwise wealthy created and substantiated the sustainability of a societal pecking order, a permanent and inviolable hierarchy incorporating a recidivistic stretching of the distance or gap between the rich and the poor.

The greatest wealth of personal property rested in the elitist ownership and control of productive land. Economic standards evolved further along the same disproportionate path. Nobles lived in protected walled castles which were necessary for housing their personal property, while peasants lived in the unprotected open surrounding countryside. Castles were expensive to build and maintain, so the migratory economics of the time became quite simple -- peasants had to be made to labor and to be taxed. Peasants paid a share of profit from their labor on the land and a tax for just living on the land owned by the noble elitists. Political or moral philosophical arguments concerning the economic validity of productive versus non-productive accumulation of wealth would linger on and be contested in every future societal arrangement of Man. During the Fourth Industrial Revolution, practitioners of Medicine were likened by corporations to peasant farmers in an agrarian societal era. Opposing philosophies had naturally and repeatedly led to protest, protest movements and outright anarchy to the point of riot, battle and revolt. Cultural evolution changes the names of the players, but never the recidivistic game played by Man and justified by Money and Medicine. Often by brunt military force, Kings and nobles took over absolute ownership of not only all the cultivated land but also all the surrounding land and lands beyond; and a fundamental migratory economic principal of that period in time became well understood by all -- the source of the wealth and power of the kingdom emanated from the ownership of large land masses. Military and political forces through war and conflict determined the de facto ownership of the land.

Control of the masses has always been through control of Man's ecology of political myths concerning economics (Money) and relative wealth/health status (Medicine). Conquest by order of the Kings led to territorial expansion and economic growth. Engaging in the act of war, once upon a time, stood as a reliable established economic advancement tool. The peasants feared to revolt against their King, for loss of protection from and through the might of their King would most likely lead to probable slavery resulting from a new conquest by a new opposing King. A new and proper myth and accompanying mythological terminology spit out politically proper words for the unequal art of living that was offered to and accepted by all the residents -- the migratory economic privileged birth myth of "Royals versus Commoners." Economic Globalization would eventually produce new rules for the source of wealth and power and elitist status would eventually not be determined by genetic bloodlines, but by global corporate interest. There are three great mythological global forces used to justify conquest – ecological-economic, political-cultural, and theological–religious. In the Third Industrial Revolution era, powerful Money-hungry corporations mimicked the behavior of those Royal Kings bent on conquest. Be it by kingly or corporate war or economic hegemony, the impacted or conquered peoples also, albeit temporarily, enjoyed economic growth through post war reconstruction projects; but no good plan or workable theory lasts forever without repeated innovation; in time, "Then leaf subsides to leaf." – Robert Frost

An aged tree must die, tumble and rot to provide the space and nutrients for new young growth in the forest. Man must die as human sacrifice so that Man may live. "The King is dead; long live the King." Myth has pointed and continues to point the way for Man to psychologically validate the transcendence of his life through death and then onto the awe of birthing a new life. Religions are merely various modalities to transmit that message to the masses. The fundamental basis of myth is inseparable from Man's "raison d'être". Myth relieves Man of chaotic mental anxiety and puts him in temporary appropriate alignment and serenity with a migratory economic reality while his culture continues to evolve, changing his mores and codes of ethics. Myth gives Man a sense of belonging to an awesome transcendental greatness far greater than himself, and allows him the pleasure and privilege to live out a tranquil life in the midst of his chaotic earthly environment -- to feel sane within his insanity -- Rocky Horror. Belief in myth does sentence and confine Man to a lifelong term in a self-made psychologically dependent jail; however, as grand mythologies evolve due to evolutions and revolutions in technologies and economics, so do their contained believable myths also evolve to accommodate Man's visions and goals. By way of his evolved myths, Man changes his mental modus operandi. The evolved thinking pathways transform his cultures and his institutions. The mythological greatness and importance of Man once came offered as a gift from the heavens, but now mythological directives apparently emanate from his Mother Earth. The present evolution of migratory economics has transformed mythologies from those having originated in a heavenly curtain then reached down to the earth to those that originate from the earth then search out beyond the universe through the imaginative eyes of Man. Man's art forms are modalities that capture his myths. His prayer and meditation concentrates transcendental thought vital to his perceived cosmos. Perhaps Man's entire planet is just one single life form; a sacred entity that cannot belong to or be owned by Man. As once succinctly stated by Chief Seattle, "Man belongs to (and is thus owned by) the earth".

Myth is a wondrous yet necessary evil that functionally unites a specific culture of Man and promulgates generalized acceptance of a specific cultural stratification mechanism. Myth provides a unified guidance and purpose for earthly existence and offers hope for everlasting life thereafter. Myth is a marvelous psychological invention of Man, giving him a prerequisite for his deductive and inductive reasoning processes, as well as an irrevocable premise that can at any time be evoked as an indisputable non-debatable alibi for otherwise reprehensible actions. Along this unfortunate line of thought, myth can become a problematic barrier to congenial inter-cultural alignment of purpose and mutual goals, resulting in inter-cultural disputes and frank aggressiveness, invariably culminating in an inter-cultural killing war. For agrarian cultural societies, the migratory economic sacrosanct inalienable myth of "human rights" had yet to evolve; that particular myth had to wait for a future period of time when contemporary technology would dictate that subjugated labor would no longer be a practical productive enterprise. Plato's concept of the "Myth of the Metals" flourished, alive and well thousands of years before being scribed by the philosopher-economist and such philosophical myths will continue to thrive thousands of years into the future. The social "needs" of the agrarian Commoners were determined by their Royals, and a mythological Royal system of "justice" naturally followed. In an evolving 21st Century democratic industrial society, social "needs" are apparently determined and next justified by various progressive liberal demographic group leaders/organizers, and then politically driven to change existing wealth-distributive and "justice" systems accordingly. One might wonder about a future migratory economic time when some contributions made by Man and an overwhelming evolving natural ecology (climate change) have exhausted natural resources to the extent that contemporary technological advancements could no longer be practically shared by all. Newly developed myths for survival, more myths invented by that clever creature called "Man", myths designed to stabilize society among the economically fittest might in some future time very well demand and then justify a return to a subjugated labor system in society to stabilize rebellion and assure the sustainable survival of those economically fittest.

Man's entrepreneurial evolution into industrialization immensely increased his standard of living (depending on where he was living, city versus country), but also brought forth some new and exciting concepts that he may not have been prepared to deal with. Agriculture, in and of itself, as well as the mining of precious metals for the production of wealth simply support the necessary GDP resulting from trade and commerce, mercantilism that repeatedly proved to outstrip them both. Thus, the merchant class inevitably rose to the nearest to the top engraving on the ecolo-nomic totem pole for wealth accumulation. Historically, that merchant class consolidated and captured the power of Money through commerce, then rose as an inspirational group to capture the agrarian landowner crown and become the new economically fittest. Man's interactions within his species became progressively more confusing and unclear, a conundrum for which he could not readily find the exact pieces to fit. To wit, at first Man's migratory economically evolving industrial corporations sought to produce productive commodities without concern for the very clearly predicted waste, deterioration of machinery/equipment, and harmful by-products that by necessity were also produced by an unchecked and often irresponsible industrialization of former manual processes.

Planet earth has a limited amount of natural resources. Monetary depletion allowances set at any cost do not and can never restore or reproduce shorted and essential limited natural resources that are totally used up or indiscriminately destroyed by industrialization or petty wars. Therefore, the importance of environmental protection ultimately supersedes both industrial production and societal need or primary right to work in a job market created by the industrialization process. Albeit that Man's primary drive to procure by hunt or job is difficult to assure or provide when Man's game stock has migrated away or when Man's jobs are simply not available. Man's primitive pecking order for tribal power is accelerated in times of want, and his selfish self-interest also rises when he perceives a foreseeable return of health/wealth, abundance and power, Medicine that can be purchased with Man's Money.

With a shift of economic power into the greedy hands of the mercantilists, greater responsibility for production would follow as paramount for a sustainably successful firm. Factory laborers assumed the role of the former peasant agrarian renters. Concern arose that these new "renters" might not want to assume that responsibility. Furthermore, an individual worker could not be practically sued (cannot get blood out of a rock) for producing a bad or dangerous product for society. The firm, on the other hand, might have the necessary deep pocket, as did the agrarian land owner. Nonetheless, the corporations of Man, like his Money, overstepped that same proverbial invisible yet very clearly understood line in the sand, and then proceeded to add much more than just a feather to the intolerable load of "inhumane" or historically human practices that finally broke the back of Mankind's societal acceptance camel. Within the structure of Man's unrestricted and unbridled laissez-faire commerce/economy, laws, rules and regulations, the three mighty musketeers of Man in his war for "humane" or "beastly" survival, would become the three sword-masters to eventually save the day for the world's environment. The majority of excessive waste and harmful or polluting industrial by-products were eventually adjudicated to be accountable to and charged back to the responsibility of the corporate interests of Man that had, if fact, created them.

Moreover, the natural deterioration of industrial machinery/equipment, that is the natural wear and tear caused by production of a commodity was also necessarily found to be an important factor in the economic/Money equation for production; depletion and limited longevity had to be considered for machinery/equipment rebuild, adjustment or replacement in order to continue to produce a sustainable work-product without process interruption or frank system failure. Expensive new machinery that could utilize new technologies had to be and was justified at additional costs to sustainably and dynamically compete in the competitive industrial markets. The increased sales generated by a superior commodity made it so. When there was unexpected and unanticipated breakdown of some component or mechanical device, simply substituting a similar device would never suffice; either the process had to be changed to accommodate the device or the device had to be upgraded at the expense of the corporation to fit an established on-going process of production.

Now, all those details concerning commodity-generating economics in the past two or three paragraphs are intellectually intuitive and painfully obvious; and even when presented to a third-grader, the Money-wise concepts are tedious and b-o-r-i-n-g. But now, if those cognitive reasoning processes are spiced up a notch or two beyond third grade level by simply substituting the former agrarian renter and now the "working Man" every time machinery/equipment/device is mentioned in the industrial process equation, then things dramatically change. The labor of Man greases and lubricates capitalistic machinery and/or socialistic industrial production. That former gut feeling of ennui now suddenly changes to emotions of conflict and challenge: "The mass of men serves the state thus, not as men mainly, but as machines, with their bodies…..and wooden men can perhaps be manufactured that will serve the purposes as well." -- Henry David Thoreau, "Civil Disobedience"

As the industrial revolution began in the late 18th Century, a new myth awareness or a psycho-social idealism tugged along downstream on the same adaptive river. Intuitively and most economically prudent, a "firm", be it a private or state run capital enterprise, envisioned the best mechanism to contractually script the labor of Man (now designated as "employees") would be the same as the scripting the labor accomplished by an inanimate industrial machine to produce a profitable product. If the product of Man's labor were to belong to the laborer, then workers could logically claim property right interests in the profitable product. He that rules it owns it, and he that owns it rules it. In an agrarian society, Man sowed the seed, but it was the land that labored to produce the product and the owner of the land claimed ownership of the profitable product. The moral/ethical argument was clearly and concisely defined. The "landlord" was literally the "Lord" of the land, the owner/operator/builder/producer and the ruler. Myth marches on, and by the start of the 20th Century, opposing rumblings concerning the owning or renting of Man as property arose and became the basis for future political divisions of rightist and leftist philosophies.

According to this altered/substitute reasoning process, the many corporations must assume responsibility for their machinery/equipment/devices singularly known as the "working Man" -- Man's maintenance, wear and tear, health, aging and eventual disposal. In addition, the corporations would also be responsible for his upgrading/vocational-training to fit any existing or technologically improved and more efficient industrial production process. Medicine related concepts -- work safety, workers' compensation for job-related acute or chronic injury, depletion of health with age and retirement compensation in the form of continued health benefits and pensions suddenly blurt out additional migratory economic cost factors for production. On the other hand, human error, breakdown, ignorance and sloth are examples of bad equipment or human machinery that must be fixed. Simply raising a wage does not begin to satisfy Man's ultimate retirement security. A negotiation held with management by one single average employee is ludicrous to envision..... A detailed discussion of collective bargaining and unionism will occur later in this text.

The recidivistic, continual and overtly acute military-economic conquests of Man and his resultant slower cultural infiltration migrations for survival, pleasure and productivity have consistently altered and uprooted his financial institutions along with his various migratory economic systems for **Healthcare Reform,** while blindly, hopelessly and yet continually re-defining the borders and the ephemeral influential jurisdictions of Mankind's so-called "sovereign" nations. These various "sovereign" geographical regions, evolved civilizations of Man designed to preserve and to protect the prized personal property of various short-lived governing or ruling institutions, likewise repeatedly lived and died, apparently all in an evolutionary process of progressive human existence on planet earth.

No matter what form of government is eventually chosen after a successful rebellion, a re-stratification of wealth eventually evolves. The migratory economic is continually driven along a repetitious Möbius strip. Capitalism drifts towards the traditional social aspects of communism and communism drifts towards the social aspects of an unbridled capitalism. Greed in a capitalist society is termed corruption in a communist society; and they are both functionally accepted by the masses. A lower level historical class, the merchant class, evolves into a business administrative and product manufacturing class to eventually float to the top in both aforementioned societies where a religious doctrine does not dominate. Communism initially endows a great public force to unite and rebel against an imperialistic state, but social reforms for the masses such as "from all according to ability and to all according to need" are gradually put to rest as a saprophytic capitalism, an unbridled capitalistic entrepreneurship emerges to be the next migratory economic fiscal model in partnership with the totalitarian communistic government, a federal model that retains ownership of all land masses and defines designated parcels for development with long term lease contracts. Democracy by its very nature likewise endows public forces to rebel in search of various reforms. Democratic capitalistic reforms are gradually put to rest as a progressive socialism along with a wealth-redistribution welfare economic acceptance for the equal-democratic equal-voting poorer masses simultaneously work to mentality penetrate the social mindset with the aforesaid wishful concepts of wealth distribution socialism, ultimately to take command of and change the formerly successful capitalistic fiscal model.

Such obviously over-simplified and sweeping generalizations as above scripted might summarize and conclude that although seemingly socialistic at first, Totalitarian Regimes that can and do control their masses are most likely to evolve to Capitalism; and although seemingly capitalistic at first, Democratic Republics that can and do evoke altruistic morality for their masses are most likely to evolve to Socialism. Furthermore, economist Cornelius Castoriadis argued that in Man's imaginary extra-social ordered societies, his government seeking to control distribution must also seek to control production. Thus there must sequentially be a natural accepted mythological-reasoned evolutionary growth from big to bigger government control. "Rational" cognitive reasoning becomes a function of the migratory economic environment that enslaves Man to the norms and mores of an evolving society at a particular point in time. Robert Herbert Simon's efforts for detailing a staged process leading to rational decision-making are excellent for a non-emotional computer to number-crunch, but those orderly sequence patterns tend to fail miserably in rational consistency once put in the slippery psychology-mythological enslaved hands of Man. Through all this evolutionary-ordained chaos, there tend to be some repeatable, come-around-again historical social patterns of Mankind that do stand out and are worth noting.

Sustainably successful and economically thriving secular and democratic industrialized nations eventually suffer from a self-induced decadence, a selfish decreased fertility of personal choice, and then they cannot replace their native-born citizenry. Not to worry, for migrating peoples from less economically advantaged areas rapidly make up for the local national or domestic population losses and initially offer hearty reproductive rates that can and do continually grow those entire national populations. On the other hand, the remaining non-thriving nations become low hanging fruit for militant or religious conquering cultures. There are three things necessary and essential for Man to declare war – Money, more Money and mountains of Money. Conquest initially forces abandonment of historical language and customs, but brings in new technologies, builds infrastructure, establishes productive manufacturing with nationally enforced low-employment that benefits both the conqueror and the conquered while also introducing a migratory economic for **Healthcare Reform**. With the prolonged passage of earth-time, those initial rules and regulations of the conqueror inevitably become relaxed, and the older indigenous customs slowly become re-established. New-formed resentment, rebellion and insurrection from the original native population mindset is either forcefully curtailed or accepted by the original or former conquering ethnic population or culture. If the rebellion is accepted, then that nation reverts back to a societal norm of free and independent high unemployment and becomes ripened fruit for picking once more, destined to once again be re-conquered through warfare or ethnic/religious/international-corporate migrations along with that trailing migratory economic for **Healthcare Reform.** This cyclic process rolls merrily along a bumpy trail resembling a twisted Möbius strip, a path upon which the evolutionary scenario continually repeats itself and thus quite effectively disperses through migratory economics the overall knowledge and cultural evolutions of Mankind throughout his known world.

A return to a life of leisure and relaxation for the rich traditionally translated into frequent famine for the unemployed poor. Although new technologies tend to improve general living standards overall and particularly for all in the lower strata, the net result is always zero change in the prescribed pecking order of life for the common Man. The conquering force that included disruptive technological enlightenment for the majority usually fails to be inclusive in substantially relieving the pain and suffering of the extremely poor. Yet migratory economics does re-equilibrate all, as fortunes inevitably rise and fall. Desperate people recognize no national borders. Theological rebellion, fed by the fear of eternal damnation and the reward of a glorious afterlife, is further justified by the eradication and extermination of the migratory economic of politically defined "evil", an ignoble task defined as a sacred human duty. Chants, defying death songs of militant soldiers, belittle and disgrace an "evil enemy" in conquering military mindsets; national slogans do the same for imperialistic nationalistic cultures.

Likewise and unfortunately, generalized ill health has been perceived as an excuse for an "evil enemy" that might arrive at a nation's emigration borders unless there was a specific national need to increase a nation's manpower in a lower economic social stratification. More than half of all European emigrated Americans before the Civil War first arrived as indentured servants. The migratory ecology and economics of the USA around 1864 revealed a nation in dire need of male workers due to losses from a war and an emergent, green-budding industrial culture. The legislated Page Act of 1865 encouraged the emigration of legalized contract labor and stated that immigration "should be fostered and encouraged by a liberal and just policy". After having endured a trans-Atlantic voyage during which one out of every seven immigrants died, 70 percent of those surviving new-comers were noted to have emigrated specifically from Southern and Eastern Europe. However, the migratory economic of American morals and ethics concerning immigration policies that were present at that particular point in time would also drastically evolve to change in the future as the economic needs of the USA repeatedly changed.

While in their various heydays, so many proud and notable civilizations of Mankind have not only repeatedly opposed, but also set up various stern but eventually ineffective barriers to cultural/economic migration and conquest. These ephemerally successful multitudes, consisting of nations, city-states and communities, continually constructed and reconstructed great piles of rock and stone into protective city and national walls with guarded gates or protected-gated seaports, with their various points of potential entry forcibly manned by armed administrative gatekeepers. Those gatekeepers, by selectively refusing entrance, repeatedly limited, suppressed, and frankly eliminated healthcare delivery or **Healthcare Reform** to any and all immigrants along with sadly defeating the hope for future economic migration among those obvious suffering poor, those begging sick and literally dying, those particular hopeless and hapless emigrants. But again, desperate people recognize no nation's border.

The famous plaque on the great standing-tall American symbol of freedom, the Statue of Liberty in New York Harbor, features Emma Lazarus's "New Colossus" sonnet:

Not like the brazen giant of Greek fame,
With conquering limbs astride from land to land;
Here at our sea-washed, sunset gates shall stand
A mighty woman with a torch, whose flame
Is the imprisoned lightning, and her name

Mother of Exiles. From her beacon-hand
Glows world-wide welcome; her mild eyes command
The air-bridged harbor that twin cities frame.
"Keep, ancient lands, your storied pomp!" cries she
With silent lips. "Give me your tired, your poor,
Your huddled masses yearning to breathe free,
The wretched refuse of your teeming shore.
Send these, the homeless, tempest-tossed to me,
I lift my lamp beside the golden door!"

However, over a quarter million "wretched refuse emigrants" were immediately turned away and put back on their original transport ships when they did not pass the administratively enforced guard-gated health inspection processing at the Ellis Island immigration portal of entry in New York Harbor.

For some, that pre-port Ellis Island stop, a stop so short of New York proper's "golden door", proved for some to be an initial pause at an Island of Hope; for others, the immigration center at Ellis Island proved to be final termination at an Island of Tears. The migratory economics of the day teased and twisted previous and then future ethics of **Healthcare Reform**. During the first years of the 20th Century, America yearned for laborers in flour-blossoming industrial sweatshops, and the immigration policies therefore remained generally freely open -- if one could pass the health inspection. For the emigrants who survived the treacherous trans-Atlantic voyage, but did not pass the health examination, "deportation" raised its ugly head as a feared, hated and despised new American word. The first induction into the healthcare delivery system of the "new world" for these immigrants consisted of a brief 30 second evaluation by a physician to determine possible deportation for "health reasons". The examining physicians routinely placed white "X" chalk marks on the left shoulder portion of whatever garment the emigrant happened to be wearing; and one out of every five emigrants at the Ellis Island center received that chalk mark, a dire omen that one might very likely be ordered to stand in a deportation line.

The even more evolved health ethic philosophy expressed by William Williams, the intermittent Commissioner of the Ellis Island facility from 1902 to 1914, stated that USA immigration should open only for "potentially productive USA residents". This migratory economic for a **Healthcare Reform** ethic readily transferred to the admission policy at the Ellis Island Hospital, which was not administratively organized to be, or ever intended to be the "Hospital for the World". Deportation procedures became quickly and quietly arranged for all those who did not show potential for future productivity in America. 90% of those hospitalized were eventually released to immigrate into New York and beyond; the remainder were deported. In the spirit of what comes around goes around, approximately 100 years later Ezekiel Emanuel was quoted to evoke the possibility of a similar "potential for productivity" criteria to determine the rationing of Medical care to all Americans, a possible **Healthcare Reform** policy dependent upon the migratory economics of medical payment coverage in the supposedly enlightened 21st Century set of ethics. The dismal consequences arising from limited and rationed healthcare access affecting select groups of individuals in the face of medically effective but extremely expensive technological advances in medical science had to be accounted for by a new believable mythological ethic of the day. Of course, the hopes, wishes and desires of impacted people to prolong their lifetime and improve their health beyond historically set goals by way of currently known Medical Technologies tore at that sacrificial myth of mores, a myth that was hypnotically touted to be mandated by the many.

Before the time of the 1929 Wall Street fiasco, migratory economics took the opportunity to twist the ethics of **Healthcare Reform** once again. Previously successful immigrants became jobless and cluttered the Ghettos of the big American cities. As an economic "correction", healthcare delivery suffered from a eugenics movement promoted by the migratory economics of that intercity crowding and joblessness: In 1912, a psychologist, Mr. Henry H. Goddard, championed that despicable American eugenics movement. He and two laymen assistants utilized a prejudicial intelligence testing program to determine a "scientific" need for deportation, totally apart from the flash rush to judgement healthy or not healthy determinations made by the physicians on Ellis Island. Mr. Goddard defiantly publicized intentionally flawed data that included such criteria as head circumference, facial width and facial expression to "medically prove" "genetic inferiority"; he then introduced such words into the American Medical literature as "moron", "imbecile" and "idiot". The affected population included mostly Jews, Slavs, and Italians who, after their successful previous emigrations, had been quite productive in their sweathouse industrial employment; but suddenly that same genetic stock as these accomplished-proven Southern and Eastern Europeans were for migratory economic reasons being considered a "genetically inferior" "immigrant menace". Popular opinion at the immigration center immediately determined that 80% of these aforementioned productive emigrants were somehow now genetically mentally deficient, apparently based on their national origin and "scientifically proven" by mathematical data analysis of invalid criteria.

Thus, the migratory economics of **Healthcare Reform** officially introduced "Racism" into the 20th Century as an accepted American political agenda item. This admittedly was not as horrid as the original U.S. Naturalization Law of 1790, which restricted the granting of naturalization citizenship solely to free (non-indentured) white-only immigrants of good character and also restricted "natural born citizenship" to foreign-born children of fathers (only) who had been resident citizens of the United States. Nonetheless, this line of radical reasoning revealed a harbinger of hate and reset a dire course for American society to follow.

The USA Congress overwhelmingly responded to that indecent bit of supposed ethical **Healthcare Reform** with the passage of equally biased immigration legislation. 1921 saw the passage of the Emergency Quota Act. The Johnson-Reed Immigration Act of 1924 further restricted immigrants from Southern and Eastern Europe, particularly Jews, Italians, and Slavs. The legislation passed with majority votes from both Democrats and Republicans in Congress and formally, shamefully and morally sinfully introduced painful "racial" or "national origin" bias into American law. The supposed mythical excuse for "primary intent" of the despicable law rested in limiting immigration from Southern Europe and Eastern Europe was "to preserve the ideal of American homogeneity". However, the Act also significantly limited immigration from Arab and African lands; the Act completely excluded immigration from Asian nations. After a dire reasoning battle of conflicting mythologies, President Coolidge officially signed that overtly "racially restrictive" Act into law, signed in the very same year that he officially dedicated the Statue of Liberty as a permanent "American National Monument". "Racism" unfortunately once again became an accepted component of the American legal justice system and executive cultural ecology. The table was set for a divisive banquet that would eventually serve up institutional racism, victimization philosophies and structural poverty forty years later in the early 1960's. This type of cultural isolationism spoiled the traditional strength of the migratory economics associated with immigration:

The secret to an immigrant's success over the psychologically stagnant local population laid and still lays in the new-comer's fortitude and willingness to educate oneself, integrate with the general population and then migrate further on to where an economically viable and feasible job opportunities exist, while striving to learn and utilize any available apprenticeship for vocational training along the way in conjunction with individually repeated attempts at risk-taking entrepreneurial enterprises.

Thus and sadly, selective American ethnic and racial emigration isolationism also survived over the next 100 years as exemplified by the "Wetback" return to Mexico program and ethnic concentration camps for Japanese-American and Italian-American citizens engineered during the progressively liberal Democratic President Roosevelt administration.

The 1995 "State of the Union" address by President William Clinton clearly asserted that "Illegal Aliens" in trouble with American Laws were to be actively tracked down and deported. He stated that, "There has been an abuse of our immigration laws and we must do something to stop it.... We must secure our boarders.... Barring welfare benefits to illegal immigrants and cracking down on illegal hiring." Then again, this type of prejudicial reawakening in political popularity was expressed through the political rantings during the U.S. Presidential campaign of 2016. Political posturing changed to accommodate and pander to a significant voting mass; the standing Democratic administration and candidate suddenly acted astonished and dismayed to hear near the exact same, now termed "racial", words formerly and very clearly expressed by a Democratic President repeatedly expressed by a Republican candidate. Boarder walls, amnesty and deportation of incarcerated non-residents were all hotly debated issues on all sides of traditional popular mass voting alignments. In dire remembrance of the "great war" – WWI – a century earlier, campaigning included a debate on refusal to allow non-vetted Islamic integration/immigration versus open boarders for immigration into the USA. Social isolationist feelings were enhanced and almost created a third political party by the young voting masses in a democratic society who feared and wished to revolt against the "rich" corporations ruling their nation, thus placing blame for loss of their expected post graduate jobs along with a deterioration in their individual standard of living onto unacceptable and supposedly one-sided contractual arrangements involving other financially competing nations. No mention was made pertaining to the degradation of a former pass or fail standard according to the traditional "3 R's" or to the lack of job-targeted vocational courses in public elementary and high schools.

Both the Democrats and the "mainstream" Republicans were also guilty of accepting the concept of "political correctness", a concept that breeds division of amalgamated multi-cultural American resident groups into single-cultural silos of hate and envy while openly opposing and preventing any and all further amalgamation of diverse cultures and citizen groups in the traditional churning crucibles of the USA, the melting pots that were once held as the American ideal to produce one unified American spirit. The popular public wish was unfortunately to get back to a former more comfortable era rather than the traditional American purpose of going forward to bigger and better possibilities, to be an ever more powerful unique and awe inspiring leading nation rather than an evolving to a liberal-progressive status of a "nation among nations". As you will eventually here read, Cicero's younger brother (Quintus) seemed to serve as the campaign manager for each and every American political candidate. Confusion abounded. Then again, according to W. Edward Deming, "If you cannot describe what you are doing as a process, then you don't know what you are doing."

Medicine also took a poke at Man and his Money. All that effort, that "racial-ethnic" medical gatekeeper migratory economics of **Healthcare Reform** in the first part of the 20th Century did little or nothing to halt or lessen the 1918-1920 global H1N1 "Spanish flu" influenza pandemic that killed so many American young and healthy first by inducing a cytokine storm, an over-reaction of the body's immune mechanism. Five percent of the world's population, 500 million people died; civilization silos were few back then and today ethnic-racial silos of human interaction for preventive health are near to non-existent. A much milder version of H1N1, "swine flu" appeared in 2009; but a potential devastating breakout of a more virulent H5N7 "avian-bird flu" strain in 2013 struck fear into the hearts of epidemiologists. Then Ebola came knocking at the American gatekeeper doors in 2014, only to be fortunately and successfully denied general public entry. Migratory economics looked to fund expensive medical research without considering many previous cost-effective delays. Healthcare delivery is, always was, and always will be expensive, but well worth that expense for the afflicted individuals. In the United States, the typical American-born citizen can expect medical insurance/payment due expenses to add up to over $600,000.00 during an average lifetime. Historical rationing by governmental gatekeepers has now been cleverly replaced with and through administratively-derived cost-effective definitions of optimal population healthcare delivery along with administratively-rationed **Healthcare Reform** management, a processed evolution in former gatekeeper enforcement and ancient stone wall construction held together with invisible migratory economic enforcement cement.

Perhaps the more migratory economics for **Healthcare Reform** change, the more they functionally remain the same. The migratory economics of today's world have constructed another "Great Wall" in China. This fiscal Chinese wall serves as a barrier to immigration as well as to **Healthcare Reform**. This new and improved Chinese great wall carries an old familiar name – citizenship. Immigrants to China as well as to children born in excess of one or two per documented citizen Chinese couples are not readily recognized as citizens of China. In such limbo status, when they are sick, they do not qualify for or receive public healthcare; when they are eager to learn, they are refused admission to public education; and when they are ready to work, they do not qualify for the endless number of jobs offered by the Chinese government. Of course, in the modern Chinese symbiotic capitalistic fiscal system, if they are wealthy, then they may partake of separately-housed private education and private healthcare, as well as various work opportunities in private industry. In partial reprieve, as opposed to the massively populated mainland, the Hong Kong District does grant a limited form of welfare for those lucky citizens who were born in and have remained to stay as permanent residents of Hong Kong.

Balancing the classical three-legged healthcare delivery stool of cost, access and quality for Man has always been viewed as a magical act of prestidigitation. Money and Medicine are strange bedfellows. Over 200 million people round and about Man's world migrated for economic reasons relating to health survival, pleasure and productivity in the year 2013. The health economic disparity and opportunistic goal, the attainment of available, affordable and less rationed healthcare delivery through **Healthcare Reform** pushes and pulls at these migratory economic patterns and further forces not only consumer but also provider economic migrations, both consumer and provider consisting of voluntary and administratively assigned or engineered origin.

Healthkeepers, keepers of "humanistic" health of all types and categories, operate within the evolving and greatly expanding technologically advanced paradigm that all Americans enjoy today. Now, more than ever, healthkeepers must envision the essence of "health" clearly and then strive to preserve Mankind's simplistic human to human concern regarding healthcare delivery within their honored and entrusted task, as caring and treating servants of the people in their stations as health quality leaders. While it seems that people all across the USA share a frustrating conundrum concerning the meaning and consequences concerning such terms as "health", "healthcare", "healthcare access", "healthcare coverage" and **"Healthcare Reform"** -- continually fitting together and pulling apart puzzling pieces of science, rites of myth, trends of culture, changing mores, and newer rules and regulations from evolving codes of law -- fear not, for such chaotic enthusiasms and controversial habits have been formed, broken and discarded many times over, throughout human history. Guiding principles for medical care and national health have had political pundits on all sides and slopes of health and healthcare modality arguments for thousands of years before the USA existed, and future pundits will continue to escalate that unending battle for thousands of years to come, ad infinitum.

Man now dominates the earth like no biological creature has ever done in the history of his planet. With Man's great power and control comes even greater responsibility, an ultimate defining lesson that Man may be just now in the slow and painful process of learning. If Man does not take heed, he may convict and then sentence himself to an unsustainable future on a planet that he has ravaged, disfigured, damaged and devastated beyond repair or replacement both physically and biologically. He risks his global extinction. Man's technology and an Atomic bomb rendered his world a shock wave, and his 12,000-year population expansion is now at an exponential threshold for the creation of a new and treacherous inter-glacial biosphere era, a geologic state shift to the begin the Anthropocene. Man's population density on planet earth now stands at approximately 7 Trillion, but Man's population is on course for growth to over 12,000,000,000 in just the next 40 years. Global-scale losses in earth's ecosystems must and will naturally follow to sustain such a biomass and continue to desecrate fresh and salt water fisheries, conifer forests, potable water supplies, agricultural land masses, social interaction, economic stability, and ultimately human life.

Man's iron sword evolved to the iron manufacturing machine and then the iron horse as Man's science marched ever onward, hopefully not into a valley of annihilation to be identified in a future time only by Man's hazardous carbon imprint. Man has mythological-morally/ethically justified continued unrationed increases in toxic environmental emissions of fossil fuels and allowed greenhouse gas consequences to support his ever-increasing out-of-control biomass on planet earth. Currently accepted political policy dictated by Man requires increasing agricultural production to feed, shelter and clothe a starving world while acknowledging the consequence of such a global policy -- a resultant run-off of the necessitated higher-production by-products which then pollute Man's planet. Such is the nature of Man's present beastly human footprint that identifies and defines the Anthropocene. The migratory economic of spreading and multiplying a growing human biomass to fill every niche of every continent and accepting a mandatory accompanying increase in per-capita consumption rate cannot continue indefinitely. For the present, Man's global population growth has demanded and propagated a mythical moral/ethical excuse for unrestricted limited resource consumption and energy production to enhance his habitat and life style, a mythical moral/ethical excuse that also cannot continue unaltered and unrationed indefinitely. Fear not, Man's mythology will march ever onward.....

A moment for pause and perspective CONCERNING MONEY:

Money has historically presented itself in a variety of physical forms. A few of the modalities by and in which it has functioned as a mechanism of exchange include: shells, IOU's, precious metal coins, banknotes, and paper backed up by metallic reserves or the promise of a thriving nation. The true and real practical purpose of Money is to express and codify Man's precariously perceived value/worth of property or services into numerical terms, an alphabetical hierarchy of numbers that hopefully hold true for some brief period of time for a specific tribe, culture, nation or group of nations created and organized by Man. Money is the transference embodiment of Man's mystically derived earthly economic values. Money, in metallic-bullion, paper-token or in endless inventive and adaptive forms of "metalism" or "chartalism", functions as and expresses an accountable commodity for integrating two primal driving factors -- firstly Man's fiscal wealth/health and secondly Man's mercantile efficiency for services, trade and commerce. The evolutionary paradigms of Money and the sometimes unimaginable circumstances offered up for Man's willingness to part with his Money follow the same ephemeral evolutionary paradigms as of Man and Medicine.

Money can independently manifest and often project an anthropomorphic life form of its own. Money can reduce the worth of Man to a commodity that can be negotiated to suit the mystical transient migratory economic-cultural wants of Man. Philosophers would argue that Man's wealth/health is not in holding large sums of Money, but rather in the productive versus non-productive societal mechanisms by which he attains those sums. Philosophers may comment upon, but do not direct the economic misadventures of Man -- there is no argument that Money and mystical fear control Man's politics. Money can be the physical manifestation of some political power's purposeful and directed influence. Institutional fear can rear its ugly head through the untouchable mechanisms of strike, organized protest and war, which are both backed by Money. The mere presence or suspected smell of Money injects an uncontrollable variable, a distinct distracting and distasteful odor, a nasty variable into all economic equations. Anarchist and historic founder of community organizing, Saul Alinsky boldly stated, "Control healthcare and you control the people". The evolution of migratory economics concerning Money has never been apart from **Healthcare Reform**, as healthcare enhances Mankind's ability to strive for and pursue prosperity/wealth/health. They share mystical convoluted but inter-linking histories: Man, Money and Medicine.

The never-ending Money-payment system saga traces: first, the creation of Money Giants; then, the Giants' transformation into Money Titans; next, the waring of the Money Titans against the Olympian Money gods; and finally, the Money Titans ultimate succumbing to the exact same fate as of the ancient Grecian Titans. This epic Money tale begins with the pre-Money process of "barter" for trinkets, favors and bits of personal property. Barter is likewise as old as Mankind's existence. When weight equivalent private precious metal stampings (monitory equivalents much before evolving to actual coinage) were introduced to better manage or serve the role of exchange for time-definite perceived values of bartered items, local governmental bodies could not resist and quickly intervened to control that primitive monetary system. Again, the government-administrative-lordly central control sought and captured the general public trust with an economic relationship that was at one time granted to the individuals within a society. The weave of Man, Money and Medicine is finely threaded and tight. Rounded metal coinage with a central hole for easy portability on a necklace or chain, the first accepted real-looking, feeling and touching Money commodity, began in China at about 1000 BC. Money became a tool, a common accepted and agreed upon commodity with which Man could easily and comfortably negotiate with his fellow Man.

Innovatively advancing beyond bare pieces of precious metals, imprinted coinage, such as the gold and silver Lydian electrum trite, originated in the iron age around the turn of the century, about 600 BC, under the rule of King Alyattes in Sardis which would be located in present day Turkey. A time-bit later, captured prisoners of war were turned into life-long Roman slaves; and at great human cost, these short-lived slaves labored for the remainder of their lives in the Riotinto silver mines of southern Spain. This commonly and culturally accepted-approved enforced human slave labor continued for nearly a millennium, to produce a coinage and create a dynamic economic advantage that would allow a reliable and sustainable wealth of Money to grow a great empire. Slavery of Man in silver mines for Man to accumulate Money is just not cost effective as an economic process for creating Money in a human-right benefit-driven society. Migratory economic policies have become much more "sophisticated" today, and of course, always with the accompanying evolution of contemporary myth.

Money "counting" evolved to "accounting"; Man sought ways to manipulate the written or carved concept of actual numbers, and in so doing Money created the science of mathematics. Still serving Man as a better prediction of outcomes than blind faith in some ideological system of accounting, down to earth Money matters mattered more and more. Around 3500 BC, 5000 years before the application of word script in Mesopotamia, ancient Sumerians invented symbolic writing to keep tally on monetary transactions. Certain historical economic modalities such as the recognition of Money in the form of international hard coinage depicting the head of Emperor Augustus peaked at the time of the Roman Empire, when as is written in the Bible, "one rendered unto Caesar that which was Caesar's". As did the

Roman denarii throughout the Roman Empire, the sea-green flavor of the U.S. buck or the expectant taste of any other stable national imprint attracts all groupings of Man to come and sit at a common dining-discussion table. The international development and growth of economics in general became stunted by the lack of new coinage for manipulation and dispersal of Money following that Roman Empire epoch, during the very Dark Ages of Western Civilization, after the fall of Rome.

Ancient migratory economic cultures used animal bones carved with notches to document debt in terms of a message defining a quantity or a number. For Man's love of Money or because of his love of Money, this counting devise was held to be somewhat sacred, akin to the counting beads in a Christian prayer-bead rosary. Again to be noted, as societies underwent further organization, the maintenance of a sustainable hierarchal structure demanded that public barter for substantial economic components be controlled by the state. The traditional single tally bone or tally stick evolved to a more difficult to counterfeit devise – a second split-stick that could "match the fit" of a set of grooves or notches. In the year 1100, King Henry I of England insisted that all public lending issuances be recorded for future repayment with that improved version of the tally stick, the split tally stick. With this second split stub or "foil" retained, the agencies of the king could accurately demand each year what had to be returned or "revenued", given back as a tax to and for the kingdom. The king's tally Man could then re-issue or lend and more accurately control the kingdom's credit balance. Coinage of solid, more durable and still more difficult to counterfeit metals eventually replaced the split tally stick or foil system.

A copper shortage in China's Szechwan province fostered the temporary use of banknotes and paper Money in the early part of the ninth century. Migratory economic development time for national monetary paper currency may have begun in the Song dynasty around the year 1023, but further development soon stood still until after the death of Genghis Khan, when the migratory economic modality of recognizable and reliable international paper Money and international contracts for those nations under Mongol rule became officially backed by governmental law and force. The death of the first Great Khan in 1227 divided his enormous empire into "Khanates" among his four sons. The geography included a vast multi-cultural land containing a supermajority of the world's civilized peoples. Within less than ten years, each son died from an unrelated cause, leaving their four East-European Christian wives, Tartar Queens, to rule the civilized world in the name of their very young children (grandsons of the Great Kahn) for about the next nine years. These dynamically competing women enabled the first use of those internationally economically contractual papers, later evolved into international paper Money under the rigorous and exacting economic rule of grandson Kublai Khan. Due to uncontrolled inflation, that temporal migratory economic modality of paper Money (which was first reported to the Western cultures by Marco Polo) disappeared in 1445. Despite this known migratory economic knowledge of a functional paper currency, not until centuries later, in 1661, did the "Stockholm Banco" of Johan Palmstruch begin to issue paper banknotes. When this inflationary Swedish effort finally failed, the Goldsmiths of England developed a similar Money system through the Bank of England in 1694, but eventually safeguarded their migratory economic paper currency from inflation by the institution of a "gold standard" in 1816.

In similar pursuit, the very first-issued USA paper notes required the secured sustainability of a silver and gold metallic reserve in the ratio of 15 to 1. In 1831, because the conversion ratio for international trade differed, the USA feared a continual slow but steady metallic gold depletion and revised the U.S. ratio upwards to 16 to 1, which then substituted that prized gold depletion with silver depletion. In the spirit of due diligence to assure the American public that one could "bank on" the fiscal sustainability of the local bank-issued USA paper notes, the federal government developed a National Bank mechanism as a backup in 1863. For a nation so rich in natural precious metal resources, these federal actions had very little influence on the migratory economic interactions of U.S. citizens freely traveling from one state to another; but eventually that economic trading freedom sadly ended. As a matter of migratory economic military strategy, a "fiat" monetary standard, not tied to metallic gold or silver reserves, persisted for paper Money during the Civil War epoch in the United States of America and lasted until 1879 when President William McKinley's administration adopted a single metallic standard – gold. There were many efforts to bring back silver into the mix and the official U.S. federal fiscal policy became confused for a while. In the year 1900, the USA officially re-adopted the 1879 administrative policy of President William McKinley by officially utilizing a free exchange of a fixed proportion of gold for currency, a "gold standard", to physically back large paper currency, while silver coinage served the need for smaller denominational commerce. At that time, this true gold standard, which persisted until 1933, temporally stabilized the USA's banking industry; but this gold standard of world peace via preserving mutual interest in protected trade and commerce arrangements may have unintendedly or insidiously led to the consequences of increasing monitory disparities between the "rich and poor".

Migratory economic forces in the course of societal development tend to naturally increase a disparity in Money distribution. Population density tends to increase in urban areas, and the ownership of property tends to be more and more restricted to the individually wealthy or the corporations of Man, who and which in turn become wealthier from the collection of more rents or payments of lower wages. Possession of manipulatable Money makes more Money, much more Money than Man can gain from his individual physical-manual labor. Income generated from wealth/Money also outstrips income from managerial hierarchy, professional acclaim or any other sort of earned income. Income from wealth is usually put toward research and development and partially saved for a rainy day nest-egg, both efforts naturally leading to the production of even more income; while the vast majority of earned income, especially low and middle class income, is usually spent on an annual basis. When wealth increases faster than national income, that migratory economic condition further depreciates the relative income of wage earners. The rich become richer and the poor become relatively poorer in their accumulated wealth and style of living. Redistribution of wealth becomes a political topic of demand without regard for supply, especially when ignited by class struggle to overcome an ever-growing actual or perceived functional economic disparity. Simply providing a significant rise in the low end numerical per/hour wage may temporarily help a few, but most likely would result in unemployment, especially if that raise is above an equilibrium point that would effectively redistribute wealth. Realignment is best achieved by a nation increasing its volume of exports and thus increasing national Gross Domestic Product (GDP) beyond the rate of accumulation of individual wealth and enabling an effective rise in relative mid-stream wages and available middle class jobs. The Capitalistic formula of increasing business activity and opportunity thus increasing the business demand to hire for newly formed well-paying jobs is so very easily and simply stated, but altering an established stratified economic process for the mutual benefit of Man is no easy task and often fraught with unintended consequences consisting, a varietal order of economic failures.

Man links jealousy over Money distribution to opportunity limitations in earning/accumulating Money. In order to have jobs, there must be businesses, and businesses need a reason to stay and not migrate from one nation to another nation. The negative effect derived from simply increasing wages alone may result in the shutting of businesses, decreased overall employment or downsizing of firms to meet the cost of doing business, increased automation to lessen costs, and an overall decrease in manufacturing competiveness compared to another nation. When the migratory economic of "following the Money" further incentivizes businesses to migrate outside of a nation's borders, an employment tail of migrating jobs will naturally follow in the exodus. The former contested and protested disparity in income of the rich versus the poor not only persists, but is then significantly expanded. Moreover, a quick governmental-enacted simple redistribution of wealth to correct such a disparity in wealth/Money has also proven to be of only temporary benefit on the world stage. As observed in Argentina, quickly-enacted governmental redistribution of wealth actually ruined the nation's future economy and resulted in so many jobs having been exported to Brazil, where there already existed a Money-hungry low wage earning population eager and anxious to gulp up the opportunity for those newly-created jobs.

The unintended consequences that had resulted from the Speenhamland system of bread laws of 1795 had been for a long time forgotten by progressive liberal thought. At that time, a "worker or non-worker right to live" guaranteed subsidies to be paid by land owners due to a migratory economic inducing the higher price of grain. In return for the "right", wage earners suffered stagnation in overall wages with a resultant very minimum wage being paid to all. The workers eventually revolted as they and the poor suffered more than ever before. The Sperm and the Ovum again rose to be the procreators of poverty. Poverty then bred disease and diseases culled poverty. Ecolo-nomics (from the Greek, environment + society + law) progressed from terribly bad to something worse. Social reactionary mores led to the still horribly inhumane Poor Law Reform Act of 1834. The fickle course of migratory economics had repeatedly allowed political corruption to propagandize a natural sub-human existence for the poor, but absolutely not also for the unaccountable actions of the rich. The ontological or metaphysical relationship between the concepts concerning the nature of being human and Man's subjective class categorizations of Man in an argumenta-database became a political subject matter simply labeled "Taboo".

There is no truly "just" tax law; some voices have indeed shouted that all taxation is simply Money robbery by the state. Money follows a cyclic course as the world goes round. Historically land is rented or taxed to temporary "owners", upon whose death or bankruptcy the land "ownership" reverts to whomever or whatever happens to be controlling the nation/state/kingdom. The controlling governing party then rents or taxes the same land once again. Stepping from the macro into the micro art of living picture, consider this: The increased Money accumulation in a profitably exporting nation brings prosperity to all and can then keep jobs at home. Therefore, more ultimately successful strategies would be economic policies that strengthen collective bargaining solitary for workers through the granting of increased power to trade unions and the middle class, including small businesses. However, it must be emphasized that such productive strategies would be destined to fail if not intimately intertwined with macroeconomic policies that would grow aggregate demand to strengthen the GDP, which might also include a sliding scale of annual taxes or a fixed percent tax for all, a tax that represents and is a true gross annual taxation without loopholes, and also a controlled/limited taxation that is not overwhelming for businesses. Only if all of the above measures and policies have been vigorously put in place with the dedicated cooperation of a society and then ultimately failed miserably would a consideration of national standardization of all incomes or the slightest thought of a frank straightforward tax on accumulated wealth be in any sort of reasonable migratory economic order.

Enjoying that anthropomorphic life of its own, Money can and often does shrink and evaporate global boundaries. Free trade works best for nations that mostly export (supply product and receive Money) and not so well for nations that mostly import (supply Money and receive product). Money is also intertwined with the misery and mysticism of politics. There has to be some sort of return on capital or other political/social advantages for any trade agreement to be successful. Some successfully trading nations have supplied product and received Money in the form of supplied emigration. The emigrated supply of low income laborers from all over the globe have historically sent and currently send back a Money product to the country of their origin, via those laborers transferring cash back to their friends and families yet living in the country of their origin. That very substantial amount of Money then significantly bolsters the GDP in the said nations of origin.

The proven power of Money does do and has done the talking for Man. New world gold and silver permitted Spain, with the help of Charles the 5th, to repel the recidivistic re-expanding Ottoman Empire in the Mediterranean, the "White Sea" of Suleiman the Great. Money talking allowed a Catholic Pope Pius the 5th to organize and allied armies to fight the forces of Islam. Moreover, that raw influence and power of Money talking goes way beyond permitting and influencing wars, the entity "Money" itself insidiously directs the economic postures and supposed paradigm ideals of Man, his politics and the structure of his societies. Money power controls beyond the point of Man's rational behavior, forcing Man to submit and kowtow to a most powerful and overwhelming addiction, further fueled by Man's overpowering innate greed for Money.

Intertwined with Medicine, Man's politics of Money power was all about who could get or got the bucks, who has or had the bucks, who is or was hiding the bucks and who is passing or passed the buck. So here in the New Western World intertwined are three more Money questions: what about that potent political force called the dollar, what about the universal monetary symbol "$" and just what is it all about with that almighty all-American greenback "dollar"?

It is perhaps slightly ironic that the Greek god Hermes carried the caduceus, a stick entangled by snakes which resembled the "$" sign, and that caduceus is now the universal symbol of Medicine. It is definitely more ironic to remember that Hermes was the god of both "Banking and Thieves". Offering an equally bewildering choice for its architecture, the United States Federal Reserve Building in Washington D.C. boldly flaunts a statue of Virgo holding a medical caduceus. The universal word "dollar" is derived from coins of silver that were mined in historic early 16ᵗʰ Century Bohemia via the German word "taler" and the Flemish word "daler". Later, Spanish-American colonial and British-American colonial coinages utilized the word "dollar". Not to be totally off the coinage bandwagon, in the late 18ᵗʰ Century the USA proclaimed the "dollar" to be the official unit of American currency. Moreover, that stand-alone mysterious universal monetary symbol "$", the "dollar sign", has its own story to tell: In the later part of the 18ᵗʰ Century, manuscripts reflecting economic dealings between English and Spanish Americans tallied up sums of "Pesos" utilizing the handwritten script "Pˢ". This scripted mark gradually transformed itself first to a "P" overwritten by an "S" and then subsequently on to the familiar "$".

What is for a time to be considered economically successful and sustainable healthcare delivery, or good or better quality healthcare delivery, an economic deliverable somehow accomplished through **Healthcare Reform,** may be just a matter of acquired or expected/perceived taste -- A migratory economic taste for the tongue of an individual or for a nation, and also a sampling taste for the world to savor. The invisible self–correcting migratory economic hand of economist Adam Smith and the heavy economic hand of government control may both seek equilibrium in the end, but as admonished by economist J. M. Keynes, "In the end, we are all dead". Therefore, **Healthcare Reform** through short term migratory economic action alone is too often justified as an appropriate action to immediately enhance the art of living for the individual, often with great similarity to economist Gary Becker's thought on crime and punishment as a migratory economic gamble on not being caught.

The evolution of economics and economic thought may not at all be any sort of equilibrator or equalization process as is classically or neo-classically described and understood. A process of dynamic change in the way that Money is created and utilized is linked to ecological and societal evolution. The industrial revolution transferred the monitory economic dominance and control of landowners to merchant organizations and then on to corporations. **Money can buy power, but power is not always for sale. – Ralzak.** The process of dynamic societal ecologic evolution serves as the mechanism to drive contrived economic equilibrium theory paradigms.

However and pragmatically, in the big picture for a nation that hopefully does not expect to be dead in the end, carefully calculated short term gain must lead to a long term economic benefit. Simply reforming healthcare delivery through projected savings derived from future mass consumption is not a true or sustainable economic investment. Economic investment represents or should represent a delay in personal or societal consumption gratification by saving economic resources to eventually increase productivity and profit by way of a planned future economic investment. With an abundance of such migratory **Healthcare Reform** strategies in dynamic competition, the most efficient and profitable will no doubt survive the test of sustainability; however, one must also be acutely aware and cognizant that that amoral greed within profit and growth might not always be desirable, especially when local economies lead to national ecologies where eventual unethical hegemony of migratory economic power can be set on exploitation of healthcare delivery on a global scale. Although locally ignored in England, Thomas Percival codified ethical conduct for a global scale in 1803 and is credited with the establishment of such terms as "professional ethics" and "medical ethics". In 1847, the American Medical Association became the first modern healthkeeper of medical standards by adapting that Percivalean code to define medical ethics in the USA.

Change in the social order with newly-acquired mores and ethics required continual migratory economic adaptation of relationships among nations. A unique interest in world peace to preserve financial stability fostered a diplomatic Plausible Deniability (PD) of any possible economic or military interest in the conquest of one nation over another. After all, those speaking on behalf of a nation had to protect their national economy. The disruptive technologies of machines eventually became powerful enough to create revolutions centering on social interactions. Disruptive technologies do not necessarily raise employment after an initial period of stabilization/equalization, and the nation's GDP is only dynamically elevated when compared to less technological innovation on a global perspective. Profit and wealth derived from manufactured products overwhelmed the profits from agricultural produce, and that newly found commerce came to surpass agriculture as the leading or primary motivator of the economy. A new top dog Money totem pole featured the image of the merchant class above all others.

With Money working wonders, Man's Western Culture World underwent a rather sudden societal reform in about that same period of earth-time. The infinite imagination within the mind of Man has fostered his technology to continually march on like wanderlust and create at least four paradigms of Industrial Revolution (so far…..). Each period created an intellectual and practical shrinking of his planet earth by means of Man's Money-driven technology continually enhancing Man's physical mobility and his intimate communication with his fellow Man.

The Nineteenth Century witnessed the beginning of these adaptive consequences with the First Industrial Revolution paradigm. Steam engine powered locomotive trains for rapid distant transport and additional lines of communication were created first with a pony express and then a clicking Morse-code telegraph system. Money made it possible for Man to work at jobs requiring few skills and long hours. Man died in battle from the trajectories of lead-laden bullets, crude rockets and cannon-fire bombardment.

A migratory economic of sudden Money held fast with an international gold standard, self-regulating markets and a global concept of liberal nation-building led by the above referenced war of unification within the USA. (WWI created political imbalance within the global system which also disrupted the international gold standard, eventually to become a factor in the promulgation of WWII.)

The first half of the Twentieth Century experienced the Money-driven technological magic of the Second Industrial Revolution paradigm, leading to discovering electricity and gasoline to power automobiles, airplanes, and a voice-transmitting telephone. Money made it possible for Man to work at jobs on an "assembly line" for greater productivity and efficiency. Man died in battle from ever more devastating atomic bombs dropped from those planes, and cars converted into heavy metal tanks with unguided missile-shooting guns adding to the horror of warfare.

The second half of the Twentieth Century oversaw Man's Money-driven technology advancing at an accelerating rate during the Third Industrial Revolution paradigm. Ground and air rapid transport systems utilized larger and larger planes designed with jet engines and super-fast 250-300 miles per hour trains with electromagnetic induction engines. Both advances eventually enabled Man to take a small step on the Moon, while mankind's communication system took a giant step forward with the development of an Internet. Money made it possible for Man to work at jobs that required increasing amounts of vocational training. Man died in battle victimized by such weapons as robotic drones, precision guided rockets, and ever so many types of bunker buster and underground bombs with the constant threat of a dirty bomb or a radiological dispersal device (RDD) always looming over his head.

The first half of the Twenty-first Century is witnessing Man's Money-driven technology doubling at a rate of every three years and a Fourth Industrial Revolution paradigm. Global and/or national mobility and communication are both almost instantaneous and seamless. Smartphones are ubiquitous. The workplace jobs of Man, his honored places of employment for earning the Money for his daily bread, are being replaced with Artificial Intelligence robotic devices. IBM's empathetic supercomputer Dr. Watson outperforms all human challengers and pretends to augment his humanity. Non empathetic Man will die in battle with the aid of high altitude electro-magnetic pulses (HEMP) – Man's blasting of intense gamma ray pulses from robotic-controlled space stations to specifically defined geographical targets on his planet, thus destroying the local functioning electric equipment and rendering that chosen area militarily defenseless; and, therefore, vulnerable for further military invasion and conquest, or alternatively, simply the surrendering of any part or whole of some nation's territory. The migratory economic maneuvers to enhance wealth and the ultimate social evolutions of "Man the technological conquistador" have been and will be not much different from the military priorities of the historic property and Money-hungry agrarian landowners, nobles, royals and kings of Man's not so ancient times. Ultimately, however, in the Fourth Industrial Revolution paradigm, Man will be evolving his role and social interactions with his fellow Man at every conceivable previously hidden part and parcel on this third rock orbiting his sun; and Man is already progressing with social and technological innovations at an exponential rate. No longer is Man faced with the problem of "could"; he is now duty-bound to the more psychologically difficult decision of "should". There will be a harsh conundrum for "latter 21st Century Man" to solve -- "Should all or only part of Man's biomass be equally and luxuriously supported at some level, or at what level, of acknowledged environmental sacrifice"? – That will present a perplexing question that Man must answer in a very painfully foreseeable time-definite future schedule. Myth will see the way.

Medieval times also bore witness to disruptive technologies: Money somehow successfully seeks and finds what Money may and can buy; and thereby all the ancient Chinese secrets concerning explosive devices immigrated to the Western Cultural World like a migratory economic bomb that was destined to burst into paradigm shattering consequences. Just as that sudden Chinese migratory economic invention of the gun and gun-powered cannons into western culture rendered useless and redundant twenty years of intensive and laborious training that once was necessary for Euro-Western Man to become an efficient horse-backed knight wielding a lance and a sword, so there is a similar paradigm shift in the medical industry of today. The creep and crawl of migratory economic "professionalism" into **Healthcare Delivery** practitioner practice is accelerated and dashing forward in the Twenty-first Century to rapidly render obsolete the traditional absolutely required ten to the fourth power (10^4) hours of rote memorization and hands-on training. That laborious work, training and time prerequisite, once essential for Man to render a quality medical practice to his fellow Man, suddenly shrunk to be barely visible and yet viable for the particular biomass paradigm. Sustainability was never assured.

Information Technology (IT) is now and finally at last delivering its intellectual and institutional knowledge directly to the masses of Man in a manner that the relatively untrained or "common" Man can both assimilate and utilize in the form of Operational Technological (OT) devices that can monitor, detect and correct (observe, diagnose and treat) the medical frailties (illnesses) of Man. Moreover, after monitoring via sensors and controls (taking a history and doing a medical examination), OT can carry on interactive conversations with other machines (and if it wished, humans) to "optimize human resources to central systematic control", directly explain a medical condition to a beneficiary (patient) and answer the recipient's or healthcare client's (physician's patient's) questions in just about any language popularly spoken and hopefully understood by Man. The supposed endpoint, machine communication to the common Man, instantly converts those new relatively untrained dumber "doctors", the cheaper-paid medical practitioners of that new brand of "professionalism" into technological geniuses in record time. These new on the horizon Money-savers are forever mesmerized from continually staring each long day into computer monitors, to audaciously bear witness to that godly communication originating from on high in some Internet cloud that instantaneously converts these so-called "professionalists" into **Healthcare Delivery** geniuses; but that final Man to machine delivery mechanism is only a small fraction of the IT involved in mutual machine communication with other machines. There is an overwhelming production and consumer demand for so many new and constantly improving or "upgraded" (up to date) OT with predictive maintenance (continuing education) of mechanical sensors (formerly known as physicians) and various controls operationalized and operated without the awkward and unpredictable interference of Man. By the way, repair and renewal of machine driven hardware and software (otherwise rest and rehabilitation of the human body and the mind of Man) are important components for reliable and sustainable systematic performance (continuing quality care and improvement). All of this IT, OT, robots, and many more robotic devices help to perform the deliverance of medical and surgical practice to Man. By way of history, in 1921, Karel Capek introduced to Prague a play production entitled "Rossums's Universal Robots". The author chose the word "robot" to describe an artificial human that could work for less Money than a real Man; a creature lacking the dignity of Man that was manufactured and solidified in a reproducible mold from a yet unhardened and shapeless chemical compound, an artificial Man that could easily and more efficiently do the work of two and one half bone and flesh real humans. Capek derived "robot" from a Czech language word meaning "forced labor". Perhaps someday in the future of earth-time all these super-smart robots of the Twenty-first Century may also come under the direct influence of that functional evil known as "Money", get the bright idea of solidarity for monetary negotiations and then, of course, unionize – to form a "Union of American Pod Devices".

A moment for pause and perspective CONCERNING MEDICINE:

Medicine is first and foremost Man's necessary and permissive ability for the transference/embodiment of Man's desire and will to gain and maintain his personal property or fiscal wealth, a task that for prerequisite requires utilizing the dynamic competitive advantage of his physical and mental wealth – Man's good and functioning health/wealth. Translation: Man's Money buys Medicine for the physical/mental/religious POWER to attain longevity and happiness during his earthly life and mystical life to come. The evolutionary paradigms of Medicine follow the evolutionary paradigms of Man and Money. As Man's longevity increased, so did his absolute increasing need for Medicine wealth/health. Thus Man became more and more willing to transfer his fiscal or monetary wealth into buttressing and prolonging his Medicine -- physical/mental/religious wealth/health.

Man, Money and Medicine and their over-riding evolving myths interact in an unending variety of ways. The Healthcare-Medicine varietal is often politically manipulated and reduced to the status of a minor "civil right" in order that this painfully obvious essential health/wealth need of Man can shore up the mythological shoe strings of so many other newly-formed otherwise previously overlooked "civil rights". Indeed, Man's Medicine is not simply a civil right – health/wealth stands on a scale firm and tall accompanied by potable water, food production and an armed military defense as absolute essentials for a nation's and world's biomass sustained survival on planet earth – not just a "civil right". Manipulation among the ingredients of Man, Money and Medicine continue on in the evolution of migratory economics; the process is as ancient as Man's history…..

In his *Odyssey*, Homer wrote, "In Egypt, the Men are more skilled in Medicine than any of human kind." Born a poor peasant in the 27th Century BC, Imhotep rose to the rank of demi-god and became the first documented "physician" in written history. He prescribed herbs for cures long before Hippocrates instituted "rational Medicine" in 469 BC. The medical school at Alexandria certainly spoke to that comment of Homer and went far beyond the former Egyptian empirical pontificators or priestly "snu". A division of Alexander the Great's empire appointed one of his generals, Ptolemy, to rule and become Pharos of Egypt. Hieroglyphics describing the Egyptian medical arts were translated into Greek, but all that Egyptian-recorded medical knowledge and much more were immediately lost after the burning of the library at Alexandria. Not until the discovery of that Greek-translated black block of basalt known as the "Rosetta Stone" was the Western World actually able to document those ancient Egyptian medical arts. Archeologists have since proven that in Egypt's Badarian age, hieroglyphics described remedies such as malachite for eye paint. In 3000 BC the "Ebers Papyrus" explained a pulse and a circulation of blood as well as many, albeit unproven, medical treatments. The "Edwin Smith Papyrus" of 1600 BC depicted many surgical procedures such as the treatment of fractures. Alcmaeon, a Pythagorean, described the function of the Optic Nerve.

Still eons before the time of Hieroglyphics or Sanskrit, the most ancient Medicine Man tended to his tribe with the one-on-one laying on and **sacrosanct holding of his patient's hand** while utilizing the penultimate quality of chants available to him. He was never disgraced for having administered a short, cheap and humiliating ineffective but cost-effective healthcare delivery chant. There was never any tribal administrative **Healthcare Reform** consensus meeting to have the Medicine Man work smarter, see more patients and spend less time procuring or actually eliminating some especially hard-to-find herbs. A more efficient for the total tribe or "optimal care" chant was never demanded nor desired by the migratory economics of his culture, and neither was such a "working smarter" chant part nor parcel of the Medicine Man's basic healing nature; that ancient healthkeeper and his tribe could not and would not ever even consider administering such a chant. A tribe with such a renowned Medicine Man tended to prosper and soon became a sort-after tribe that economically pulled in new tribal immigrants to marry into or join up with in some migratory economic fashion. The migratory economic factor of healthcare delivery always pushed and pulled migrations for **Healthcare Reform**. Those chanting have also survived over the millenniums – 21st Century yoga enthusiasts chant and meditate for pain control.

Eventually, the imprecise, inexact and inaccurate changing oral transmission of medical knowledge became systematically recorded and standardized: Before 1000 BC, Agnivesa, under the tutelage of Atreya, compiled and named this landmark-written medical diagnosis and medical treatment record, the "Carakasamhia". A congregation of sages reviewed his sacrosanct writings and officially stamped and applauded the prized work and its humble author with great admiration and approval. Migratory medical knowledge evolved as time passed over a few centuries and old fundamental questions certainly demanded newly evolved answers. The great Sanskrit scholar and highly esteemed itinerant physician practitioner and teacher, Caraka, updated that classic healthcare delivery volume to a newer and scientifically improved version in about 800 BC. His pre-Buddhist Brahman masterpiece, the revised Carakasamhia, stood the test of time for sixteen centuries as the most authentic of all the Ayurvedic medical teachings until eventually translated from Sanskrit into Persian then Arabic in the 8th Century. The medical knowledge and doctor-patient medical practice of the time was unquestionably sacrosanct. Only men were believed to be pure enough to graduate from India's fist nursing school in 250 BC, and women were not accredited with nursing duties until the time of Phoebe (Romans 16:1), the first female nurse.

Time's passage changed Caraka's name to Sharaka Indiansus in the eventual Latin translations, but his fundamental ingredients for healthcare delivery remained the same. The functions of mind, body and nature were all interrelated and there were things and practices that caused diseases and other things and practices that cured diseases. He outlined a scientific approach to medical treatment by eliciting an authentic one-on-one account of the illness (a patient history), directly observing his patient (later to be called a physical examination), and then arriving at a conclusion (diagnosis) by logically comparing and contrasting the history and physical exam with the known disease states of his time. Caraka was also deeply concerned about medical ethics and developed an oath of initiation for those few who were "worthy" to practice Medicine and partake of a sacrosanct physician-patient relationship. He was also a political activist and demanded that the "state" protect true physicians from pseudo-practitioners.

The 2100 BC code of Hammurabi also defined an ethical position for the physician in society and introduced a state-mandated and enforced sliding scale fee payment schedule based on the patient-recipient's societal position and financial ability to pay. Thereby, payments to the physician were assured by the state. (According to Murray N. Rothbard, this is a viciously unstable economic/tax system and charity, albeit unequal, is a more sustainable modality of wealth/services distribution than mass welfare.) The migratory economics of **Healthcare Reform** and politics were, are, and always will be inexorably intertwined. In return for those politically granted guarantees, the quality of the physician's care was also audited and evaluated by the state. If the quality of healthcare delivered was determined to be poor and the physician did not act with the best of intentions (as consensus-determined by politically appointed administrators), then the punishment for the physician was quite severe. An eye for an eye repayment philosophy was clearly enacted and recorded. Sacrosanct mores were disregarded under the state-run universal healthcare delivery system. The actions or autonomy of the actual medical practitioner physician became more deliberate and restricted under the yoke of that administrative scrutiny. Man's Money and Medicine galloped on together. Medical practice always came with risk and risk-taking; there never was such a thing as a free lunch in medical practice for the hands-on practitioner. When the consequences of that medically necessary risk became too great a burden for the practitioner, then the physician refused to take on that particular risky patient. Physicians preferred to pay the state to be excused from taking on such a risky burden rather than be paid by the state to perform the medically necessary task. This migratory economic situational decision offered way back then lends perhaps a very early peek into the free-market "at what personal cost" 20th Century philosophy of Milton Friedman. Entire countries would one day need to decide "at what national cost" universal healthcare should or would be funded. The migratory economics of basic beastly human nature prevailed then as they still do today.

Moses escaped from Egypt in the great migration of 3500 BC, but the Bible and the Dead Sea Scrolls did not come to light until after 1000 BC. In Leviticus, the importance of healthy dietary laws, sanitation, and medical quarantine are expressed in many passages. Certainly ancient civilizations were anxious to preserve the healthy, but let's not forget the regularly expected humiliation and crude deaths imposed by Man upon lepers and such people with deformities by utilizing the common popular practices of stoning and abandonment. Luke, with a gentler hand, was noted to have been formally educated as a common-place physician. When William Tyndale published the first English translation of the New Testament, he translated the Latin word "medice" into the English word "physician". "Jesus, the Great Physician" was known as both a spiritual healer and a spiritual teacher; from that inference, physicians are also teachers. From the Latin word "duceo" (I teach) is derived the word "doctor" and a later word "master" in academics, all emanating from the original physicians (teachers) such as those apostilles who taught the Christian faith.

In and about 460-370 BC, Democritus, a Greek from Thrace, rejected Plato's "Myth of the Metals" and insisted on a "materialistic" philosophic cause and effect for every natural and Man-made phenomenon. He taught that Medicine-diseases were not curses sent by the mythical gods of Olympus, and for centuries to come befuddled the scientific community with concepts of time, space, void and movement that prevailed until the time of Einstein's revelation of "relativity". Democritus dismissed the concept of a celestial curtain that surrounded the earth at night, proved the world to be basically spherical in shape, and postulated the future ephemeral existence of planet earth in accordance with an infinite number of other worlds and suns throughout an unexplored universe. During the period of his lifetime, national cultural myths continually collided and were continually revised. The Persian King Darius introduced gold currency Money and held a treasure of Egyptian Medicine knowledge. The Greeks were constantly at war with the Persians and their Royal Mounted Persian Mail Carriers -- "Neither snow, nor rain, nor heat, nor gloom of night stays these courageous couriers from the swift completion of their appointed rounds." Thereby the concept of **Healthcare Reform** did travel on those rounds saddled on the omnipresent accompanying three horses – Man, Money and Medicine.

Hippocrates, the famous Greek healthkeeper from Kos and a contemporary of Democritus, subjected various and varied clinical practices to a detailed meta-analysis in order to develop approved and sacrosanct prescribing practices. Hippocrates is most remembered for writing the classical medical or surgical practicing physician's sacrosanct vow and oath of medical practice. Up until the later-half of the 20th Century, every graduating American medical student formally stood and swore to follow the dictum of these words:

"I swear by Apollo the Physician, by Asclepius, by Hygieia, by Panaceia, and by all the gods and goddesses, making them my witnesses, that I will fulfill according to my ability and judgment this oath and this covenant:
To hold him who has taught me this art as equal to my parents and to live my life in partnership with him, and if he is in need of Money to give him a share of mine, and to regard his offspring as equal to my brothers in male lineage and to teach them this art - if they desire to learn it - without fee and covenant; to give a share of precepts and oral instruction and all the other learning to my sons and to the sons of him who has instructed me and to pupils who have signed the covenant and have taken an oath according to the medical law, but no one else.

I will apply dietetic measures for the benefit of the sick according to my ability and judgment; I will keep them from harm and injustice.

I will neither give a deadly drug to anybody who asked for it, nor will I make a suggestion to this effect. Similarly, I will not give to a woman an abortive remedy. In purity and holiness, I will guard my life and my art.

I will not use the knife, not even on sufferers from stone, but will withdraw in favor of such men as are engaged in this work.

Whatever houses I may visit, I will come for the benefit of the sick, remaining free of all intentional injustice, of all mischief and in particular of sexual relations with both female and male persons, be they free or slaves.

What I may see or hear in the course of the treatment or even outside of the treatment in regard to the life of men, which on no account one must spread abroad, I will keep to myself, holding such things shameful to be spoken about.

If I fulfill this oath and do not violate it, may it be granted to me to enjoy life and art, being honored with fame among all men for all time to come; if I transgress it and swear falsely, may the opposite of all this be my lot."

There have been many guiding principles for an individual physician, physician group, or any type of economically migrated healthkeeper to consider in their especial relationship with a patient. All these ethical directives, current and ancient, really boil down to one marvelous Medicine prescription, a prescription dispensing just four wonderful and powerful ingredients: **Justice, Autonomy, Non-Malfeasance, and Benevolence.** Perhaps these four especial ingredients are what it truly takes and sincerely means to be a patient's trusted physician healthkeeper:

Justice: to treat all patients equally and fairly and to the very best of one's ability, regardless of disparities in social ideals, social status, race, religion, ethnicity, gender, or ability to pay; and to keep confidential all that is discussed.

Autonomy: to alone and freely without external threat or monetary coercion decide what is best for individual patients; to respect all patients equally; to not alter a patient's carefully considered life-decisions in informed consent and/or advance directives, and to honor the patient's right to refuse treatment where no one else will be affected.

Non-Malfeasance: to honor the ancient Roman creed of "Primum Non Nocere"; to first do no harm or malice to the individual patient in the face of contrary societal or economic pressures; and to be truthful and not advocate that which is known to be ineffective.

Benevolence: to have a special place in one's heart to freely and without charge provide service for those patients in urgent medical need and for those patients who cannot financially afford doctoring, while always acting in the individual patient's best interest. *"The practice of Medicine is an art, not a trade; a calling, not a business; a calling in which your heart will be exercised equally with your head."*-- Sir William Osler

That hopeful sacrosanct physician-patient relationship and those historic medical principles, when not forsaken, are embodied spirits of humble honor and privileged pride that must be possessed by all categories of modern healthkeepers as a **uniform envisioned goal** to enable overall healthcare delivery quality to increase and thus enable a patient to maintain an exceptional quality of health for a lifetime and truly enjoy the art of living.

Increasingly expensive medical technology must continually seek a better quality end product; this concept unfortunately becomes an increasing variable in a migratory economic cost-value equation. Therefore, the same traditional economic criteria for calculating value, like adding cost-effective technology to make more and cheaper widgets of the same quality in an automated manufacturing industry, may not apply to effective or value-based innovation for true Health Quality, national healthcare delivery or true **Healthcare Reform**. Troublesome yet to ponder, health is not a fixed quantity, but a second unstable and deteriorating variable within the migratory economic cost-value equation of **Healthcare Reform**. In addition to changing migratory demographics, the human life cycle adds a set of variable demographics all its own. Therefore, quite naturally, variably adjusted according to age and gender, Medicine progressively demands more and more Money to keep healthy, well and alive as time goes on throughout the human life cycle. That very cycle is now extended more than ever in the past; the USA now has an expanding culture of older Americans. Aging is popular and hopefully will continue to be so. USA citizens in the 21st Century have to openly confront evolving migratory economics for **Healthcare Reform** as Americans now face **AADD** – Aged American Disability and Depression along with increasing persistent and chronic disease on a scale never before imagined. An evolutionary **Healthcare Reform** migratory economic in healthcare delivery must be dynamically structured and restructured to compensate for what is obviously just not problematic in the very near future, but subsuming the traditional American economic structural allocation allotments this very day. Economic migrations of consumers and providers of healthcare delivery will always seek a balance, a dynamic equilibrium point in the ever-evolving migratory economic **Healthcare Reform** equation.

A private relative value system (RVS) for equating the Money value for Medicine services in terms of time, and effort began in the 1960's. The RVS was approved and trusted by various medical specialty groups and their patients also concurred. However, the U.S. government reacted quickly to negate the system as a form of contra-competitive price fixing and then replace that RVS with their own devised maximal pricing system, a Resource Based Relative Value System (RBRVS), which plagiarized the criteria of the original RVS including multiplication factors for geographic variance, but placed a cap on the maximum pricing regardless of medically adjuvant care.

Obviously impacting the delivery of healthcare and healthcare reform, the migratory economic of public health and related social consciousness evolved in the 20th Century. Direct public health service measures included fluoridation of drinking water, food safety standards, immunizations and control of infectious diseases, while indirect measures included heightened awareness of public health safety at work and at play linked with environmental awareness for health, to include the dangers of tobacco, diabetes, obesity, and smog. Seen again and again -- Man and his migratory economics of Money and Medicine.

Adjusted for inflation, the actual dollar amount spent by an individual healthcare consumer at the doctor-patient level has decreased in the past ecolo-nomic paradigm; but because there are increasingly and more progressively older people needing and truly enjoying their wonderful increased longevity resulting from an expanding list of expensive technologies, total healthcare delivery cost has increased beyond the reasonable out-of-pocket spending range for most people. The insurance industry has avariciously jumped in to sell "financial protection" for an onerous and usurious non-productive middle-man profit. The unique USA legal profession has found a bonanza of profitable lawsuits increasing in proportion with advancing medical technologies. The healthcare delivery cost at the point of service is only a small percentage of the total insurance premium cost. The cost of an office visit, an office cardiogram, or an office-based surgery has not significantly increased. And yes, profiteering in healthcare delivery has always been present in the American medical economy: Doctor McBurney, the inventor of a surgical technique in 1894, was paid over a thousand dollars for an appendectomy in the very early 1900's, an amount equivalent to an average yearly income at that time. By way of contrast a century later in the early 2000's, Medi-Cal paid a surgeon $400.59 for performing an appendectomy. The total cost for physician-paid visits, moreover, is a tiny line on the total healthcare delivery balance sheet, way lower than the cost of vital and essential drugs or the cost of new life-expanding technologies and organ transplants. A practicing physician doctor is lucky to receive 9-14 cents out of the spent healthcare delivery dollar. As healthcare delivery cost has increased in the past few decades, adjusted for inflation, that doctors' income percentage per patient has proportionately decreased.

A bit more about beastly human nature: Perhaps an added sense of choice and independent authority gives one a false perception of getting a better deal with a greater chance for a successful outcome. Total independent healthcare spending by the general public far exceeds total spending at the point of formalized healthcare delivery. Americans spend more on alternative remedies than they spend on doctor-prescribed remedies. An additional shameful fact is that too many people choose to stay relatively sick and pay for viewing movies and basketball games from their bedside, rather than spend a few out-of-pocket dollars on their much needed minor healthcare doctor visits. Here again is a choice among what activities one believes to constitute quality in life, and then a weighing in, an independent cognitive reasoning but not necessarily a reasonable or logical balance to determine what the benefit of quality is worth to a given individual. When people who neglect their health become sicker, the expense for their treatment becomes more than they can afford, and then their formerly independent authority over remedy choices becomes restricted by arbitrary insurance company affordable benefit lists. Here is some simple arithmetic: if Harry had 36 candy bars and he ate 30 candy bars, what would Harry have now? ….. Diabetes.

Out-of-pocket payers demand value, but third party recipients suffer from the overly demanding moral hazard of expecting quality service without concern for cost or concomitant of personal responsibility. Bankrupted third party recipients of medical care know that, like the fraudulent investment banks after the 2008 bursting of the housing bubble, federal government funding will bail them out from the burden of any personal unpleasant consequences that may result from their bad choices or grave errors in their judgment. Having removed the risk of personally paying for or being penalized for those consequences, their demand for benefits and the frequency of their future inappropriate healthcare behavior naturally increases -- the moral insurance hazard. In response, insurance carriers incorporate cost reduction restrictions, a rationing of healthcare delivery that does not solve the basic problem. 20% of healthcare recipients are responsible for 80% of the healthcare premium costs. 20% of total healthcare recipients utilize near to all of truly essential healthcare delivery services. Unrestricted availability of various healthcare remedies produces a supply-induced demand; more elderly patients produce a longevity-induced demand; and ecolo-nomic entitlement consumerism ("I want my "Maypo" now") produces a patient induced demand. Total cost naturally increases with all that popular demand. Given the restraints of a limited budget in which huge increases in funding for direct healthcare delivery are increasing, the amount and extent of presently existing and functioning direct healthcare delivery services become overwhelmingly strained. Healthcare administrators, politically appointed by government agencies, are supposedly forced to doggedly chart a possibly unpopular yet statistically proven economic course with hard data to determine what best can be done within the bounds of the present economy to most assuredly and most effectively improve and sustain true Health Quality. However, it is only a skip, hop, and jump from migratory economic political correctness in **Healthcare Reform** to migratory economic political pandering in **Healthcare Reform**. Plato might have commented that one of the penalties for refusing to participate in politics is that you end up being governed by your inferiors; and he also admonished that you may refuse to get involved with politics, but politics will never refuse to involve you. That should hopefully at least give up a possible clue of what is about to arrive from the efforts of politically assuaging lobbyists who influence legislative governmental regulations, carefully packaged as what is really necessary to achieve true **Healthcare Reform.**

Apart from the much more prominent demographic, a select niche group of physician healthkeepers enacted their own brand of **Healthcare Reform** and economically migrated into some exclusive private medical practices of today, such as "Concierge Practice Physicians". They yet regard the personal, one-on-one, private relationship between a physician and a patient inviolate and sacrosanct. This functional relationship of mutual individual trust is what traditional medical societies such as the Los Angeles Medical Association (LACMA) defined as the "bedrock of excellent healthcare in any free society". Economic migratory patterns induced by **Healthcare Reform** have changed and continue to change the demographics of the medical societies; and, of course, the contemporary, "Demographics are Destiny" (Arthur Kemp) or from the 1800's "Demography is Destiny" (Auguste Compte). The traditional medical societies once insisted that any proposal to improve healthcare financing and healthcare access must be first tested in the light of the sacrosanct physician-patient relationship, and rejected out of hand if said proposal degrades that sacrosanct relationship. But can this functional arrangement really be part of or even considered in a cultural mores plurality value-based genre of migratory economically driven **Healthcare Reform**? Certainly there must be an ultimate degree of mutual trust between an individual patient under general anesthesia and a surgeon expertly whittling away with a scalpel; but beyond that type of life or death scenario, the doctor-patient relationship may have to be more precisely defined or perhaps continually redefined by provider and physician healthkeeper migratory economic patterns, perhaps creating a new set of demographics for True Health Quality induced by said **Healthcare Reform**.

Historically, the greatest advance in promoting True Health Quality began with the building of Aqueducts and the Cisternae Magna during the time of the Roman Empire. Marcus Tullius Cicero wrote, *"Hominem ad deos nulla re propius accedunt quam salutem hominibus dando",* in nothing do men more nearly approach the gods, than in giving health to men. What would Cicero say about Man's situation today, where medical ecolo-nomics seems to have become a purely migratory economic political process with only a mere suggestion of True Health Quality overtones, and migratory medical economic theory has become encumbered by vote-popular emotionally-derived socio-economic goals and visions? One must never forget that the primary directive action for any legislator once elected is to be re-elected. -- Ralzak. During the Greek and Roman times, Man's migratory economics and prevailing myth/mores dictated a sorely severe unequal distribution of health and wealth – Money and Medicine. The then popular myth of many gods stabilized those societies. Suicide was an accepted outlet for crippled unproductive starving individuals. According to that prevailing myth, Asklepios, the son of Apollo, held a staph with an encircling snake in the Asklepion, the healing sanctuary and alter dedicated to the god. After drinking poison to avoid his jail sentence, Socrates has been credited with uttering, "I owe a cock to the sacred alter of Asklepios." A short time later, as in Greece, the Roman Laws of the Twelve Tables legally sanctioned murder for those unfortunately born mentally and physically deformed. But myth marches on......

Contrary to the dire direction driven by the Western World's unstable and faltering migratory economic culture after the fall of the Roman Empire, the Far Eastern and Arab peoples kept to an informed, intellectually stable and sustainable migratory economic culture. The "down–to-earth" ancient Chinese doctor learned to diagnose by "LLAF" – look, listen, ask, and then feel. Arabic medical tradition likewise withstood the rigorous test of time and evolving myth since the Second Century. Islāmic and Christian beliefs, functionally united myth modalities, depicted human life as a trial to determine worthiness for a greater destiny. Mohammedism sustained the great Arabic empire during the 6th and 7th Century. The first awarding of an actual academic Medical Degree had to wait till the Islamic Golden Age, about 790 AD. About that same time, Sharia Law, the fundamental concept of Islām, held to two tenants: A Moral Code of strict religious discipline in an earthly life, and a Devine Favor during a transcending after-life following mortal death. Utilizing the resultant cultural stability brought about by that particular and often mimicked myth modality, Muslims were able to lead the forefront of scientific development in healthcare delivery for more centuries than the "Western World" would like to admit: Islām kept safe and intact the ancient Greco-Roman scientific secrets of healthcare delivery that were totally lost to an evolved mythology and resultant inferior technological culture in the Dark Western Middle Ages. Islām was not naïve to the migratory economic scientifically devolved mythological ways of the West; Islām simply neither intellectually nor morally accepted Western Middle Age cultural concepts as reasonable, logical, viable or enduring. With variations in spelling, the name Muhammad remains as the most popular first name for a male child in the world today.

During those aforesaid very Dark Middle Ages, the entire Western Civilization lost the knowledge and ability to make cement, which led to the loss of infrastructure and public health construction projects such as clean water delivery and sanitary sewage disposal. Thus, loss of the functioning Roman Aqueducts and Cisterns resulted in a gain of massive pestilence and disease, with a concomitant atrocious and enormous net loss of human life. A plague of rats became the dominant European life-form. Healthcare delivery knowledge also deteriorated and then became completely forgotten in Europe during the Middle or Dark Ages. The scientific teachings of Democritus were also totally forgotten, and Man's entire planet earth was once again thought to be flat by its Western-cultured population masses. Medical science and knowledge stagnated, stumbled, and then fell, crumbling into indistinct particles of dust. However, most all of that ancient medical knowledge was serendipitously, almost miraculously resurrected or born again in Hesperia, the western land of the setting sun, at the historic medical school of the University of Salerno in the 10th Century. Constantine the African, a former Muslim, translated 37 preserved Arabic books concerning the ancient healing art of Medicine into Latin and educated the West (Hesperia) in Islām's extensive continued and unforgotten knowledge of and practical improvements to the ancient Greek medical arts. Constantine also taught a fundamental standard for providing healthcare delivery and re-set the direction for **Healthcare Reform** to follow for centuries, a direction that remains true to this very day.

Man, Money and Medicine can and have accomplished greatness in the USA -- an unrivaled expertise in healthcare technologies, an undefeatable military preparedness, and the highest average standard of living of any people anywhere else on planet earth. But wait just a moment for another pause…. Now, just a word of caution to readers who wish to go forward within this book: There is an enormous amount of editorial commentary and uncomfortably awkward, actually outrageous metaphorical phrasing, that is best understood by understanding, hopefully with some moderate degree of empathetic compassion, a bit about this book's obviously and painfully overly-opinionated author:

I was born with a great dynamic competitive advantage over most – a 95% head and shoulders tremendous global population advantage over anyone and everyone else who happened to be born on this blue-spinning sphere that rotates third in order around with the solar system of Man's sun – an overwhelming starting advantage that is equally shared by anyone and everyone fortunate enough, like me, to have been born in the United States of America. Yes, I am a pantheist enthusiastically enjoying the long term sequelae of many myths; I welcome and embrace them all; but as for myths, I believe in and rigorously abide by none – I rigidly hold my dying loyalties to the present migratory economic that has resulted in the shifting mythology to the present way of life in the USA. I have solemnly chosen my own personal designated path in life, and even if need-be stand alone, would willingly defend that particular course for human existence well beyond the point of personal financial or bodily harm -- forever – unto my finite point of my demise:

In the USA of today, the accepted and workable stratification/division of labor and the stratification/division of levels of production both combine to produce a maximum fiscal profit that enables a migratory economic proportional set-aside known as accumulated wealth. Wealth is a scarce resource, a functionally limited asset dependent upon a dynamically sustainable system of economics. In order to generate wealth, a person or entity must be willing to postpone leisure in anticipation of a possible but not guaranteed greater leisure satisfaction at some future defined time-definite period. Thus, in the USA, a productive generation of wealth through capitalism/entrepreneurship provides the ecolo-nomic fiscal mechanism that allows and supports an equilibrated welfare system. Those excess profitable dollars from this limited and scarce productive resource, known as wealth, also flow down a one-way street to adequately satisfy dependent leisure yearnings among the non-productive masses; note well that the reverse of these circumstances is obviously impossible. The sustainable proportional population size of the dependent leisure or welfare component in a society is a critically evolving biomass dynamically dependent upon a nation's advancing technology and concurrent surplus wealth production. Uncontrolled or unrationed, that critical biomass of dependent leisure population can potentially disrupt the entire ecolo-nomic system, destroy initiative for concurrently accumulating surplus wealth, kill the functional mechanism for entrepreneurial success and ultimately lead to its own segment of society's self-destruction.

I am a cynic, but favor the USA's order of democratic government over and in place of any previous alternatives, and I anxiously willingly pay my taxes to keep me safe and alive. Man's concept of "capital" is a not a thing, it is a process in which Money produces more Money to construct more points of Money production which in turn produces more Money etc. Capitalism is an economic mechanism that provides for wealth accumulation. Capitalism is a powerful weapon that cannot, in and of itself, be blamed for any potential danger it might bestow. A society must decide where to point their powerful Capitalistic weapon, how to best shoot out their fiscal rockets and when the time is best or needed to do so. Capitalism allows for the material might of a nation, a national potential to successfully and sustainably mobilize for global economic battle or frank warfare partly through the expression of an economic index, the Gross National Product (GNP); but Capitalism also permits for an abundance of human development which may or may not be on a global scale, such as the health, longevity, and welfare of individuals and the population of mythical beastly humanistic human beings as a whole. It is Man who must decide on allocations of Money and Medicine. A difficult to titrate two-sided societal balance must weigh increasing personal property (one's personal "freedom TO" act, a non-governmental liberty) against redistribution of wealth (decreasing harm to others with "freedom FROM" prejudicial acts through enforced governmental human "rights") to best benefit that said society's national goals. Charity and Medicine-Charity for the circumstantial non-affluent must arise from Man's generosity with his Money and not betray the utility of self-fulfillment. If in a theoretical world where Man might exist as devout saints, then fear, jealousy and maximizing Man's "utility" would be eliminated; there would be no need or purpose for personal property, and stratification of economic divisions would be an amoral process as all of Mankind would virtuously labor solely for the benefit of others. Karl Marx had advocated for governmental control of the economy, media and, "From all according to their ability and to all according to their need". That wealth redistribution mechanism may have been or may still be possible in a rigidly religious totalitarian state. But Ann Rand asked, "Who is John Galt?" – Man's personal choice must be passionately respected as a primal human instinct; but there are known consequences which must be accepted, including the interference and balancing of such choices made by those who absolutely refuse to labor for the fulfillment others and those who absolutely refuse to labor for the fulfillment of themselves. In a situation of such hostile consequences, from where shall arise the mechanism to provide for wealth accumulation and the safeguarding of a sustainable future for Mankind?

I do admit that a fundamentally capitalistic democracy must carefully and cautiously walk along a high-strung tightrope while delicately balancing the art of living along with an increased healthy quality of life for its populous of individuals at one end of a balancing pole against that capitalistic nation's Gross National Product at the other end of the pole. I do also so admire and praise the wondrous and marvelous accomplished efforts of the United States of America in exquisitely balancing those opposing forces during my dear country's unending precarious walk along that dynamic human existence tightrope. "Medicare is just one result of a continual dynamic migratory economic force in America that defines and redefines capitalistic production and value in terms of evolving societal norms for health and the art of living." The migratory economic material might and power, in and of a vigorously thriving USA, has continually capitalized on individual opportunity for Man's phenomenological development and social wellbeing. Social advancement and welfare programs are homogenously integrated as a natural consequence of my America's brand of capitalism, accomplished through taxation of yearly accumulated wealth, accomplished without the need to yearly tax any individual's put-aside net worth. There is evidence everywhere in the USA that evolving and competing migratory political influences will continue to do whatever is necessary to continue to provide a securely balanced walk along that aforementioned tightrope, even though the foreseeable path's delicately-needed balance might be now temporarily strained by the uneven heaviness exerted by overly-liberal progressivism.

To wit, multitudes of naysayers decrying and denouncing America's economic and cultural future I hear resounding all about me. Crying the tyranny of taxation without representation for the upper middle class, they are overtly angry, frustrated and resentful concerning the economic and cultural direction for the future USA. Others blame unresponsive governmental cronyism, corporations and the "rich" for loss of American jobs and stagnation in their opportunistic advancement. As far as I am concerned, they must not yield to the fork in their road constructed by continually evolving yet disruptive technologies; they must rather follow the fork-disruptive advice once offered by Yogi Berra: "Take it", don't stand in line; carve out not one, but many newer paths to the future, and forage ever onward. Those naysayers must become enlightened to see and behold the vision recorded by Dante Alighieri: When his path came to an apparent end in the forest of life, "I looked up and saw its shoulders brightened with the rays" of hope and light. Creative human imagination knows no end. The USA reigns as the foremost world power, a nation developed and made great by the descendants of former slaves, indentured servants, immigrants and indigenous natives – new-comers to imperialistic power all and all bearing an ancestral gene pool of risk-takers, get-goers and doers -- all striving to be the best of the very best in their continual pursuits of happiness. There is a uniquely refreshing revitalization of happiness in those pursuits, for the laborious yet joyous attempts put forth for winning are far more thrilling than having won.

I envision my USA as a unique peaceful human experiment for the amalgamation of diversity, a syncretism of cultures, and a unification of ideals and goals. Yes, I am optimistic; I celebrate American free enterprise and the American brand of dignified capitalism. My dedicated resolve concerning the USA remains unbroken: I am humbled, privileged and honored to live in an esteemed and celebrated indivisibly-united land where personal liberty, freedom and free speech are not encumbered or coerced by pressures or persuasions from outside social or religious influence. ("Liberty, the greatest of all earthly blessings - give us that precious jewel and you may take everything else!" – Patrick Henry) There is no exclusive or restrictive Royal Bloodline in the USA; there is still an abundant and unique opportunity for a great number of hard working individuals to be fortunate enough to rise from rags to riches in one single generation; there yet remains a chance for dedicated American children to strive and then enjoy a better life and art of living than their parents. My cherished and honored personally preferred ethnocentricity lies strictly in being known as and performing all my life-long tasks and actions as an "American" of the good old USA -- and absolutely not defined by any ethnocentric political grouping of some shade of skin color or any other ethnocentric grouping of "gender-family-origin-land-race/American".

My ancestral germinal cells did once live and thrive in Cicero's aforementioned Republic, a Republic that ruled the entire known world; and I was serendipitously born into a Republic that has surpassed that former super-power's might and yet prevails as the undisputed number one world power in this and any other new century for my entire lifetime and hopefully, I pray, long thereafter. I was born into a unique era for my very special beloved country, born into a generation of contagious capitalistic and imperialistic conquest for a super-power nation, a nation with migratory economic policies that demand constant alertness and occasionally war to courageously preserve an ideal of fundamental sacrosanct liberty, indivisible unity and personal freedom. America, **the United States of America, is (not are)** a geo-political nation that is not defined by the geography of its land mass, nor is my country defined by any particular grouping of cognitive reasoning *Homo sapiens*. A miraculously God-sent amalgamating melting pot for all human types, races, religions and nationalities, my America is defined by continuing and courageously defended ideals, by a fundamental root of common law that embraces individual "freedom to" as a way of life, as the joy of life, as the penultimate "art of living" in a constitutional democracy.

My nation, a Republic, stands for and demands, mandates, defends and delivers fearless equal opportunity for every citizen to diligently work hard, so that each and every citizen can be effectively endowed with the unique global opportunity to pursue and perhaps hopefully attain independent economic security along with the opportunity to earnestly pursue happiness for each individual person -- a unique global opportunity window for all the people, like me, fortunately blessed to live in my great and wonderful USA. Looking, searching and sifting through the entire past history of life on planet earth, I could not possibly have chosen a better time or finer place in this great world for myself to have been humbly born, to honorably work for my daily bread and much more -- to proudly live out my entire thrilling and uniquely spectacular U.S.-AMERICAN way of life.....

MIGRATORY ECONOMIC FACTORS & PATTERNS EVOLVING MAN, MONEY & MEDICINE

PART TWO

GOVERNMENT-IMPOSED
MEDICAL DOCTOR EXCLUSIVITY
MEDICAL ECOLO-NOMICS

The first half of the 20th Century from 1910 to 1950 was a physician-driven iatrogenic healthcare delivery era in the United States. The Flexner Report of 1910 hallmarked a migratory economic that resulted in a Healthcare Reform watershed event.

Healthcare policies are the spawn of political ecologies and economic mores. Such ingredients are the raw materials that simultaneously simmer to reduction in an epicurean evolutionary stew pot and then yield the various flavors and refined tastes of Healthcare Reform.

--Ralzak

"Health" for a nation is an ephemeral and perceived state of societal wellbeing that is reflected by the physical and mental condition of its inhabitants. This most often inadequately defined and illusive visionary concept referred to as "health" is unfortunately too often inaccurately summarized and touted simply as a United States national longevity, a longevity that is ranked 27th among industrialized nations by the World Health Organization (WHO). The mass media and appropriate political pundits gloat to dwell on and unjustly magnify this unexamined statistic of longevity and make an inappropriate inductive leap to define that longevity statistic as the major factor directly related to healthcare delivery in the USA. The unquestioned bias media opinion then concludes that "health", alias longevity, is presumably an easily correctable and primary definitive deficiency in the American healthcare delivery system. The common notion of **Healthcare Reform** is thusly often unjustifiably aimed at improving that particular definition of "health-longevity". But changing delivery access processes and monitoring mechanisms within that change register only relatively minor effects on improving a nation's health. Actually, direct healthcare delivery adds only one small contribution towards the goal of a nation's overall true health and well-being, but the service or perhaps commodity of healthcare delivery has always been held in penultimate importance. One can readily grasp and criticize healthcare delivery because the concept can be too easily but falsely envisioned and packaged as a clearly defined product, a marketable item of goods and services that greatly satisfy perceived wants and needs of both individuals and populations. In that respect, healthcare delivery continues to be regarded as a unique economic commodity for modern industrial cultures, a deliverable that has always been of great economic importance, ever since Mankind existed as a primitive hunter-gatherer scavenger cave culture. Healthcare delivery coverage then vies with true and effective healthcare delivery availability in every stratum of America's modern society. The three-legged stool of access, cost, and quality has been and continues to be most often unbalanced.

Traditionally, historians most often first credit Otto Von Bismarck as the 1883 craftsman of a method to pay for healthcare delivery through an insurance mechanism. His social scheme to insure healthcare delivery costs by spreading them across a greater population base so that German workers could remain healthy and increase their productivity was touted as a method to "wean away from Socialism" one third of the German population. Interestingly intriguing, the near to exact same verbatim quote, about avoiding socialism by means of a unique cost-effective modality in healthcare delivery, is attributable to Henry Kaiser during his innovative healthcare delivery announcement of a formula for a prototype Health Maintenance Organization (HMO) at the opening ceremonies of the Sunset Hospital in 1953 at Los Angeles, California.

In 1751, Benjamin Franklin and Dr. Thomas Bond found it necessary and proper to fund the construction costs for the first hospital in America, Pennsylvania Hospital, "to provide charitable healthcare delivery to the sick-poor and insane that wandered the streets of Philadelphia". Many Philadelphians complain that the indigent homeless street situation in parts of downtown Philly is not much better today. To this very day, hordes of poor and chronically ill homeless citizens still wander there and wander elsewhere in and about the great cities of the USA in dire need of health maintenance counseling and guidance in the art of living.

Around the turn from the 19th to the 20th century, academicians, industrial leaders, and some governmental officials, referencing vague and unsubstantiated data of the times, became increasingly concerned that a new migratory economic path needed to be cut for national healthcare delivery. There were no time-marker milestones of meaningful and measurable monitored metrics and measures that were considered or even envisioned; but they all did charge ever onward into a potential valley of death through a rocky sharp and bumpy pot-holed well-trodden path, a long and winding calloused switchback road filled with trenches which rolled on to a wishfully promised national single payer health insurance destination, hopefully to originate early in the first half of the 20th century. As always, culture drove economics and economics drove adaptive selection for healthcare delivery mechanisms:

As hopeful and industrious immigrant patient groups arrived in America during the last part of the 19th Century, they created clubs, fraternal organizations, lodges, and benevolent societies in the big American cities. Many of these local ethnic-orientated organizations -- French, German, Italian, etc. – offered direct healthcare delivery to their members on a pre-pay basis. A diverse group of ethnic-oriented healthkeepers economically competed among themselves for this unique group or cache of patients. Then there seemed to be a rather sudden increase or a reactionary migratory economic demand, a dynamic competitive advantage increase in these clustered immigrant groups which successfully offered economically sustainable pre-paid medical care to their members in the form of "Lodge Medicine". Unfortunately, these economically viable **Healthcare Reform** demographic patient cohort groups were broken apart and dispersed, economically forced to migrate elsewhere with a good deal of "help" from or by the order of state government-legislated regulations sponsored and lobbied by the economically competing American "medical societies". Cultural ecology melded with migratory economics to evolve "ecolo-nomics". It was simply a matter of gaining migratory economic dynamic competitive advantage and the elimination of competition that drove the American Medical Association and medical societies, in an organized economic effort, to monopolize and protect their "fiscal risk pool of payers"; and to oppose that practice of "Lodge Medicine" during the evolving medical ecolo-nomic environment of the first half of the 20th century. Needless to say, the "economic attributes" within the migrated cohort populations (greenback dollars) were compelled to a parallel migration, into the welcoming open hands of the "approved" medical establishments. It was all too simple to follow Man's Money flow in Medicine.

Thus, the well-organized and well-respected medical societies eventually completed and basked in all three necessary components attributed to a perfect economic marriage with their paradigm membership, at that time totally composed of very private fee-for-service practicing physicians:

1. Production complementariness – increasing referral sources for its members.
2. Consumption complementariness – containment of profit among its members.
3. Pooling of risk – sharing of malpractice costs among its members.

Physician medical quality performance and the multi paternal types of doctor images, like politics, were based solely on perception, not reality -- or perhaps perception was and remains today as the true reality or at least the reality of the moment. Doctor image in the United States at the turn of the 19th century included an art form of infantile prejudices, fears, and desires expressed as popular public opinion. Doctor image was related to medical science through a habituation modality similar to spin in relation to political science. Throughout the first half of the 20th Century, the patients' image of the doctor and the doctors' image of the patient were both of mutual high esteem and respect. The relationship was indeed sacrosanct.   In the late 1920's, mutual trust in the doctor-patient relationship crested at an all-time high mark, as did individual doctor concern for charity care. The American doctor maintained an image of a kindly and charitable gentleman, making a house call with a black "doctors" bag gripped by his **healing hand**. The humble and honored physician of the times carried every bit of necessary pharmacy and up to date medical technology, all neatly packed into that wonderful and wondrous old black "doctors' bag".

The ability to practice Medicine and the receiving of medical care were considered mutual privileges; and for the favor of privilege and trust, doctors felt a deep indebtedness to their patients, especially the poor and illiterate. A doctor stayed loyally married to the practice of Medicine, for richer or poorer, for a lifetime -- till death did they part. Stephen Paget characterized Medicine as a "divine vocation". The imagined image of the concerned paternal doctor became the idealized wish and dream of the child-minded patient, both magically transformed into the reality of life-long unwavering dedication to medical practice.   The demographics of medical school graduates accurately reflected that popular physician image. The demographic count revealed an obvious and overwhelming predominance of male physicians genetically owning North European ancestries. Before 1930, Jewish medical students found it necessary to attend medical school in Germany before "qualifying" for admission to American Medical schools. Women medical school graduates remained uncommon, and women surgeons were especially rare. However, as the image of the physician negatively evolved along with the passage of time, that paternalistic perception became even more imaginary and vague in the public mindset. The aforementioned demographic changed in turn as the medical provider migratory economic patterns changed.

Meanwhile, all sorts of businesses were booming in the USA, blossoming for the greatest and fastest growing economy in the world. American mining and railroad workers suffered extremely high rates of industrial injury at isolated and distant locations, far and away from big city hospitals and big city medical societies. These isolated work-places were also far and away from any big city migratory economic risk pools cohorts of potential payers. The railroad employee injury patterns and medically necessary treatments required long range medical transport and extensive work absenteeism, both unduly costly items for the railroad employers. Desperate need does slowly finally find a way to overcome the shackles of undue governmental regulation; and of course, necessity is the Mother of invention, allowing administrative decisions to succumb to medically-necessary and cost-effective migratory economic patterns. On-site psychological, physical therapy, occupational health, and emergency medical services were essential; therefore, railroad officials offered lucrative salaries to young professional physician healthkeepers willing to sign on for short term contracts. It was like working today in the oil fields of Alaska or Northern Alberta Canada where the average per capita income is in excess of $190 Thousand per annum. Those temporary migrated industrial pre-pay physician medical practices of the early 1900 years generated the necessary capital, an adequate grubstake, for a young physician practitioner to shortly thereafter economically migrate once again and start up a private healthcare delivery practice in a big city or small town. Big businesses, the owners of those unique local patient care contracts, ran the entire medical care show. The Industrial Indemnity Exchange in the Southern California desert near Indio was such an entity, and Henry Kaiser was a major shareholder in that exchange. The economically migrated contracted physician healthkeepers remained contented employees and generally desired and therefore demanded no medical practice autonomy. A few, such as Sidney Garfield, MD, were more entrepreneurial. They sought and found the means to additionally build a variety of healthcare delivery systems. Nobody complained about **Healthcare Reform**. The on-job medical work was accepted by all as economically migratory and temporary. The price was right. Competition flourished and resulted in a win–win migratory economic windfall for all.

In the early 1900's, 20% of the American population consisted of foreign immigrants, and Medical transportation was both difficult and dangerous. The time was ripe for migratory economic migration in healthcare delivery. The migratory economics of **Healthcare Reform** most naturally reacted and evolved to satisfy that existing culture. At about that same time, there was no uniformly accepted standard for educating a medical practitioner in the USA. Curriculum content and teaching practices in what were termed "medical schools" varied from the philosophical esoteric to the practice-oriented incompetent, according to the medical migratory economic future interests of the American Medical Association (AMA). All sorts of educational and apprenticeship mechanisms, offered by individual existing practitioners or through organizations, produced a wide and varied spectrum of "doctors", from ritualistic and religious-oriented doctor healthkeepers to health food advocates and also to itinerant Medicine men – professorial cure-all potion pontificators. Medical therapists of every possible type abounded. Marginal, yet profitable, physician-run proprietary training programs, some by mail-order, enlisted, without exam requirements, all-comers who desired entrance, thus providing an easy economic migration into the possibly lucrative medical profession. Demographically poor and ethnic-cultural needs were serviced and appreciatively met primarily by proprietary-trained practitioners. There were true and sustainable dynamic competitive healthcare advantages as well as varied medical payment mechanisms – all varieties of **Healthcare Reform** -- offered by each type of economically migrated healthkeeper-practitioner.

In order to teach some healing art in medieval times, a mandatory license was required. This license was granted by the Catholic Church only after a rigorous examination and a swearing to an oath of allegiance, and of course the paying of a certain fee. Man, Money and Medicine! Eventually, university guilds offered apprentice programs leading to a "masters" degree such as "Master of Arts" and then onto higher degrees such as a MT degree – Master of Theology or a "MD" degree – Master of Divinity. By academic evolution, medical science was separated out into two separate sub-doctorial programs, a MB – Bachelor of Medicine and a BS – Bachelor of Surgery. The two degrees were sometimes combined as a "MBBS". Credentials were then inflated at the academic level from master to doctor without the traditionally required presentation of a thesis, much like untrained lay healthkeeper jobs are presently inflated to degrees of "Professionalism". The final end result was the awarding of a new type of "MD" – a "professional" Medical Doctor degree having nothing to do with the original Master of "Divinity" – or maybe not?

Turn of the century times in America also saw the need for a mandatory license requirement. All the varied medical practitioners of the later part of the 19th Century had to be organized under one governmental umbrella and then charged that all important fee for the privilege to practice Medicine. At the supposed very top of this diverse practitioner heap of healthkeepers stood the big three -- the AMA-sanctioned homeopathic doctor (DH), the osteopathic doctor (DO), and the allopathic or medical doctor (MD) practitioners. The idea of having some reliably reproducible scientific method to determine treatment remedies was not novel for the time, and generally encouraged by all types of healthkeepers; but the precise scientific methodology necessary to train for and then achieve this end became a matter of great dispute.

John D. Rockefeller extended his philanthropic interest in education to medical education and founded the Rockefeller Institute for Medical Research in 1901. An allopathic (MD) pathologist on his board of directors, Simon Flexner, had his brother Abraham placed on the staff of the Carnegie Foundation for the Advancement of Teaching. Abraham Flexner (1866-1959) had returned to graduate school at Harvard following a 19-year career of teaching in high school. After additional training in educational systems at the University of Berlin, he championed strict academic preparedness for higher education and was determined to raise the standards of high school education in the United States with a duel system of education -- literacy training for all and rigorous higher education for the academically gifted. (All animals are equal, but some animals are more equal than others." — George Orwell, Animal Farm) To better dynamically compete for academic-scientific advantage in a world market that has already adjusted to stratified and functional educational systems, something like Flexner's dual system of education for the United States is yet touted today by some, but progressive political influence and re-election fright regarding incumbent social prejudices within the voting public majority usually leads to an ecolo-nomic rejection of the duel standard educational concept. Backed by no real proof and substantial data to the contrary, a migratory economic of political correctness from both sides of the political aisle insists that universal higher education is a practical solution for decreasing income inequality in the USA. Back at the early 1900's and by strong contrast, having been steeped in German traditional learning, Abraham Flexner advocated for an isolated and stratified academic group from the general population having a strong background in the sciences as a pre-requisite for a higher level of experimental-derived medical school education, and he further envisioned a system that would eventually replace didactic learning at that higher level of medical practice education.

Thus the stage was set for the USA's first migratory economic watershed event in **Healthcare Reform**. No Nostradamus needed calling; sparks were already flying in the air; a non-negotiable hundred-year war between supposedly selectively organized highly academically trained practicing medical-theoretical scientists (physicians) opposing diversely organized practically trained medical practitioners (all other types of healthkeeper-practitioners) was about to begin: Simon Flexner nominated his brother Abraham to be the General for this centurial campaign. With $10,000 of Carnegie financing readily in hand, Abraham Flexner set out on an amazing adventure in 1908. In 1910 he published the very first detailed and "authenticated" high quality study of medical education in the USA. Flexner had (reportedly)[1] visited and evaluated 155 graduate and a dozen postgraduate centers of medical education in the United States and Canada. Aided by an unholy alliance struck among the AMA, the Carnegie foundation, and the Federal Government (which produced proper financial and political backing), wide public acceptance flourished, and the United States government permanently closed half of all standing medical schools, thus mandating and creating a select undermanned monopoly cartel for the migratory economic supply side of USA healthcare -- by legally equipping only a select chosen "more than equal" with the exclusive right to practice Medicine. That migratory economic for the most part yet exists today in a substantially lessened form, but that politically determined diminished supply side economic could not and has not stood up to future testing by ticking time.

The "Flexner Report" recommendations included: consolidating the number of "medical" schools, **reducing the total number of graduates**, increasing entrance standards with a prerequisite basic science curriculum, and somehow increasing a yet poorly or really undefined "quality" of medical care. Motherhood and apple pie concepts included increasing the study and use of new to be discovered pharmaceuticals (an allopathic strongpoint) and scientific research methods to enhance didactic learning in medical schools. Of course, most of the schools that had enough faculties and could afford to do research were those associated with economically stable universities. However, the Flexner Report also closed down the medical school at UCLA. Some have been critical of Flexner's methods:[2] "Abraham Flexner's evaluation of education on the North American continent in the early twentieth century proceeded at a rapid pace. The itinerary emerges from the footnotes Flexner left in his Report reveals periods during which he would have had only a fraction of a day to travel to and visit a school. Either Flexner was strikingly efficient or his efforts lacked thoroughness. In any event, a Report of such repercussions warrants further study of the methods used in its creation. Certainly Flexner, allegedly the promoter of the scientific method in medical education, would have approved of such perusal."

Half of the graduates from purported schools of Medicine were suddenly, through a governmentally decreed migratory economic, deprived of obtaining and legitimately employing various medical therapies, and by further governmental decree, restricted from legally using government-approved new and developing

---

[1] Griffin, Edward G., World Without Cancer: The Story of Vitamin B17, chapter 18
[2] Hiatt MD, The Medical Sentinel 2000;5(5):167-168,2000 AAPS

medical technologies as well as future innovative healthcare delivery techniques. Rather than allowing free laissez faire à la economist Turgot natural forces in a capitalistic society to best determine the direction for **Healthcare Reform,** the American healthcare delivery system became further subjected to the horse-eye blinders imposed by methodological nationalism. A U.S. federal government audaciously and arrogantly acted and reacted, unconcerned and apparently unaware of any possible unintended consequences. The federal government essentially hand-picked and dynamically advantaged the future fiscal medical economic winners and losers in the healthcare delivery arena. The federal government's intrusion and interference quite unjustly and unfairly tilted the medical ecolo-nomic healthcare delivery playing field of free market dynamic competitive advantage away from all medical practitioners other than Allopathic, Homeopathic and Osteopathic physicians.

The Flexner Report thus proved to be an evolutionary migratory economic Healthcare Reforming watershed event. Only 80 out of 160 schools of medical education survived to represent a new healthkeeper set in an evolved medical ecolo-nomic environment following some years of expressive delay after release of the Flexner Report. "Real" doctors, now reduced to only three types – allopathic, homeopathic, and osteopathic -- waged a political battle among themselves. Eventually the allopathic ranks predominated and became the gold standard doctor, "Mr. MD". The new dominant healthkeeper set – The MD -- became entrenched in a medical ecolo-nomic environment that was willing and able to accept Carnegie foundation financing, along with AMA influence and control, to supposedly once and forever hopefully firmly establish the "MD" as the U.S. Government's predominant migratory economic monopoly, the one and only certified and legal provider of healthcare services.

MDs openly applauded this consolidation movement as a reaffirmation of the Oath of Hippocrates,[3] to teach to "disciples bound by a stipulation and oath according to the law of Medicine, but to none others". The pen again proved more powerful than the sword as Allopathic, Homeopathic and Osteopathic coffers became enriched by a unique and exclusive legal ability to write for and dispense a drug "prescription". Of the big three, the MD predominantly enjoyed a near exclusivity of medical practice, medical autonomy and medical authority. No non-MD competitive healthcare delivery system had the legs or standing to bark or whine any significant threat to MD power and control. Quality and cost in

---

[3] The Oath of Hippocrates: I swear by Apollo, the physician, and Aesclepius and Health, and All-Heal, and the gods and the goddesses, that according to my ability and judgment, I will keep this oath and stipulations.....

healthcare delivery increased and access decreased while the MD Physician had near total iatrogenic autonomy over healthcare delivery during the first half of the 20th Century.

A popular Norman Rockwell poster depicted the idealized imaginary early 20th Century physician, seated at a patient's bedside, waiting for a potentially deadly fever to crescendo then break. That watchful wait was filled with anticipation, much like waiting for one of the seven heavenly archangels -- Raphael -- to appear and cure any dire disease with his miraculous golden staff. The early 1900's role of a doctor was that of a facilitator in that miraculous process. The dedicated doctor was greatly honored to be that facilitator because the process was saintly and spiritual. Repeating once again, the American doctor sustainably maintained that image of a kindly and charitable gentleman by making "house calls" with a black "doctors'" bag in his **healing hand**. The vastly unproven medical quality outcomes from such medical practices were not necessarily better than those administered by the many other previously existing ancillary healthkeepers. However, to put things in further perspective, there was no great pharmaceutical industry then in existence. There were no antibiotics. The greatest and most useful medical tool to be found in an honored doctor's black bag was a bottle of leaches. However, by contrast to years to come, there would be no honor or **healing hand** for a physician equally named and classified along with many other healthcare providers-facilitators in a technologically advanced pharmaceutical arena utilizing an algorithmic protocol of computer-generated population step-based treatment programs that fit standardized approved cost-effective administrative guidelines, especially during the third and fourth overlapping medical ecolo-nomic generations (1990-2010 and 2010-2030) of organized healthcare delivery.

Nonetheless, after the watershed year of 1910, MDs serendipitously acquired the ammunition, and officially/legally, with a diploma stamped "Flexner approved", acquired the affidavit to further promote themselves as the only "real" doctors in the USA. That perception or spin became immediately accepted, as the mind of popular public opinion also readily agreed with the concept. Patients openly praised and demonstrated gratitude for the care that they received. The cost of healthcare was not excessive at that time, as expensive medical technology remained very limited. Perhaps because doctors stayed few in number and their alternatives for medical treatment were also limited, their unique health-benefit role remained unquestionably honored. The MD, DH and DO of that time became accepted as and were in fact true and real professionals who held not a legal contract, but a public trust to perform medical work and do no harm in a spirit of fairness, with a trusted respect for individual patient autonomy, and overt generosity for the general public good.

The saga of malpractice evolution in **Healthcare Reform** is a tale peculiar to the USA. At one time, all doctors swore to and stood loyal to the oath of Hippocrates: "While I continue to keep this oath inviolate, may it be granted to me to enjoy life and the practice of the art, respected by all men at all times; but should I trespass and violate this oath, may the reverse be my lot."[4] In the USA that "reverse lot" soon became known as a medical malpractice judgment. "In 1906, the Los Angeles County Medical Association raised its yearly dues from $4.00 to $5.00 a year. Half of the increase was put in a fund to reimburse physician members for malpractice claims. Before this action, physicians were supported only by the generosity of their colleagues, who would pass "the hat" around the room when the need was announced."[5] Again, the functional structure of the medical associations provided that aforementioned perfect three component economic marriage: -- Production complementariness, consumption complementariness and pooling of risk. Never so sweet a migratory economic deal was ever to present itself again to the medical community.

The topic of economics or more specifically medical finances always remained a forbidden point for open discussion in or out of medical school. The medical associations went to considerable effort to portray the typical doctor as usually well-dressed, but exhausted and occasionally disheveled from work and in no condition to discuss detailed medical charts. Doctors, however, went a bit further; they refused to discuss case studies of medical malpractice, and were accused of having taken an "oath of silence". "Never listen to a tale told to the detriment of a brother practitioner.....Let not your ear hear the sound of your voice raised in unkind criticism or ridicule or condemnation of a brother physician."[6]

Physicians volunteering at County Hospitals were, for a time, immune from lawsuits. Nevertheless, all healthkeeper forces recognized intuitively that physicians could not be and in fact were not infallible; they too were naturally subject to all sorts of human frailties. Mistake, misjudgment, rush to judgment, and lapses in the reasoning process happened and were generally tolerated; but not ever forgiven. Patients were not treated according to some standard pathway or algorithm. The physician had to be forever mindful not to jump too quickly to

---

[4] The Oath of Hippocrates: I swear by Apollo, the physician, and Aesclepius and Health, and All-Heal, and the gods and the goddesses, that according to my ability and judgment, I will keep this oath and stipulations.....
[5] Gray, Barbara B., 120 Years of Medicine, Pioneer Publications, Inc.; 1991, p. 61.
[6] Bean, R., Sir William Osler Aphorisms, C.C.Tomas, Illinois, 1961, p.72.

what seemed to be an obvious conclusion; the good physician needed to deliberately spend the extra time prerequisite to engage one's Betz cells in consideration of a complete list of likely differential diagnoses and outlier "Zebras".

As the daily volume of patient visit encounters increased for an individual physician, and while the same routine patient diagnosis repeated itself redundantly like a boring epidemic, a uniquely human frailty process rendered an even greater opportunity or temptation for the physician to make and then act upon false assumptions. The error-committing end result became finalized because of a silly human mind trick of stepwise disorderly logic that went and goes along something like this sort of unfortunate mal-reasoning pathway:

First, by not constantly searching out for an oddity within a stressing, large and boring repetitious patient care experience – by not looking out for the outliers with due diligence, the so called "Zebras".
Then, by the dreadful but common process of "mental reinforcement habituation from constant repetition" – by expecting, actually hoping and wishing the end point or medical diagnosis to be something that it is not.
Next, by looking only with that same old set of "horse-head blinders", looking along the same methodologically worn and very wrong random reasoning pathway – by arriving at a false conclusion and finding a wrong medical diagnosis.
After that, by unquestioned faith and submission to believing -- like a "stubborn mule" -- that the now false and formerly repeated diagnosis is in actual fact truly true. And…
Finally, – by confidently acting upon that false conclusion or medical diagnosis.

That was and is the unfortunate and tricky disorderly logic ball game. A triple play of outs and end of inning -- from zebra to horse to ass. That above described "too quickly to reflexively react" medical practitioner who swung at a self-thrown a curve ball usually got called "out" with a malpractice suit.

Since the time of Hippocrates, and throughout previous unrecorded history, questions about the ills of Mankind have always been the same. The answers, however, constantly changed and continue to change with increasing frequency. Historically, medical practice had never been scientifically validated. Theoretical dogma (an oxymoron) necessary to pass the licensure examination in Medicine (USA national board exam) changed over each five-year period to the degree that the previous five-year-old "correct at the time" answers, when given subsequently, changed a newer exam's passing score into a failing grade. Medical practice was considered an art, but an evolving art. A physician practiced the then "art" of Medicine over a lifetime, usually until death. Communication and validation systems were not yet adequately developed. A physician did not have the time nor circumstance to keep current over a lifetime of medical service. Times were difficult for extended travel, and continuing education difficult and unreasonable to demand in remote areas – effective mass communication systems were yet to be developed in the first half of the 20th Century.

In that old and former context, the practice, or practice standards, of a physician were difficult to define. Malpractice judgments depended on defining a selective practice that was divergent from an accepted norm. Since it was difficult to define the norm, malpractice claims for outliers were difficult to prove. Gross malpractice meant outright negligence – a grossly unreasonable action under the circumstances. The healthcare delivery circumstances were difficult to standardize and reasonableness was also ill-defined. Therefore, the actual total number of malpractice claims became artificially reduced and did not coincide with the actual rate of medical errors and wrong doings. Malpractice judgment awards very gradually evolved during the first half of the 20th Century:

First, the Flexner report was released and demanded more standardization in medical education and practice. Some semblance of a normal standard was just beginning to develop. Malpractice claims naturally increased.
Then, as the public sense of medical practice became more scientific than artistic, greater consistency with end results was expected from medical treatment. Malpractice claims increased further.
Next, the courts ruled that if the end result from the medical treatment was obviously not an expected end result, then some medically negligent act was committed on the legally accepted basis that the end result spoke for itself (res ipsa loquitur).
Finally, the legal community overly touted malpractice awards as the only supposed practical mechanism of the times to regulate the quality of medical care. This, of course, also led to an ever increasing number of malpractice claims.

Additionally, with time and research during the second half of the 20th Century, medical technology advanced and concomitantly produced increased public risk and morbidity from newer procedures and powerful pharmaceuticals. However, with that increasing risk came along a welcomed companion known as "medical progress". Unfortunately, looking at the migratory ecolo-nomic mechanism in place, that increasing number of malpractice claims stood by and accompanied this progress – that increased the supply side for the migratory economics of malpractice events. At the same time, the forever-fiscally-vigilant legal profession became more aware of medical malpractice lawsuits as a lucrative source of income – that increased the demand side for the migratory economics of malpractice claims. Workers' Compensation claims, offering a reliable deep Money pocket, became more abundant – that increased product production from the lawsuits. Lawyers employed by injured workers then dug more deeply into cash awards beyond monetary losses for "pain and suffering". If an injured worker completely recovered, then the lawyer did not do as well in recovering legal expenses that were set solely on a percentage of the final award. Expensive legalistic digging into a cause for existence of a continued lifetime of pain and suffering was rewarded by an extended concomitant search for physician-related malpractice causes. Next, big business corporations sold increasingly expensive malpractice insurance coverage to physicians like organized crime sold protection, while the number of and cash awards from malpractice suits continually increased, actually skyrocketed. Migratory economic supply malpractice criteria gradually increased by creep and crawl to meet the increasing migratory economic demand. At first, but only at first, pre-paid healthcare organizations seemed to be immune from the sting of enterprise liability and malpractice. As Scott Fleming, a Kaiser executive, expressed in a 1989 interview with Rickey Hendricks, "It was "virtually impossible" to hold a corporation responsible for the maintenance of standards of medical practice."[7] That line of thought continued into the second medical ecolo-nomic generation (1970-1990), but by the third medical ecolo-nomic generation (1990-2010) evolving migratory medical ecolo-nomics made that aforesaid "virtually impossible" statement not only very possible but also extremely legally probable. Finally, as medical ecolo-nomics evolved, so did the concept and consequences of medical malpractice along with more technological opportunities, ways and means for documenting all sorts of medical errors.

The worldly general public always felt that physicians, as a group, should be only tolerated as poor and penniless servants of the people. Remuneration from the practice of Medicine was always resented by the public. Even back in the year 1390, inference that a physician's greed superseded his interest in patient care was not so subtly scribed by Chaucer in the "Canterbury Tales, "He kept the gold he gained from pestilence…..Therefore he loved his gold exceeding all." Another interesting observation was and is that while people thought and think of their personal physician as a wonderful and honest practitioner, medical practitioners in general were and are thought to be greedy, untrustworthy and sometimes

---

[7] Hendricks, Ricky, A Model for National Healthcare, Rutgers Univ. Press, New Jersey, 1993, p. 14

dishonest. Per Ralzak, Ockham's and Hanlon's razors often collide with their sharp crossing blades, for there also always persisted a general attitude that doctors (as opposes to the legal profession) were getting paid something for nothing in giving medical advice if the end result was not a cure. So, even if one does not jump to assume malice where ignorance will suffice, in the 1666 "Le Médecin Malgré Lui", Molière did state, "Médecin c'est métier le meilleur de tous; car, soit qu'on fasse bien ou soit qu'on fasse mal, on est toujours payé de même sorte." Always getting paid anyway – Money and Medicine,

During the first overlapping medical ecolo-nomic generation (1950-1970), the progressive migratory economics of medical insurance and financed governmental programs permitted an open path for doctors' per capita income to rise sharply. Physician equity holdings also ostensibly and quite visibly increased as did their malpractice insurance coverage. Following and sniffing this newly-arrived alluring "Money scent" along first generation medical ecolo-nomic physician equity streams, voraciously hungry legal sharks lurked and abounded in the litigation waters of every California community. The sudden sweet sanguine scent of new currency burdening the hands of physicians flowed from the tidewaters to attract even bigger sharks in the deep dark sea. The aroma of legally delicious deep pockets from those newly-acquired physician equity holdings and increased malpractice coverage hovered about the legal airways to be sniffed into the nares of attorneys as a delightfully intoxicating pleasure drugs continually oozing from exposed and unprotected physician net worth statements along with those new higher-coverage malpractice insurance policies of first generation (1950-1970) medical ecolo-nomic physicians. Positioning themselves to hopefully evade a potential gnashing of teeth and a feasting blood bath in stormy malpractice seas, physicians stripped and shed (transferred and hid) their liquid assets and equities to establish zero net worth statements. They then went into and performed their medical practice "bare". Those non-bare or otherwise insured physicians who were not able to boast "ain't got nothin, ain't got nothin to lose because I'm bare" grasped for lifelines, further increased insurance coverage in the range of millions of dollars, thrown from corporate business world "rescue" ships, captained by malpractice insurance carriers. That shark feeding frenzy malpractice "umbrella" insurance protection lifeline was quite mistakenly though by the "un-bare" physicians to be the first generation of a medical ecolo-nomic last best hope for preserving and protecting quite substantial acquired life savings. A regretful and sad state of fiscal circumstances naturally followed.

Corporate insurance industries (would-be future Health Keeper Organizations (HKOs)) perpetrated a sanctioned organized crime spree. As doctors sought more and more umbrella coverage, insurance companies steadily increased their malpractice rates to coincide with the increasing coverage amounts, size and number of lawsuits, and increasing risk resulting from more complicated advanced medical technology. The cost of healthcare delivery increased sharply because doctors were emotionally drawn into the game of legally "Defensive Medicine", overspending in testing and referrals, by a rational fear of not possible but probable impending malpractice suits. A "defensive" and supposedly protective medical-legal work up greatly increased medical costs. Many costly tests and procedures were ordered and performed that were superfluous; the added expense contributed nothing to medical quality and had no logical rational for existence in the medical work up. The common phrase heard in a busy hospital setting was, "You better cover your butt and order a "......." Termed "medical-legal" testing, the expensive act became the only prophylactic precaution that a physician could employ. If every possible real and imaginary diagnosis was not completely worked up, then the physician would look and feel embarrassingly incompetent at deposition time when consistently and repeatedly asked two giant illogical and ambiguous, yet routine and seemingly sequentially-related incriminating questions: "Doctor, did you consider a diagnosis of "......"? -- Then, "If not, how did you rule it out?"

Fear of malpractice reprisal also stunted the growth of utilization review for medical quality. Doctors were further drawn into that self-protective code of silence and were reluctant to make it any easier for the lawyers to find causes for litigation. Malpractice litigation stung medical progress like a bite from a split-tongued viper. Lawyers claimed to improve medical quality by calling attention to and punishing wrong doings, but lawsuits also inhibited the growth of medical quality by preventing initiative for honest quality medical review. Overall, a malpractice investigation, as viewed by physicians, was medical review performed by serpents possessing deadly poisoned venom. Lawyers, on the other hand, altruistically envisioned themselves as necessary and essential public healthkeepers, because the actions taken by the angelic lawyers served to assure quality in healthcare delivery. (There was, is, and always will be an important third side to any two-sided dispute.)

Physicians acknowledged many medical errors or mistakes, but there was not yet a dignified data compiling or statistical analysis computer during that once golden era of medical practice. Medical practitioners routinely kept the dire malpractice event locked away like a skeleton in their closets. Physicians did not want to hear about errors, did not want to deal with errors, and made insufficient efforts to proactively do something about medical errors or mistakes. With a righteous indignation, the lawyers dominated over malpractice issues in the second medical ecolo-nomic generation (1970-1990). Perhaps the lawyers actually might have had a valid fallback point of view, but their overwhelming greed overran their stated reasoning and hastened unintended but not unexpected consequences.

The pendulum of payment on the award balance to compensate for pain and suffering in malpractice suits swung so far to the expensive extreme during the early 1970's that nearly all national malpractice insurance carriers abandoned the California market, as they had done in Florida, Ohio, and other states. The legal beagles sniffed out those deep-pocketed physicians with millions of dollars in umbrella insurance coverage – perhaps it was a mistake to have purchased progressively increasing coverage. Malpractice premiums jumped threefold and attained an all-time high. Many physicians made plans to leave those aforementioned states in the event of impending financial bankruptcy, while others, acting proactively, sought out financial planners to transfer ownership of their net worth so that there would be no assets to freeze or sue. As previously pointed out, those deep pocket-less physicians could then practice without insurance (go bare) and be functionally immune from lawsuits. At one point 60% of California doctors were practicing without malpractice insurance.[8] In 1974, the California Medical Association (CMA) organized a physician protest march on the California state capitol building in Sacramento. The white coats came in a great parade, onto the capitol mall in tree town.....

As a result, along came MICRA – The Medical Injury Compensation Reform Act. The act placed a quarter-million-dollar cap on pain and suffering, with no limit on actual damages, but one might just take pause and ask -- what really and truly is just and satisfactory compensation for a fatal injury? In truth, there is no amount of Man's Money or Medicine/wealth that can ever replace a loss such as a dead child. The grief, pain, and suffering among the child's family remain as an enormous hurt, and the family's pain and tears can never be halted by mere Money in any form. Prayer and meditation, over time, remain their only possible cure. MICRA enforced a dollar limit on awards for pain and suffering at $250,000, with no cap, no limit, on awards for economic loss and/or medical bills – past, present, or future. The injured party was also free to pursue retribution from hospitals and/or physicians in the form of punitive penalties for egregious malpractice. Such lawsuits for valid punitive damages were not inhibited nor affected by MICRA legislation. MICRA, then, really existed to reduce the cost of healthcare delivery to the general public and to reduce the cost of malpractice

[8] CMA government relations MICRA briefing sheet 1998.

insurance to physicians. MICRA did not need to and was not intended to punish physicians and hospitals. Punitive damage awards were specifically set apart for that purpose. MICRA limited attorney fees by discouraging nonsense or frivolous lawsuits, while placing no dollar limit on economic damage awards for patients. MICRA held back but did not stop increasing healthcare cost inflation; even when accounting for general inflation, the number of lawsuits and the dollars in awards seven years before MICRA became law were significantly less than the numbers and dollars in a similar period seven years after the passage of MICRA.

The third ecolo-nomic generation (1990-2010) brought further changes into the migratory economic malpractice arena. Sophistication of the patient-consumer shot to an all-time high. The typical patient, having now officially become a "patient healthkeeper" through education and the Internet, was "previously informed" regarding most common medical treatments. The patient heard and read about a surgery in the second medical ecolo-nomic generation. In the third medical ecolo-nomic generation, the patient saw the procedure on public television and interacted with the procedure on the Internet. In July of 2001, The Joint Commission on Accreditation of Hospitals and Outpatient Centers (JCAHO) surveyed for disclosure to patients concerning unexpected or adverse treatment outcomes. A "prudent layperson" would expect more than an explanation of surgery, risks, indications, alternatives, and outcomes. If an orthopedic prosthesis was to be implanted, then a discussion of the manufacturer, appropriateness of various models, metallurgy, longevity, plastic, ceramic and metal component ware complications, outcomes, risks, alternatives and "use variation" rational was expected. Any drug prescribed for an "off formulary" purpose naturally mandated a very detailed explanation of possible adverse side effects or reactions.

Because of overhead expenses such as malpractice insurance, a great economic migration began concerning a physicians practice process and environment. Fee-for-service physicians felt more secure as salaried employees under the aegis of large institutions. Some Health Keeper Organizations (HKOs), who saw malpractice as just another line under "negotiable business expenses," paid the physician's malpractice premiums and extracted the Money back through increased patient dues and lowered physician salary payments. HKOs were more concerned about the ever-rising specter of enterprise liability in malpractice judgments. HKOs, the ultimate "big pockets" wanted to direct, but not be responsible for, medical care. HKOs wanted to keep their cake and eat it too. The new HKOs and the old malpractice carriers both refused to pick up insurance coverage for left over "tails" from former and premium cheaper "claims made" physician malpractice insurance policies. Physicians who had purchased the more expensive or "claims originating but not yet made" time-period of practice insurance remained covered after economically migrating to work for a HKO. Patients were allowed to sue their fee-for-service indemnity insurers in the first medical ecolo-nomic generation, but this ability was taken away with the federal Employee Retirement Income Security Act (ERISA) protections offered to the Health Maintenance Organizations (HMOs) in the second medical ecolo-nomic generation. Because of outcries from both patients and physicians, the newly evolved HKOs soon found themselves unprotected. In the second half of the third medical ecolo-nomic generation, the HKOs completely lost their malpractice immunity; and attorney-calculated award judgments resulting from that aforementioned new type of malpractice, enterprise liability, reared their new ugly corporate-hungry heads while anticipatory thoughts of tasty tidings dripped hot saliva from the jowls of those corporate litigation attorneys.

The federal government previously (and successfully) had sued "Organized Crime" on the grounds of illegal conspiratorial collaboration to further a business interest (a crime). HKOs of the third medical ecolo-nomic generation found themselves entered on the government's hit list because of similar activity. HKOs became under fire for racketeering according to the civil provisions of the Racketeer Influenced and Corrupt Organizations Act (RICO). AMA and CMA lawsuits on behalf of physicians and patients claimed that their plaintiffs were economically harmed because of a conspiratorial collaboration of misconduct. Plaintiffs alleged that the HKOs entered into medical decision-making and placed unreasonable restrictions on the level of medical care, without the consent from or the knowledge of consumers. The good (financial/fiscal) of the health plan was allegedly placed ahead of the good (quality healthcare/outcomes) of the collective patients. With a successful suit under RICO, financial damage awards multiplied to a product three times the traditional malpractice lawsuit damage awards. "After the gentleness of Apollo, the words of Mercury are harsh" (Shakespeare's "Love's Labour's Lost"), but "through the earnest joy generated from a physician's medical practice, such labor is of love, that love's labor's is never lost" -- Ralzak

Back in the day and as it is today, a physician or some form of healthkeeper still had to migrate from somewhere to fill a great void in accessible healthcare delivery for the masses. Many non-sanctioned methodologies along with unapproved closed panel medical services slowly arose once again like a Phoenix from the rubble and ashes of former quasi-medical practices bankrupted by the Flexner Report. Then, more political tampering by State Governments sprinkled additional poison on the peculating political pot by rigging the allocation of customers and territories, requiring individual state licensure for medical practice and effectively restricting physician economic migration by restricting interstate medical commerce. Pure unadulterated political pandering into **Healthcare Reform** -- Those resultant silos of state-only medical practice thus formed blocked what should have been a natural evolutionary growth in a national networking of healthcare delivery and medical modality communication, common national physician licensure, and enterprise intermingling of various forms of economically migrating healthcare delivery systems.

Migratory economics continued to evolve **Healthcare Reform**: Soon to follow in the second half of the 20th Century, physicians were no longer expected to provide free charitable healthcare for financially poor patients in hospital settings; and before long thereafter, physicians would also be reimbursed for indigent healthcare delivery services outside of the hospital setting – soon to say good-by to all pro bono healthcare delivery and non-payment "medical courtesy" for physicians' families.

A great debate arose concerning possible and probable methodologies to provide healthcare delivery that would include access for the entire citizenry of the United States. All of these recurring arguments took and take place while migratory economic driven medical ecolo-nomic evolution slowly yet steadily churned and churns out a steady stream of temporary generational paradigms or eras of medical practice. The process for **Healthcare Reform** was always the same:
Myths beget Cultural mores;
Cultural mores beget medical ethics;
Medical ethics beget a medical ecology;
Medical ecologies beget medical economics;
Medical economics beget healthcare delivery systems;
Healthcare delivery systems beget **Healthcare Reform**s; and…..
All of this is simply an evolution of medical ecolo-nomics first described by economist Anne Robert Jacques Turgot, Baron de Laune in 1750. In his *Philosophical Review of the Successive Advances of the Human Mind,* Turgot described such a step to step progression that evolves to change the various and varied ecologies of a culture.

Even though technology advanced while medical quality and medical costs arose concomitantly, interest in indemnity health insurance grew at a relatively slow rate through the 1930's. World War II medical experience controlled exposure to Typhus, but evolving mores exposed many sticky cultural norms for the migratory economics of the day to adhere to. In 1942, the United States Congress saw an economic need for and passed the Wage Stabilization Act. Mid and post war businesses desperately competed for a limited employee pool, but were forbidden to raise wages to attract new employees. The business community then found a dynamic competitive advantage in a medical economic loophole: Employment Based Health Insurance stayed exempt from that Wage Stabilization Act and was also tax-deductible as a business expense. Thanks to a National Labor Board ruling in 1949, employee based health insurance benefits officially became a negotiable item on the American trade union collective bargaining table. Employee Based Health Insurance not only became a tax-free wage increase for employees, but also an income tax write-off for employers. That double benefit also seemingly assured both healthier workers and less employee sick days off for the business entity. **Employee-Based Healthcare Insurance proved to be a migratory economic evolutionary Healthcare Reforming watershed event.** Exponential growth in healthcare insurance corporations immediately followed. (After Y2K, employees were abundant, and the per-tax dollar expense was out of proportion to the perceived loyalty gained. Employers then balked at the increasingly expensive healthcare insurance and became more amenable to partial payment as a form of healthcare rationing.) Nonetheless, Employee Based Health Insurance stood out as a **Healthcare Reform** migratory economic event to continue the changing evolutionary medical ecolo-nomic course of healthcare delivery in the United States.

Routinely referenced from both sides of argument are the supposed wishes and ideals of the American Founding Fathers concerning a set, resistant to change and loyal to the letter fundamental United States Constitution versus those favoring a flexible, dynamic progressive interpretation of the spirit rather than the letter of United States Constitution. The Founding Fathers were perhaps both capitalists and budding socialists. Thomas Pane advocated for common sense, including common sense in managing a welfare state.

There have been many political advocacy efforts for **Healthcare Reform** to bring about universal healthcare or "coverage for all" since the beginning of the 20th Century, and all federal legislative attempts directed at single payer governmental plans have failed miserably. The real accompanying topic of "universal access for all" with mandatory rationing trade-offs had and has remained a consistent "hot potato" topic. A definition of "basic" healthcare seems to elude all political thought. The goal of universal medical "coverage" is equally elusive. Program cost versus program rationing, these very practical and basic balance of care issues were not and have not ever been settled in American society, a society that demands the best technology regardless of public cost and personal individualized healthcare delivery from MD or DO physicians who still have no real competition in the American healthcare delivery marketplace. So exactly where does this poorly definable winding road to national single payer healthcare, the path that leads Americans into hotly fired current and future political debates with no real solution from either side, where does its footpath seem to originate and possibly end?

There were a few preliminary attempts to get things sorted away, cleared in some sort of order a bit before the design or engineering of that so difficult to build road began:

The first recorded political advocacy for governmental national health insurance in the United States began as a plank in the platform of the socialist party in the early 1900's. The socialist party, of course, lost the election at that place and time; but their influence eventually prevailed in the progressivism movement, and fired by the millennial generation, threatens to emerge as a separate political party today.

Eugene Debs, after founding the first industrial union, the American Railway Union, ran and lost five times in attempts to become a U.S. President. As a socialist, he advocated for women's rights, social security, and national health insurance. Such ideas were considered to be "un-American" around the turn of the Nineteenth to the Twentieth Century.

Just about all futuristic societal science fiction tales of today sadly portray a deprived and depressed futuristic American society where the economy is top-notch in terms of GDP, but the majority of American people suffer from inadequate to complete absence of technological and social amenities: Electricity limited to 3% of the population, running water limited to 33% of the population, mechanical transportation limited to 5% of the population, with no public welfare and a paucity of healthcare delivery seem to be the expected futuristic norms of a vast USA population living to suffer in abject stark poverty, according to the majority of the Hollywood script writers of today. About the turn of the 19th to 20th century, the American economy found itself vibrant and booming, the western migratory expansion of a great nation had been completed, natural resources were abundant and easily transportable, industrial development flamed, hot and cracking like a wildfire. And oh yes, by the way -- those above mentioned futuristic societal statistics and percentages scripted by Hollywood futurists happen to be the exact statistics and percentages for the population of the United States of America in the year 1900. In spite of what one's current propagandized, habitual and learned mythological societal-social concepts might lead one to believe, the American society at the turn of the century was fairly content with their state of affairs and confidently trusting that things could and most assuredly would just get better as time went on. There was some hesitation and fear to deal with banking institutions holding or more properly put, not holding enough Money, but the level of mistrust remained quite acceptable, enough for those institutions to run a sustainable profit in spite of the migratory economic force.

About the same time as the Flexner report for **Healthcare Reform**, further citizen mistrust and demand for economic reform ran ramped in the USA. According to economist J.A. Schumpter, the banking crisis of 1907 resulted from improper "controls" (i.e. regulation) in the banking system which let to inappropriate utilization by the general public. Citizens feared that the smaller banks were lending dollars well beyond the capacity of their capital reserves. There was a "run on the banks", an effort by the American public to hoard and hold their hard earned dollars and a concurrent international effort to do the same with gold. A "Rich Man's Panic" lowered the value of the stock market by 18%. Landsteiner had just recently discovered the human blood groups and the **Healthcare Reform** methodology of human blood transfusion suddenly became more palatable and popular, but economic transfusion was more the word of the day. In order to allay the fears and provide a method of stabilization, J.P. Morgan organized a migratory economic transfusion of private monetary funds to the rescue and aided in the passage of the 1908 Aldrich-Vreeland Act. The banks created the Federal Reserve, a private-central organization formed by a dozen banks scattered across the USA in 1913, which allowed the temporary issuance of non-redeemable currency during a national economic crisis and guaranteed a 40% holding reserve of metallic gold for the remainder of the currency, (a guarantee which would eventually be completely and totally denied once President Nixon eliminated the "quasi gold standard" for the USA). Individual bank coinage as practiced in the USA prior to 1914 continued in Canada after 1914. The USA Federal Reserve Concept had failed twice before 1914 as the heavy hand of government's awarding of monopoly status to a private firm to decrease competition had been deemed to be economically unfeasible. However, the majority of officers that ran the new Federal Reserve were appointed by the Federal Government, so that the private entity, the Federal Reserve, was and is really an arm of the Administrative branch of Federal Government, armed with the ability to tighten up the total Money supply, set a lender interest rate to banks, and set the amount of reserve funds that a local bank is required to hold, all completely and legally without the consent of Congress. With a federal governmental guarantee on their bank-held savings, American citizens became less likely to hoard their Money supply, at least for about half a generation or so.

In 1911, before he became a Supreme Court justice, Louis D. Brandeis gave a speech advocating for **Healthcare Reform** with a goal of national health insurance and quickly found the subject to be rather unpopular with the voting public, especially for popular political debate.

President Theodore Roosevelt's progressive party made national health insurance one of the major planks in his party's 1912 Presidential campaign platform. National health insurance, however, became another forgotten **Healthcare Reform** campaign promise once Roosevelt took office. A tax from everyone earning Money to pay for mainly the unfortunate as well as other socialistic concepts did not bode well with the migratory economics or the cultural mores of the time, but some things do and inevitably will change with the aid of Tolstoy's two greatest of all warriors -- time and patience.

In 1915, the American Association for Labor Legislation (AALL), which was established in 1912, lobbied a congressional bill to cover professional and hospital health costs for citizens earning under $1200 per year. The bill offended a spectrum of political-interest groups and failed because the proper progression of aforementioned medical ecolo-nomics had not yet evolved; but the increasing cost of medical care and the economics of American wages lost due to sickness were indeed debated nationally, ad nauseam. As physician income increased so did private practicing physician autonomy, influence and prestige, along with their medical associations' well-organized and natural entrepreneurial opposition to government-run healthcare delivery. Time and patience would also war in opposition and eventually defeat and conquer physician entrepreneurialism in healthcare delivery.

Meanwhile, nationalism and militarism grew in Europe at a proportionally faster rate than various national emissaries could effectively control. World War I (1914–1918) erupted. Although at first neutral, by 1917 the Woodrow Wilson Administration entered the USA into the horrible fracas while boasting a world order for progressive democracy. America subsequently suffered the loss of over one hundred thousand lives, half of which succumbed to the infamous H1N1 influenza pandemic. Women were actively recruited into military service for the first time, and the war effort grew the U.S. military and the U.S. economy at exponential rates. Wars generally kill interest in progressive reformers and domestic **Healthcare Reform** programs alike. Therefore, when a 1918 U.S. Congress dared to propose national health insurance, that proposal immediately died, especially when the AMA lobby spun the proposal as an "insidious German idea".

In November of 1918, a proposed California senate constitutional amendment (sca26) authorized the legislature headed by Governor Hiram Johnson to enact state healthcare delivery insurance for low-level wage earners. The measure failed a public ballot proposal; 26% for and 73% against. The exact California numbers were 133,858 for and 358,324 against. Destiny however would eventually be determined by an evolving population and legislative demographic. An egg and a sperm are Ralzak's greatest demographic sculptors for war and migratory economic concerns over Man, Money and Medicine.

At the 1926 annual meeting of the AMA, a minority committee of five academic leaders considered changing the way in which medical care was then delivered – a seemingly new concept, called it **"Healthcare Reform"**. Technological intrusion, economically disruptive technological advances, were also at their naissance in functionally disrupting the course of **Healthcare Reform**: Two medical researchers, Banting and Best, discovered Insulin; and Fleming discovered penicillin during those "Roaring Twenties", when my then girlish mom and "flappers" wildly danced to a folk rhythm that originated from an Atlantic Ocean harbor city in South Carolina, the "Charleston".

As a result of necessitated politico-scientific admixtures, in 1927 Ray Lyman Wilbur, MD, secretary of interior and president of Stanford University, presided over the Committee on the Cost of Medical Care (CCMC), whose fundamental hard work and admiralty exquisite basic research findings for a governmental committee commendably consisted of three boiled down concepts that are yet touted today:

1. Fee-for service private medical practice must end;
2. Corporate insurance group models or federal government models must replace private practice for the general public; and
3. Academic Staff models as Centers of Excellence must be fed by multiple grass-root, non-physician basic healthcare delivery facilities.

In 1932, **IN BOLD**, above the fold front page headlines in newspapers such as *The New York Times, The New York Herald-Tribune and The Wall Street Journal*, the words all shouted out, "Socialized Medicine is urged in Survey" and the newspaper articles below the fold read out, "Return Medicine to the status of a public service". Were these headlines outrageous and disgraceful for the times? Yes, during the 1930's and 1940's popular media -- beltway spin and the powerful

AMA lobby ever so successfully portrayed and demonized National Health Insurance as a dreaded "Soviet-inspired" notion.

Alas, the virtuous Committee on the Cost of Medical Care (CCMC) had tried but tried in vain to reform the American healthcare delivery system before the end of the first quarter of the 20th Century. The CCMC failed because the powerful political forces of medical associations, not unlike some early trade unions, stood as a federally created monster, effectively swaying public opinion and blockading further innovative governmental **Healthcare Reform** legislation. The varied and multiple-suited lobbyists portrayed themselves as standing for the continued preservation of physician autonomy along with public choice (for those who could afford it) in all aspects of medical care. However, those three often-repeated 1927 CCMC conclusions were more persuasively brought forward as time went on, especially during 2010. After the enactment of the Accountable Care Act (ACA) in 2013, "federal government-funded think centers" (an oxymoron?), which were established to effect cost reduction in new healthcare delivery systems, "brainstormed" the literally exact same edicts as the 1927 CCMC -- just an astounding and amazing coincidence (certainly no plagiarism?) -- "round we go again". It also became painfully obvious to governmental and corporate healthcare entities after 1927 that **Healthcare Reform** required that trade union-like political power of the medical societies and medical associations to be drastically curbed then totally dismantled and thus effectively destroyed. The political power and political direction of the medical associations evolved over approximately one hundred years to finally drastically evolve change and progressively adapt to avoid extinction on both of the above counts. Medical Association membership that originally represented a collective cohort of private fee-for-service physicians shifted to represent a collective cohort of organized medical groups and insurance corporations that employed physicians. Governmental favor was then granted to competing large health insurance plans. Although the sellers of "health plans" were initially duped by greedy expectation of great profits through collusion with the government, future loss of health insurance corporate autonomy would most naturally follow in the second half of the 21st Century -- Adaptive evolution takes its time and takes its toll – Ralzak.

After World War I, American nationalism and the American business economy continued to accelerate like some kind of jet plane or rocket ship that had not yet been invented for or at that time in history. The roaring twenties brought: that dance -- the Charleston, the time and dress for characters like the fictitious Great Gatsby, the paradigm of loose Money and the speculative era of buying stocks on a wide percentage margin. The unfortunately induced migratory economic habit of acting in the present based solely on the teachings of the past, rather than information available in the present (like the Y2K and beyond housing bubble) assured a great public confidence that resulted, for an ephemeral period of time, in a continuing and endless rise in the DOW from the huge public purchase of speculative stocks on wide margin. (Warning: Past performance does not guarantee future earnings – during the housing crisis at the beginning of the 21st Century, Americans one again succumbed to the same smooth blarney-pitched malarkey.) Insight into migratory economic future and a ten-year-old future economist, Hyman Minsky, were yet too young and immature to advise the public as to the value of profit-backed "hedge" borrowing versus speculative "Ponzi" borrowing in an economy where "stability is unstable". This obvious but unfortunate migratory economic policy of acting on "adaptive expectations" rather than "rational expectations" was to be again problematic with the inappropriate DOW bubble just before Y2K and the overlooking of the recurring migratory economic that continually haunted realistic efforts towards **Healthcare Reform**.

There was no gleaming gold standard for healthcare delivery at the beginning of the twentieth Century. The perennial problem with the migratory economic gold standard became sub-acute around 1920 when the USA was forced into a short recession in response to a raised federal lending interest rate, prescribed in order to compete with foreign nations who had raised their interest rates in a vain effort to hoard the shiny yellow metal during a global gold rush. The USA's reactively increased interest rate had to be dealt with politically. The federal government mandated that for safe-keeping, Americans must turn all their bright yellow coin currency over to the federal government in exchange for paper Money. Shortly thereafter, that unfortunate knee-jerk reaction raised a federal interest rate that also was finally reduced and brought under control with the passage of Father Time.

The unfortunately misguided USA migratory economics of the late 1920's evolved from a bewildering dilemma to perplexing trilemma – poor control of monetary policy led to exchange rate controversies and decreased capital mobility. To start with, the Federal Reserve became worried that the economy was proceeding at a faster rate than any normal or planned growth could eventually sustain without upheaval or collapse. In order to slow down the economy and tighten things up a bit, the Federal Reserve supposedly sweetened the micro economic stew pot by increasing its offering of bonds to the public; and the public readily purchased that touted lucratively stable product. Unintended migratory economic consequences ensued -- when these bonds were eventually cashed by the public at their local banks, the Federal Reserve's previously established and required withheld stash of liquid reserve funds at those local banks became depleted; and thus, the Federal Reserve's mandated liquid reserve requirement for the local banks was then suddenly, unexpectedly and unintentionally not met. Responding in turn, the local banks called in the numerous loans that so many of the American public had acquired solely in order to buy those aforementioned speculative stocks on wide margin in the era of an escalating DOW. The profit-driven rotating fiscal wheel of demand side confidence lost its spokes. The marginal worth of the purchased stocks had very little cash value; the general public investors suddenly could not pay back the balance on their loans; and the stock market "crashed" in 1929. **Healthcare Reform** no longer could be found on anyone's immediate migratory economic agenda.

Easy Money quickly becomes sloppy Money, resulting in a migratory economic Mad Mania as was seen in 1929 and again in 2007, when a house mortgage financing structure, previously politically engineered and constructed like a house of cards, suddenly collapsed. The same sort of collapse was touted and feared for the 2018 and beyond future of the Accountable Care Act, where the overwhelming number of enrollees in the state and federal healthcare exchanges signed up for an expanded but time-limited federally subsidized Medicaid rather than the politically promised "audacity of hope" in a 21st Century myth of the metals for percentages of coverage. Magic had abounded once again in political prestidigitation. An expected illegitimate commerce clause condition judicially turned into federal tax by the Supreme Court mandated healthy young individuals to enroll into private insurance exchanges or buy private insurance and thus help lessen the medical ecolo-nomic burden of overall cost in that initial **Healthcare Reform.** That was the necessary migratory economic cost to keep alive healthcare delivery insurance corporations rather than the cost of healthcare itself. Or perhaps it was quite cleverly all planned that way......? Was the entire process just a stepping stone for national single payer health insurance or just another chapter depicting entrepreneurial Man haphazardly manipulating Money in the supposed cause of Medicine?

In remembering and learning from history, one must be constantly cognizant and vigilant to consider the totality of the cultural mores and economic policies that were in place before suggesting that a similar solution might be effective in a present time, where the circumstances are almost never exactly the same. The children of the future are due that due diligence of questioning, even to the point of questioning any preached or academically "intuitive" understanding or concept that apparently takes nothing for granted:

The migratory economic policies at the beginning of the Herbert Hoover administration dated back to the classical "substances have intrinsic value" and "no need for government" self-correcting economic theories of Jean Baptiste and David Ricardo in the late 1700's, where output product value was deemed directly proportional to the cost of production. French Physician, Surgeon and Economist François Quesnay had previously led innovative economic thought in the early 1700's with a "phisiocratic" or natural power analytical analysis that he summarized in his *Tableau économique*, which is similar to a modern day algorithm. He saw a comprehensible and rational interconnection, a natural order that justified an economic stratification of resources and labor for a common (defined today as capitalistic) harmonious good for humanity. His hypothesis -- As goes the land owner (not GM) so goes the nation -- remains pertinent today in recognizing the role of large corporate interests (formerly landowners), who direct the acquisition of natural resources (formerly farming), as well as the research, development and production of commodities including healthcare delivery and **Healthcare Reform** (formerly the work of artisans). According to Quesnay, the efficiency and productivity of sustainable interdependent interaction among these three groups and the instinctual driving migratory economic interest of his landowner class to benefit itself through benefiting society is unjustly tampered upon and restricted by administratively legislated laws and regulations which are neither in accord with natural human interactions nor the ultimate law of Mother Nature. Economist Quesnay also strongly supported a strict and rigid written constitutional rule.

Therefore, still not recognizing the imperfections of "Perfect Competition", such as the painfully obvious natural volatility of short term markets and the influence of monopolies, President Hoover confidently assured the American populace with the often quoted phrase, "Prosperity is just around the corner"; but when Americans looked around the corner all that they could see were either their next-door neighbors desperately selling apples and chestnuts for migratory economic survival on the next street-corner or someone in a business suit leaving a tall building in a single bound without a red cape or a big "S" on his jersey and then landing "splat" right there just beyond the corner sidewalk. As a possible proof of Milton Friedman's future "permanent income hypothesis", Americans hoarded their savings; but because employment opportunities did not exist, they paradoxically became progressively poorer in spite of their thrift. Healthcare delivery mechanisms and **Healthcare Reforms** were sorely needed, but the obvious downtrodden migratory economics of the time did not smile nor even once flirtatiously glance in the direction of Medicine.

In all fairness, President Hoover may have been the unfortunate recipient of bad political advice right around re-election time. He did diligently try to inject capital into the Money supply with public works projects such as the Hoover Dam; and he did finally realize that taxes take buying power out of the economy, and therefore, instead of taxation incurred a federal debt to ease tension on credit. Presidential candidate F. D. Roosevelt gained political capital by unjustly criticizing those worthy albeit end-of-term migratory economic actions and then convincing the superficial-superfluously-thinking and reactionary American voters that the federal budget should be and must be immediately balanced or else….. Where one sits is most often a prerequisite for where one stands. (Wait till you read the quote attacking the President Bush administration from Senator Obama in 2006.)

In the absence of **Healthcare Reform**, the moral-ethical doctor-driven force of charitable concern remained a non-reimbursed propensity to help and serve the sick and injured, regardless of personal or financial risk. "Charity" or donations from rich patrons with bona fide philanthropic aspirations supported many private hospitals of the era; but, unlike physicians, most of these charitable-financed hospitals showed no propensity to actually serve the less fortunate. Even though America was far and away from the Greek island of Kos, doctors were honorably entrusted to care for the poor with equal "purity and holiness;" and in the first half of the 20th Century, hordes of charitable-minded physicians did just that:

The Los Angeles County Board of Supervisors constructed the Los Angeles County Hospital during the time of the great American depression. In 1929, an inscription, carved in the frieze stone, atop the parapet, supported by immense Doric columns providing grandeur to the entry alcove, at the top of the pyramiding stone stairs of the main grand entrance to old "Big County" hospital, boldly proclaimed:

"ERECTED BY THE CITIZENS OF LOS ANGELES TO PROVIDE HOSPITAL CARE FOR THE ACUTELY ILL AND SUFFERING TO WHOM THE DOCTORS OF THE ATTENDING STAFF GIVE THEIR SERVICES WITHOUT CHARGE IN ORDER THAT NO CITIZEN OF THE COUNTY BE DEPRIVED OF HEALTH OR LIFE FOR LACK OF SUCH CARE AND SERVICES"

Similar structures to L.A.'s "Big County" were built with tax-funded **Healthcare Reform** initiatives in other metropolises: Boston City Hospital, Bellevue of New York, Charity Hospital of New Orleans, Cook County Hospital of Chicago, and the former Osler Hospital -- Philadelphia General Hospital, just to name a few. These county hospitals proudly stood erected tall and strong as an important and vital investment in the American migratory economic **Healthcare Reform** culture. The national county hospital system was a great and wonderful idea, a working concept to help solve a national social problem for the medically needy indigent in an evolving culture that finally recognized and acknowledged a social and moral obligation to provide some level of healthcare delivery for all; but like a falling star, the beacon light shining from the county hospital system that welcomed one and all to gratis basic level medical healthcare delivery gradually dimmed and faded away over the next generation or so.

That great American depression of 1929 also lessened interest in national healthcare programs. During the 1930's and 1940's beltway spin and the AMA continued to repeatedly portray national health insurance as a "soviet-inspired" notion. New York Governor Franklin Delano Roosevelt supported a laissez-faire economy; but having to deal first with a post-depression jobless recovery and then a World War, newly elected President Franklin Delano Roosevelt's overtly progressive administration pushed a bit too far to the left for the progression of ecolo-nomics of that time to bare, a bit more beyond the tolerance of the American people. (Remember -- Where a politician stands -- depends on -- where a politician sits.) In the first 100 days of his presidency, the 1933 National Recovery Administration (NRA) forced the dynamic American industrial machine to create "codes of fair competition", set price floors and minimum wages/maximum hours, and ended the true classic "gold standard". Paper Money issued by the government could no longer be converted into gold and vice versa. Americans were advised to hand in their gold coins for the new paper Money which merely defined the American dollar as an evolving legislative decreed percentage of gold. Moreover, the NRA laid down a non-specific but positive progressive foundation for what could possibly be seen as a migratory economic that would someday develop an evolutionary branch, a nascent branch budding a **Healthcare Reform flower** that could grow and then bloom as a national governmental single payer health plan. Then the 1935 Supreme Court, in the *Schechter Poultry Corp. v. United States 295 U.S. 495* verdict, determined the formation of the NRA to be unconstitutional. All supporting efforts for **Healthcare Reform** fell to their begging knees and nobody wanted to listen to or even hear those seeking Medicine delivery alms.

Charity healthcare was always an essential part and parcel of medical practice until the political pandering of government regulation stepped in. In 1931, California Welfare and Institutions Code #1700 statutorily mandated California counties to provide for their medically indigent. Physicians were next to ephemerally benefit from the pandering, and for the first time, actually had the backing of government regulation mandating that they be paid to care for the poor in County Hospitals. Those formally "free hospitals" or "charity hospitals" all eventually fell into fiscally unsustainable further financial difficulties, especially after the advent of government-sponsored entitlement programs in the 1960's. Physicians were again governmentally mandated, but now to be serendipitously paid to deliver healthcare to the poor in luxurious private hospitals of their choice, privately funded hospitals that now could at will "bill the government" for hospital services directed to the indigent. There was, is, and never will be a governmental Money tree; the human ego defense mechanism of denial overpowers rationality in accounting for the spending of taxes paid by the citizenry that finance "the government's ability to pay". The federal government carelessly stepped into and left a permanent great footprint in the brownish mud stuff just beyond a **watershed of Healthcare Reform** once again. Caring for the poor and unfortunate uninsurable citizens and residents in the USA during the 1st half of the 20th Century was known as "charity" among the doctors, hospitals and populace; after 1965 all Americans were to forever refer to that formerly honorable pro-bono service as a magically reimbursed "government-paid" **Medicaid**.

In 1935, the California Medical Association House of Delegates astonishingly recommended that, "legislation be proposed seeking to establish a health insurance system, mandatory as to certain population groups and voluntary as to certain population groups". This unintended consequential action toward universal coverage in **Healthcare Reform** was then later dismissed by a majority of the doctors as an unfortunate example of an Abilene Paradox, groupthink, herd mentality, pluralistic ignorance and/or an innate fear to confront reality. Name-calling, if loud, repeated and unchecked, has always overpowered and defied basic logic.

The Roosevelt administration, meanwhile, was subsequently forced to ignore the Wagner National Health Act and allowed it to die shortly after coming out of committee in order to gain passage of the Wagner National Labor Relations Act, which included a few of the previously rejected NRA provisions. Nonetheless, President Roosevelt's progressivism took a big leap forward in 1939. Having switched his alliances, and although unable to solve the problem of post-depression joblessness in America, President Roosevelt championed a bill of Citizen "Civil Rights" as an on-going migratory economic evolution to replace traditional "constitutional rights", and the President additionally pushed through a "New Deal" philosophy that eventually led to the passage of the National Social Security Act. However, still limiting the practice of Medicine to a select chosen few, Section 1395X of the Social Security Act clearly defined the term "physician", when used in conjunction with the performance of any function or action, to mean -- "a doctor of medicine or osteopathy legally authorized to practice medicine and surgery by the State in which he performs such function or action", and none other.

When President Roosevelt first took office in 1933 and someone whispered the name "John Maynard Keynes" into his presidential ear, he may at first thought that the John Maynard Keynes "hoarding Money theory" was "Too easy an explanation", but he had to do something to reduce out of control inflation and an unacceptable unemployment rate of over 25%, so he initiated public work projects and eventually sought to "prime the pump" of the national economy with Keynesian-styled federal funds. After the engendered increased nationalism and formation of vital jobs necessary to support World War II serendipitously increased federal spending funds, the President touted a "miraculous" recovery, and the American migratory economic economy reversed its downward trend to sing and shout, "Good times are here again".

"Single men had marched away to war, and both single and married women economically migrated to work in job positions that up till then had been the "exclusive province of men". No feminist sub-culture led the way; no woman cast her national patriotic American duty as an expression of independence for her sex from her home environment. Those brave and strong women assured a strong and vibrant backbone for the continued dominance in economic prosperity of their beloved nation. Those twenty million strong American women were responding to that mother of all mothers, the mother of necessity, the necessity for the cherished survival of their families and of the USA. Women not only ran their homes, but they also brought home the bacon; and the courageous "we can do it" women working on the vital United States of America labor force would never ever again let any of the male sex living or yet to live in the USA forget it." (Approximately written as first stated by my mom.)

Healthcare Reform in medical decision making by physicians was also subjected to and not very gracefully enduring a very rocky course. "Organized Medicine" existed in the form of medical societies and associations, but at the turn of the 19th

Century, the science of expert healthcare delivery lacked any effort toward organization. The life-long course of medical practice was considered a continuous learning experience for an "art" of Medicine, and individual experience stood as the sole standard basis for most judgment decisions. Older physicians in the first half of the 20th Century were honored mentors for younger physicians, both in private practice and in the emerging organized group delivery systems. Financial risk-taking and legal liability were recognized entities, but did not dictate or influence method or time allotments in medical care examinations, testing procedures or prescriptions. Results from physician-directed medical care were not critically analyzed, yet believed to be generally good; but those results often proved to be quite variable. Although the diagnosis, clinical course, pathophysiology, and etiology of many diseases were well understood, there was neither a local nor national unified gold standard of quality medical treatment to strive for or rely on. Various medical "experts" offered varied and unproven recommendations in treating clinical problems. There existed no reliable evaluation of risks versus benefits, safety or efficacy for any therapeutic option. The concept of such a thing as a benchmark or Plimsoll Bar Line for medical practice had not been considered, and just thinking about the cost of medical care was, well, absolutely unthinkable. Limited diagnostic and therapeutic choices also made the practice of Medicine much simpler, but did little, for instance, to save millions of Americans who died of the H1N1 flu in 1918. Infectious diseases remained feared the most, but the quality of healthcare delivery in the Public Health Service fortunately stood out as the best and most efficient in the entire world in providing for the health, welfare, and longevity of the American citizen.

Just considering the concept of physician profiling immediately became absolutely unconscionable. Credentialing and privileging processes were nascent and inconsistent. Molière's misanthropic "Le Médecin Malgré Lui", "Doctor in Spite of Himself", would soon find that he had no place in the **Healthcare Reform** and the subsequent practice of 20th Century American Medicine.

A few physician-philosophers thought and pondered long and hard about scientifically improving healthcare delivery practices by utilizing analysis of treatment outcomes; but even revered sages atop the high ivory towers of Harvard University rejected such concepts as unworkable. Doctor Ernest Amory Codman's concept of "the end result idea"[9] did not latch on to the seemingly non-scientific medical community, yet his physical therapy exercise program for shoulder rehabilitation is still followed by orthopaedic surgeons of today, and his

---

[9]Codman, E. A., The Shoulder

original book, <u>The Shoulder</u>, is a collectable which increases in true value and with less risk than stocks or bonds. Documentation of medical observations or "charting" was quite scanty and doctors had no real concept of valid statistical evaluation techniques. Vilfredo Pareto Diagrams (bar graphs) were developed in the 1800's, but doctors of the first half of the 20th Century could not imagine those diagrams or migratory economic considerations as having any place in medical practice. The term medical science was truly an oxymoron in the evolutionary process during the first half of the 20th Century, even after the Flexner report.

Patients were promised that "everything possible" would be done to cure their diseases, and that promise was honored by physicians, but an untold and elusive cure was not so frequently accomplished. One-sided intellectual stagnation prevailed due to enslavement of "rational" cognitive reasoning to the norms and mores of a non-questioning society. Doctors' intentions remained for the attainment of good (in the moral sense) quality healthcare delivery; therefore, their actions remained regarded as honorable and morally reasonable. Physicians, unfortunately, overlooked the fact that the roads of hell were, are, and always will be paved with those same good intentions of Man. A logical concept of end result analysis was not even considered; and in spite of contemporary physician publications, Doctor Codman's "the end result thing" was largely not yet invented or not yet discovered as a valid public piece of knowledge. Trotting along established yet unproven clinical treatment paths; doctors appeared to don methodological horse-head blinders that enforced tunnel vision decision making. Since end result analysis was not considered, it could not be ruled in or ruled out as an important factor for good (in the mathematical sense) quality healthcare delivery. Medicine was not exactly still a mythological religion practiced by witchdoctors, but doctor decision making certainly needed and deserved a more scientific footing.

In the first half of the 20th Century, third party healthkeeper concerns about patient care originating from insurance companies, drug companies, and for-profit hospitals did not exist to alter the course of healthcare delivery. Medical report cards and Harvard "B" School balanced scorecards were inconceivable. The 1906-1910 Flexner report was the key watershed event during the first half of the 20th Century, a report that also effectively and unfortunately reduced the number of medical schools and the subsequent physician pool for over a century to follow. Without a cane or support, **Healthcare Reform** stumbled along slowly onward in an awkward Trendelenburg gait guided by the heavy hand of government: In 1946, coupled with tax free health insurance from wage price freezes of the previous post war Roosevelt Administration, the Hill-Burton Hospital Survey and Construction Act became a part of the watershed event to start the first overlapping medical ecolo-nomic generation of change in the second half of the 20th Century. Unchecked hospital expansion was let loose to populate the American countryside with no qualitative regard for appropriateness or any quantitative regard for reasonable medical necessity (as the elusive concept was gasping to be defined at that time). Federal tax incentives for employee healthcare delivery programs naturally gave migratory economic **Healthcare Reform** birth to an overwhelming abundance of carpet-bagging indemnity insurance salesmen.

Considering the government as the ultimate land owner, the wealth of a nation ultimately rests in two mutually shared economic disciplines:
1. The dynamic production confidence of the nation's individual peoples, especially with economic acceptance of a societal-structured work ethic that sustainably maintains high production. And
2. An acceptable life style from adequate profits with dynamically competitive overall wage and rent income capital that grows the GNP faster and better than a competing nation.

Were these aforementioned classical economic norms, tried and true economic tenets of economist Adam Smith, put into practice in the USA, then there would never have been a self-serving economically driven decrease in the total number of trained physicians and fewer yet trained physician specialists. According to French economist Jean Baptiste, maximal productivity results when there is a vibrant work force in a growing job market that tends to multiply itself because it is free and unencumbered by the forces of political or economic power. Where there is overabundance of self-interested power such as governmentally mandated monopolistic control of healthcare delivery, corruption is inevitable, especially where the limited number of American physicians had exclusive rights to supplies of effective innovative technological advances, which independently created their own demand (Say's Law). It was painfully obvious that the sustainable economics of reasonable and necessary medical practice yearned to be integrated interstate, nationally and internationally with adequate numbers of practitioners in dynamic competitive alliances. An unbounded, dynamically competing universal and ubiquitous very basic healthcare delivery system bolstered by free medical education for all demanded a place in the great American society. However, it was also woefully realized that such political occurrences aimed in that direction by **Healthcare Reform** would be continually and successfully suppressed by the unintended consequences of the monopolistic dynamic competitive advantage within a government-engineered academic establishment. After the passage of the

Flexner report, the medical school academicians raised their wine glasses high while shouting a toast in Italian for a hundred future years of living well -- "Cin Cin"; their unchallenged "big brother" influence lasted just about that long.

In 1945, a freeze on wages balanced by a tax write off for employers providing financial coverage for employee healthcare expenses also gave rise to the supposed "health" (oxymoron) insurance corporations.   President Harry S. Truman supported Wagner-Murray-Dingle legislation to expand the social security system and included a single payer system of national health coverage, but interest in the Korean War took precedence in the minds of the American people.   The AMA lobbied against the plan and a congressional sub-committee denounced the legislation as a "communist plot".   Congress sorely defeated the measure.   President Truman became quite upset and declared, "I've had some biter disappointments as President, but the one that has troubled me most, in a personal way, has been the failure to defeat the organized opposition to a national compulsory health insurance program.   But this opposition has only delayed and cannot stop the adoption of an indispensable federal health insurance plan." President Truman was the very first of many U.S. Presidents to directly and formally endorse **Healthcare Reform** with a direct proposal for national health insurance to the U.S. Congress.

Ever-changing cultural mores continued to evolve, and a new ecology of ethics drove medical ecolo-nomics once again.   The neoclassical synthesis of Keynesian style economics by John Hicks and Paul Samuelson praised classical Keynesian economics for short term governmental intervention and regulation, but followed the classical school of reliance on self-regulating markets that better reflected individual preferences and thereby knew better than the government for producing a long term stabilization of the economy.   In 1948, Governor Earl Warren electrified the country by proposing a compulsory state healthcare insurance program to the California legislature. After a prolonged and expensive political battle, his proposal was defeated. However, that liberal-progressive cultural ecology shift in California had only just begun and would soon drive the local medical-economics and then spread across the nation. Pre-Paid Group Organizations (PGOs) that delivered a brand of healthcare to a select niche of the general population had commenced their rise to prominence in California during the first overlapping medical ecolo-nomic generation of evolutionary change (1950-1970) and now were gathering more momentum.   Another healthcare delivery mechanism, an adaptive ecolo-nomic that mirrored the 1927 CCMC's recommendations was being independently selected by the private corporate ecolo-nomics of the time; but another "police action", the "Korean War", diverted interest away from domestic policy for **Healthcare Reform** once again.

"Irrational rationality" yet consumed the world. Logical and rational minds cherished human life and continually sought to find extraordinary means to preserve life at all costs through **Healthcare Reform**; but then so callously and repeatedly destroyed masses of mankind through human-instigated wars. However, when the "A" bomb burst in 1945, that atomic shock shook the entire world: Any conscionable concept of a successful world war became instantly and most logically rejected as obsolete by any truly rationally thinking human being. Contagious diseases that could affect the masses were falsely thought to finally come under technological control. Even more haughty human mind tricks prevailed: Birth control and human abortion knelt to be knighted as workable mechanisms to limit world population biomass, resource consumption and alter forever British economist Malthus' 1778 concept of economics which had been termed a "dismal science" by Thomas Carlyle in the 19th century, because it was then believed that (underclass) population numbers, the growing human biomass would eventually and ultimately outstrip food resources. The suffocating dangers of industrial pollution affecting health, longevity and food supply were overtly unrealized during that former time, doubted and unaccounted for during the mid-20th Century, and still not totally accepted and certainly not resolved by **Healthcare Reform** in the mid-21st Century, while the human biomass accelerated in growth.

Bad Medicine -- Man cannot allow substitution of the words "depletion of natural resources and the environment" for the words "food supply" in Thomas Malthus's 1778 classic description or Thomas Carlyle's 19th Century forecasted interpretation of economics as a "dismal science". Man must forever look forward to the future with migratory economic planning and remember the economic teachings of Claude Frédéric Bastiat in his 1850 essay "Ce qu'on voit et ce qu'on ne voit pas" (What is Seen and What is Unseen). Bastiat's parable of the broken window introduced the concept of opportunity cost and defined a good economist versus a bad economist. Henry Hazlitt summarized that classical work in 2013: "The bad economist sees only what immediately strikes the eye; the good economist also looks beyond. The bad economist sees only the direct consequences of a proposed course; the good economist looks also at the longer and indirect consequences. The bad economist sees only what the effect of a given policy has been or will be on one group; the good economist inquires also what the effect of a policy will be on all groups." In the process of balancing the benefits of industrialization with the unintended costs to the healthy art of living and the environment, the migratory economics of Man and his Medicine must first "remember from the future" – Ralzak.

Newly derived and continually cyclically evolving migratory economic patterns sets new mass migration patterns for the world's people. After a five-year delay, an inevitable new paradigm with its own unique ecosystem and economic system mysteriously arrives. The quality-driven golden era of medical practice in the first overlapping ecolo-nomic generation seemed to slip along unnoticed until confronted by a watershed migratory economic event that changed that era's paradigm and then once again evolved a new ecolo-nomic environment of Medicine for all types of healthkeepers.....

MIGRATORY ECONOMIC FACTORS & PATTERNS EVOLVING MAN, MONEY & MEDICINE

PART THREE

ORGANIZED HEALTHCARE DELIVERY PLANS: MODELS FOR MILESTONES OF MEANINGFUL AND MEASURABLE MONITORED METRICS AND MEASURES

There have always been social and economic imperatives from all humanistic cultures to prevent, treat, and/or cure a state of ill health produced by circumstance or disease. Any person or institution that takes on this esteemed charge or righteous duty to keep the health within a politico-economic culture hopefully performs that task or causes that labor to be accomplished under a dignified and honorable state of affairs for varied and diverse patients or particular group-patient populations, while at the same time being ever respectful of each individual patient's associated pain and suffering. Such an honorable and dutiful task is easily defined, but not so easily accomplished; and those dutiful persons or institutions, hopefully trying and laboring with due diligence their sincere and honest best efforts -- they are, they have been, and with Godspeed they will forever be known as virtuous and revered American "HEALTHKEEPERS".

"Médecin c'est métier le meilleur de tous; car, soit qu'on fasse bien ou soit qu'on fasse mal, on est toujours payé de même sorte."[10]
-- Molière, Le Médecin Malgré Lui (1666)

Expectations from the past may have no place of honor in the future.
-- Ralzak (2016)

---

[10] Medicine is the best of all trades; for if one performs well or if one performs badly, one is always paid just the same. (1666)

Those soldiers returning home from the Christian crusades bore witness to the construction of the first formal hospitals in Man's Western culture. Brittan established "Poor Houses" for the parochial poor. The healthcare delivery systems of Europe transferred into an American **Healthcare Reform** movement during the colonial days. The sick in the early 1800's usually died quickly and quietly; therefore, there was no need for long term care. Organized healthcare delivery remained an undiscovered and un-evolved healthkeeper species, but Mother Nature does demand that adaptations to new species will be necessary for future survival; and in fact new species of healthcare delivery concepts and temporary functioning **Healthcare Reform** entities that are grossly unfit for future survival do regularly appear......

The process of evolution to any new species demands geographical isolation and environmental advantage for genetically rare adapted forms to gain dominance and then genetically separate themselves from their ancestors as a new variant, a form better suited for a migratory economic paradigm. Western America, the great expanse of the American West, in the early part of the 20th Century provided the ideal separation ingredients to flavor and cook to perfection a delicious organized healthcare delivery evolutionary soup – new and varied healthkeepers for a migratory economic paradigm era. The larger sustainable groupings of these "healthkeepers" adapted further and then economically migrated into various **Healthcare Reform** forms that eventually consolidated into varied genetically separate species for enacting healthcare delivery. Allopatric adaptation evolved to speciation of healthkeepers as well as healthkeeper niche populations, arising slowly, gradually and deliberately in California; but those many newly evolved Pacific coast species were then perceived to economically migrate even further, to abruptly appear far across the North American continent, all the way to the Atlantic coast.....

With help from the Los Angeles County Medical Association (LACMA), the Los Angeles County Hospital System began in 1875. The medical society along with the Los Angeles County Board of Supervisors appointed a physician to be the first official public health healthkeeper. This **Healthcare Reform** evolutionary adaptation to a county hospital and public health system greatly improved the health and wellbeing of residents in the metropolitan area.

Further evolution of the Genus "healthkeepers", such as grouping some of them as "organized healthcare delivery systems", first sparked California legislation and later ignited federal legislation, controversial legislation which ultimately heat-sealed Medicine's evolutionary fate in providing healthcare delivery. Indeed,

California, "the hot oven", was not only the place of kneading the healthkeeper dough, but also the place of baking the healthkeeper bread. Those "golden state" loafs were eventually served as two basic national standards of organized healthcare delivery. California, a mere state, with the seventh largest economy in the world (often politically spun as the fifth largest), was both nidus reservoir and bellwether location for healthcare delivery's evolutionary course in the United States. Understanding what organized healthcare delivery migratory economics and healthkeeper development took place in California during the early part of the 20th Century is an essential prerequisite for the study of subsequent federal governmental **Healthcare Reform** that eventually affected national healthcare delivery outcomes. Comprehending the circumstances and events that set off an unstoppable chain reaction in California is essential for a valid appreciation of the evolved organized healthcare delivery products that exists in America today.

As immigrant groups settled in California during the last part of the 19th Century, they created clubs, fraternal organizations, lodges, and benevolent societies in the growing big cities. Many of these organizations -- French, German, Italian, etc. – offered Medicine services to their members on a pre-pay basis. As previously noted, the Los Angeles County Medical Association (LACMA) and other county medical societies, in an effort to protect part of their own income derived from a competing risk pool of payers and also to altruistically promote a consistent high quality level of Medicine, successfully opposed those healthcare delivery practices of "Lodge Medicine" utilizing political and governmental pressures, but they did so only within the confines of the greater metropolitan areas.

Healthcare delivery practices for the migrating and migrant healthkeepers outside of the metropolitan area were quite different. Adaptations were essential to meet the medical and social needs of the unique migrated patient population and their families. On-site occupational health fulfillment as well as medical care and compensation for unique on-the-job injury patterns were new and important matters to be attended to by the varied healthkeepers, each in their own particular mode, means, method and manner. Somehow and in some way they all got the job done and evolved a learned expertise in **Healthcare Reform**, each in their own particular migratory economic interest. For example, before the advent of workmen's' compensation legislation (later changed to workers' compensation), the Los Angeles Board of Public Works recognized the need to provide medical care for industrial injuries. So, while the Flexner Report committee was busy cleaning up medical education,[11] the Public Works Board formulated a closed

---

[11] DiLibero, Ralph, The Business of Medicine, 978-0-9815969-3-8, 2007.

panel private business contract with Dr. Raymond G. Taylor between 1908 and 1913. Ten thousand Los Angeles Aqueduct project workers, employed at a great distance from the metropolitan city environs, exclusively contracted for healthcare delivery with Dr. Taylor and his associates. Work injuries were first treated in crude emergency field hospital stations. The injured workers were at first medically stabilized, then transferred to the Los Angeles County General Hospital. By the end of the contract period, Dr. Taylor's gross return was $164,000.[12] By contrast, from 1920 to 1950, "emergency hospital physicians in San Francisco usually earned less than electrical line workers, plumbers, and fire captains."[13] Regional cultural ecologies fostered regional migratory medical economics. Combining those two concepts, a painfully obvious medical "ecolo-nomic" fact became clearly evident, yet continually denied for more than a century by most American physicians to protect their dear egos: From the very start of the 20th Century, great wealth could be derived from organized healthcare delivery, and that wealth was primarily derived from the migratory medical economics of third party contracting arrangements. Man's Money in Medicine went primarily to the middleman. The practical quick-handed business of administering, rather than the actual careful and deliberate hands-on point-of-service in Man's Medicine – healthcare delivery -- is what really brought home the prized economic bacon. Contractors, sub-contractors and other "middlemen arrangements" involved in organized healthcare delivery always produced a greater total profit – they always made more Money than their contracted hands-on physicians or any other type of healthcare practitioner-worker.

Dr. Michael Shadid, a self-proclaimed socialist who was born in Lebanon in 1882, the same year as Henry Kaiser's birth, created a pre-pay consumer healthcare delivery coop to serve the out-patient and hospital needs of rural farmers and their families in the Great Plains adjacent to Elk City, Oklahoma.[14] This organized healthcare delivery plan was based on the concept of a farmers' cooperative that existed in the area. Profits from Dr. Shadid's former lucrative and capitalistic private practice, along with newly generated pre-payments, were used to build a private hospital. This doctor's contracted organized healthcare delivery system never expanded extensively, but lasted up until 1965.

The Group Health Cooperative of Puget Sound's organizational structure mirrored Dr. Shadid's **Healthcare Reform** design. A peek into the future -- Yet remaining as a "Non-Profit", in the latter part of 2016 Kaiser Foundation Health Plan

[12] Hendricks, Ricky, A Model for National Healthcare, Rutgers Univ. Press, New Jersey, 1993, p. 13
[13] Hendricks, Ricky, A Model for National Healthcare, Rutgers Univ. Press, New Jersey, 1993, p. 14
[14] HEALTHKEEPERS, Ralph J. DiLibero, MD, June 17, 2002, TXu 1-054-120

negotiated to purchase Washington State's Group Health Cooperative for 1.8 Billion dollars. The previous year, Kaiser reported operating revenues of $56.4 Billion and Seattle's 78-year-old Group Health Cooperative reported $3.7 Billion in revenues. This officially 2017 acquisition deal brought near to 600,000 new enrollee members under a continually growing national Kaiser Foundation umbrella.

In response to the great depression of 1929, while governmental bodies of diverse economic philosophies argued laissez-fair versus increased spending and lowered taxes to spark the economy, administrators at Texas Baptist Memorial Sanitarium, a Baylor University Hospital in downtown Dallas, created an organized healthcare delivery system which they named the "Baylor Plan". This **Healthcare Reform** type of contracted hospital service pre-payment insurance plan for financing healthcare delivery would eventually evolve into Blue Cross and then WellPoint-Anthem.

The much overly debated philosophical contest between economists John Maynard Keynes and Milton Friedman had not yet begun, but the medical ecolo-nomics of the times characterized profit/loss business possibilities for organized healthcare delivery contracting into four classical migratory economic survival categories. A description of the flow of Man's Money in Medicine:

1. Excess profit,
2. Normal profit,
3. Loss, and
4. Shut down.

When there was unexpected excess profit, new competitors entered into the dynamic medical ecolo-nomic healthcare delivery marketplace. When there was induced strategic loss, the smaller sized competitors dropped out. When there was shut down, the medical service business could not be re-started, and patients usually dispersed and economically migrated to the security of larger organized healthcare delivery organizations. The ideal medical ecolo-nomic business model geared production and allocated efficiencies to seek an equilibrium of normal profit. At that point, a dynamic competitive advantage prevailed because new competition was not encouraged to enter into the migratory medical ecolo-nomic marketplace. Normal profit kept marginal revenue equal to marginal cost, stabilized competition, increased medical product demand, and gradually increased price/profits. However, near to a century later, when powerful organized healthcare delivery organizations reached oligopolistic dynamic competitive advantage, all these classic paradigm rules of migratory medical economics evolved to change and reflect a different corporative business environment in a new migratory economic paradigm for **Healthcare Reform**.

Most organized healthcare delivery contracting arrangements in the first half of the 20th Century involved a single physician bargaining on behalf of a group of physicians. The restrictive yoke of anti-trust legislation did not yet exist to encumber physician collective bargaining while exempting the same for insurance corporations. As compared to fee-for-service, the early rates charged to patients for specialty physician services provided through and under the aegis of organized healthcare delivery systems were lower and generally fixed. Economy of large numbers in patient-payer risk pools and an economy of ancillary payrolls trimmed repetitious fat and produced leaner P/E ratios. This migratory economic was simple, could be and would be expanded to larger contracting arrangements with sure success. At that paradigm of time, however, there was no anticipated concern that corporations might grow to exert oligopolistic medical ecolo-nomic control, and then transform to gain their ultimate control of legal and viable physician-run healthcare delivery systems with little or no regard for the classical doctor-patient relationship. The undesired, unintended and then truly unimagined consequences of the "lay practice of Medicine" were neither yet debated nor even envisioned to exist during the legislature sessions in Washington, D.C. during the early 1900's.

Meanwhile, contemporary American proprietors of many and various small business enterprises other than medical businesses expressed a great deal of concern that large business monopolies would or could totally control and therefore stifle their free or "laissez passer" business enterprise. Therefore, in 1890, President Benjamin Harrison's administration passed the Sherman Anti-Trust Act to protect small, cottage industry businesses, including the migratory economics of the small "doctor"-owned medical business. Restraining competition or monopolizing trade became a felony. Collective bargaining by one physician or healthcare practitioner on behalf of a group of healthcare providers, however, was not determined to be illegal until the migratory economics of that Sherman Anti-Trust Act evolved in a future time. The Act eventually extended its influence to cover the "learned professions" in the second half of the 20th Century -- in 1975. 1982 federal legislation further evolved the Sherman Anti-Trust Act to mandate price-fixing within a "learned profession" business group illegal, even if that price-fixing benefited the general public and encouraged competition by significantly lowering customary and usual prices charged by physicians. Migratory medical ecolo-nomics evolved along a one-way street with a constantly changing yet steadily increasing significance attributed to newly-erected governmental-enforced traffic signals. If the full scope of the Sherman Anti-Trust Act had been in effect during the first half of the 20th Century, there would have been little to no development legally possible for physician led, corporate or "lay" organized healthcare delivery systems.

The business contracting mechanisms of organized healthcare delivery were never taught nor ever discussed in medical schools; that focus of migratory medical ecolo-nomics had to do with Man's Money. More than in bad taste, any discussion of Money's association with Medicine within the hallowed academia of medical schools always was and apparently still is taboo. Unfortunately, physicians graduated relatively unprepared for dealing with the reality of migratory medical economics in their lifetime of medical practice. Uniformly uninformed as to the contemporary and historical nature of the dynamic healthcare delivery marketplace, the evolutionary migratory economic value of healthcare delivery was traditionally overlooked and never seriously considered until the consequences were forced upon the medical profession. Likewise, patients never possessed a true grasp of healthcare delivery's financial worth or of healthcare delivery quality systems or mechanisms. Never an unexpected consequence to the eyes and mind of any economist of the times, economically speaking, naïve patients became the unfortunate migratory economic sheep of tragically lost and wandering physician shepherds. When organized healthcare delivery systems matured to be ripe for harvest, corporations (neither patients nor physicians) did the harvesting. Big business corporate boards, well trained in the migratory economic administrative processes and also in the persistent art of following the flow of Man's Money in Medicine, took the leadership roles and controlled the finances in the yet evolving healthcare delivery systems.

In 1910, the Western Clinic, in Tacoma, Washington, contracted with a lumber mill owner and his employees at lumberyards at a cost of 50 cents per member per month.[15] As steady income flow, Man's Money was thus adequately provided for Man's Medicine -- at that time the contracted doctors. Such a pre-pay concept was needed and necessary because fee-for-service Medicine alone did not then satisfy the Medical needs in the Pacific Northwest and would not in the foreseeable future suffice to satisfy the total Medical needs of the American society. The Western Clinic's organized healthcare delivery concept would much later lead to the establishment of a health plan, Group Health Cooperative of Puget Sound, and very much sooner point to similar contracting arrangements in California that would ultimately evolve into much larger national conglomerate

[15] Mayer, T.R. and Mayer, G.G., The New England Journal of Medicine, 590, 1985.

organized healthcare delivery organizations.

Regardless of possible initial anachronism or Gestalt perception and behaviors compared to healthcare delivery systems elsewhere in the world, the course of organized healthcare delivery in the United States indeed proved to be a roller coaster ride through time during the 20th Century. This exciting and exhilarating ride for the most part predominantly began with the start-up of three distinct pioneering and sustainable medical groups in California. Each espoused three initially variant philosophies for the accomplishment of the very vital healthcare delivery process. Their ups and downs, their successes and failures, were directly related to an evolving migratory medical ecolo-nomics. Along the bumpy way, self-centered feelings, prejudices, altruistic motivations, and ambitions of patient healthkeepers, systems of healthcare delivery, physician healthkeepers and third-party healthkeepers eventually evolved to accept a common understanding or at least a forced consensus. This evolutionary process was perhaps inevitable, yet still wonderfully surprising. California was among the first to hear a muted scream for migratory medical ecolo-nomic evolutionary change. That same scream increased in intensity, and then suddenly broadcasted itself to pierce the eardrums of healthkeepers and citizens all across America.

The three ultimately most successful early organizations during the 20th Century's evolution of organized healthcare delivery in California had some very deep roots. More important for their success than their roots, however, was their ability to keep survival alive by continually adapting to uncertainty, reaching for the sun to promote evolutionary trunk growth, while avoiding poorly planned side growth off into dead-end evolutionary side branches. As the organized healthcare delivery systems increased their migratory economic penetrance into the healthcare marketplace, certain of these California organizations established a trunk on the evolutionary tree that flourishes today in the rain forest of contemporary organized healthcare delivery eco systems. Each of these three filled a temporally needed niche in the changing migratory medical ecolo-nomic climate of California's healthcare delivery.

An extraordinary entrepreneurial individual led each organized healthcare delivery organization. Capitalistic super administrators, all with a spirit of entrepreneurial competition racing through their blood, and all possessing a firmly-established, gut-wrenching wealth accumulation goal. These extraordinary men, once again came to enact the ancient and repeated migratory economic cycle of Man, Money and Medicine. Capitalistic organizers of pooled human labor in the practice of Medicine, they, the great leaders, will forever be recognized and honored for that particular migratory economic of their creation. Collectively, these three pioneering doctors of uncanny vision and magnetic personalities set a renaissance stage for the constantly mutating action plans that assured success for their individual-styled medical organizations: Doctor Loos, Doctor Garfield, and Doctor Lee were astonishing men of truly dedicated character -- physician healthkeepers who forged ahead, against all the odds of popular tide in the general public mind-set, traditional corporate business oppositions and medical society "organized Medicine" spin, to bring organized healthcare delivery to the forefront of quality healthcare delivery in California:

Dr. H. Clifford Loos set a leadership pace that was, at times, hard for his partnered physicians to follow. He was a truly unique politician. He clearly set standards and rewards for his organized healthcare delivery pre-pay group practice doctors, but did not make a great effort to develop future leaders from his senior or junior partners. Dr. Loos did not coach the other group practice doctors to fit his leadership shoes, yet his leadership shoes were not acknowledged or at any time alleged by him to be unique. There was just no one physician groomed to walk the proverbial mile in the well-worn soles of his leadership shoes. Within the limits of his variable-asset partnership structure, Dr. Loos was even-handed and empathetic when dealing with the other doctors. Dr. Loos's organized healthcare delivery business plan was oriented to his own natural life span. Physician partnership financial interests were divided annually on an individual basis according to a rough senior partner longevity formula. The partnership created pooled assets for physical plant expansion, but never created a common pool of assets dedicated to future doctor-partner group expansion. A short passage of time was kind to the early generations of Ross-Loos doctors, but with the eventual longer passage of time, that kindness did not remain, especially for those doctors who joined the organized healthcare delivery system during later migratory medical ecolo-nomic generations. Dr. Loos unfortunately finished his final years of medical practice as a post CVA invalid in a wheelchair.

Dr. Russell Van Arsdale Lee approached his medical ecolo-nomic organized healthcare delivery game plan like a coach's coach. He set a leadership example of excellence that his physician associates found irresistible to follow. He sold his vision of "we are the champions" to the other organized healthcare delivery pre-pay group practice doctors with an empathetic appeal for them to emulate their very best. He created consensus and commitment among extremely self-directed entrepreneurial physician leadership personalities by establishing an emotional bonding for the production of a superior product. Being the best of the best was his personal best self-directed reward. The arches in the shoes of all his pre-pay group practice doctors were admiringly fabricated to also fit those shoes belonging to Dr. Lee. Dr. Lee's physician hiring practices emulated the great master, Leonardo da Vinci's Renaissance proclamation -- "Only a poor master would not be surpassed by his apprentices." By providing for future leadership and setting a vision that went well beyond his own life span, Dr. Lee set a sustainable course for his organized healthcare delivery system to adapt, evolve, and prosper for future generations to come.

Dr. Sidney Roy Garfield was a leader with a great vision, but he did not lead his doctors riding a charging horse and carrying his visionary flag. He was a quiet, empathetic, and equalitarian leader. Rather than demand, he influenced. He set an example that autonomous-directed personalities could follow with pride. All who followed his self-directed leadership experienced and reactively felt a sense of commitment and responsibility. Dr. Garfield wore a unique pair of leadership shoes that fit the feet of no other doctor in his entire group. Never was it feasible nor was it even possible for any of the other organized healthcare delivery doctors under his command to walk that proverbial mile in Dr. Garfield's shoes. Not unlike Dr. Loos, Dr. Garfield also oriented his business plan to his own natural life span. However, the limited tincture of time remaining to sustain his original business plan was miraculously rescued and extended in the nick of time. Fortunately for the generations of organized healthcare delivery healthkeepers that followed, an anticipatory strategic planning industrialist rescued, revitalized and reconstructed Dr. Garfield's original business scheme with innovating, adapting, and evolving dynamic competitive business plans that set a chameleon tapestry both for dynamic competitive advantage and for perpetual fiscal sustainability.

The idealized mission or purpose of an organized healthcare delivery system was and is to provide, through a common administrative structure, integration of the cost of healthcare with the delivery of healthcare. Within the structure of the healthcare delivery system, there had to be both politically-driven and altruistic mechanisms, diverse yet interrelated and interdependent, all hopefully acting and interacting in unison to continually improve upon an agreed vision and goal for **Healthcare Reform** -- quality in healthcare delivery for all. With that projected endpoint, healthkeepers must be ever mindful of "public trust" as the basic fundamental of their raison d'être. The general public served deserves a confidence that, in the course of an organized healthcare delivery system's activities, one's health and wellbeing are significantly improved.

Many healthcare delivery systems tried and strived to meet those fundamental expectations; many also failed. The development of organized healthcare delivery

118

systems in California, and also as echoed throughout the United States, has been too often termed random, confusing, and erratic. Such unwarranted conclusions arise because there seems to be no obvious logical or sequential reasoning pattern (algorithm) to explain developmental changes in the delivery processes of the organized healthcare delivery systems. Nonetheless, an easily recognizable common thread exists in all surviving healthcare delivery systems -- the linking thread of migratory ecological and economic evolutionary survival.

The three aforementioned entrepreneurial physicians each expertly wove that chameleon thread into beautifully unique individual designs that accurately expressed their particular personalities and leadership abilities to successfully overcome future ecological and economic uncertainties:

Born in the USA, Dr. H. Clifford Loos received his surgical training in California, became president of the San Diego County Medical Association and then a member of the California State Board of Medical Examiners. With the advent of World War One, Doctor Loos joined the military and rose to the rank of Colonel. After the war, he started a successful surgical practice in the metropolitan area of Los Angeles. With some family ties to the La La Land entertainment industry, Dr. Loos's sister wrote the screenplay for "Gentlemen Prefer Blondes".[16] Being an individual of ever-broadening horizons, his private medical practice alone was not fulfilling enough for his abundant entrepreneurial energies. Therefore, he chose to sell his economically stable private surgical practice to Doctor Ross and embark on a prolonged trip about the world with his family.

Donald E. Ross, MD, born and surgically trained in Canada, went on to more advanced surgical training in Edinburgh, England. He then worked in a pre-pay environment for the Canadian-Pacific railroad to gain the necessary financing for a private surgical practice. After accumulating sufficient funds, he immigrated to Los Angeles where he purchased an open-ended fee-for-service surgical practice from H. Clifford Loos, MD and continued an amicable relationship with Dr. Loos who, while abroad, continued to direct many medical-surgical referrals to Dr. Ross.

Upon Dr. Loos's return to Los Angeles from his world tour, he resurrected his politico-administrative talents and formed a recruitment consultation alliance with Mr. Daniel Parks. Parks was a personnel officer who was currently in the process

---

[16] Interview and personal communications with Timo Baladi, former Ross-Loos department head and medical director.

of developing strategies and formulating various insurance plans for recruiting physicians to work under contract with the DWP (Department of Water and Power). After reviewing multiple options for systems of organized healthcare delivery along with possible insurance mechanisms for Mr. Parks, Dr. Loos formulated a unique plan of his own – a periodic payment plan, capitated within a closed physician panel. Utilizing that mechanism of affordable pre-payments taken from an average worker's salary structure, Dr. Loos's organized healthcare delivery system would then develop a large liquid working risk pool of funds to cover a variety services.

Having maintained that continuing and ongoing extremely amicable relationship with Dr. Ross, Dr. Loos next took Dr. Ross to heart as a trusted colleague. He convinced Dr. Ross to call upon personal past pre-pay healthcare delivery skills in an effort to help administrate an expanded healthcare delivery partnership. Doctor Loos purchased back half of his former private practice, and this newly combined medical-surgical practice enlarged to accommodate both individual private practices and that aforementioned anticipated periodic pay plan healthcare delivery practice contracted with the DWP.

By April 1, 1929, while construction of the Los Angeles County Hospital was nearing completion, the two doctors finally and officially establish the Ross-Loos Medical Clinic (RLMC) in Los Angeles. This was truly an historic event, for it marked the very first time for a budding, urban-centered, pre-pay organized healthcare delivery administrative structure to offer comprehensive healthcare delivery to a budding large city business employee group -- and then blossom in a metropolitan area. The flowering practice delivered organized healthcare to the city workers and dependents of DWP's newly named Los Angeles Metropolitan Water District (LAMWD) at an original subscription rate of $1.50 per employee per month. The two founding doctors hired on a Canadian physician, Dr. Allen Ross, as the general partnership's first contracted employee to help service over 2000 LAMWD workers in the RLMC's first year of business.

The Ross-Loos Medical Clinic's patients were mostly of a working class payer pool niche that was unable to pay the average full doctor fee; but the individual patients within that niche were able to pay a diluted fee resulting from the spread of individual debt over a great number of patients by risk-pooling the pre-payment funds. Moreover, the ingrained cultural ecology of this same payer pool niche of patients seldom sought medical care in the past, and was unlikely to abuse the pre-pay system with less than essential medically necessary care demands. The cultural work ethic of the patients at that time did not encourage, seek, or expect preventive, early diagnostic, long term or rehabilitative healthcare/services. This niche of selected healthy working patients was exceedingly grateful for whatever medical care it could obtain. Therefore, all pre-pay group health plans in the first half of the 20th century were blessed with limited healthy consumer demands and provided only selectively needed and reasonable medically necessary organized healthcare delivery, along with only a relatively few related services.

The Ross-Loos Medical Clinic (RLMC) offered a system of arbitration for what amounted to a very limited number of patients unhappy with their medical care. Arbitration kept costs down and benefited both patients and the clinic. The Kaiser Foundation Health Plan (KFHP) would eventually incorporate this migratory economic principle and go one step further by contractually demanding of their patient pool compulsorily non-binding arbitration for malpractice disputes.

As the RLMC group practice grew, the insurance end of the business required an evolved migratory ecologic and economic adaptation which otherwise may be termed **Healthcare Reform**. The senior Ross-Loos partners purchased the Independence Insurance Company of Pasadena and solely profited from the dividends until they sold their various scattered clinics in the second half of the 20th Century. Because of this arrangement, a number of younger physicians left the partnership.[17] The senior partners alone also owned the original hospital-clinic building at 947 West Eighth Street, which was eventually sold to downtown LA Macy's via the May Company Department Stores. Other sub-partnerships, made up along the way with the current partners of those particular times, purchased buildings in North Hollywood, West Covina, and Santa Ana, which were then leased back to the Ross-Loos Organization at lower than local rents while continuing to make small returns on the investments. Obviously, the more senior a partner, the greater were the allocated assets. A new partner could accumulate assets from new ventures, but not from established ones. However, the medical group paid physicians a minimum yearly salary of $4,200 to $6,000 in 1931, and that was at a time when concomitant private physician net income had rapidly declined after the depression, from $6,500 in 1929 to $3,000 in 1931. Physicians who worked at Ross-Loos in the second half of the 20th Century enjoyed the group relationship and medical practice that was offered, but felt that they could have made more Money and accumulated more assets for a future net monetary worth by working in a private practice fee-for-service relationship.[18]

---

[17] Personal communication, Richard Onofrio, MD, Ross-Loos executive committee member, July, 2003.
[18] Survey taken by author in June, 2000.

The same negative competitive advantage in immediate total wealth generation over private physician practices was true for the Permanente physicians working at KFHP hospitals and clinics, but only during certain selected time periods -- in the golden era (1950-1970) and the greater part of the entitlement era (1970-1990). Going forward and at other times, the group practice doctors gained a higher immediate financial return than their colleagues in private practice and partnered physicians in Southern California were also assured a lucrative pension plan upon retirement. An onslaught of private practicing physicians migrated to join group practices during the organized healthcare delivery economically lucrative times, and those medical groups were then able to be more quality selective and work-hour restrictive in their physician hiring policies. After 2010, planned federal legislation would forbid physicians the opportunity to venture into ownership of hospitals and medical clinics. Had that been true in the first half of the 20th Century, then none of the ultimately successful organized healthcare delivery systems would have developed, lived long and sustainably prospered.

Recruitment and retention of physicians for pre-pay organized healthcare delivery systems in California during the first half of the 20th Century proved to be especially successful. Migratory medical ecolo-nomic niche needs in the medical marketplace along with a volatile financial market in the private fee-for-service sector gave a dynamic competitive advantage to employment opportunity with the early pre-pay organized healthcare delivery plans. "In 1941, the average U.S. doctor netted less than $3,912, and less than 1% had a yearly income of $10,000. Permanente doctors in California received a minimum of $4,800 a year with top salaries of $24,000."[19] (It might be noted here that most all the actual practicing physicians in the medical group received the minimum salary distribution).

Doctors D. E. Ross and H. C. Loos were both members of the Los Angeles County Medical Association (LACMA). In 1931, Dr. Loos surprisingly advised LACMA that all periodical pay medical groups or clinics should be supervised by organized Medicine.[20] The vision and mission that inspired this keenly calculated advisory were both altruistic and migratory economic. Dr. Loos believed that the ultimate success of his pre-pay health plan depended on the preservation of a unique medical ecolo-nomic risk pool of "healthy enough to do hard work" payers. Dr. Loos's strategic plan, to preserve that risk pool, depended on both some help and a lot of good will from "organized Medicine". The means of oversight that he suggested was periodic inspection by the California Medical

[19] Hendricks, Ricky, A Model for National Healthcare, Rutgers Univ. Press, New Jersey, 1993, p. 221
[20] Letter from H. Clifford Loos MD, to Carl R. Howson, MD, President of the Los Angeles County Medical Association, September 30, 1931.

Association (CMA). Dr. Loos put forth three politically appealing reasons to justify the potential migratory economic political action:

First, was to safeguard the public in the furnishing of proper and adequate medical attention.
Second, was to safeguard the medical profession at large against unfair competition.
Third, was to legitimize the aberrant form of practice (organized healthcare delivery) and have it under proper ethical administration order -- to prevent -- the development of such entities as State Medical Practice, practice in the hands of unethical men, large insurance companies entering into the field, and the continuance of lay-owned organizations for the practice of Medicine.

Politically echoing the God-sent devotional loyalty and determined determination of a Saint Teresa d 'Avila, Dr. Loos utilized humility and obedience strategies to give the perception of conforming to the ideals and standards of the medical establishment and organized Medicine societies. He effectively warded off most suspicions and beliefs about his "socially disruptive" type of organized healthcare delivery. Nonetheless, negative implications for future medical practice and healthcare delivery as unintended consequences resulting from Dr. Loos's "illegitimate, aberrant and socially disruptive" form of medical practice yet lingered and festered among LACMA member physicians. Looking a bit forward however, Dr. Loos never envisioned that most of his founding principles and well thought-out medical practice precautions (the aforementioned legitimatization of "aberrant forms of medical practice") would ever evolve to be completely eroded; and that those anticipated possibilities that he listed as the worst and most feared of all organized healthcare delivery nightmares were to be realized migratory economic probabilities, completely accepted by Organized Medicine within the passage of his own lifetime.

The Ross-Loos practice of pre-paid organized healthcare delivery serendipitously enjoyed increasing popularity; the RLMC subscription rate increased 33%, to $2.00 per month, and for a few of the early years, the group grew exponentially, especially among the public service and educational institutions. Los Angeles County employees, LA fire, LA police, and LA teacher groups quickly signed contracts, followed by industrial employees, tripling group enrollment by 1931 and approaching 40,000 enrollees by 1935.[21] Medical office buildings expanded

---

[21] Kisch, Arnold I., Viseltear, Arthur J., The Ross-Loos Medical Group, U.S. Department of Health, Education, and Welfare, Arlington, Virginia 22203.

and then had to be rebuilt to accommodate the increasing group-worker membership. Satellite clinics opened. Doctors Ross and Loos employed 40 physicians and surgeons on a full-time basis at a salary much above the California average, at a time when fee-for-service doctors' incomes were dropping to one third the pre-depression level. This coincidental temporary crisis in physician income made it possible for the clinic to hire highly qualified physicians to work on a salaried basis, a situation which was to repeat itself not only for the emerging groups of the first half of the 20th Century, but also for the Health Keeper Organizations (HKOs) after the year two thousand. Several other doctors, especially specialists, contracted with the Ross-Loos Clinic on a part-time basis. When they rendered healthcare delivery within the clinic, the specialists were paid a per diem wage. When they delivered specialized healthcare delivery in their own private offices, the specialists returned near to 50% of their usual and customary fees to the clinic. (This well accepted practice of "kickbacks" for referrals became illegal in the second half of the 20th century and significantly lowered the income and power base of primary care physicians, but then resurrected itself in the reverse and unpleasant form of "selective contracting" when Insurance Corporations, further lowered the practicing physician percentage cut from the healthcare dollar.) The Ross Loos Medical Clinic (RLMC) full-time employee physicians also administered healthcare to private patients, for which they were reimbursed 50% of their collected private fee.

By 1934, the RLMC was turning a 12.8% profit. Doctors Ross and Loos privately invested 70% of this clinic profit in the form of member benefits and development.[22] That dynamic competitive strategy induced rapid clinic expansion. In 1936, 16 new doctors were admitted to full partnership, setting the number of general partners at 18. Partnership became an individual financial affair, and no pool of Money for future Medicine or any other type of asset reserve was put aside for future partnership or plan development/evolution.

Although eligible to buy into the voting partnership after two years of employment, not all qualified and eligible employee physicians were made general or full partners. A yearly meeting at the Jonathan Club in Los Angeles elected an eleven-member board of directors and a medical director from the partner physicians. New partner physicians were also nominated and elected at that meeting. Since they owned the largest percent of fixed assets, an inner group of senior partners ruled and controlled the Executive Committee with iron hands.

---

[22] Kisch, Arnold I., Viseltear, Arthur J., The Ross-Loos Medical Group, U.S. Department of Health, Education, and Welfare, Arlington, Virginia 22203.

The power of the controlling shareholders naturally satisfied their personal interests first. Looking at the real world, the main purpose or primary function of any committee meeting is simply to acquire and secure a documented "consensus" for a course of action the committee chair has already determined and decided to pursue. Decisions were thus made by a few and OK'd by the rest with only modest and polite debate. Unfortunately, not much attention was paid to group administrative growth.[23] The total number of partner physicians comprised approximately 25% of the total physicians in the RLMC. Voting clout weighted in according to the number or percent of partnership shares owned, giving the original (and older) partners a controlling vote at all times. Therefore, as the voting partnership majority approached their natural retirement age, the thrust, vision, and action plan of the entire group structure was likewise bent in an angle pointed at retirement. Young entrepreneurial physicians and professors of medicine were never encouraged to join the group. The effect of this skewed selection, comparable to a genetic inbreeding of a single-minded generation, was not to be seen until the need and desire for strong internal leadership could not be found at a critical point for economic survival in some decades to come.

By 1941, the number of enrollees, including subscribers and dependents, was approaching 80,000. However, over a quarter of a century later, by 1967, there were only 45 full partners, and the total enrollment was only near 140,000, with nearly one third enrolled as individual subscribers.[24] After 1940, a review of RLMC statistical growth curve revealed a steady but very controlled slow stable increase in membership. During that same time period, other organized healthcare delivery groups grew much more rapidly throughout the state of California.

The spectacular early growth of pre-paid organized healthcare delivery was not viewed with any kindness or open mindedness by the establishment -- the private practice, small business fee-for-service "Organized Medicine" physician community. Undocumented propaganda regarding migratory economic and quality issues ran rampant in that general medical community. Rumors flew abundantly in the gossiping winds and included mostly unfounded charges of: unethical conduct, restriction of patients' rights in physician choice, along with false, isolated and incomplete testimonials. Whispers buzzed to saturate the air; unnamed unfit physicians, inadequately trained physicians and overzealous physicians were allegedly undertaking complicated medical procedures for which they were unqualified. Negative organized healthcare delivery gossip was not only

[23] Personal communication, Richard Onofrio, MD, Ross-Loos executive committee member, July, 2003.
[24] Kisch, Arnold I., Viseltear, Arthur J., The Ross-Loos Medical Group, U.S. Department of Health, Education, and Welfare, Arlington, Virginia 22203.

often openly discussed among fee-for-service doctors at private social gatherings, but also a common topic for gab among patients and staff at the doctors' private offices. Community physicians openly accused the Ross-Loos clinic doctors of practicing "communistic" and "socialistic" forms of organized healthcare delivery. The anti-capitalistic fear became an anti-democratic thought and such thinking was (at that time) unthinkable -- the thought was "un-American", an anti-national interest, a disgrace. The root cause for the ecology of propaganda rested in fear-mongering for dynamic migratory economic Money advantage. The dreaded and very legitimate fear that such closed panel organized healthcare delivery plans could and would gradually infiltrate, dynamically compete against, and then totally eliminate the private practice of Medicine could not be denied in the history of American **Healthcare Reform**. In the first half of the 20th Century, that real fear arose to such a horrid point that just possessing the thought that the government would eventually run the show was not just unconscionable; the mere thought was hyped as despicable. However, the cultural ecological mindset within the cognitive migratory economic rationality of the American people would evolve and adaptively change to give a renewal of hope for organized healthcare delivery as a routinely accepted part of **Healthcare Reform**.

For a considerable while, doctors Ross and Loos were the only two doctors in their medical group who held active membership rights at the Los Angeles County Medical Association (LACMA). Projecting an eventual future restriction in patient choice to acquire private medical healthcare, "Private Organized Medicine" plotted to discredit these two doctors, and by so doing, hoped to discredit their organized healthcare delivery system and hinder organized healthcare delivery's further evolutionary development. The Board of Councilors of LACMA served doctors Ross and Loos notice to appear before LACMA on March 5, 1934, in order to answer questions regarding unethical physician conduct. The accusatory charge was "soliciting and advertising for patients".[25] The two summoned doctors were to show cause as to why they should not be censured and/or suspended and/or expelled from LACMA for such egregious acts. The heart of the evidence against the doctors involved a recruitment bulletin sent out to Los Angeles school teachers, and articles favoring the Ross-Loos Medical Clinic published in the Los Angeles County Employees' Magazine by the All City Employee Association. (Anything more than distributing a simple matter-of-fact business card was considered "unethical conduct" for any doctor, according to generally agreed upon and accepted cultural or ecological mores at that time.) Dr.

---

[25] Notice served from Harry H. Wilson, MD, Secretary LACMA, to Dr. H. Clifford Loos and Dr. Donald Ross, 2/22, 1934.

Loos appeared, and rebuked the charges. He vehemently denied any direct involvement and/or any payments made to publish the cited articles. There was no other proof, disproof, nor witnesses to offer testimony for or against. Two days later, the verdict came down: and the two doctors were expelled from LACMA. Absence of evidence did not prove or satisfy the non-existence of evidence for conviction, apparently.

A true and verified profession, by traditional definition, self-regulates its members. If that right of mandatory enforcement is taken away, then the profession, its foundation and its organizational structure are weakened and subjected to the dynamic competitive advantages of competing organizations. In The Federal Trade Commission vs. the American Medical Association (1975), Organized Medicine was put on trial and sorely lost the verdict. The Court denied the AMA any right to hold its physician members accountable by self-regulating, mandatory enforcement to abide with AMA organizational mechanisms and guidelines in regard to advertising, solicitations, and contract practice. This decision nearly destroyed the AMA and its affiliate state and county medical societies because the court order completely cut the economic umbilical cord that bound practicing physicians to the societies. The AMA's dynamic competitive advantage to ward off HMOs and the AMA's then branded lobby as "THE" national physician spokesperson disappeared forevermore. Organized Medicine splintered apart like a splattering Humpty-Dumpty with the changing migratory ecolo-nomics. Physician specialty and sub-specialty practice models which had been organizing as separate national groups (such as the American Academy of Orthopedic Surgery (AAOS) or the American College of Cardiology (ACC)) suddenly gained special-interest dominance, but never to a point of being even close to the level of national influence and lobbyist power once upon a time uniquely held by the formerly mighty and powerful AMA.

However, during the first half of the 20th Century, loss of LACMA membership foretold of dire circumstances to come for physicians in private practice. Admitting privileges to local hospitals and memberships on hospital medical staffs were routinely denied without a proven prerequisite LACMA membership and concomitant compulsory AMA membership in hand. Also, prerequisites for certification by American Medical Specialty Societies could not be met without the same valid proof of a current county medical association membership. Collegiality and referrals within the local physician community were naturally refused to non-members. Loss of LACMA membership was, once upon an ecological time, truly a form of migratory economic shunning.

Doctors Ross and Loos appealed twice to reverse the dismissal verdict against them, first to LACMA, and then to the California Medical Association (CMA); both appeals fell to no avail. Nonetheless, by June 1935, with the support of public opinion and the local and national press, national interest and favorable recognition became bestowed upon the pre-pay Ross-Loos plan. The migratory economics of medical ecology had changed. Dr. Loos then filed a further third appeal to the American Medical Association (AMA), and the AMA's ruled in favor of the filing plaintiffs. The AMA verdict accomplished the task of overruling LACMA's guilty verdict of soliciting for patients (albeit on technical grounds). Doctors Ross and Loos were immediately reinstated into LACMA, and LACMA issued a report that basically applauded the practice of risk pooling **by physicians** as a relatively superior form of care for the "average" working man when compared with two possible feared and horrid futuristic alternatives:

1. An organized healthcare delivery system funded and run by lay insurance corporations which would financially reduce patient choice and kill the private practice of Medicine, or
2. A federal/state taxation mechanism that would create a federal/state organized healthcare delivery system that would legislatively restrict patient choice and ultimately kill both the private practice of Medicine and lay corporate organized healthcare delivery.

These very real alternatives were feared back in 1935 because futuristic thinking in LACMA, the CMA, the AMA, and certainly in the logical reasoning of Dr. Loos all too clearly understood that corporate or governmental control of Medicine would permanently and irreversibly reduce doctors to the role of dependent, fix-salaried, time-card employee workers with no true professional autonomy in an economically efficient and ecologically well accepted and competing organized healthcare delivery business market.

Moreover, these fears did not originate anew in 1935. In the first quarter of the 20th Century, the medically indigent were great in number and available physician services were erratic, as erratic as the stability and demographics of medical practices. There existed also a financial-cultural dichotomy between medical and surgical services; and the inability to provide adequate continuing education for a uniform standard of care also stood out as a matter of concern. In response, as a reader might recall, the President Hoover administration between 1927 and 1932 commissioned the Committee on the Costs of Medical Care (CCMC).

The CCMC members clearly saw that the existing contemporary medical practice in the United States was out of step with the rest of the world, and certainly not what a progressive industrial culture should have to offer to its citizens. The findings of the committee, once again, were not much different from the findings of every single governmental study before or since. Ancient Chinese Confucian philosophers might have very well previously carved these fundamental conclusions into stone. Much like the previously paraphrased biblical handwriting on the wall, "Mene, Mene, Tekel, u-Pharsin", the CCMC seemed to have miraculously re-written the Book of Daniel. Mene – foresaw that the days of private medical practice were numbered and soon to come to an end with a decline and fall of the physician-controlled physician-centric establishment. Tekel – weighed private medical practice in the balance and found it wanting. u-Pharsin -- predicted that after physician power and control was taken away, private patients would be divided among the two administrative rivals for future organized healthcare delivery products -- corporate insurance conglomerates and the federal government. The CCMC's "best care" working model mirrored an academic, top-down, training and practice organization with centers of "excellence" for healthcare delivery referrals from grass root "basic care" organized healthcare delivery centers that did not necessarily include "physicians" or "doctors" of any sort, kind or rank as the practicing gatekeeping healthkeepers.

Although continually building and funding duplicative administrative structures to the contrary, the federal government always envisioned **one** centrally controlled system to be the most efficient way, and often the only way, to eliminate costs and duplication of administrative and physician services. However, decreasing the job employment-numbers and governmental expenses attributable to multiple layers of duplicative administrative practices and the duplicate work from federal or state governmental employees was never ecologically acceptable or politically feasible. If the federal government totally controlled an organized healthcare delivery system, then the profit motive in providing excessive medical care might hopefully or wishfully be reduced or eliminated. At least that was the thought of the CCMC and a multitude of other economists since then. Along that line of reasoning back then, one idealized organized healthcare delivery model might be group physician practice solely and directly associated with compulsory, federally mandated health insurance. A discussion of whether or not compulsory mandated insurance would be offered, by whom, and administered, by whom, -- the medically necessary migratory economic details -- were totally avoided at that time. Moreover, physician practice autonomy and the physician-patient relationships never achieved the status of meaningful metric factors in any of the federal government's equations. In regards to that time-honored physician-patient relationship which some physicians and patients held as sacred or sacrosanct -- the duly appointed true and ultimate committee masters of organized healthcare delivery always and forever regarded such concepts as pure fantasy.

What was the AMA to do -- the CCMC recommendations were, quite unexpectedly, threatening to medical physician establishments, medical societies and medical associations – "Organized Medicine" in any shape or form. A clever spin campaign organized by the AMA doctors successfully hid the CCMC findings from public scrutiny. Physicians at that time had both of the public's ears because physician power and influence had invented, controlled and administered the existing, highly trained, and personnel intensive healthcare delivery services. Ecological times evolve an unending list of migratory economics. Generations later, when physicians had by unintended consequence reduced themselves to an unproductive, ineffectual and solely oppositional political role in healthcare policy-making, then those future physicians would, one side at a time, permanently lose meaningful access to the public's ears. In several decades to come, an American migratory medical ecolo-nomic paradigm would not be ineptly blinded; those eventual eras of equalization and enlightenment would and did most certainly and boldly act upon that dauntless and brazen CCMC handwriting on the wall albeit time-dated from 1927-1932.

Meanwhile, the political lobby force of the AMA had more chores to do and remained polished and accomplished in getting them done. The Roosevelt Administration passed the Social Security Act, in which, due to lobbying by the AMA, there appeared no provision for financing of healthcare delivery via taxation. One year later, in 1936, the CMA successfully lobbied the state legislatures to vote against a compulsory California health insurance bill. Live testimonies on behalf of the CMA from patients treated at the Ross-Loos Clinic became the deciding factor that finally killed the bill.

Those American West Coast medical ecolo-nomic evolutionary genetic separation and speciation ingredients necessary to produce a new species of **Healthcare Reform** were also diligently at work in Northern California:

In the year of 1924, the political and social milieu south of the San Francisco Peninsula echoed a slightly different migratory ecolo-nomic from those cultural ecologies in the emerging big California cities. In one such geographical location, the factory working-man's labor movement had been crushed and social propaganda worked effectively well in promoting privatization as a better and more efficient form (therefore spun as a more socially righteous or just form) of doing business. There suddenly existed a medical ecolo-nomic niche risk payer pool opening for businesses catering to those adequately employed middle class American patients who preferred a service that offered "a cut above" the envisioned illusion of an average "run of the mill", a healthcare program for patients who were also willing and able to pay a bit more for such a service. Agrarian reform of any evolves species was not an issue in the farmlands about Palo Alto, and a prosperous middle to mostly upper-middle class community rapidly grew and prospered about the Stanford College environs.

A former Stanford College star football player, Dr. Tom Williams, opened a surgical practice in Palo Alto after training at Columbia Medical School. He then formed a partnership with Dr. George Barnett, who soon vacated the medical practice for a professorship in internal Medicine at Stanford Medical School. Dr. Williams needed to replace his former partner and recruited Dr. Russell Van Arsdale Lee, an internist, educated at Stanford Medical School, and at that time enjoying a fairly lucrative private practice in San Francisco. Dr. Lee immediately injected a boost of energy into the existing velocity of Dr. Williams's now medical/surgical practice and prices for all doctor services were accordingly increased, hoping to stem an increasing and potentially unmanageable patient flow. However, the price increase had the exact opposite effect, increasing the price for services actually quadrupled the practice[26] and further evolved a migratory economic environment that allowed for the birthing of the Palo Alto Medical Group (PAMG). A successfully pre-planned planting of practice and business criteria nurtured PAMG to sprout deep and permanent ecological roots into the economically fertile soil of the future Silicon Valley in Northern California.

Energetic and charismatic, Doctor Lee was quick to learn effective business practices from his own experience and the experiences of those about him. That unique understanding of and continued learning from dynamic competition in an ever-changing healthcare delivery marketplace proved to be Dr. Lee's most sustainable dynamic competitive advantage. He established a group practice in a middle class risk payer pool community, an economically sustainably successful medical practice which was not unexpectedly abhorred by the surrounding solo private MD practitioners, who were already undergoing financial cutbacks as a result of the Great Depression. Dr. Lee's medical group created a referral style of practice. Unlike the Mayo Clinic, PAMG was, at its onset, a community-primary care oriented and not originally trademarked as a specialty care organization. The surrounding solo private practitioners in the Palo Alto area felt that the organized

---

[26] Palo Alto Medical Foundation Annual Report, 1990, p.3.

healthcare delivery group practice exuded an undeserved air of snobbery. Snobbery yes, but "undeserved" remained in the balance for future discussion. At the same time, the local solo practitioners despised PAMG for collecting "socially unacceptable" pre-payments for healthcare delivery. Doctor Lee understood that there was an additional motive of resentment; the organized healthcare delivery group practice framework offered cross medical coverage encompassing a larger geographical area on a 24-hour basis that could not possibly be matched by any one solo practitioner. This full-time healthcare delivery coverage gave his medical group an additional dynamic competitive economic advantage. In response, the local doctors grumbled and expressed charges of "socialized medical practice", but the detrimental propaganda failed to influence the capitalistic minds of the local population's middle class payer risk pool. The AMA included the PAMG on its list of branded "medical soviets".[27] Additionally, an unsuccessful resolution introduced at the annual meeting of the Santa Clara County Medical Society would have banned doctors who practiced in the Palo Alto Clinic.

Dr. Lee's perspective envisioned a two-phase migratory economic **Healthcare Reform** plan to forever change the perception of his organized healthcare delivery medical group. The first phase planned to take measures to shore up PAMG's basic internal reserves and strengths in an effort to give the group's existing patient customers even more than what they expected in healthcare delivery – set, meet, beat and repeat: He beat his previously set and promised goals, and thus gave PAMG's patients more incentive and desire to continue contracting with the upper-crusted ecological niche payer risk pool organized healthcare delivery system. Dr. Lee's second phase planned to create new horizontally expanded positions in organized healthcare delivery that would make PAMG more attractive as a trademark or branded product in a dynamically expanding healthcare marketplace. His community niche payer pool need basically outweighed any social stigma of Communistic medical practice. Group branding switched from quality primary care to superb sub specialty care. Superior care through cutting edge specialization in the hands of respected Stanford Medical School graduates became Dr. Lee's new drawing card. By 1930, the partnership offered orthopedics and sports Medicine with Dr. Fritz Roth, pediatrics with Dr. Esther Clark, allergy with Dr. Milton Saier and surgery with Dr. Blake Wilbur, who also replaced the retiring Dr. Williams. The associated group practice of the Palo Alto Medical Group (PAMG) expanded into a contractual permanent partnership, The Palo Alto Medical Clinic (PAMC) now offered services much like the future to be Mayo Clinic; but again, the patient base was not selectively referral, and the payer

---

[27] PAMF Annual Report, 1990, p. 8.

risk pool remained rooted in primary care. Community need remained paramount, and Dr. Lee's vision continued to provide all possible horizontally expanded services under one roof. Local support from the city of Palo Alto paid half of the fees charged to the fortunate local Palo Alto residents. With an increasing number of physician house calls constituting a common daily practice for the group, reimbursement for the healthcare delivery service often found itself in the form of local garden produce.

During the early post-depression years, the clinic slowly expanded in membership. Due to dropping doctor incomes in the fee-for-service world, the physician recruitment and retention policies of PAMC created a buyers' market for new partners, and the clinic bought in three more physicians, Drs. Niebel, Sox, and Dunn. This raised the partnership number up to eight physicians, who would eventually be known as the "Founding Fathers" of the Palo Alto Medical Clinic. Growth in the physician partnership stayed quite slow up until the post - World War II era. Half of the physician-partners served in the military and supplemented military service salaries with their Palo Alto Medical Clinic profits. PAMC hired local doctors on a per diem contractual basis to keep the clinic afloat during the war and to continue to generate profits from an ever-increasing patient base. Growing exponentially in the visionary mind of Doctor Lee were two organized healthcare delivery concepts:

First, to have experts in various medical and surgical specialties in a practice partnership with each other -- specialists in partnership with specialists, and
Second, to set up a fiscal profit sharing arrangement within a defined common or shared physical/mechanized working environment.
Dr. Lee envisioned absolutely no type of mechanized or body and flesh "gatekeeper" to delay the delivery of the most up-to-date medical care.

Switching back to a Southern California dateline, the nascence of limited organized healthcare delivery within the LACMA organization began in 1913. Doctor Ray Lyman Wilbur proposed a voluntary type of pre-payment insurance plan that would be under the auspices of LACMA.[28] That pre-pay healthcare delivery strategy proved to be a very unpopular concept for the overwhelming majority of the LACMA members, but interest in the concept did gain support, albeit at an extremely slow and painful snail's pace. Not until twenty-five years later, on December 17-18, 1938, did the council of the California Medical Association (CMA) grant approval – that was an extremely long migratory

---

[28] LACMA, A struggle for Excellence, Anderson, Ritchie, and Simon,1971, p.52

economic crawl.

Adding to the various simmering evolutionary soups of organized healthcare delivery, a totally different set of circumstances and spices would soon seek out new species dominance with a drastic **Healthcare Reform** turn of events in Southern California:

Henry J. Kaiser, born in 1882 of a nurse mother and shoemaker father, was a man gifted with an irresistibly mesmerizing smile. His formal education ended at the age of 13, but that age also marked the time when his leadership development began. He immediately started his career as a builder and industrialist with a day job followed by entrepreneurial after–hours work as a photographer. His pacesetting and affiliating personality drove him on with an inner strength of self-determination and direction, coupled with an outward demeanor of emotional bonding and harmony, and of course, that ever-present seducing smile could never be discounted. At the age of 24, he fell desperately in love, but circumstances found him to be too poor to be granted permission to marry Bess Fosbough. "Her father insisted that he build a house, save $1000, and earn $125 a month first".[29] Therefore, he relinquished his interests in three eastern photographic studios and moved to Spokane, Washington. That year was 1906, the exact same year that Doctor Sidney Garfield was born. Two years later, after rescuing the McGowan Brothers Hardware store from a devastating fire and reconditioning their merchandise, Henry Kaiser found himself gainfully employed as a hardware salesman and with sufficient funds to call on Boston for his bride to be. Five years later, with two young sons to feed and clothe, he was serendipitously fired from his job. In that time of deepest desperation, he rekindled the embers of an entrepreneurial fire that had always been burning in his heart. With a $20,000 loan and the insatiable vigor and stamina of a 32-year-old man, his first venture, the Henry J Kaiser Company Ltd., won a contract to pave two and one half miles of roadway in Vancouver, BC. Further contracts followed; and at the age of 39, he jumped off a train nearing a mail drop to secure a bid on a thirty-mile road strip between Red Bluff and Redding, California, which led to establishing his permanent headquarters in Oakland. At the age of 41, Henry Kaiser proceeded to build a sand and gravel plant in Livermore, CA; and in 1928 at the age of 46, he joined the then exclusive societal rank of net worth millionaires by completing a roadway in Cuba two years ahead of schedule. Through further networking in this exclusive social class, he became acquainted with Amadeo Giannini, the founder of Bank of America, who in 1933 wrote a letter of introduction to President

---

[29] Julie Sullivan, jailhurwitz.com/media/Kaiser, julies@spokesMan.com

Franklin Roosevelt, thus enabling Mr. Kaiser to be a political insider in Washington, DC.

About this same time, when Henry Kaiser was 51 years old, Dr. Sidney Garfield went about finishing his residency training in general surgery at the Los Angeles County General Hospital. Dr. Garfield's eventual ecolo-nomic goal was to establish a private surgical practice in the metropolitan Los Angeles area, but he lacked the immediate funds for such an endeavor. In order to build up that fiscal nest-egg, he applied for employment at the Ross-Loos Medical Clinic, where he entertained an offered position on the surgical staff; but Dr. Garfield had more ambitious entrepreneurial goals and felt that the quite adequate Ross-Loos monetary offer failed to be sufficient enough to build up the necessary cash reserves for financial backing that he would eventually require to open and initially sustain his envisioned private surgical practice.

Also of public concern in 1933, the population density in the City of Angles had continued to increase rapidly, beyond what natural resources could satisfy. An increasing ecosystem need for water and power became critical in the smog basin that the Native American Indians had previously named "the valley of smokes". The Los Angeles Metropolitan Water District (LAMWD) found it necessary to take on additional projects outside of the metropolitan LA area. A portion of the LAMWD's aqueduct project from California's eastern desert at the Colorado River to the city of Los Angeles excluded approximately 5000 workers from the existing contract with the Ross-Loos Medical Group. The distant desert workers and their families urgently needed healthcare delivery and the functional economics of the day proved to be preciously costly and time consuming for the LAMWD to send workers way back to Los Angeles for their healthcare delivery. Henry Kaiser and other large contractors had Workmen's Compensation (later renamed Workers' Compensation) requirements to fulfill and had previously set up an entity, the Industrial Indemnity Exchange, to cover healthcare delivery expenses for these 5000 and other workers at various construction sites.

Therefore, the stage was set to open up a second dynamically competitive shop many doors and miles away from the established payer pool of the Ross-Loos organized healthcare delivery program. Dr. Garfield signed a contract with the Industrial Indemnity Exchange to care for those 5000 exempted workers. Two encouraging factors aided his decision -- a little help in the form of partnership with a friend concurrently practicing Medicine in Indio, Gene Morris, MD, and a little cash, $2500 borrowed from his father. These factors provided the means and the ability for Dr. Garfield to secure the occasion and gain a foothold on a stepping stone that would eventually lead him to develop his evolving systems of organized healthcare delivery. That stepping stone might also have led him instead to a more luxurious private practice in the Los Angeles area, but as one history is recorded, "Garfield and his physician associates enacted a creation myth of corporate medical culture."[30]   They constructed "Contractors General Hospital", a physician-owned twelve bed hospital/clinic six miles west of LAMWD's construction site at Desert Center, 60 miles east of Indio. A window of opportunity opened for Dr. Garfield, the senior partner, and Dr. Morris to deliver healthcare more efficiently, more economically, and with greater access and quality, but there was a significant problem with their revenue stream. Insurance payments were at first calculated from past billings submitted on a case by case basis. Inadequate and not forthcoming to the existing private medical practice, those inadequate insurance payments arrived at a slower than snail's pace. Payment denial problems arose with recipient utilization review, prior approvals, and eligibility requirement review. Industrial Indemnity Exchange frequently questioned the scope, the amount of services and the extent of hospitalizations and treatment protocols, and too often severely cut back, reduced the amount or frankly denied those individual reimbursements.

Dr. Garfield's initial payer risk pool saturation niche specified the level of care, the cash flow, the geographic boundaries, and the payable socioeconomic occupation. LAMWD industrial injuries and off the job LAMWD minor traumas satisfied that niche. Treatments for minor injuries remained lucrative; however, the Industrial Indemnity Exchange never adequately reimbursed expensive medically necessary healthcare delivery costs for the seriously injured and functionally disabled.   Cherry-picking the cases was neither ethically nor practically possible. The medical-surgical practice and hospital costs for the treatment of major injuries that required hospitalization soon exceeded collections from billings, and a pile of aging past-due accounts eventually had to be retired as an un-collectable loss. It became painfully evident that the existing healthcare delivery insurance funding system was inadequate to provide for a sustainable and financially successful medical-surgical practice plus a hospital for all-comers. Increasing access while maintaining quality increased cost; all three migratory economic healthcare delivery components had to evolve, and eventually would evolve to balance Dr. Garfield's present and very wobbly three legged cost-quality-access stool.

In less than one year, the hospital bottom line accounting scribed near to financial

---

[30] Hendricks, Ricky, A Model for National Healthcare, Rutgers Univ. Press, New Jersey, 1993, p. 12

collapse in numerical terms. By necessity, the traditional billing schedule had to be immediately revised, as Dr. Garfield's employee payroll obligations could not be met. In desperation, Dr. Garfield sought counsel from two Industrial Indemnity Exchange executives, Harold Hatch and Alonzo B. Ordway. To avoid this very probable impending financial disaster, Dr. Garfield negotiated a new contract that still provided quality healthcare delivery to the LAMWD worker group, but now as a whole entire group on an enforced individual pre-paid basis. The new Industrial Indemnity Exchange contract offered basic pre-payments of 17.5% of premiums by collecting capitated payroll deductions of 5 cents per worker per day, taken directly from the LAMWD employees' paychecks to cover the workmen's' compensation portion of expenses. There were no state insurance mandated rules and regulations or myriads of restrictions in setting up such an insurance payment system at that time. If there were, the entire venture would have quickly ended in bankruptcy. Dr. Garfield envisioned a new strategic migratory economic **Healthcare Reform** plan to increase the percent collectable from his patient-payer risk pool. His primitive organized healthcare delivery plan additionally covered non-industrial conditions for an extra deduction of 5 cents per worker per day or $1.50 per month.[31] Before long, the organized healthcare delivery plan moved back into the fiscal black – profitable range. Dr. Garfield now also became able to repay past withheld employee salaries, build two new field hospitals, and oversee the labor of ten physician associates as a senior partner in his newly organized and suddenly lucrative migratory economic **healthcare delivery contracting** venture.

The common thread that characterized Doctors Loos, Lee, and Garfield was not limited to a weave of bright ideas. Their strategic planning and anticipatory project management of organizing and directing the work of multidisciplinary professional and administrative staff, from local hospital involvement to community and county action projects and eventually onto state-wide ventures, knitted that common thread into an exquisite weave that reflected a chameleon array of colors. They all utilized personal modifications of the principles and practices of Continuous Quality Improvement that originated in the existing business community for processes efficiencies in making recommendations for effective courses of action. Taylorism, the scientific management resulting from an analysis and synthesis of workflow, made a migratory migration into Medicine. These entrepreneurial **medical-contracting** doctors all tempered their actions with unique appreciations for the actual processes involved in creating real value through innovation. After final implementation, they immediately started the

---

[31] Foster, Mark S., Henry J. Kaiser, Univ. Texas Press, Austin, 1989, p.213

thinking process over again, re-evaluating every step in a continuing cycle of dynamic competitive advantage. They did not just dream about their finished product; they were the living embodiment of their finished products, yet their personal mindsets never could imagine their organized healthcare delivery **contracted products** as ever being truly finished or even adequately updated. In the tradition of the first Republican President of the USA, Abraham Lincoln, they all rediscovered that, "The best way to predict the future is to create it."

Dr. Garfield had introduced a visionary technological advance to his desert hospital operations. He fitted one of his hospital/clinics with skids so that the facility could move along with the construction site[32]. More serious injuries were still shipped west to the established hospitals in Los Angeles for definitive care. Present day preventive care and patient education to increase "on the job" time in Industrial Medicine were also visionary concepts that Dr. Garfield introduced into his healthcare delivery organization. This concept in migratory economic **healthcare contractual financing** and delivery had no name in 1933, and today would involve expensive insurance licensing contracts before state approval of the registered insurance business. The desert health plan became feasible and financially sustainable, yet was soon to undergo another drastic migratory medical ecolo-nomic evolutionary adaptation in its administration.

A bit earlier, in 1931, it became obviously apparent to LACMA that migratory medical ecolo-nomic changes had restructured the California patient population's ability to pay for healthcare delivery. Lucrative risk payer pool demographics had changed. LACMA could no longer ignore the potential benefits and absolute necessity for some healthcare delivery in a pre-pay form. A paradigm shift in the LACMA philosophy towards organized healthcare delivery stood out as essential for financial survival. Acting on Doctor Ray Lyman Wilbur's originally proposed voluntary type of pre-payment insurance plan, LACMA also negotiated a pre-pay contract with the Los Angeles Metropolitan Water District (LAMWD). This contract uniquely upheld and preserved the autonomy of private medical practice. The LACMA contract differed from the Ross-Loos and Garfield agreements in that there was no allowance for a closed panel of doctors. Each employee of the LAMWD could freely choose a fee-for-service LACMA physician. This **contracting arrangement** was more of a PPO rather than a PSO.[33]

In April of 1932, LACMA's Council agreed to "purify the Association, study

[32] Kay, Raymond M., Historical Review of the SCPMG, SCPMG, LA, Calif.
[33] Preferred Provider Org., Physician Sponsored Org.,
HEALTHKEEPERS, Ralph J. DiLibero, MD, June 17, 2002, TXu 1-054-120

(with a study of) the conduct of practice of various groups then carrying medical service (organized healthcare delivery) on a monthly fee basis and employing medical talent (MDs) on a salary basis. In the event members of the Association are deemed guilty of unethical practice, expel them from membership in the Association. In other words, after careful deliberation, a decision should be made as to whether certain practices now conform to the Code of Ethics or not, and that we no longer temporize, but arrive at a standard and adhere to it."[34] (As previously described, Doctors Ross and Loos were expelled from LACMA in 1934. They were reinstated in 1935.) The migratory economic concept of a contractual arrangement within the ecology of a booming metropolis in which physicians would be paid essentially as employees remained horridly despicable.

Meanwhile, LACMA further developed its own Medical Service Plan with provisions for free choice among fee-for-service physicians. That non-profit corporation set up and controlled by the doctors, provided healthcare delivery for metropolitan workers. All LACMA physicians were able to participate. The stated emphasis of the organized healthcare delivery plan sought to adequately make financial ends meet with no lay influence, no union influence, and no governmental influence. The general LACMA membership approved the plan in October of 1933. The need for hospital insurance became painfully obvious, and LACMA members hotly debated that topic until November of 1938, when, after recommendation by the AMA, a combined pre-pay plan, the California Physicians Service Plan of the California Medical Association, gained final approval from LACMA. The next step for LACMA was to obtain CMA's approval blessing on the contractual agreement that basically embraced most the elements in a self-insured PPO.

Just one month later, the Council of the California Medical Association approved the pre-pay plan, officially named "California Physician Services". The name, however, soon changed and the plan sought a brand more commonly known to provide primarily physician payments for professional services rendered in California – "Blue Shield" of the CMA took its first official breath in 1939. For a time, Blue Shield covered both hospital and physician services. To insure customer financial responsibility, a 20% co-pay for each service rendered rested in the pocketbook of the individual patient. **The contracting arrangement proved to be quite profitable.** In order to simplify bookkeeping and billing, and to satisfy internal philosophical differences, Blue Shield eventually split from the CMA and evolved to be an independent non-profit (at first) organization. Blue

---

[34] LACMA, A Struggle for Excellence, p. 53.

Cross absorbed the small hospital service plan remnant, and sold Blue Shield as a companion physician service coverage policy. In the third medical ecolo-nomic generation (1990-2010), Blue Cross further integrated and evolved economically to become America's largest for-profit Health Keeper Organization (HKO). Blue Shield continued on, like Kaiser Foundation Health Plan, as a non-profit corporation into 2014, but significantly trailed Kaiser at that time with 3.4 million enrollees and $13.6 Billion "non-Profit" revenue. Not minding the books registered a surplus stockpile of cash ("deferred earnings") amounting to $4.2 Billion, four times as much reserve funding that would be necessary to cover future claims and protect their solvency. Therefore, the California's Franchise Tax Board revoked their non-profit status; Blue Shield filed a protest and did not pay assessed penalties well into 2015. (In Illinois, Provena Covenant Medical Center lost its property tax exemption in 2004.) The ecological trend in the newer migratory economics looked unfavorably upon multi-million-dollar service agencies getting multi-million-dollar non-profit tax-brakes without actually earning that privilege by way of providing a significant amount of credible charitable services that were actually vital and needed by the poor. Perhaps Blue Shield should have been more in tune with their humble physician origins and paid their doctors a one-time bonus from those overly-abundant "deferred earnings" by way of a "stratified retention fund formula" -- like the one so effectively used by Kaiser. The battle over non-profit status went on; and Kaiser, in spite of powerful lobby efforts and clever-creative bookkeeping, feared that they might be on deck and next up -- for and possibly on this future 21st Century migratory economic chopping block.

1938 stood out as an historical a landmark year for **developing contracting** in organized healthcare delivery. LAMWD completed work on their desert aqueduct, and Dr. Garfield achieved his previously desired financial nest-egg to the tune of $150,000.[35] He returned to metropolitan Los Angeles and enrolled at Los Angeles County -- USC hospital for advanced surgical training with the expectation of opening that always envisioned private surgical practice. However, other forces were afoot in the evolving migratory medical ecolo-nomic landscape of that magical year, and soon newly evolving paradigms would not only postpone Dr. Garfield's immediate desires, but would also change the future direction to be taken for his life ambitions.

Henry J. Kaiser and son Edgar F. Kaiser contracted to construct thc upper half of the Grand Coulee Dam project in Eastern Washington State. Henry Kaiser had

---

[35] Hendricks, Ricky, A Model for National Healthcare Rutgers Univ. Press, New Jersey, 1993, p. 28.

some experience with pre-pay healthcare delivery coverage while supervising the Hoover Dam project as chairman of the "Six Companies" construction partnership, and he found himself again sorely in need of a method to provide healthcare delivery for thousands of workers, and eventually those workers' families. A. B. Ordway, Henry Kaiser's first employee and former officer in the Industrial Indemnity Exchange, brought the history of Dr. Garfield's experience in **organized healthcare delivery contract financing** to the Kaisers.[36]   Edgar Kaiser set up a meeting with Dr. Garfield and persuaded him to again postpone his private surgical practice gratification goals. Fulfilled with the excitement of anticipatory planning, Dr. Garfield moved his organized healthcare delivery institutional knowledge base to the dam site in Washington. There, he, as **contracted supervising director** again, along with a newly formed associated physician staff consisting of a few young doctors just beginning their medical practice, established a capitated pre-paid organized healthcare delivery health plan in collaboration with the Kaisers.[37] After Dr. Garfield accepted the basic offer, he added on a family plan for worker dependents to again enlarge the organization's patient risk pool to include 15,000 workers and their families. For a calculated risk-acceptance next step, he invested two thirds or $100,000 from his previous LAMWD nest egg fund to buy and renovate Mason City Hospital and hire seven additional physicians to work for him, including Cecil C. Cutting, a Stanford-trained surgeon.[38]   Unrealized at the time, but of much greater future historical significance, Henry J. Kaiser, age 54 and Sidney Roy Garfield, age 32, met for the first time, smiled together and immediately became inseparable, life-long friends with a common spirit and mission to innovate new frontiers in **contracted organized healthcare delivery.**

After 1940, work ended on the Coulee Dam project. Dr. Garfield sold his hospital to a group of local physicians and returned to Los Angeles to once again pursue long overdue postponed gratifications that would hopefully result from a private surgical practice in the metropolitan area. Meanwhile, the words that came from the smiling lips of Henry Kaiser called out: "Caput Diem". Mr. Kaiser, with absolutely no prior experience in shipbuilding, negotiated a sizeable contract to build "Liberty Ships" in Fontana, California. Simultaneously with the signing of the new contract, he and his irresistible smile came a-calling upon his new old friend, Sidney Garfield. Dr. Garfield, mesmerized by his good friend's smile once again, put his personal plans for a private surgical practice aside once more and

[36] Adelson, David, History of the Kaiser Permanente Medical Care Program, Bancroft Library, U.Cal Berkeley, 1990, p.i.
[37] Kay, Raymond M., Historical Review of the SCPMG, SCPMG, LA, Calif.
[38] Hendricks, Ricky, A Model for National Healthcare Rutgers Univ. Press, New Jersey, 1993, p. 28-35.

responded to Henry Kaiser's call. In Fontana, Dr. Garfield, a capitalist and entrepreneur, along with his associates, (who were generally not capitalistic nor entrepreneurial, but rather more idealistic socialistic crusaders),[39] provided a pre-paid **organized healthcare delivery contract system** for over 200,000 shipyard and steel plant employees and their dependents.[40]

Dr. Garfield's physician group set up a formal immunization program and a patient education program in preventive health maintenance that improved overall health and reduced both the incidence of serious illnesses along with a concomitant reduction in medical costs for his organization. This collaborated physician migratory economic effort of **Healthcare Reform** would eventually become an applied concept of medical practice throughout the entire United States. In Dr. Garfield's healthcare delivery system's incipient form, however, the organized healthcare delivery system functioned as a Physician Sponsored Organization (PSO), the kind of relatively simplistic organization that physicians in the future year of 2000 begged for and advertised as a "last chance" to recapture "dignity, strength, and self-respect"[41]

A Spanish Conquistador, Permanente, gave his name to a small creek in Northern California – Rio Permanente. Henry Kaiser built his first cement factory near the creek and, unknown to the conquistador, the new firm took on the name Permanente. That facility was just the first of several future Kaiser enterprises/facilities to bear the Permanente trademark. In November of 1941, Kaiser formed the Permanente Metals Corporation to further shipbuilding activities. Again, World War II found the Kaisers also building Liberty ships in Richmond, California and on an island in the Columbia River between Vancouver, Washington and Portland, Oregon. Henry Kaiser built hospitals and field stations on all these sites. Dr. Garfield headed each arm of a **contracted administrative triad** that oversaw the medical group, the health plan, and the hospital/clinic operations while his hired physician associates delivered point-of-service healthcare to a multitude of workers from various Kaiser industrial organizations. The **contracted organized healthcare delivery system** grew and added more hospitals to enhance Garfield's personal good fortune. The Fabiola hospital in Oakland and the Maritime Hospital in Vancouver added sustainable assets and stability to his PSO. Eventually, **funds derived from medical contracting** enabled Dr. Garfield to personally finance the building of hospitals to

---

[39] Marcus, Raymond, MD, personal communication
[40] Smillie J., Can Physicians Manage the Quality and Costs of Healthcare? The Story of SCPMG, McGraw-Hill, Inc, 1991
[41] Physicians Care of California ad., May, 1999, LACMA Physician p. 7.

service the communities of Richmond/Oakland, Portland/Vancouver, and Fontana.

Actions always spoke louder than words and soft-spoken Dr. Sidney Garfield was obviously a man of action. He innovatively designed the construction of his Richmond, California field hospital (1942) with functional counters, and modified upward his business plan profit expectations by cutting costs and increasing access simultaneously. His new ecological migratory economic plan boasted to be able to deliver that greater patient access at less organizational cost by utilizing Dr. Garfield's existing medical staff as a quality constant while concomitantly implementing the true efficiency of a counter-service business enterprise for healthcare delivery. His doctors worked behind a long counter that remained opened to a waiting-in-line public on one side while partitioned into separate doctor cubicles on the other side. His physical plant utilized the same style of patron service that is used in banking today, where the individual bank teller stations would have functioned as separate doctor stations. He next extended wait-line partitions on the patients' side to form two cubicles per doctor station with a wall between the cubicles to offer a bit more patient privacy. The wall extensions also muffled conversational noise from the larger waiting room outside the cubicles. Patients waiting in line to be serviced sat on long benches in a large waiting room and were, in turn, called to the cubicles by the doctors, thus efficiently eliminating an intermediary personnel expense as do restaurants today with electronic beepers and Kaiser pharmacies do with electric signs. Restaurants also profit from pre-dinner patron time by sitting them at a bar; this concept of selling or educating large groups of patients while they were waiting for medical care kept budding in Dr. Garfield's healthcare management thoughts, but had to wait till the year 2017 to fully blossom for KFHP. The 1942 patients eventually sat on fixed stools in the cubicles. The doctors, who remained behind the counter on wheeled stools, could also freely move from one cubicle to the next in a production line fashion, thus saving further time, energy, and equipment expense. The counter, a great barrier of wood fitted with a sink at each cubicle station, physically **separated the arm-length and hands-on intimacy** of the physician-patient relationship. This closeness of the physician-patient encounter had been re-examined and then administratively reduced as one of many fundamental steps necessary for efficient, less physician-centric patient processing in the organized healthcare delivery system. The next step for Dr. Garfield included developing a similar physical system to speed along patient prescription fills and refills from a pharmacy. Some patients preferred the efficiency of the innovative counter-service; others resented the depersonalization of having to sit there "on the other side". With the forgiving passage of time to lower expectations, however, habituated patient expectations evolved, resulting in more and more acceptance of the counter-service Medicine concept within the migratory medical ecolo-nomic payer pool niche of patients served. When the migratory medical ecolo-nomic payer pool niche expanded to include migrations of patients more financially successful in society, that newly migrated niche (for a fixed paradigm and time) demanded greater healthcare expectations in direct proportion to their economic plateau. A new "risk" pool niche of payers had to be served. Accordingly, drastic migratory medical ecolo-nomic accommodations became necessary for business survival, and the evolved business plans then dynamically competed. Technology eventually found a new and accepted medical economic answer; but for the subsequent time being, counter service Medicine found a lonely place set aside from the mainstream of healthcare delivery, at least for over half a century or so. When the niche medical ecolo-nomic base of patients became simultaneously altered demographically and increased in numbers, patients also became more active participants in the healthkeeper arena. Dr. Garfield's successful organized healthcare delivery system appropriately changed to yield to the ecology of cultural mores present at that time, the changing migratory ecolo-nomic force of "patient concerns". The continually evolving migratory ecolo-nomic mores and cultural desires of the risk pool of payers -- patient, business, and government -- always drove the migratory economic strategic planning and **Healthcare Reform** for sustainably successful organized healthcare delivery plans.

After the great depression and well into the end of the first half of the 20th Century, fewer and fewer Americans could afford to pay for all healthcare needs out-of-pocket. The CCMC federal government survey had given yet uneaten feed and fodder to pre-pay organized healthcare delivery systems, while multiple indemnity carriers and a virgin Blue Cross and Blue Shield captured the healthcare delivery market for fee-for-service Medicine.

The importance of **Healthcare Reform** in accordance with evolving migratory medical ecolo-nomics became increasingly obvious to Dr. Garfield. He devised a more comprehensive plan for a more diverse payer risk pool by expanding coverage to the non-industrial maladies of the shipyard workers. His pre-pay closed panel health plan, created in 1941, became an offered reality in 1942. He named the health plan "Sidney R. Garfield and Associates". This taxable, for-profit plan represented a change in plan orientation from workmen's compensation-occupational Medicine to a physician-oriented working family medical practice plan. Physician equity interest consisted of land, real estate, and medical equipment; and all those financial assets exclusively belonged to one and only one physician, the contracting physician, Dr. Garfield. Additionally, his solely-owned intellectual property included plan management, medical group management, and organized healthcare delivery system structure. This concept of organized healthcare delivery was at first novel when presented to the Kaiser trustees, but both the concept and the practice were familiar, old, tried and true, for Dr. Sidney Garfield.

Dr. Garfield's newest organized healthcare delivery system blossomed, blessed with sustainable success, and immediately caught the attentive eye of H. J. Kaiser. The industrialist wanted and needed to expand his financial empire. True wealth – Money and Medicine -- was, is, and will always be measured and valued by the degree of control and power attributed to Man. Money can usually buy power, but power is not always for sale (Ralzak). For Medicine, Henry Kaiser envisioned the purchase of a healthcare delivery organization as a powerfully unique investment opportunity. The boom in wartime profits from shipbuilding had to be effectively sheltered in some sort of tax-exempt retention plan to provide funding for future industrial expansion and for possible need in lean years ahead. An investment in healthcare delivery through innovative **Healthcare Reform** beckoned him onward.

Therefore, in August of 1942, just in the nick of time, two months before the passage of the Roosevelt administration's Emergency Stabilization Act, a federal price-freeze stabilization act, Dr. Sidney Garfield, with the help of Henry Kaiser, created two non-profit charitable trust foundations for his medical group. In acknowledgement of that same conquistador and small creek in Northern California near the Permanente Cement property, the two trusts took on the conquistador's name -- The Permanente Foundation and The Northern Permanente Foundation. The trust foundations oversaw the equity interests of real estate and business property --- land, buildings and equipment. Dr. Garfield (as an individual) and Kaiser Industries jointly undertook the administration duties for these non-profit charitable trusts. These new sub-species in organized healthcare delivery **Healthcare Reform** soon would undergo evolutionary genetic transformations and adaptations to meet the changing ecologies in American cultural values and migratory economics. Even as their first fittest specimen emerged, newer innovations were on their way; the two newly named Permanente conquistadors were idealistic, but they in no way resembled or would ever resemble a conquistador such as Don Quixote.

The "Foundations" assumed ownership of hospitals. A reimbursement bank-note check for $50,000, representing a previous personal interest share pay-off from the Fabiola Hospital, bore the name of the payee as Dr. Sidney Garfield. For sure the Money was reassuring, but an ideological conflict yet festered in his mind.

Dr. Garfield continued to truly believe that he correctly and effectively continued to ware two separate and distinct hats. One hat served as head of an organized healthcare delivery salaried-contracted physician medical group, in which role he had total control over administrative and individual salary functions. The other hat functioned as CEO administrator of a pre-paid insurance health plan, including the administration of associated real estate -- hospitals within that plan. However, Henry J. Kaiser believed that he ultimately owned both of those functionally-controlling hats proudly worn and displayed by Dr. Garfield. Moreover, Dr. Garfield's obvious conflict of migratory economic interests plus his close association with the Kaisers through second marriages were soon to become painfully sore points when making administrative decisions involving the other doctors in his organized healthcare delivery medical group. The migratory economics of Medicine and Money may have been tricky, but the tax-exempt non-profit realization of actual dollar contractual involvement lit up to shine all to brightly -- "The stated purpose of the Permanente Foundation was the accumulation of funds to be used for such charitable purposes as medical research and the extension of medical services into neglected areas and sections of the population."[42] The year of 1943 accounting records showed the sum of $250,000 in "deferred earnings" (non-profit word for profit) credited to the Permanente Foundation.[43]

That aforementioned favorable financial time-niche existed for the recruitment and retention of salaried physicians into organized healthcare delivery systems during the wartime epoch, and government-needed recruitment and retention of physicians became further competitively advantaged by the Kaiser Industries' identification with that war effort. Primarily for these reasons, Dr. Garfield and his employee physicians recruited for salaried work in the "Sidney R. Garfield and Associates" pre-pay plan were additionally granted federal government draft-exempt status. Many of the shipyard workers also attained a classification of "4-F" draft-exempt status. Local physicians accused "Kaiser Doctors" of evading the draft. That stigma existed in the minds of the general fee-for-service medical community, but not so in the minds of the lower socioeconomic class payer risk pool in need of medically necessary healthcare delivery. Migratory medical ecolo-nomics also favored the side of the Permanente Foundation and Kaiser Industries; the contracted dynamically sustainable business risk payer pool niche in the medical marketplace reaped good profits. The Garfield-Kaiser medical-industrial association made good migratory economic sense and satisfied that

---

[42] Smillie J., Can Physicians Manage the Quality and Costs of Healthcare? The Story of SCPMG, McGraw-Hill, Inc, 1991, p.43

[43] Hendricks, Ricky, A Model for National Healthcare, Rutgers Univ. Press, New Jersey, 1993, p. 82

needed medical ecolo-nomic niche.

Even after doctors Ross and Loos were reinstated into LACMA, newly made partners in the Ross-Loos clinic and Permanente physicians ("Kaiser Doctors") were repeatedly denied membership in LACMA. This repeated rejection practice ended suddenly in 1938, when the ever politically astute Dr. Loos testified regarding professionalism, in Washington, DC, on behalf of the AMA. Professionalism was a common autonomous ideal for all physicians. The AMA and Dr. Loos defended charges of monopolistic practices against pre-paid groups. From that time forward, all the Ross-Loos physicians as well as pre-pay plan physicians in "Sidney R. Garfield and Associates" were smoothly admitted into LACMA; and, additionally, Dr. Loos, short of being an actual officer, was elected to be a member of the LACMA Board of Councilors.

All AMA opposition to closed panel pre-payment plans ended in January of 1943. A USA Supreme Court decision, AMA vs. USA, 317 U.S. 519 (1943), found the AMA and the Medical Society of the District of Columbia guilty and in violation of the Sherman Anti-Trust Act. "These purposes, it is alleged, were to be attained by certain coercive measures against the hospital and doctors, designed to interfere with employment of doctors by Group Health and use the hospital by members of its medical staff and patients." The judicial findings were: guilty of conspiring to hinder and obstruct a membership corporation engaged in business and guilty of restraint of trade. That last charge was the most devastating because it clearly defined a judicial decision that could be cited or summoned before a court of law where and when the profession of Medicine would be declared a "trade" and a professional organization declared a "trade organization". The repercussions from this landmark decision would never cease to plague the medical establishment. Physicians defended their egos with a massive organized denial of the fiscal-social ecological reality, which persisted throughout the 20th Century. Perhaps old Molière[44] had it at least partially correct a few centuries earlier in his play, "The Physician in Spite of Himself", when he clearly defined the practice of Medicine as "the trade, the best of all trades" – "le métier, le métier le meilleur de tout".

From 1949 to 1954 the AMA became a supervisory overseer for voluntary pre-pay plans and developed a politically inspired listing of approved plans for the general public. The Ross-Loos Medical Group and only five other groups throughout the United States received recognition of especial merit – the AMA's highest honors.

---

[44] Molière, "Le Médecin Malgré Lui", 1666.

LACMA's final attempt to censure physicians in medical practices that were working under the lay-influence of corporate entities in a closed panel system as "unethical" ended in 1953. The then concurrent LACMA president wrote articles condemning closed panel practice and submitted a similar resolution to the CMA that was to be forwarded to the AMA for national action. The resolution was favorably passed in the CMA House of Delegates, but was refused placement on the agenda for the subsequent AMA House of Delegates meeting. Tempus fugit, ecologies evolve. Tincture of time doth heal all; and before the passage of four more decades, another closed-panel group physician became President of LACMA's LA City Medical Association branch. Then, just a short 53 years past 1953, an overwhelming majority of actively practicing fee-for-service LACMA physician members went about their business to vote and to duly elect him their 135th LACMA President. That year was 2006; and that newly elected President of the Los Angeles County Medical Association happened to be an actively practicing, general partner Orthopedic Surgeon in the Southern California Permanente Medical Group.[45] Migratory ecolo-nomics had marched ever onward.

Open opposition to compulsory health insurance yet continued well into the second medical ecolo-nomic generation of organized healthcare delivery (1970-1990). In 1971, the LACMA centennial anniversary book reaffirmed the opinion that the doctor-patient relationship was "being threatened by the specter of compulsory health insurance".[46]

Post WWII years were medical ecolo-nomic boom years for the Palo Alto Medical Clinic. The partnership, patient membership, real estate acquisition rate, and expansion project development all were dosed with growth hormone. The organizational structure for healthcare delivery at first remained a Physician Sponsored Organization (PSO), but the confining walls of that structure had to burst. Migratory medical ecolo-nomic evolution once again ran ramped. Ever diligent and alert to the changing healthcare marketplace, Doctor Lee recruited the most qualified doctors in the local area to join up, thus further dynamically decreasing the threat of competition. In 1946, he negotiated a pre-pay health plan arrangement with Stanford University, which deducted medical coverage payments from student tuition fees. In that same year, he championed twelve new physicians to join the clinic, allowing the organized healthcare delivery clinic to boastfully advertise as a "full range multi-specialty group, capable of handling the

---

[45] Ralph J. DiLibero, MD
[46] LACMA, A Struggle for Excellence, p. 15.

entire spectrum of healthcare".[47]

After 1945, World War II ended, and the Kaiser shipyards shut down. Patient enrollee membership in Dr. Garfield's organized healthcare delivery plan dropped from a high of 90,000 to a low of 11,000. A new migratory ecolo-nomic need for increasing medical care shifted to the community at large, and Dr. Garfield quickly responded by offering his pre-pay healthcare delivery system to the general public. His new risk payer pool niche grew exponentially. Migratory medical ecolo-nomic adaptations catered to the evolved risk pool. In September of 1945, the functionalized pre-pay concept expanded further and offered more enrollment opportunities to the general public along with a hospital service plan touting a new name for the pre-pay hospital service contracted component – the Henry J. Kaiser Company. As previously noted, Dr. Garfield, with the help of Mr. Kaiser, had established the Permanente Foundation, a non-profit charitable trust,[48] still basically a PSO, but with a capitated flavoring to neatly mesh with the hospital service component. Dr. Garfield held the reigns for direction as the CEO, but he did not own the horse or the carriage. The Foundation contractually allowed H. J. Kaiser to own tax-exempt hospitals, which were, by contract, exclusively leased to and run by Dr. Garfield. The Permanente Health Plan and the Permanente Medical Group, both also with Dr. Garfield as CEO, continued to oversee and develop expanding intellectual properties of evolving health plan administration and management.

A bargain struck with the Longshoremen Union of California enabled the opening of similar Permanente Health Plans in the port cities of San Francisco, Seattle, Portland, San Diego and San Pedro (Los Angeles). From 1945 to 1955, patient enrollee membership in Garfield's administered pre-pay organized healthcare delivery plan grew from 14,500 to 301,700.[49]

In the 1950's, during the first overlapping medical ecolo-nomic generation (1950-1970) of changing healthcare delivery, the Palo Alto Medical Clinic again modified its structure; PAMC evolved with **Healthcare Reform** as the migratory medical ecolo-nomic times changed. Touting an enlarged medical group, the PAMC partnership developed a new vision for future management. They developed into a vertically integrated group under a common delivery organization. The delivery organization eventually contracted to own and

---

[47] PAMF Annual Report, 1990, p.12.
[48] Smillie J., Can Physicians Manage the Quality and Costs of Healthcare? The Story of SCPMG, McGraw-Hill, Inc, 1991, p.143
[49] http://insidekp.kp.org

managed the individual doctor practices, and the physicians then became employees of the organization -- a transformation fostered by forces similar to what occurred with the Kaiser organization in 1955, but with drastically different consequences. The physician partnership maintained contractual ownership of the land, buildings and equipment. PAMC created a separate research institute and educational division. Doctor Lee's continued commitment to a superior medical practice became the clinic's strongest and most positive element for survival in the dynamic competitive migratory medical ecolo-nomic marketplace.

Perhaps the original idea and concept of charitable trust foundations belonged to H. J. Kaiser, not a brainstorming concept of Doctor Garfield.[50] A charitable trust fostered continued expansion of the organized healthcare delivery system into the consumer marketplace. As a non-profit, the trust avoided paying taxes. A charitable trust foundation posed a distinct competitive advantage in the medical marketplace and a future organized healthcare delivery marketplace, seen through keen eyes of an industrialist in the dynamic business world. There were of course trade-offs, and the trade-offs may not have been so obvious to Doctor Garfield.

The at-large public officially owned the hospitals – not the doctors. Power and control over the real estate rested with Henry Kaiser. Hospital plan decision-making then became a joint venture with the Kaiser organization, the de-facto administrator of the tax-free Foundation. Doctor Garfield was always an idealistic physician innovator, bent to the calling of contracting methodologies in doctor-patient medical practice at heart, not an industrial magnet; and of that purpose and dedication, H. J. Kaiser was quite well aware. However, the salaried doctors in the pre-pay organized healthcare delivery group all naïvely believed that they had absolute control and would always retain control over the hospitals; a control that they never at any time really possessed by any contractual agreement. This unintended consequence bare truth about shifting ownership and control was not too soon to be revealed by Mr. Kaiser or Dr. Garfield for fear of spoiling the on-going Post-Nuptial Romance of successful healthcare delivery through **Healthcare Reform**. A five-year sustainable honeymoon (1942-1947) followed that marriage, but the assumed and unwritten, (hard to believe today, but apparently not so uncommon then) yes, the assumed and unwritten contractual agreements among the various parties developed a disruptive, exfoliated seven-year itch in 1949. From 1955 forward, the entire healthcare delivery plan stayed in the pocket of H. J. Kaiser; and his friend, Doctor Garfield, necessarily became a rubber-stamping CEO administrator to assuage the unsubstantiated ownership

---

[50] Kay, Raymond, interview, 1985

feelings of the practicing salaried doctors.

Before that point of migratory economic evolutionary **Healthcare Reform** development, there were five healthcare delivery program entities that linked and tied the entire healthcare delivery system together without any written contract:

1. The Henry J. Kaiser Company, -- a corporation with a Board of Trustees administratively overseeing the expansion and penetrance of a pre-pay hospital service plan and hospitals.
2. The Permanente Foundations, -- non-profit public trusts for tax-exempt hospitals, administered by the H. J. Kaiser Company.
3. The Permanente Health Plan, -- a for-profit organized healthcare delivery association with undefined ownership administered jointly in conjunction with salaried doctors acting as limited partners in a clinical group practice that employed one general administrative partner -- Dr. Garfield.
4. Dr. Garfield – CEO -- administrative head of the organized healthcare delivery plan, physician association, hospital service plan, and hospital-clinic administration.
5. The entity "Sidney Garfield and Associates" – a contractual unit of physicians linked in a medical practice association with no net assets that jointly held an exclusive lease on hospital real estate that was previously owned by Dr. Garfield and currently administered by a Henry J. Kaiser Company trust, a "Permanente Foundation".

Due to ill-defined control mechanisms and a lack of a prescriptive business plan, this medical ecolo-nomic business structure teetered from its foundation with increasing instability and soon would crumble and fall in despair. The pre-pay organized healthcare delivery insurance plan, however, generated capital from a stable and sustainable risk pool of individual patient and group business payers. Control, as in all businesses, follows the Money and vise-versa. (Ralzak)

Doctor Garfield and his medical practice association of doctors working with/for him viewed that entire set of five programs as one single un-partitioned organized healthcare delivery system, while continually exuding a pride of ownership and a satisfaction derived from their mutual creation endeavor. The personal eyes of H. J. Kaiser saw the same for himself; he also viewed the doctors as simply additional employees in his industrial empire. Although accused of socialistic, communistic and lay control of medical practice, H. J. Kaiser was neither a communist nor a socialist. He was an entrepreneurial corporate industrialist driven totally by innovative capitalistic intentions. The charitable trust was his

151

business venture, a dynamic competitive strategy that would primarily benefit the Kaiser corporate interests and the risk pool community of needy patients and the businesses that employed them – not the hired help of health workers, the actively practicing doctors. "Henry J. Kaiser declared that the Kaiser organization ran anything in which it was involved."[51]

Right before this controversial time, the federal government engineered a dynamic cultural change that stood out as a migratory medical ecolo-nomic watershed event. The previously mentioned Stabilization Act of 1942 froze wages to halt inflation and opened the door for employers to contribute sums in the form of benefits to attract new employees in a highly competitive job marketplace. While the Revenue Act of 1942 provided the largest tax increase for 27 years to come, President Truman's administration passed the Revenue Act of 1945, the biggest tax decrease of that era, which additionally allowed employers to deduct the cost of employee healthcare insurance from their federal taxes and offered the incentive of healthcare coverage as an employee benefit – **A migratory economic watershed event in Healthcare Reform**. Business timing concomitantly arrived at a perfect place for payer risk pool expansion in organized healthcare delivery.

As with the Ross-Loos Medical Clinic and the Palo Alto Medical Group, the new Permanente Health Plan (PHP) intimidated and frightened traditional fee-for-service medical practitioners, and the PHP salaried physician fee schedules were especially terrifying: "Physician salaries ranged from $3600 to $6000 a year, rising to a ceiling of $8400 in 1945, at a time when the average doctor's income in the United States was $5000, with 50% of the nation's physicians netting less than $3912 per year."[52] In May of 1946, the Alameda County Medical Society accused and charged Dr. Garfield with violations of the California Medical Practice Act. The charges did not stick. An unsuccessful attempt to remove Dr. Garfield's California medical license because of alleged laymen influence in directing the practice of Medicine ensued. In June of 1948, the Alameda County Medical Society again unsuccessfully charged Dr. Garfield with the now over-worn and beaten to death accusation of "unethical practice" in "closed panel Medicine". That unethical conduct charge just would no longer stick as the mores and customs of the times had since evolved. The charges encompassed wrongdoings consisting of a "mass-production style of medical practice" and limiting patients' free choice in selecting a doctor and/or course of treatment due to "financial

[51] Smillie J., Can Physicians Manage the Quality and Costs of Healthcare? The Story of SCPMG, McGraw-Hill, Inc, 1991, p.143
[52] Smillie J., Can Physicians Manage the Quality and Costs of Healthcare? The Story of SCPMG, McGraw-Hill, Inc, 1991, p.46

hamstringing" incumbent in a closed panel system. During the third generation of overlapping change in organized healthcare delivery (1990-2010) "financial hamstringing" became known and accepted as politically correct "cost effectiveness", and "mass production style of medical practice" became known and accepted as politically correct "population-based medical practice guidelines". Ah yes, so much can be done with just a "wordsmithing" name change. After 2010, as outlined in the American Recovery and Reinvestment Act, a centralized federal health policy decision making body, the Institute for Comparative Effectiveness (ICE) utilized a new politically proper or politically correct "word-speak" term for all those guidelines and former unethical charges. The ICE committee sought to develop a system of "Coordinated Healthcare."

Further ineffective charges against Dr. Garfield included public advertising and the soliciting of patients, which were practices continually and rigorously forbidden buy the AMA until 1975.[53] Largely due to the extensive county, state, and national political efforts accomplished by Dr. Loos and his political action activities within the Los Angeles County Medical Association (LACMA), and then having these political efforts bolstered by threats made directly to the AMA by H. J. Kaiser, the charges against Dr. Garfield of unethical practice of closed panel Medicine failed to materialize. However, in 1946, the California Board of Medical Examiners, or Board of Medical Quality Assurance (BMQA), (later termed the Medical Board of California, (MBC)) brought forward new allegations and charges of "illegal medical practice". The BMQA accused Doctor Garfield of employing doctors with revoked medical licenses and employing doctors with no current medical licenses in the state of California. The accusations were eventually softened, but this time they never completely went away. The BMQA found Doctor Garfield guilty of illegally employing two physicians. The expected repercussions became exaggerated in the press, and falsely tarnished all the good names of the remaining "Kaiser Doctors" in the medical community. In proper and good response to the verdict, many administrative tasks within "Sidney Garfield and Associates", such as due diligence in documented review of medical credentials and privileges, gained an important and deserved stature which then demanded and received adequate funding in ongoing and future yearly budget projections. A series of federally ordered third medical ecolo-nomic generation unfunded administrative mandates would eventually rigidly require the same for all of the then re-named Health Maintenance Organizations (HMO's) to the newer designation of Health Keeper Organizations (HKOs).

---

[53] Federal Trade Commission vs. AMA, 1975.

Driven by risk payer pool protectionism, the Ross-Loos and the Garfield-Kaiser organized healthcare delivery systems both favored the rights of laborers and union workers in general. That favoritism alone was enough to be more than a squeaky wheel, more like a lynch-pin on the propaganda wagon of the American Organized Medicine's mind-set. Continually rebuffed charges of labor unions practicing Medicine and unethical closed panel practice arose once more. In response, both organized healthcare delivery plans offered "Dual Choice" whereby union enrollees were offered an alternative choice of healthcare delivery plans. Still and in vain, local medical societies feared for the financial survival of their members and responded with propaganda campaigns aimed against all pre-pay organized healthcare delivery plans. "Kaiser made it worse by bombastic pot shots and threats of litigation against them."[54] In 1953, Henry Kaiser responded to a series of defamatory articles published in the Los Angeles Times newspaper by declaring, "American labor is making it clearly known that working people demand better ways of meeting the crushing costs of illness."[55] Also in 1953, at the opening of the Sunset Hospital in Los Angeles, similar to the 1883 proclamation of Otto Von Bismarck, Henry Kaiser proclaimed, "to stop the socialization of Medicine in its tracks", physicians everywhere should accept pre-paid organized group healthcare delivery.[56] A true clairvoyant, Henry Kaiser clearly foresaw the day when insurance corporations would come to battle big government for control and ultimate possession of the healthcare delivery dollar; the continuing interactions among Man, Money and Medicine.

At that time, however, those anti-socialization words fell mostly on deaf ears; but the very same words, at the end of the third overlapping medical ecolo-nomic generation of healthcare delivery, were clearly heard as a battle cry for physician survival, not just acceptance. Eventually, just after the third medical ecolo-nomic generation (1990-2010), most but not all physicians finally kowtowed and struck their heads nine times on the ground while begging Health Keeper Organizations (HKOs) to keep the practice of Medicine under the control of industrialists like Kaiser rather than have medical control totally secede, into the hands of the federal government. The larger and remaining group of physicians at that time divided themselves into two ideologies on either side of the insurance corporation HKO brand of medical practice. One group championed fee-for-service medical practice, while the other anxiously awaited a federal single payer government-run brand of **Healthcare Reform**. The conflicts and resolutions of conflicts between the Kaiser organization and the Garfield physicians during the period of 1948 to

---

[54] Hendricks, Ricky, A Model for National Healthcare, Rutgers Univ. Press, New Jersey, 1993, p. 10
[55] Hendricks, Ricky, A Model for National Healthcare, Rutgers Univ. Press, New Jersey, 1993, p. 10
[56] Hendricks, Ricky, A Model for National Healthcare, Rutgers Univ. Press, New Jersey, 1993, p. 10

1953 were identical to those conflicts and resolutions between private practice physicians and Health Maintenance Organizations (HMOs) in the second medical ecolo-nomic generation of overlapping changes in organized healthcare delivery (1970-1990). The old tattered and torn physician-written Kaiser chronicles from 1953 to 1955 were freshly rewritten without much rewording or "wordsmithing" in the physician-HKO contracting disputes during the third medical ecolo-nomic generation (1990-2010).

On February 20, 1948, sealed with a $150,000 loan from the H. J. Kaiser Company,[57] all Permanente Hospitals were brought together into one charitable corporation -- the Permanente Foundation. Dr. Garfield profited from the buy-out; Kaiser paid Garfield in installments amounting to $257,500, and in return, Garfield no longer held total command.[58] Again, Money can buy power, but power is not always for sale (Ralzak). Anytime that healthcare delivery power, such as control of the hospitals, became available for sale, Henry Kaiser seized the opportunity to quickly buy that power with quick and ready cash, a fiscal funding mechanism. As a matter of historical fact, the salaried practicing physicians and/or the partnered practicing physicians at that time never-ever possessed such true power, control or the sufficient cash. Again the story of Man, Money, and Medicine repeated itself.

The very next day, February 21, 1948, the business association of limited partner doctors in association practice with Dr. Garfield evolved into a new organizational structure. A general and equal group practice general partnership entered into the organized healthcare delivery migratory economic environment. Following the previous paths cut by Drs. Loos and Lee, Dr. Garfield declared and officially contracted each Permanente limited partner associate physician to become a true and legal general group partner for the very first time. The intellectual property of patient care systems mutated to evolve, and the adapted **Healthcare Reform** gave birth to The Permanente Medical Group (TPMG). The seven "Founding Fathers" included: Dr. August Lamonte Baritell, Dr. Morris F. Collen, Dr. Cecil C. Cutting, Dr. Robert King, Dr. Paul Fitzgibbon, Dr. Melvin Friedman, and Dr. Sidney Garfield. Dr. Wallace Neighbor, medical director of the Kaiser hospital in Vancouver, WA was among the first to join this new group of general partnered physicians. As a functional concept in the organizational plans and in the minds of the doctors, but without officially written words on a holding paper contract

---

[57] Smillie J., Can Physicians Manage the Quality and Costs of Healthcare? The Story of SCPMG, McGraw-Hill, Inc, 1991, p. 76
[58] Smillie J., Can Physicians Manage the Quality and Costs of Healthcare? The Story of SCPMG, McGraw-Hill, Inc, 1991, p.76

(littera scripta manet), their pre-pay organized healthcare delivery system was now assumedly divided into three branches:

1. The Permanente Health Plan, a non-profit corporation (of which the doctors unfortunately "assumed" ownership without legal or written documentation);
2. The Permanente Foundation of Hospitals, a charitable trust (of which the doctors knew absolutely nothing and inquired even less regarding their legal requirements or responsibilities); and
3. The Permanente Medical Group, a for-profit, egalitarian general partnership of physicians in group practice with no tangible financial assets.

Painfully apparent, no attempt to do due diligence and omission of forethought both prevailed. No paper document contractually stated functional and operational boundaries that might have clearly and ultimately legally defined who or what owned and/or controlled/administered each entity. A fundamental decision point moment, a crossroads choice, or perhaps a timely test, suddenly set a window of hope and prayer opportunity that would inevitably be put before the practicing doctors: The doctors would eventually have to consider if they were willing and able to act alone, to take command, to control and direct the future management and repercussions thereof in the entire administration of this three-part organized healthcare delivery organization. The Permanente Medical Group general partnered doctors would have to act as a cohesive group to both govern themselves and act as one united, unfreezing, and evolving unit. They would also have to make a crucial decision regarding future group survival and hopefully be visionary, see beyond the natural course of their own life span and make the necessary sacrifices and business adjustments that future long-term medical practice autonomy within a continuing and sustainable organized healthcare delivery system would painfully demand. There had to be a willingness to share their good fortunes with newer partners in an expanding **Healthcare Reform** system that would take on a life of its own; an unwillingness to act in such a manner would result in a future sadly restrictive medical group longevity, by unintentionally copying the then currently successful model of the Ross-Loos Medical Group. The new general partner doctors had to independently act in a timely fashion or else accept some outside influence to foster their own cohesiveness. They had to develop a business plan that was legally valid, well-planned and adaptable to dynamically competitive advantages in the changing business world. However, in reality, the partnered physicians never thought to have any kind of business plan at all. They had to be fiscally sound, but there never were medical group cash-transferable financial infrastructures or any significant cash reserves, present or planned, to sustain their assumed organized healthcare delivery business venture in times of temporary financial need. There was no concept introduced into their imaginary business plan that included a rainy day or deferred earnings set-aside. The doctors would alternatively need to have ready access to, or the ability to independently arrange for large capital financing; needless to say, that was also lacking. Time's passage and migratory ecolo-nomic evolution could be their enemy or their friend. It did not take much time at all to tell that failure to plan was and is planning to fail. They should have considered the "7-P" Military Adage from the Brits – "Proper Planning and Preparation Prevents Piss Poor Performance"; or at least the American Boy Scout Motto – Be Prepared – by means of the ever vigilant meticulous pains of carefulness "Curum".

Not unexpectedly, barely a year after its evolutionary birth, in July of 1949, The Permanente Medical Group underwent a further migratory economic adaptive **Healthcare Reform** change. The majority of the general partnership felt that the Kaiser Industries' influence upon Dr. Garfield provoked too much of a strain on The Permanente Medical Group. While all of this talk and gossip regarding conflict of interest ensued, Dr. Garfield first sensed, then he personally developed, a progressive distance involving his personal relationship to and with the general medical partnership of physicians. He had overtly refused to become a working associate physician employed by Ross-Loos in the distant past, and this current step-down arrangement as an associate general partner physician did not fit in well with his entrepreneurial administrative talents.[59] He looked to see what else might be available in the migratory economic job market for an entrepreneurial CEO physician whose expertise involved **medical contracting arrangements**. After a series of interviews, the Health Insurance Plan of New York offered him their CEO position. Dr. Garfield strongly desired to be in such a leadership position once again, but after much personal contemplation and persuasive discussions with his best smiling friend and confidant, Henry Kaiser, he declined the offer.

Permanente Health Plan leadership and management festered and posed a different conundrum. Doctor Garfield lived in close proximity to H. J. Kaiser and eventually moved in next door. In 1951, Henry's wife, Bess Kaiser, died after a long illness that had been attended to by Dr. Garfield and his nurse, Alyce Chester. A short time later, Henry Kaiser took Alyce for his second wife and convinced Dr. Garfield to marry her sister. The two men, already social companions, now became brothers-in-law via second marriages to sister nurses once employed by the medical group. Dr. Garfield's total earnings were six times

[59] Herman, Cornelius (Pappy), interview, 1975

that of the average physician in the general partnered medical group.[60]   Dr. Garfield's supposedly two distinct hats became increasingly more similar on closer inspection. These two hats seemed to meld into one, and that one remaining hat fit the head of the chief executive officer -- CEO – of a yet undeclared and yet un-named Kaiser Industries' health plan. With Dr. Garfield's wish and consent, the general physician partnership revised their physician agreement; Dr. Garfield instructed and accomplished the removal of his name from any direct ownership and all general partnership rights and privileges within The Permanente Medical Group.   Dr. Garfield effectively, willingly and freely granted the power of attorney, the intellectual property, and control of the medical group to the remaining TPMG general partners. He truly hoped and expected that the remaining partners would carry on successfully without him, and he looked to be involved only in peripheral management responsibilities. Dr. Garfield's total time as a general partner in The Permanente Medical Group was limited to a total of only 18 months.   Revision of this general partnership agreement may have symbolically removed a seemingly perceptual overt cause of health plan vs. doctor unrest; but it was quite evident that the true and real insidious cause of the conflict remained intact, and its symptoms were simply stayed, disguised but unabated, while the true insidious migratory business-economic disease festered toward eruption.

There were also legal and ethical risk issues involved in the crossing of the legal "corporate bar" and entering into the "Lay Practice of Medicine" -- having laymen (Kaiser Industries) direct medical care, albeit indirectly via selective financial incentives to the physicians. To that end, the concept or perception of a doctor-owned medical group helped dismiss publicized (horrific for its time) propaganda that group practicing physicians were direct employees of a lay corporation. The Kaiser organization did not want to be exposed to enterprise liability or the consequences resulting from violation of generally accepted existing business codes such as the corporate bar on medical practice. These exact same social/legal issues were to burden the majority of organized healthcare delivery systems in the third medical ecolo-nomic generation (1990-2010).   (In the fall of 2016, California Governor Jerry Brown signed AB 2024, which nullified the corporate bar or ban on medical practice for small hospitals.)

In an abrupt change of attitude, suddenly neither H. J. Kaiser nor the partner physicians were satisfied with Dr. Garfield's other hat, his acclaimed health plan management abilities. The temporary awkward conundrum involving Dr. Garfield

---

[60] Herman, Cornelius (Pappy), interview, 1975

seemed never to be solved. Dr. Garfield was really an inspiring leader and builder of healthcare delivery systems, not ever a happy middle manager. The organization already had an industrial magnet in a leadership position where there was only room for one at the top. As with most entrepreneurial types, Dr. Garfield's entrepreneurial drive gear did not shift well into a management strategies sprocket. Dr. Garfield wished to continue to develop unique and innovative approaches to healthcare delivery, but he was forced into administering a status quo system. His innate long-range perspective and kindness of attitude inspired trust in people to investigate and challenge the future with him, but that now really became Mr. Kaiser's job. Dr. Garfield's job description devolved close to one of middle management administration. He was empowered only to maintain, manage, keep the peace, act like a good soldier, rely on control rather than trust, and to only ask how and when, rather than so ever gently demand what and why.

The general working structure of Dr. Garfield's administered organized healthcare delivery system that existed from 1945 to 1955 combined three distinct entities whose names and functions would soon change:
1. The Permanente Health Plan (PHP), (PSO doctor-insurer trust);
2. The Permanente Foundation (Kaiser hospital-clinic trust); and
3. The Permanente Medical group (TPMG), (general-partnered physicians)

In spite of those political oppositions from local medical associations to the concept of "unprofessional" closed panel medical practice, patient membership increased at a slow but steady and financially sustainable rate. The projected yearly expense budget remained sustainable over the long term, but varied with growth and often arose too high to be matched with the current-year pre-payments. Adequate reserve liquid funding within the doctor group such as "deferred earnings" never did exist. The doctors continued to falsely assume and continued to truly yet recidivistically believe that they shared management in the hospital service and also assumed and believed that they shared in the ownership, management, and intellectual properties within the health insurance plan.

All these unconfirmed shareholders agreed to one part of a vision and action plan. That dynamic competitive strategy was to establish a one-stop shop with everything under one roof for a patient – a medical department store. Continued risk payer pool expansion, however, was not a common partnership goal for a physician partnership like The Permanente Medical Group (TPMG) or the Ross-Loos Medical Clinic. On the other hand, for a corporate industry, as H. J. Kaiser realized early on, the organized healthcare delivery system must first and foremost be a business enterprise; and to sustain itself, the business needed to grow and enter into competition with others in the healthcare delivery marketplace. To maintain this essential competitive edge and assure sustainability, a dynamic business-like approach became overtly and obviously essential. Kaiser's vision demanded continued health plan growth to best avoid extinction of the business venture, an extinction that would ultimately neither benefit Kaiser Industries nor patients in need of affordable healthcare delivery. For the sake of the patients, the doctors agreed to the health plan insurance expansion vision without much complaint, questioning or contractual investigation. The subsequent migratory economic history of **Healthcare Reform** for the doctors and the corporate industry was set and about to tell an interesting tale:

With Kaiser Industries as a co-signer, The Permanente Medical Group physicians (yes, the general partnered physicians) secured a $250,000 loan directly from Amadeo P. Giannini, the founder of the Bank of Italy in America (Bank of America) and good friend of Henry Kaiser. Utilizing these funds through the authorized auspices of the Permanente Health Plan (not the medical general partnership), the Permanente Foundation purchased and built two new hospital-clinics. Capital generated by a contractual real estate lease payable to the vibrant TPMG general partnered doctor organization repaid their loan in nine months.[61] Renters do not ordinarily borrow Money to pay for their landlord's real estate or mortgages, and renters usually do not celebrate when their landlord's mortgage is finally paid off, but the Permanente general partnered doctors certainly did both. They also wore horsehead blinders to methodologically direct and obscure their future vision and goal -- they intellectually could not and did not see themselves as renters-only. Denial is a strong and powerful ego-defense mechanism.

In the earliest beginning of the first medical ecolo-nomic generation of overlapping change in organized healthcare delivery (1950-1970), dissatisfaction among the physician general partners continued to escalate. This dissatisfaction was not publicly acknowledged in 1950, but the unhappy distrust was not unnoticed by the calculating eye of the ever diligently watching industrialist. In line with Kaiser's commitment to run "his" health plan according to good competitive business principles, Henry Kaiser devised a scheme, an act of supposed concern and understanding as a potent political business strategy-ploy. He initiated and oversaw surveys that were taken to determine satisfaction among patients and doctors. Push-pull polling was and still is an effective feedback

---

[61] Smillie J., Can Physicians Manage the Quality and Costs of Healthcare? The Story of SCPMG, McGraw-Hill, Inc, 1991, p. 43

mechanism to keep one step ahead in the dynamic competitive healthcare delivery marketplace. In order to assuage the tension among the doctors and to showboat an overt attempt at appeasement, the Kaiser organization proclaimed that a "neutral-interest" assistant should be appointed.

Therefore, Henry Kaiser hired Dr. E. Richard Weinerman from Yale University to assume the role of health plan managerial assistant to Dr. Garfield in 1951. Dr. Weinerman was never granted partnership in The Permanente Medical Group. Dr. Weinerman worked diligently to distil out what, in the evolving organized healthcare delivery system, appeared to be inconsistent with the prevailing partner physician ideals and values. He became quite popular with the physician-partners. After a thorough study, he determined that Kaiser's lay industrial influence remained a key factor in disruption of the perceived sacrosanct doctor-patient relationship. Also, an unwritten business plan had directed and originated all administrative decision-making from a top-down direction; and Henry Kaiser held that penultimate position -- the top boss of all the healthcare delivery plan's bosses – "Capo di tutti Capi." This corporate administrative top-down structure, according to Dr. Weinerman, stifled both medical and political physician autonomy; and further, a workable mechanism overtly stood lacking for clear grass root working doctor concern to be ever seriously considered and evaluated by the Kaiser trustees. Forgetting exactly who was paying his bill and thus not considering the unintended consequences of such omission, Dr. Weinerman falsely trusted his contracted "neutrality" and naïvely let his findings be equally known to all parties involved. As a result, the Kaiser management did not consider him much of a "team player", at least on the Kaiser Industrial side of the team competition. Administrative propaganda insidiously leaked a fatal message – "administrative incompatibility"[62] – the days remaining for this pretend-assistant or "neutral interest" ombudsman became rapidly numbered. After a few short months, his tenure with the currently disgruntled and disorganized healthcare delivery system was, by executive decision, terminated. Dr. Weinerman returned to Yale. An additional eerie coercive note of trepidation sounded in the hearts of the remaining physician partners. Non-conforming doctor philosophies and moral ambiguities swore their tongues to a private silence, "Omertà", while their guts yearned for vendetta. Sophocles would have summoned to action the mythical conflict within Electra.

Henry Kaiser next conferred with his son Edgar, and together they determined to

---

[62] Smillie J., Can Physicians Manage the Quality and Costs of Healthcare? The Story of SCPMG, McGraw-Hill, Inc, 1991, p.118

bring in a truly solid, trustworthy and reliable Kaiser "Company Man", Clifford Keene, MD, to run the healthcare delivery organization, not as an assistant to Dr. Garfield, but as the true CEO. The proverbial hammer was about to fall; but to start things off and give the appearance that nothing had changed, Henry Kaiser first gave Doctor Keene that temporary old Dr. Weinerman title of assistant to Dr. Garfield; but it was soon quite clearly revealed that from the very start this preordained arrangement would evolve to become something quite different; and Dr. Keene would really and truly be "The Man" in charge with the big hat and bigger axe to grind. His title was rather quickly next changed to "Executive Associate". Dr. Keene saw his exact directed role without any confusion about multiple hats. He fit and assumed the role of ironhanded fiscal manager for his direct employer, Henry Kaiser. Dr. Keene was not at all sympathetic to what he interpreted as "petty doctor causes". The doctors suddenly faced a demanding, authoritative and no-nonsense administrative leader. Dr. Keene set clearly understood standards with very little room for flexibility. Harmony and empathy were overtly absent items in his leadership toolkit. He exercised little or no effort in any direction to in any way encourage or develop future administrative leaders from the existing general partner physician pool.

Eventually and certainly not unexpectedly, overt and open conflict arose between the partner physicians and the Kaiser-industry management concerning management decisions affecting both the hospitals and the health plan. In 1952, Dr. Garfield quite sadly announced to the Permanente Medical Group that Kaiser and the partner physicians might have to go their own separate ways. The basic inevitable conflict arose over who would control the PHP doctor-insurer trust (health plan) – The PHP would have to be administered either through the Kaiser corporate management team or the general partnered doctors, but not both – there was only room for one at the top. The control and power position of the Kaiser trustees stayed immutable. An escalating implacable attitude from the doctors just made matters worse. Tensions arose and escalated to the point of nearly destroying the entire relationship and abandoning the pre-paid organized healthcare delivery system forever. Neither the physician general partners nor the big business administrators trusted the other to in any way run any part of the PHP doctor-insurer trust.

Meanwhile and concurrently, as a result of union tensions between the United Mine Workers (UMW) and the Congress of Industrial Organizations (CIO), Permanente physicians who treated the UMW were targeted as scapegoats and alleged to have Communist ties. "Henry Kaiser made relations with the doctors worse by attempting his own anticommunist purge..... and..... devised a loyalty oath for physicians.[63] One of the founding fathers, Dr. Paul Fitzgibbon, resigned because he correctly concluded that Henry Kaiser planned to push out the doctors and then personally run/administrate the entire organized healthcare delivery system.

Next in 1953, with an obvious overt act of psychological and political posturing, Henry Kaiser ordered a revision of the company names:
1. The Kaiser Health Plan; (insurance agency);
2. The Kaiser Foundation (hospitals/clinics); and
3. The Permanente Medical Group (healthcare delivery physicians).

Although the Permanente Health Plan and the Permanente Foundation suddenly changed their names to "Kaiser", no overt management changes were made. Actually, none were needed. Now officially named, a Kaiser Health Plan and a Kaiser Foundation Hospital entered into the organized healthcare delivery medical ecolo-nomic marketplace; but there was no Kaiser Medical Group – a mere consolation made to hopefully and effectively assuage Permanente general partnered physicians who rebelled against the other changes. The physicians refused to accept the name of "Kaiser" for their general partnership; therefore, Henry Kaiser simply tossed them that crumb and let the general physician zero net asset partnership retain their original name -- The Permanente Medical Group. The separate name, however, did not offer the doctor group any inkling of independent identity in the public mindset. They still suffered under and from the "Kaiser" stigma and stayed branded as "Kaiser Doctors" by their local and distant physician colleagues, who also despised Henry Kaiser's public prominence.[64] A second founding physician father, Dr. Lamonte Baritell, became enraged and resigned when, at Henry Kaiser's direction, funds that Dr. Baritell originally earmarked for renovation of the Oakland Hospital were, by executive order, withheld then transferred and finally used for the Walnut Creek facility.

"The Medical Group considered the Kaiser Health Plan as an adjunct agency intended to provide a mechanism to enroll members, set rates, and collect pre-paid fees. The physicians considered Kaiser Hospitals as workshops intended to provide them an adequate setting for the practice of Medicine."[65] The physicians ignominiously and falsely assumed that they owned the entire organized healthcare delivery program.

---

[63] Hendricks, Ricky, A Model for National Healthcare, Rutgers Univ. Press, New Jersey, 1993, p. 9
[64] Hendricks, Ricky, A Model for National Healthcare, Rutgers Univ. Press, New Jersey, 1993, p. 9
[65] Smillie J., Can Physicians Manage the Quality and Costs of Healthcare? The Story of SCPMG, McGraw-Hill, Inc, 1991, p.119

"Internal problems intensified as a result of Henry Kaiser's provocative conduct and imperious attitude towards doctors."[66] In an interview, Scott Fleming, Kaiser legal counsel, was noted to have said, "Henry Kaiser hoped to control the doctors just as he controlled his manufacturing and other operations."[67]

Early in 1955, the physician partnership sent a memorandum of understanding (MOU) to Edgar Kaiser, outlining the "partner physician point of view" as to the development, management, and future direction of the health insurance plan. The MOU clearly demonstrated both physician frustration and their total lack of business acumen. TPMG partner physicians clearly and succinctly outlined their falsely assumed understanding that:
"The basic concept" of integrated operation of all medical care entities under "physician management" was sustained from 1948 through 1952, when a radical change (Dr. Keene) occurred."[68] The physician partners still failed to appreciate the administrative corporate significance of a non-profit hospital and naïvely recollected that the non-profit hospital: "was created" -- they did not state by whom or what entity was responsible for administering the charitable trust, but they did state that the intended purpose of said creation was – "to convert a maximum amount of "our" funds (those aforementioned physician-secured, Kaiser co-signed loan funds from Bank of America) to the construction of facilities."[69]

Henry Kaiser functionally snatched the alleged physician control over the health plan like taking candy from a baby. The Permanente partnered physicians naïvely expressed their blindly distorted vision of the corporate-spun process. To wit, the doctors further documented in the memo:
"because of problems with the medical societies" (a true event falsely expanded by Henry Kaiser to use as a propaganda tool or scare tactic to coerce the partner doctors) "contrary to the desire of both the trustees and the doctors" (another successful Kaiser "please don't throw the tar baby in the briar patch" maneuver) "it became expedient" (Kaiser corporation trustee translation = irresistible) "to change the direct relationship between the doctors and their patient members by setting up an intervening" (more intervening than the doctors' wildest dreams could imagine) "third party in the form of a Health Plan Trust."

[66] Hendricks, Ricky, A Model for National Healthcare, Rutgers Univ. Press, New Jersey, 1993, p. 162
[67] Hendricks, Ricky, A Model for National Healthcare, Rutgers Univ. Press, New Jersey, 1993, p. 165
[68] Hendricks, Ricky, A Model for National Healthcare, Rutgers Univ. Press, New Jersey, 1993, p. 185
[69] Hendricks, Ricky, A Model for National Healthcare, Rutgers Univ. Press, New Jersey, 1993, p. 185

Again, as was with the hospital trust, the doctors still did not understand the practical or legal significance of a health plan trust or any trust for that matter. At this point, any businessman would have guessed that the Kaiser trustees were falling off their corporate meeting room chairs with hilarious laughter as they read further in the preposterous memo from the physician general partners:

"There was never any question but that we (physicians) were participating in the physician operation of a medical care plan including all of its parts – direct operation of hospitals, direct management of clinics, and direct agreements with the patient membership. Kaiser "sponsorship" gave us the backing and security we needed to do the job."[70]

Perhaps at that point, it was not clear to the Kaiser trustees whether the doctors had just fallen off a turnip truck or if the doctors were actually living on some other planet in a distant solar system, perhaps on Kepler-452-b. Dr. Lamonte Baritell, one of the founding fathers of TPMG, who had previously resigned because of that aforementioned Kaiser lay management interference in fundamental healthcare delivery policies, influenced Cecil Cutting and the remaining general partners to finally draw up some sort of business plan. The medical partners drafted a "Statement of Fundamental Policies" which defined the role of the physician to include a role of responsibility for quality and costs in the entire organized healthcare delivery system. This feeble attempt at writing a post-facto business plan proved to be too little, much too inadequate and very much too late. To a "Man", physicians had not adapted to the migratory economic of **Healthcare Reform** in sufficient time, and now medical ecolo-nomic evolution sought and demanded the extinction of physician "Money control of Medicine", the Medicine of organized healthcare delivery systems. Yes, Man Money and Medicine: déjà vu all over again Yogi.

Of Sardonic interest in the migratory economic history of **Healthcare Reform**, lawsuits between doctors and Health Keeper Organizations (HKOs) in the third overlapping medical ecolo-nomic generation of organized healthcare delivery (1990-2010) used near verbatim wording as in the Permanente doctors' arguments. Times had changed, but the sequence of prose had not. Thus, "those who do not read history (George Santayana) and those who do not learn from history (Winston Churchill) are doomed to repeat it". Migratory medical ecolo-nomic history was to redundantly repeat itself again and again. The Kaiser evolutionary process in organized healthcare delivery during the first half of the 20th Century proved to be

---

[70] Hendricks, Ricky, A Model for National Healthcare, Rutgers Univ. Press, New Jersey, 1993, p. quoting from memorandum sent to Edgar Kaiser. P. 185

a well-trodden adaptive path for survival for the medical ecolo-nomic genus "HKO" the Health Keeper Organization. The genus HKO first produced an immense spawn, an array of various organized healthcare delivery species. The HKO genus then self-selected out through dynamic competition the ones most akin to the Kaiser corporate pathway for ultimate adaptive migratory ecolo-nomic survival.

That aforementioned "Statement of Fundamental Policies" overtly offended the entire Kaiser corporate business management team. Corporate decision-making unanimously agreed that their de facto control had to be made legally undisputed and contractual for once and for all. Therefore, on May 19, 1955 Henry Kaiser devised a clever political ploy. Much like a high stake poker-card game gamble, he offered to sell the entire healthcare delivery system to the physicians, if the physicians would or could assume the organization's debts of $14 Million that were currently being guaranteed by his Kaiser Industrial Companies. It would have been the penultimate financial deal of a lifetime for all the physicians. Unfortunately, the physicians apparently (obviously to the corporate strategists) could not raise the necessary capital for the purchase. Dr. Raymond Kay led the many attempts to raise these funds.[71] The physicians were out of chips in a high stake poker game and had no choice but to fold over their dealt hand of very probable winners, now transformed into losing playing cards for lack of adequate ante funding. In the future, this poker game would be off limits and permanently closed to the amateur Permanente partner physician players. At that time in medical ecolo-nomic evolution, there was no other corporate entity willing to come forward and co-sign a loan agreement that would back up the doctors' insufficient quantity of chips; and the doctors had not had the foresight to set up any reserve monetary "retention fund" of "deferred earnings" in their previously non-existent business plan that could have quickly bailed them out. The physicians simply could not call Henry Kaiser's bluff, and he obviously knew that well established fact well in advance.[72]

This magnificent bluff led to many meetings and debates between the physicians and Kaiser Industries that the physicians termed "The Tahoe Wars".[73] Although there are no truly accurate official records of what transpired at these meetings, Dr. Jack Hallat recorded a few of the proceedings on his crude "wire tape" recorder.[74] A number of options were discussed, all leading to one single

---

[71] Dr. Raymond Kay, personal communication, 1975.
[72] Smillie,J.G.,Can Physicians Manage the Quality and Cost of Healthcare?, McGraw-Hill Inc., 1991, p. 151.
[73] Kay, Raymond, personal communication 1975.
[74] Hallut, Jack, personal communication, 1975.

inevitable conclusion. As with most wars, the decisive battle was won or lost before it had begun. The foregone conclusion, an accord, was finally reached at the Kaiser "Fleur De Lac" estate on the north western shore of Lake Tahoe, from July 12 to July 15, then finalized on July 19 in 1955. (Ironically this very same compound served as the set for the infamous "Godfather" to hand out favors in the Hollywood production with the same name.) The accord was "a masterpiece of ideological ambiguity and political consensus"[75] Specific details of the contractual agreement were to be worked out at later date in the near future, with no specific set time-definite. Basically, a trade off of all future management and property rights granted the doctors a yearly negotiable and renewable exclusive contract to treat Kaiser-enrolled patients. The Southern California Permanente Medical Group (SCPMG) officially signed the yearly renewable exclusive "Medical Service Agreement" in June of 1956. Separately and apart, each Permanente physician group entity annually negotiated with Kaiser Foundation for their personalized "Medical Service Agreement". The Northern California organization, The Permanente Medical Group (TPMG), signed on March 27 of 1958. Each contract linked together three separate and newly-created entities:

1. The Kaiser Health Plan (a non-profit trust of Kaiser Foundation),
2. The Kaiser Hospital Foundation Hospitals (a charitable trust of Kaiser Foundation), and
3. Permanente Medical Groups (each having an exclusive geographical agreement to treat Kaiser Health Plan patients by means of annually contracted and globally funded physician general partnerships with no tangible physician group assets in place or to be accumulated).[76]

Now no longer a Physician Service Organization (PSO), this organized healthcare delivery system evolved the physician group into a rigid internal staff model, globally funded Physician Group Organization (PGO)[77] with the intellectual property of present and all future health plan management owned solely by Kaiser Industries. The various geographic medical group partnerships retained ownership of intellectual property consisting of patient care and internal physician group management systems. With land, real estate, business property, and all tangible equity interests now contractually signed over to and by written contract bound solely to the administration and/or control of Kaiser Foundation, Henry Kaiser appointed Dr. Sidney Garfield to the position of Medical Director in the ever-expanding newly certified Kaiser Foundation Health Plan (KFHP).

---

[75] Hendricks, Ricky, A Model for National Healthcare, Rutgers Univ. Press, New Jersey, 1993, p. 2
[76] Smillie J., Can Physicians Manage the Quality and Costs of Healthcare? The Story of SCPMG, McGraw-Hill, Inc, 1991, p.168
[77] HEALTHKEEPERS, Ralph J. DiLibero, MD, June 17, 2002, TXu 1-054-120

KFHP carefully orchestrated each individual geographic "Medical Service Agreement" structure for medical group funding. KFHP wisely chose to control the doctors through a globally funded group financial model, thus removing the corporation from frustrating involvement with internal disputes. A rigid self-governing administrative staff model within each physician group provided an effective managerial and direct hierarchal communication link to KFHP. With the combined entities, KFHP created a secure, top-down administrative and budgetary structure and also provided for "single signature contracting" with a geographical physician group leader on a yearly basis. The individual physician medical groups designated their own specific individual physician to sign each yearly cleverly scripted KFHP "Medical Service Agreement" contract on the KFHP provided dotted line after KFHP management had thoroughly discussed and set funding and growth goals for the year to come.

The internal staff model structure for the globally funded, physician group economic model flowed from an adaption of traditional academic-university top-down management plans. A board of MD directors (some appointed and some elected from the general partnership) elected a single MD regional medical director, much like a dean of a university. That regional medical director then assumed the potential power to collectively "bargain" yearly with KFHP for the "Medical Service Agreement" dollar amount, and then sign that yearly contract on behalf of all the partnered physicians within the specific geographic region. The regional MD medical director, functioning much like a dean, also appointed MD area medical directors, who in turn appointed MD medical department heads and MD medical division heads. As each region geographically expanded medical services to various areas within the region, the regional medical director would appoint additional geographic area medical directors, who would in turn make the local area MD appointments. Each MD department chairman chose the MD department physicians and the non-physician department staff. Department chairmen were directly responsible to their area medical director for administrative and budgetary concerns. The area medical directors were, in course, responsible to the regional medical director. They all agreed to work within a prescribed cost-effective area plus regional budget. An attitude of local budgetary control was thusly extended through to the entire medical staff. KFHP held the regional medical director directly accountable for the contracted efficient utilization of the global dollar expense. Medical decision making remained generally unhampered unless some medical practice autonomy conclusion found itself in direct conflict with the self-imposed budgetary restraints inherent in the globally funded rigid staff structure. Each physician practice area also independently elected non-administrative working physicians to serve on a regional board of directors along with their appointed area medical directors and other administrative physicians.

Meanwhile, a bit more insidiously inspired government engineering of cultural mores simultaneously transpired in Washington. **April 10, 1965 marked another medical ecolo-nomic watershed event. The federally legislated Mills bill, HR 6675, took on the name of Medicare.**[78] Indemnity insurance sales and fee-for-service billings took off like they were shot directly straight out from a cannon. Price controls did not exist, and it was painfully obvious that this unsustainable condition of rising prices and services could not exist for very long. All of Medicine, including organized healthcare delivery, would soon have the piper to pay for inflicting economist Milton Friedman's most sever order of moral hazard perception -- paying for a group of demanding other people with funding taken from some other unknown group of "other people" – enjoying unrestricted and un-rationed benefits derived from some "other peoples' Money".

Unlike underpaid or unpaid MD administrative duties in a traditional fee-for-service Medicine delivery system, financial incentives for MD administrative duties in the KFHP system proved to be doubly rewarding. Appointed administrative physicians received both extra salary and additional time off from their physically-demanding clinical productivity schedule to accomplish their administrative functions. These beneficial perks or adaptations for administrative duty recipients proved to be great incentives for encouraging physicians to actively seek such administrative appointments, which then encouraged those administrator MD's to further strengthen and unify their internal staff model hierarchy. Permanente physicians nibbled then bit into a 20th Century version of Plato's "Myth of the Metals". There was no escape from the baited KFHP hook, line or sinker. Delightfully satisfied and in response to the new business plan, by 1967 patient membership in the KFHP organized healthcare delivery system topped the one million mark.

The KFHP hospital division administrator chose and appointed the MD Chairman of the hospital executive medical staff (traditionally the area medical director that was designated by the medical group's regional medical director). This appointment, made by the local KFHP hospital division head included a proviso that he or she could, at will and at any time, unilaterally change the MD hospital staff Chairman--appointee. Although in direct violation of CMA's hospital

---

[78] Ralph DiLibero, MD; The Quality of Medicine, 978-0-9815969-4-5, 2008.

medical staff model by-laws, this written hospital administrator proviso remained locally suppressed and therefore never officially questioned by the Permanente physician partners or the CMA Institute for Medical Quality (IMQ) surveyor teams that certified California hospitals along with the Joint Commission on Accreditation of Hospitals and Outpatient Facilities (JCAHO). Perhaps simply looking the other way served convenience and avoided unwanted litigation. The local area doctors then elected local practicing MD's to the office of President, Vice President, and Secretary of the local hospital executive medical staff -- to serve under the appointed MD Chairman of the hospital medical staff and rubber stamp hospital administrative policies. A top-down from KFHP to practicing physician staff-administrative structure therefore reigned over both medical group activities and hospital staff activities.

Academia followed suit, and in the third medical ecolo-nomic generation (1990-2010), many university faculties negotiated a global group funding arrangement through a single chosen negotiator with HKOs. Thus, the KFHP concept of top-down administration with single signature contracting became independently re-validated for physicians outside of the Permanente Medical Groups forty years after KFHP's inception.

KFHP became the enemy of a practicing individual physician's hope for a lifetime of medical practice well into the aging beyond traditional retirement years and the savior of employment opportunity for a future young physician group. With Henry Kaiser's long term business plan, both the existing physician partners and future generations of physicians could be assured an organized healthcare delivery medical practice that could sustain them, but for a time-set limited lifetime of personal medical practice. Like professional athletes, the young and exuberant were chosen, but there was no oil depletion allowance for the maturing physician who wanted to practice less hours or slow down the prescribed number of patient to be seen per hour and in turn agree to a lowered salary per hour. Individual doctors continued to object to various aspects of the business plan, but any sustainable and competitively advantaged business plan would not appreciate a migratory economic allowance for natural changes in an individual doctor's life style or the physiological aspects of aging related to actual on-the-job work to be done per hour/day/week by a physician. The health plan, like any other of today's HKOs, was set for perpetuity and continuous high level productivity from the physicians; the organization was never envisioned to be physician-centric and die along with the inevitable apoptosis of any biological system. Coveted medical practice autonomy and gradual reduction in productivity with the increasing age of a physician were and are not so set and envisioned. The organized healthcare delivery plan held its functional orientation to the continued and uninterrupted sustenance of the many patients, not to the few physicians who temporarily provided medical services during the very most physically healthy, sprightly vivacious and productive period of their lifetimes. The classical revered image and deep paternal regard for "good old doctor so and so" were already shattering like fine crystal and soon both would be swept away, forgotten and gone forever.

In October of 1977, during a second-generation ecolo-nomic environment (1970-1990), KFHP changed very little, but took on the popular title of a Health Maintenance Organization (HMO) solely to increase market advantage, since all businesses with 25 or more employees were federally required to offer an HMO as one of their health insurance benefits. The species adaptation "HMO" was another uniquely carved temporal paradigm in the evolution of organized healthcare delivery. During the third overlapping medical ecolo-nomic generation (1990-2010), the Kaiser Foundation Health Plan further evolved and expanded its patient-business-government payer risk pool to become the largest group model HKO[79] in the United States with over 10,000 doctors and 90,000 employees nationally. Health insurance corporations encouraged buy-outs and mergers of the remaining HKOs to dynamically compete with the Kaiser giant. The events that made this all possible and predictably probable were the changing dynamic forces of cultural ecology and migratory economics – Man, Money and Medicine -- the ecolo-nomics[80] of doctor, patient, and third party -- during the 20th Century.

After 1955, Dr. Garfield's influence in California Permanente Medical Groups' physician affairs decreased to become virtually non-existent. In 1957, The Permanente Medical Group (TPMG) of Northern California elected Dr. Cecil Cutting to the position of Executive Director, and Dr. Raymond Kay had already signed the first Medical Service Agreement for the Southern California Medical Group (SCPMG). In 1958, Henry J. Kaiser appointed Dr. Sidney Garfield to the office of Executive Vice President of KFHP in charge of facilities and planning. Not long thereafter, Dr. Garfield and his dear irresistibly smiling close friend, Henry Kaiser ventured to Hawaii with plans to build a new Kaiser Health Plan and hospital in Honolulu and a Kaiser City -- Hawaii "Kai" -- on the windward side of Oahu. Other projects included a 1,146-room Hawaiian Village Hotel, a $13.5 Million cement plant, and radio/television broadcasting facilities. Industrialist Henry Kaiser died in 1967 at the age of 85; Dr. Keene remained as Edgar Kaiser's fiscal manager until 1975. Medical service contractor par excellence, Dr. Sidney

---

[79] Ralph J. DiLibero, MD, HEALTHKEEPERS, TXu 1-054-120, 2002.
[80] Ralph J. DiLibero, MD, MEDICAL ECONOMICS, TXu 981-118, 2001.

Garfield died on December 29, 1984, at the age of 78.

""I made two big mistakes," Garfield later admitted. "I turned over control of the Hospitals to the Board of Trustees (Kaiser Foundation) with complete faith that we (the doctors) would continue to run it in the way we wanted to. I turned over control of the (doctor) Partnership to the partners with complete faith that they would let me work with them and continue as I had been. I learned my lessons.""[81]

Disagreements, along with partner versus partner versus management crisis and clashes, were in no way unique to KFHP. There were ongoing conflicts between the "juniors" and "seniors" as to the future direction of the Ross-Loos Medical Clinic. Walter Halloran, a general surgeon and a few others were instrumental in the construction of the main RLMC clinic/hospital building, just east of Hollywood, California. This group of physicians partnered with William and Robert Powers in a joint venture and convinced the Los Angeles Department of Water and Power to issue construction bonds payable to their retirement fund. Ownership of the facility fed through a separate partnership whose individual interests mirrored the interest of the medical partnership. After just a few years, everyone involved admitted that this arrangement could not survive for a variety of reasons, mainly because of those financial inequities forced forward by an administrative leadership program that had been ignoring a steady decline in enrollment and more recent drop in the RLMC's payer pool base. A sale of the RLMC plan, RLMC group, and RLMC group assets to INA/CIGNA saved the integrity of the physician medical group and profited a great number of the senior partners.

PAMC was also having unique financial and management problems of its own. Further business strategies had to be developed in quick response to actions taken by the government and other organized healthcare delivery systems. A new medical ecolo-nomic adaptation serendipitously appeared as a road to salvation. The clinic rapidly responded to the new dynamics and chose to evolve along a newly adapted path rather than sell out like the RLMC. Still always striving to provide a surviving and sustainable upper echelon, risk payer pool niche point of service in the delivery system, the clinic contracted with a variety of Health Maintenance Organizations (HMOs) in the second overlapping medical ecolo-nomic generation of organized healthcare delivery (1970-1990). Interacting in

---

[81] Smillie J., Can Physicians Manage the Quality and Costs of Healthcare? The Story of SCPMG, McGraw-Hill, Inc, 1991, p. 157

this new medical ecolo-nomic environment, competitive influences pressured an even newer vision to provide for future PAMC survival and continued care to a middle class community in a changing cost-containment migratory economic medical marketplace. PAMC physicians came to a group consensus that would adapt the clinic for evolutionary change -- a desire to innovate and merge. Furthermore, senior PAMC physicians possessed absolutely no desire to sell and retire their organization, as was the case with the Ross-Loos physicians. Therefore, survival dictated that the Palo Alto clinic, institute, and division had to be brought under one non-profit economic umbrella. That migratory medical ecolo-nomic adaptation became sustainably essential for species survival, and the fabric of this new structure looked and felt remarkably similar to that exact fabric previously woven by KFHP. A magically invisible hand of balancing migratory economics again wove that same common chameleon colored thread. Economist Adam Smith's invisible hand wove again and wove well:

In 1981, a newly evolved Palo Alto Medical Foundation (PAMF), a non-profit foundation, began to receive funding from the land, buildings, and equipment being sold by the PAMC medical partnership. In 1987, before the end of the third ecolo-nomic generation, all those tangible assets were purchased by PAMF. The nonprofit umbrella organization (PAMF) oversaw 150 physicians, an independent research institute, and a health education division. Patients enrolled directly with the foundation. The foundation contractually granted exclusive rights for organized healthcare delivery to the medical group. PAMF formulated a common governance mechanism through a community board of directors. Again adapting to the dynamics of changing migratory medical ecolo-nomics, in 1989, 35% of PAMF's patients were associated with Managed Care, and PAMF officially became an HMO.[82]

Dr. Weinerman may have been one of the first to express his objections to a deaf-eared healthcare administration, but he certainly was not the last to be never heard. In the final analysis, business plans for organized healthcare delivery systems were really the property of businesses, and physicians were only relatively short-termed tenants whose personal interests were bought and sold along with the property. Nonetheless, the undisputed ultimate benefactor became the average blue collar working patient, the common Man.

The Permanente Medical Group (TPMG) in the "Northern California Region" incorporated in 1982, while the "Southern California Region" Southern California

---

[82] www.PAMF.org, "the Sutter Connection"

Permanente Medical Group (SCPMG) remained a general partnership. Neither group retained any tangible assets. Each group had separately traded any perceived tangible business or real estate assets for the exclusive right to treat the Kaiser Foundation Health Plan (KFHP) patients by the terms of the previously described annualized Medical Service Agreement. The accord drama between the physicians and KFHP played out as a tricky performance by master magicians whose sleight of hand prestidigitation mesmerized the physicians. This strategically planned business plan, however, stood the strength of time and proved fiscally sound, extensively studied, and rigidly standardized throughout the United States as a lucrative and sustainable mechanism for quality organized healthcare delivery for the average American worker. KFHP and the PMGs together truly discovered or more likely fell upon this truly magical formula.

During the second overlapping generation of ecolo-nomic change in organized healthcare delivery (1970-1990), the Ross-Loos Medical Clinic recognized a patient-customer need for healthcare services at multiple geographic locations throughout California. May of 1972 was the penultimate point for group morale at the RLMC. With the same golden spade that went to the moon, Los Angeles Mayor Sam Yorty led a groundbreaking ceremony, celebrating the construction of a contiguous hospital and clinic. With construction finally completed, the edifice opened for business in 1974. Growth was essential to prevent business loss and eventual shut down. When, in the early seventies, RLMC first applied to become a HMO, many partners objected to that new trend or direction in migratory medical ecolo-nomics, therefore the actual application was first withdrawn and then resubmitted along with an application for a second pre-pay (PPO-like) license. The second license permitted RLMC pre-pay organized healthcare delivery to operate at a reduced cost, with a decreased benefit package. The second license also enabled the Ross-Loos doctors to continue seeing patients who could not or did not want to qualify for the HMO plan. After a year's delay, the federal government granted both licenses. This was unique for the RLMC; no other pre-payment organized healthcare delivery organization ever possessed two separate licenses. The RLMC partnership was also able to hold onto their private practice sub-culture during the first part of the Managed Care era, but that "un-chameleon-like" attitude would unfortunately prove to be a future stumbling block.

As a consequence of their physician-culture-related organizational structure, the Ross-Loos partners finally sold their medical group in that aforesaid horizontal merger during the second overlapping generation of medical ecolo-nomic change in organized healthcare delivery (1970-1990). The time had come for the older partner physicians, the overwhelming controlling shareholders in the Ross-Loos

Medical Clinic, to retire. Accordingly, the older physicians also retired their medical group. Because of the uneven manner in which equity shares were divided among the partners and the lack of a vitally necessary physician group retention fund or cash reserve, both finding a buyer and negotiating a sales contract became problematic. This unfortunate situation reflected something similar to but not exactly like the dilemma that faced the cash-poor Permanente Medical Group in 1950. Lending institutions were not anxious to finance a business expansion because there were no common assets -- each partner had a different sized personal piece of the pie and there were no extra pieces. Therefore, the Ross-Loos organized healthcare delivery system hired an outside manager to procure a buyer.

Dr. Joseph Macarelli and Dr. Cliff Harris consolidated a medical group practice in Phoenix Arizona that was then sold to the Insurance Company of North America (INA). The head office moved to Dallas, Texas, and Dr. Macarelli became the CEO of INA (and later the combined "CIGNA"). INA developed a niche Medi-Cal (Medicaid) practice to serve the Los Angeles area, and then searched for a merger to horizontally expand the INA organized healthcare delivery system. Visionary realignment demanded diversification in their payer risk pool. On March 10, 1980, INA purchased the Ross-Loos Medical Clinic for $33 Million.

Mergers were absolutely necessary for dynamic competitive business strategies, but mergers were quite uncomfortable for the doctors. A physician to physician culture clash in financial reimbursement, medical practice autonomy, medical practice style, and doctor-patient care philosophies accompanied the INA/RLMC merger. The former Ross-Loos physicians abhorred the work-harder efficiency and the ecolo-nomic culture of a Medicaid-oriented organized healthcare delivery system. In addition to their lump sum takeover payment, INA granted the Ross-Loos partners a contractual ten-year extended tax deferred salary pay off. Therefore, INA initially paid former Ross-Loos partners at a higher rate than the original INA doctors. INA paid the non-partner Ross-Loos physicians at the lower INA rate to keep the transition running smoothly, but those formerly non-partnered physicians still benefited with more vacation time allotted than the original INA doctors. The original INA doctors were quite obviously resentful. An on-going conflict came to a head on "black Friday", Friday November 13, 1981. Several non-partner Ross-Loos physicians found themselves suddenly fired in a business realignment to downsize and maintain group harmony. The next day, a new medical director took over the leadership of INA.

Three years later, in April of 1983, further horizontal expansion resulted in an

INA merger with a former fire and property insurance company that had just recently entered into the healthcare delivery marketplace -- Connecticut General Insurance (CGI). This combined new entity juggled and shuffled the old names about to spell out a new acronym -- CIGNA.

Benefits in the original RLMC partnership agreement which CIGNA had to contractually remain maintained proved to be a continuing sore point with other non-RLMC CIGNA contracted physicians because of the contractually agreed periods of paid time off and paid sabbaticals. The new administration led a concerted effort to get those former Ross-Loos physicians to pursue retirement or transfer to another form of practice. The Ross-Loos concept for organized healthcare delivery had proved to be vital and viable in a past medical ecolo-nomic era, but the essential needed adaptation to an evolving new migratory medical ecolo-nomic environment did not take place. When that Ross-Loos chameleon threaded vision failed to adapt and change its colors, the non-adapting species rapidly became extinct. Accordingly, as the older physicians retired, the heart and spirit of the Ross-Loos Medical Clinic also retired.

Government-engineered cultural migratory medical ecolo-nomic evolution struck again. Twenty years after the passage of free-for-all Medicare entitlements, the equalization era piper demanded immediate payment. The accumulated debt challenged the continued sustainability of the Medicare program. In the Ronald Reagan Administration, a specified currency for capping repayment took the form of price-fixed **DRG (Diagnostic Related Group) payments, a migratory medical ecolo-nomic watershed for Healthcare Reform driven by the painful reality of economic cost factors. Man, Money and Medicine.....**

Therefore, in the third overlapping medical ecolo-nomic generation of organized healthcare delivery (1990-2010), PAMF reexamined and redirected its vision. The healthcare marketplace was always dynamic and complex. Big fish ate small fish in big ponds. Too many large and hungry HKOs with big mouths, sharp teeth, and insatiable appetites continually swam by and snapped to gulp small healthcare delivery organizations. Public policy ignored technology changes as they both continually ran afoot on a path with no defined destination. PAMF had to avoid entering into a twilight zone of: "High end Hell – a prisoner in its own gold-plated niche"[83] risk payer pool. The migratory economic **Healthcare Reform** survival game played on, move after move, like an animated chess match.

---

[83] Day G.S., Riebstein,D.L., Gunther,R.E., Wharton on Dynamic Competitive Strategy, John Wiley & Sons, Inc., New York, 1997, p. 6

PAMF put principles of dynamic competitive strategies into place and reevaluated the ecology of the organized healthcare delivery marketplace. PAMF re-reviewed contemplated action plans, arranged in perspective, from the eyes of the competition, to determine chances for success. PAMF also added into the calculations possible successful counter-plans that could be initiated by the competition. After a variety of strategic further moves were contemplated, PAMF accomplished a long-term analysis of the evolving migratory economic dynamic. All of this was done under the stress of time restraints, as the "next move timer" aside a migratory medical ecolo-nomic chess board clicked away, nearing ever-closer to the sounding of its bell in a dire championship migratory medical ecolo-nomic chess match for sustaining ultimate survival.

PAMF concluded that a successful future survival depended on alignment of its incentives with a much larger and ecolo-nomically broader-based organization in order to promote growth and efficiency in contracting with major payers. PAMF's protected niche payer pool had to be expanded to a broader risk payer pool. PAMF took that chameleon-colored thread of evolutionary medical ecolo-nomic survival and success, placed it into Adam Smith's invisible migratory economic hand, and then searched for a securing stitch to link to that ultimately sustainable broader base. PAMF sought out an outpatient-based, not-for-profit Health Keeper Organization (HKO). Sacramento based Sutter Health, which started as a small hospital service plan, had matured to a sizeable vertically integrating and growing HKO. Sutter serendipitously and simultaneously sought avenues for expansion into the San Francisco south bay area, and an affiliation with PAMF proved to be a perfect life-long match.

PAMF sold its intellectual property, governance, and oversight powers to Sutter Health for $50 Million. The Money immediately went to develop clinics adjacent to the San Francisco Bay peninsula, in the south bay area, and help finance campus development for PAMF. This merger looked to be typical of the megabuck financing maneuvers for control of organized healthcare delivery that took place in the third medical ecolo-nomic generation (1990-2010). The small ecolo-nomic niche risk payer pool Palo Alto Medical Group practice that once flourished no longer could stand alone, unprotected and unsupported in the highly evolved third generation equation of migratory medical ecolo-nomics. PAMF also became a not-for-profit umbrella for Sutter to expand by merging with the Santa Cruz Medical Clinic. Continuing to increase horizontal integration in the second half of the third generation, after Sutter Health became affiliated with PAMF in 1993, Sutter merged with California Healthcare System (CHS) in 1996.

Stanford University Medical Clinic's contracted IPAs operated in the red during 2001. University physicians cancelled the IPA contracts with many HKOs, including Aetna U.S. Healthcare. PAMF arose to the occasion and absorbed those patients from Aetna, but with much different critically evolved organized healthcare delivery contracts. That chameleon silent threaded hand, the secret of PAMF's success, wove another vital stitch; and in 2008, the non-profit Palo Alto Medical Foundation for Health Care, Research, and Education, an organized healthcare delivery system, merged three groups to form a single medical group. The Camino Medical Group (CMG), Palo Alto Medical Clinic (PAMC), and the Santa Cruz Medical Clinic (SCMC) became PAMF's Camino Division, Palo Alto Division, and Santa Cruz Division. Before 2010, the merged physician group employed over 900 physicians and served more than 600,000 patients, while an additional funded project forged ahead to utilize a unified electronic medical record (EMR) for all the divisions.

By the end of the third overlapping migratory medical ecolo-nomic generation in organized healthcare delivery (1990-2010), the chameleon colors of PAMF looked a lot like the chameleon colors of Kaiser Foundation Health Plan (KFHP) and vice versa. That common thread fostered a common political action group. The two health plans politically aligned themselves by forming the California Medical Group Association (CMGA) for the purpose of California state legislative advocacy in Sacramento. Both plans wanted to preserve their de facto exemption from Knox-Keene legislation that the CMA's AB-1600 was seeking to disrupt.[84] Both lobbied against "national catastrophic healthcare delivery" as well as "consumer directed healthcare". Both were protecting the exact same risk payer pool in different and sometimes shared geographical locations. Seemingly quite divergent paths had come together and bonded as former dynamically competing HKO combatants now temporarily allied in a common foxhole to wade off common political enemies. Both organized healthcare delivery systems also found themselves once again perfumed with that sweet, sweet smell of success.

To assure the continuance of those success stories, the organizations sought to dominate a 21st Century healthkeeper environment, with a constant alertness and awareness that patient-healthkeepers likewise continued to ecologically evolve up to an elevated position and enjoy greater political and medical ecolo-nomic clout; that clout would demand further adaptations on behalf of the medical groups. (Evolution never stops.)

---

[84] HEALTHKEEPERS, Ralph J. DiLibero, MD, TXu 1-054-120, 2002.

A philosophical Dodgers baseball double play in organized healthcare delivery medical ecolo-nomics might have been touted or announced over live media as: "From Plato to Hegel to Marx." Social gradations, an acknowledged prerequisite for any civilization, were an essential part of the Kaiser business plan in organizing the doctor groups and the doctors within the groups. Progressive socialism sold as a group ideal. Administrative physician spin condemned capitalistic intent among the doctors. Group administrators spun capitalistic intent as a stigma, a lacking in dedication for patient care, all preached from a "holier than thou" administrative pulpit. The physician administration carefully hid their personal clandestine capitalistic intent behind a broad open "progressive" liberal front. However, when KFHP's administration unilaterally reorganized a structure for negotiating with the two regional medical groups in California by declaring that the two physician groups were in fact only one entity, the Permanente administrative physicians could not accept the obvious intended consequences that would have deprived them of their appointed administrative hierarchies. If each physician group was to maintain any portion of their individual business autonomy and keep their prized administrative business positions intact, KFHP corporate capitalistic firepower had to be fought by a defensive show of strength; and that demanded a significant return of capitalistic firepower. This new battle did not involve docs vs. businesses; the new war saw business vs. business. History proved that particular KFHP administrative "reorganization" decision of 1997 to be an ill-advised and an unnecessary rub sorely lacking in well planned anticipatory dynamic competitive counter strategy from one administrative body to another administrative body. KFHP had failed to do a SWOT analysis to gain a better grasp of their competitor's current business as well as anticipated business behavior and intentions:

In a calculated business response, the exciting migratory economics of **Healthcare Reform** took another twist. During the third overlapping generation of organized healthcare delivery, Permanente administrative physicians created two physician-owned offshoots -- a Permanente Federation to centrally organize the various Permanente medical groups throughout the USA and a for-profit Permanente Company for accumulating financial assets. Finally, a half century long overdue workable migratory economic "reserve fund" or "retention fund" through a group venture capital investment in medically-related enterprises became a reality. The practicing doctors in the various regional medical groups ratified and contributed cash assets to these administrative and equity-building business entities. The basic idea intended to show Kaiser Foundation Health Plan (KFHP) that Permanente physicians could (alas and finally) become independent, collectively organize throughout the United States and possibly create a competing autonomous health insurance plan by building an equity property power base through their venture capital investments. (Thus creating a reserve fund to provide the Permanente physician partnerships with a positive equity position, an equity position sorely lacking in 1955, when the medical partnership suddenly found itself unable to "call" Henry Kaiser's infamous strategic bluff and buy the whole kit and caboodle for $14 Million.) This probably perceived and/or possibly real Kaiser trustee-calculated future Permanente Medical Group autonomy threat resulting from that future equity accrual, significantly aided the Permanente doctor administrators in their very next Medical Service Agreement negotiation with Kaiser Foundation Health Plan. Needless to say, KFHP quickly and quietly retracted the proposed plan to unite the two medical groups in California as one single entity.

To wit, the Permanente Company provided tangible assets for all Permanente physicians, distributed back to individual physicians as cash value of shares at the time of retirement from the partnership. The Permanente Foundation organized a national partnership agreement that was signed between Kaiser Foundation Health Plan and twelve (later to be eight) regional Permanente Medical Groups throughout the United States. KFHP restored the separate medical service agreements as well as independent regional status to each of the two California groups. The Permanente Company evolved and softened its response to the rub of 1997. In May of 2001, SCPMG's Medical Director's Bulletin Board newsletter stated, "Perm Co was set up not only for venture developments, but also for consulting with other regions on Kaiser Permanente expansion efforts. Frankly, there is little need for the latter at this time." In addition to the economic vertical layering, the doctor-owned intellectual property of patient care delivery systems also sought horizontal expansion to include population management, quality control, and hopefully electronic medical record management systems.

However, when electronic medical records (EMR) were finally implemented, KFHP clearly made the system and all future EMR development solely their intellectual property. In a contractual agreement with EPIC EMR systems, KFHP stipulated that modifications to the EPIC EMR system that was originally purchased by KFHP could not be marketed by EPIC to any other customer. In addition, KFHP required each and every physician to sign a confidentially agreement which stated, "With respect to medical information, I will only access or use such information as it is necessary to provide medical care to the member …. I know that confidential information that I learn on the job does not belong to me and that Kaiser Permanente may take away my access to confidential information at any time".[85] Some, at first, refused to sign, but they were few and insignificant to the big picture.

The HKOs (Health Keeper Organizations) were the organized healthcare delivery systems of the third medical ecolo-nomic generation. HKOs contracted with physician groups and/or hospitals through various organized care modules as previously described. The HKO health plans owned or had exclusive contracts with some of the hospitals and medical groups and were loosely affiliated with others. The medical groups under HKO ownership or direct control fared better financially for three basic reasons:

1. They were generally larger and could better spread the debt, especially from risk pools. Simple mathematics would have readily proved to physicians that it was near to impossible to be able to break the bank at Monte Carlo with a two-dollar stake, but that same reasoning process carried over to risk pools was, unfortunately, not understood by so many uninformed private practice physicians who joined several soon-to-fail smaller groups.
2. The mandated administrative tasks (continuing quality improvement, credentialing, and hospital risk integration) were generally not pushed onto the exclusively contracted medical groups.
3. (Also often a just cause for lawsuits which stung the HKOs), some HKO plans conspired to save costs by preferentially shifting referral and primary care benefits of enrollees (patients) to contracting systems (IPAs) or medical groups under the HKOs direct control or ownership, thus contributing to bankruptcies in competing entities.[86]

Despite the fact that some were actually more efficient and cost-effective, small HKOs quickly realized an economic reality; they had to price their product at the equivalent level of a large HKO to prevent the larger enterprise with enormous financial reserves from entering into a price reduction competition that would eventually bankrupt the smaller HKO.

As a major component in the American "pursuit of happiness", equality in pursuit of access to healthcare delivery might finally be considered essential. The inalienable right to pursue intelligent health choices for personal happiness is the constitutional right to do rather than the egalitarian entitlement right to get. Evolved mores dictated social and economic standing not to supersede an

---

[85] KFHP: OBLIGATIONS REGARDING CONFIDENTIALITY, version 120401
[86] East County Physicians Medical Group Inc. vs. Aetna Life and Casualty Insurance Co.; 4th district court of appeal; San Diego, Ca.; 4/2000

entitlement right to basic healthcare delivery. The entitlement right to healthcare delivery evolved and became engrained as a basic cultural and ecologic medical economic, an "ecolo-nomic" in the United States. It was, therefore, quite natural to expect KFHP with the Permanente medical groups, the ultimate organized healthcare delivery system, to be fundamentally socialistic. However, capitalistic enterprise within such a system, such as the Permanente Foundation, gave rise to fundamental questions of political idealism and once again echoed Henry Kaiser's words ("to stop the socialization of Medicine in its tracts") that were spoken in 1953 at the opening of the Sunset Hospital.[87] The new organized healthcare delivery system in the USA would shortly, and of course temporarily, become a government-sanctioned capitalistic corporate insurance industry organized healthcare delivery monopoly. Evolution then would eventually see these economic monopolies versus a socialized federal government organized healthcare delivery system in the heat of battle for ultimate survival – the finite battle of the Titans versus the gods.

In order to satisfy the fundamental sustainable prime directive need for species survival, all types and models of surviving health care entities took four basic ecolo-nomic forward steps:

1. Reduce fragmentation; establish a delivery system; consolidate and downsize.
2. Realign payment systems.
3. Restructure; reduce health benefits.
4. Inject market discipline; increase productivity.

Downsizing for HKO health plans meant firing middle management and anyone else whose position could not be clearly identified with the continued sustainable production of capital. For hospitals, downsizing meant firing nurses and closing down hospital wings and floors that did not show full occupancy rates. For physician groups and practices, downsizing meant firing or not hiring new physician staff whose work could be done by a cheaper ready-to-train employee or physician assistant. In general, downsizing meant cutting away the fat along with a substantial portion of the juicy red lean.

Realigning payment systems demanded some deeper introspection during an era when the paradigm doctrine of comparative effectiveness ratings for remaining patient life years was not yet socially acceptable. Being that the best defense was

---

[87] Smillie J., Can Physicians Manage the Quality and Costs of Healthcare? The Story of SCPMG, McGraw-Hill, Inc, 1991, p. 76

and is both a good offense and a dynamic awareness of the competition, there were some general measures that each physician had to consider when overviewing the financial structure of a healthkeeper business practice. Unlike accident insurance or catastrophic insurance, health insurance (alias healthcare delivery bill payment insurance or wealth insurance) became to be culturally understood as a misnomer – the yearly insurance premium amounted to really only a small partial payment schedule for a life-long healthcare delivery maintenance policy. Physicians learned the hard way to understand risks before signing contracts and not to depend on cash risk reserves as part of their contract assets – those cash risk reserves and contingencies eventually got set up independently. A plan and vision in a dynamic changing migratory medical ecolonomic market redefined the needs of management for the healthkeeper delivery business. Realignment included structuring new management that was skilled in rapidly unfreezing while quickly adapting to dynamically changing healthkeeper market strategies. Fewer dollars had to travel further for sustainability. A Darwinian survival of the fittest – an adapt-or-die Herbert Spencer economic fundamental -- predominated in evaluating healthkeeper business philosophies and documented "best-practice" scenarios.

A fundamental goal of restructuring is to put advancing technology in place to actually reduce cost -- a previously (apparently) never before conceived concept. When added to a fixed financial allocation agenda, the politically correct terminology spoke of "Optimal Care". End result studies, outcomes, were used to restructure patient care along set and cheaper clinical pathways that yet gave an "acceptable" percentage of good results. Many costly testing procedures could be and were eliminated without significantly affecting that type of outcome study. Decreasing hospital length of stay became a top priority. Non-reimbursed hospital care reverted to the home environment expenditures with the help of social services, friends, and family. Health plans restructured (down-coded) physician reimbursement fees, requiring physicians to both increase their productivity per hour and increase the total number of hours worked in order to maintain the same level of income. Was that philosophical epiphany really working politically "smarter", or was there an unintended consequence of such a new work ethic? Would an immediate and albeit limited number of physician producers fall into a consequential limiting of further years of their productive life expectancy on the supply side of the economic balance because of their "smart work" fostered early "burn out" accidently overlooked, blatantly refused to be considered or ignominiously inspired in "working smarter"? Taking the restructuring concept into hand and not considering future dynamic competitive agenda, physicians themselves promoted the development of cheaper nurse specialists, psychologists, therapists, and physician assistants to do tasks and take on the responsibilities of higher paid physicians. Physicians also championed cheaper-still licensed vocational nurses, clinic assistants, medical technicians, and therapeutic assistants to perform the tasks of their higher paid upper echelon certified "physician extender" counterparts. An ill-defined increased patient satisfaction concept, fostered by a strange but consistent habitual phenomenon that limited patient expectations, became the primary goal for a more "productive" medical practice. The uncomfortable and seemingly moralistic bottom line boldly stated that if the healthkeeper business failed as a sustainable and profitable business economic commodity, then any and all idealized altruistic physician goals to treat a medically needy patient for pain, disease, and suffering relief would never be accomplished, not at all. So they all had to bite the bullet really hard and long or else – or else the bottom-line would fall apart and the entire business of medical care would come crashing to the ground.

In addition to lowering patient expectations, another process of engineered change in cultural mores utilized a well-described dynamic to increase plan profit by hopefully limiting utilization: A physician with a self-suspected malady historically sought out the advice of another physician only as a last resort. A doctor who treated himself was universally said to have "a fool for a patient". Nevertheless, self-treatment was and is basic to the nature of medical knowledge. That knowledge and means to medically treat drove or were responsible for what made physicians treat themselves. Corporate ingenuity plotted to capitalize upon replication of that precise behavioral pattern. Extensively informed patients would first battle within themselves regarding treatment for a personal disease state. Then those informed patients would utilize services that were convenient, respected and non-judgmental, such as family, friends, self-help groups, and Internet services. Next, such now newly defined "patient-healthkeepers" would seek out possible alternative medical treatments that were benign and non-invasive. Only after all the aforementioned actions were thought to be ineffectual, be it by failure after trial and error or misaligned intellectual judgment, would the medically knowledgeable patients -- the patient-healthkeepers -- finally seek out the advice of a physician. No media article ever suggested or even hinted that patient-healthkeepers who were naturally driven to treat themselves also had fools for patients. What had been proven disastrous for doctor goose now apparently became not only OK, but also accepted and encouraged for patient-healthkeeper gander. At last, the traditional and expensive dependence on physicians could be dramatically reduced, and an overly labor-intense, physician-oriented and physician-centric industry could be relieved of dependency upon a single significant ecolo-nomic "burden" -- the physician. Automation of the **Healthcare**

184

Reform commodity would naturally follow.

The popular politically correct phrase for increasing professional staff productivity became working smarter, but, in fact, really meant working harder. Physicians were actually working both harder and longer. Working an increased number of hours per day and processing more patients per hour became the new gold standard for doctor-patient encounters. The level of stress upon physicians obviously increased and those physicians who could not take the heat of the HKO kitchen either needed to retire, work as a non-benefit employee in a large physician group on a part-time basis, move into medical administration, or transfer/transform their career into a totally different type of employment or entrepreneurial endeavor. The traditional deep desire to persist and practice Medicine drove the overwhelming majority of remaining physicians to accept increased stress, repress anxiety, and adjust their lifestyles to be compatible with (accordingly or unfortunately depending on one's political bent) progressively lowered overall income per increased productive hour worked. Without this discipline, the LD-50 for sustainable physician economic survival time in the newly evolved healthkeeper ecolo-nomic market projected to be critically short-lived.

Some standardized statistics concerning the aforementioned advice stated as, "injecting market discipline and increasing productivity":
Primary care physicians increased their productivity by 11.6%, which only increased their compensation by 3.4%.[88] The net increase after taxes seldom met the increase in business expenses or the pay per hour when working more hours. That increase in physician productivity was not by choice, increased productivity suddenly became essential just to stay economically alive in business. Most physicians were more than unhappy with the newly-mandated and essentially enforced arrangements. Southern California Permanente physicians voted down the automatic unopposed reappointment of their medical director in 2008 and forced a run off to keep that medical director in place. After being painfully and thoroughly educated to and then grudgingly accepting the ecolo-nomic realities of the day, they, the exact same partnered-physician body then re-elected their same medical director by an 80% majority vote. Reality stings. Those vibrant young physicians in active medical practice accepted their sentence like repenting for the sins of Sisyphus because they had nowhere else to go, nowhere to run for fiscal forgiveness. Of 2,300 physicians responding to a CMA survey in 2001, 1,513 or

---

[88] "American Medical News", November, 2000, p. 13.

66% were not advising their children to choose Medicine as a career.[89]

So the word went out and action plans spontaneously set themselves into perpetual motion. The health plan, hospital, group, and individual practice responses varied -- some were able to accommodate and others were not. Approximately 130 medical groups declared bankruptcy, and 2000 physicians ceased medical practice in the state of California during the three years prior to Y2K. That Darwinian selection prevailed once again. Those who were able to adapt survived and then helped to hasten the extinction by the culling of those unfortunately unable to adapt. That new destined healthkeeper corporation species for the third medical ecolo-nomic generation of overlapping change, the Health Keeper Organization (HKO), emerged, like an insect nymph, up to the river surfaces in the evolving organized healthcare delivery waters. These HKOs basked a tiny bit to grow their new-formed wings in the sun, and quickly flew off in a swirling spawn to rapidly compete, merge, and aggressively mate in a still ever-evolving medical ecolo-nomic environment.

After Y2K, KFHP had both secured oligopolistic marketplace permanence and optimized physician behavior dynamics. Their ducks were placed all in perfect order. The time was ripe to initiate bold new dynamic competitive advantage strategic sales and marketing moves. For all the HKO's -- Déjà vu Tombstone Arizona -- the competitive business mood brought about an anxiety similar to the nervousness which prevailed prior to the gunfight at the OK corral. The time was ripe to sort out and determine which would be the last big-gun HKO standing or more realistically, the last few of big-gun HKOs still standing.

Competing HKOs primarily developed by organizing physicians from former fee-for-service practices. Control and regimentation of financially abusive patient practices and at-risk physician economic reimbursement were both served by a system of patient co-payments. The traditional KFHP no co-pay dynamics evolved out of line with significant new HKO patient co-payment systems. Moreover, an absolute rejection of co-payments, an essential pawn played and maneuvered so well and effectively by KFHP in previous American medical ecolo-nomic paradigms, no longer stood its ground to remain as an economically feasible bait and switch tactic. By Y2K KFHP sacrificed that former old pawn in anticipation of a future co-pay checkmate. Long term dynamic competitive strategy moves became clearer and competitive healthcare delivery market advantage grew stronger. In the second half of the third medical ecolo-nomic

---

[89] "California Physician", CMA, Summer 2001.

generation (1990-2010), the KFHP chessboard queen let down her veil. KFHP's new marketing dynamic was not just to get in line with other HKOs or to get on any other HKO bandwagon. A new competitive advantage propelled KFHP to the very front of the co-payment parade. Those new dollars realized from significant co-payments quite effectively cost-shifted previous KFHP expenses directly into and onto the pocketbooks of pre-pay patients. Co-payments became required for hospital admissions, emergency room care, maternity and delivery services, physician clinic visits, and prescription drugs. An additional yearly expenditure cap, once exceeded, placed the full burden of prescription drug cost onto the enrolled pre-pay patient. A formerly "free" Senior Advantage Medicare plan also suddenly required a monthly patient co-payment.

Marketplace confidence made these cost-shifts economically feasible and certainly possible. KFHP achieved two goals concurrently: First, double digit increases in health plan dues remained in a dynamically competitive range as bottom line profits increased. And second, cost-shifting reversed previous adverse patient selection and migration; KFHP no longer suffered the economic burden from adversely attracting patient enrollees who were high users and/or abusers of "free" drugs and services. After an effective habituating "re-education" of the existing patient enrollee population, KFHP demonstrated that their health plan enrolled members were in no rush to disenrollment over the co-pay issue. Their existing enrollees really had no better economical place to go or invest their healthcare dollar. Evolving migratory medical ecolo-nomics protected that new and very precious high and moderate demand payer risk pool. Once again, KFHP prepared to place itself in an acquisition mode; excitement abounded; further expansion seemed inevitable.

What worked well, really had worked well for KFHP -- In the year 2000, the California division of Kaiser Foundation Health Plan (then a powerful third medical ecolo-nomic generation (1990-2010) Health Keeper Organization – HKO) revealed a capital-spending budget of over ten billion dollars. And worked the best -- "Consumer Reports" rated the Southern California organized healthcare delivery region (a $2.3 billion budget in 2002 with SCPMG) the #3 HMO in the nation. At the end of 1996, the national program boasted 13 with a "B" -- that is $13,241,000,000 in total revenues.

However, that same medical ecolo-nomic evolution of co-pays next placed the KFHP slight and no demand payer risk pool in jeopardy. In 1998, KFHP CEO Dr. David Lawrence, posted the organized healthcare delivery plan's first major paper loss at $270 Million of $14.5 Billion total revenues. It was determined that most of the losses were attributable to reimbursements to "Non Kaiser" hospitals and physicians for Kaiser–enrolled patients treated "out of network". An Emergency Patient Repatriation Program (EPRP) to immediately transfer patients back to Kaiser hospital facilities after those patients were either seen in out of network emergency situations or treated at non-Kaiser facilities quickly reversed this loss. Competing HKOs next championed a dynamic advantage of their own to induce consumer cherry-picking among the low and no demand risk groups. As a result of this smoking gun, KFHP again lost a small battle in the overall HKO war and posted a second paper loss, $300 Million in 1999, mainly due to the abandonment of the Texas KFHP organization and trouble with enrollee growth in the Carolinas. Funds that were loaned to Texas KFHP from the two California KFHP groups' profits were never repaid. Independent catastrophic medical insurance policies and a possible national catastrophic medical insurance financed by the government were like the great elephants in Hannibal's army, set in place to conquer the imperial KFHP empire. KFHP could have offered its own catastrophic coverage, but such an optional coverage benefit might have risked the possibility of existing full coverage healthy enrolled patients switching to that cheaper plan option, a cost-shifting that would have future dire consequences for KFHP. Concomitantly, at both of the mighty empire's flanks, employers were limiting their total dollars paid for healthcare delivery and therefore indirectly encouraging healthy employees to pick and choose a catastrophic coverage plan. Was the KFHP defense of their payer risk pool market share by means of increasing co-pays enough, or would KFHP have to introduce additional secret dynamic competitive strategies? Was that army of catastrophic healthcare delivery elephants to be victorious or conquered by a carefully controlled pack of imperial Roman "Canis Pugnax" war dogs, KFHP's evolved and modern "Cane Corso" HKO war dogs, armed with dynamic competitive advantages consisting of report cards boasting high grades in selected, cost-effective, and evidenced-based outcome and patient satisfaction statistics, report cards that would bite off the toes, weaken the knees, then hopelessly collapse those would-be grandiose catastrophic medical insurance elephants to the ground?

As always, moving right along, KFHP re-evaluated (PDSA Plan Do Study Act per W. Edwards Deming) and made adjustments to their strategic plan by re-examining the migratory healthcare delivery market and competitive environment. KFHP then hired from Blue Cross of Ohio a new CEO, George Halverson. Looking at their current and potential penetration, Halverson assessed the HKO market in terms of where new physician groups could be developed and serve large potential risk pool groups such as senior advantage and large industrial complexes. Acquisition of large existing physician groups into the Permanente culture was weighed against a slower and more expensive building from small groups that would be easier to self-adapt and then assimilate. Buying out the bigger groups proved to be faster, more efficient and a winning strategy in the long run.

Major national competitors, namely United, Aetna, CIGNA, WellPoint, and Anthem were assessed by SWOT (Strengths, Weaknesses, Opportunities, and Threats) analysis as well as in terms of membership, operating margin, and performance to improve margin expansion. The most successful competitors seemed to be those focused on delivering an efficient and migratory innovative menu of health insurance options, supported by competitive physician contracts and with less focus on care management mechanisms (only for a short while). Dynamic migratory economic competitive advantage rested with increased size and strength of reserve revenues that would allow investing in enhancing enrolled member and administrative services such as internet capabilities and electronic medical billing records. Competitor HKO approaches to risk segmentation, deductibles, and coinsurance continually threatened KFHP's risk pool revenue flow. Upcoming mega-mergers were also feared to decrease competition and raise prices. The race for the golden ring of power and control was definitely on and running with the expectation that in the end there might be only one mega insurer fiscally fit to remain standing.

By utilizing a temporary migratory economic, the cutting of benefits, competitor HKO healthcare insurers were able to cut premiums to the point where their cost savings outweighed the KFHP cost savings that arose from efficiencies and care management mechanisms. Similar to the classical 20-80 rule of economist Vilfredo Pareto, one percent of KFHP members were utilizing 30% of healthcare dollars and 5% of KFHC members were utilizing 50% of total healthcare dues. (An amazingly consistent statistic, the "5-50" held true for all health plans including government–run plans such as Medicaid.) If KFHP were to lose 10% of its healthiest members, the overall cost of care would not change by one cent. Therefore, the former migratory economic conundrum now expertly defined the correct and accurate placement of feasible puzzle pieces: The existing risk pool of patients had to be retained and protected in the system while new deductible options and consumer cost-sharing schemes (co-payments) were being initiated to provide the cash flow necessary for growth. Progressive social determinism provided the backdrop for the Madison Avenue performance to come. The primary or key initiative became increasing retention through patient satisfaction with flexible migratory benefits and changing (lowering, brainwashing) consumer expectations to accept a documented consumer perception of high quality healthcare delivery, propagandized perceptions achieved both at the point of service and through intensive consumer advertising. KFHP was not then and was never to be hampered by capitation of patients into a narrow network of provider types; they did not have to apologize for the lack of availability and access to any highly specialized physician. Their media performance became a perfect play for sustainable fiscal prosperity.

A new KFHP electronic medical record system had to be purchased then modified in the wake of a $1.6 Billion fiasco that resulted from an effort to create the entire EMR system internally. EPIC systems now had arrived like Mighty Mouse, "to save the day". The new system hoped to reengineer healthcare delivery by utilizing a fully automated and integrated electronic medical record to support administrative and billing practices while coordinating and directing physician charting functions with maximized code choices to achieve the maximum from third party payments at the point of actual healthcare delivery in both the hospital and clinic environments. KFHP evolved a migrating economic factor for Healthcare Reform into a Paradigm. Dr. Robert Pearl, The Northern California Permanente Medical Group (TPMG) medical director, reported a 1.2 Billion Dollar profit in 2013. Kaiser Foundation Health Plan had the competition on the run -- in 2014, the income-profit-reserve-retention fund revenues increased to $2.2 Billion; all this "non-profit" set aside profit was gained from their active operating revenue of $56.4 Billion. By 2015, Kaiser Foundation Health Plan had cornered approximately one third of the total healthcare marketplace in California and was drooling with anxiety to purchase established health plans in other states such as Washington State's Group Health Cooperative.

Dr. Sidney Garfield's visionary migratory economic concept of efficient, productive and cost effective counter-top healthcare delivery had evolved over a century in time. Disruptive technologies paved the way to even more cost-effective methodologies yielding still greater productivity. From that original counter-top modality were added the magical ingredients of TV -- video displays, computers, touch-tablets and the Internet. Together these new modalities paved the way for a telemedicine-telehealth migratory economic commodity. Beginning in 2016 and utilizing a portion of their $60 Billion profits in operating revenues from 2015, KFHP and SCPMG, under the direction of CEO Bernard Tyson, transformed and evolved the popular concept of a "medical home" to better organize patient care into "health hubs". SCPMG invented a new dynamic process to describe their antiquated patient healthcare encounter. (It is the process that always determines the best and finest cheese.) Dr. Garfield's functional counter-top medical service was technologically rebuilt to add many vertical services such as yoga and diet planning in a literally-speaking medical garden of "community rooms" featuring well-spaced informational counter-tops where patients could linger until being electronically requested to enter into a cozy examination room. (It was like having a drink and some tasty hors-d'oeuvres at the bar before being called to dine in the main dining room at a plush restaurant.) After checking in at stations akin to electronic boarding pass dispensers at airports, the dispensed computerized electronics summoned each patient in chronological order to enter and be seated on a comfortable leather recliner in the center of that examination room, perfectly positioned to view a huge life-sized video wall display, not face to face, but "eye to eye". This re-built environment in the 21st Century created unique examination rooms utilizing more efficient collaborative work flows in a virtual medical home. A para-medical practitioner sat adjacent to the patient and recorded pertinent medical findings while simultaneously controlling the enormous wall-mounted display and various images, all accomplished by way of a laptop touch-pad. X-rays, Lab tests and instantaneous telemedicine consultations with social workers, psychologists and life-sized virtual physicians became resultant by-products, all packed into a fifteen-minute patient visit. When necessary, the telehealth option on the touch pad produced an array of sub specialty medical expertise, appearing intimately involved and truly immediately available, thereby increasing total work productivity by 40%, cutting costs by 10% and saving an enrolled patient the time and expense of scheduling diverse multiple future visits to boot. By 2016, the Permanente Organizations had already proven themselves adept in training over 600 resident physicians in their current educational programs, and in 2019, a Kaiser Permanente School of Medicine would open its 501-c-3 doors in Pasadena California. (I can readily recall that recognizable "follow me" familiar smile on Dr. Sidney Garfield's friendly face; and I am certain that it now projects down from heaven with rejuvenated joy, shouting out, "keep on going guys".)

On the hands-on side of direct patient healthcare delivery, progressive social determinism drastically changed mass public doctor perception from a loving and caring paternal character to a contemporary-class worker, but overall quality in medical practice outcomes had significantly improved. Never again would physician decision making be based on the non-statistically significant opinion of a few. Hopefully there would not ever be a recurrence of the disastrous consequences such as arose from traditional Thalidomide and peptic ulcer therapy, which resulted from a false universal opinion that originated with just a few "experts" and then went unchallenged. Economist Schopenhauer's "Herd Mentality" in the choice of medical treatment was replaced by a scientifically proven ranking of evidence for the effectiveness of medical treatments, screenings and testing. Existing medical practice decision-making became under strict scrutiny utilizing reasonably achievable time-marker milestones of meaningful, measured and monitored metrics and measures. The U.S. Preventive Services Task Force (USPSTF) developed a system to stratify medical evidence by examining the quality of that evidence and grading the reliability of that evidence, from reliable to questionable, according to a scale:

- Level I: Evidence obtained from at least one properly designed randomized controlled trial.
- Level II-1: Evidence obtained from well-designed controlled trials without randomization.
- Level II-2: Evidence obtained from well-designed cohort or case-control analytic studies, preferably from more than one center or research group.
- Level II-3: Evidence obtained from multiple time series with or without the intervention. Dramatic results in uncontrolled trials might also be regarded as this type of evidence.
- Level III: Opinions of respected authorities, based on clinical experience, descriptive studies, or reports of expert committees.

Steven Toulmin's classical logical study of moral language denounced as "unethical" any consideration of cost in contractually designing a treatment plan for a patient in the first medical ecolo-nomic generation. Migrating cultural mores and morals changed medical ecolo-nomics. The language also changed; politically correct wordsmithing evolved with advancing progressive social determinism. By the same logical study, therefore, not to consider cost within a fixed societal healthcare delivery budget in the third medical ecolo-nomic generation became "unethical". Did the new migratory medical ecolo-nomics redefine the meaning of "ethical"? No, ethical concepts were defined before the migratory economic change. Migratory morals, followed by mores, evolve and necessarily change to produce a new migratory ecology comprising a variety of current migratory societal ethics tethered to the economics of the time – "ecolo-nomics"…..

Economist David Ricardo taught that all trade is an advantage to all competing parties because of individualized efforts to increase efficiency of production through specialized advantages. Theorist and economist Claude Frédéric Bastiat took that thought one step further and insisted that even without those individual specialization migratory economic advantages; simply increasing trade alone is beneficial for all because of the realized increased total abundance. Without competition, human nature forgets how to do nearly everything, like the absurd and unimaginable loss of knowledge during the "Dark Ages" when nobody in the Western World of culture could even make ordinary concrete cement to hold bricks together. So, had the period of open conflict, the continually "warring for dominance" competition in the trade of healthcare delivery among the HKOs come to the end of Dante's callused path in an Inferno of organized healthcare delivery and looked into the pathless forest ahead with an epiphany of pure delight? "La Vita Nuova" was retranslated in the Healthkeeper version to mean that a continual new and excitingly unknown organized healthcare delivery course certainly lay ahead. Would the next step for the future of healthcare delivery be the universal practice of some type of "virtual Medicine"? What would become of the traditional "laying on of hands"? Greater than those many-chaptered great books and records of human memories of past achievements is the infinite chaptered book of human imagination. Once the latter is opened, the chapter on the migratory economics of **Healthcare Reform** will clearly show that Healthkeeper possibilities in organized healthcare delivery will forever become limitless for **Man, Money and Medicine.**

MIGRATORY ECONOMIC FACTORS & PATTERNS EVOLVING MAN, MONEY & MEDICINE

PART FOUR

THE CORPORATE PRACTICE OF MEDICINE
THE INTEGRATION OF HMO, MANAGED CARE AND
INDEPENDENT PRACTICE ASSOCIATION (IPA)

The first overlapping medical ecolo-nomic generation from 1950 to 1970 was a quality-driven golden era of and for medical practice. Employee Benefit Insurance, beginning in 1945, hallmarked a Healthcare Reform watershed event.

The second overlapping medical ecolo-nomic generation from 1970 to 1990 was an access-driven entitlement era of and for medical practice. The enactment of Medicare-Medicaid in 1965 hallmarked a Healthcare Reform watershed event.

The cultural ecology of an epoch, the socio-economics of political culture, and the moral-ethical character paradigm of people residing in any particular region are all expressed in contemporary territorial design – all art as well as the arts of migratory economics and healing are also so designed.
-- Ralzak

"For those of us who devoted our lives to reshaping the health system – and where our motives were typical of many physicians, trying to make the health system better for patients – the thing (Health Maintenance Organization - HMO) has been a profound disappointment."
-- Dr. Paul M. Ellwood, HMO founder,
Medical News and Perspectives,
December 1998, vol. 280, No.24

In 1962, at Madison Square Garden in New York City, President John F. Kennedy, an extremely popular, young, handsome and exquisitely charismatic President, addressed the nation to sell an omnibus healthcare delivery package based on a new healthcare delivery King Anderson Bill, the prelude to the Medicare provisions which provided hospital and nursing home coverage for citizens over the age of 65, but limited payment of formerly outpatient x-ray and laboratory diagnostic services to the hospital setting. He packed the Garden to standing room capacity and his address was covered on all three major TV networks at that time (ABC, CBS, and NBC).

The very next evening, addressing a totally empty Garden and carried only by ABC, the President of the AMA, Dr. Edward Annis told the nation "the other side of the story, a sense of fairness". In reference to defeating the King Anderson Bill, Dr. Annis asked: "Who read it"? He declared to the American public, you have been "blitzed, brainwashed, and bandwagoned."..."Your children will have to pay more than they will be willing to pay."..."The government will stand between the patient and his doctor."..."People will eventually have to buy private insurance on top of the cost of a government-run program which they choose not to use." …….. Are those not the exact same phrases that were heard again and again during the tea parties, town hall meetings, walks on the Capitol, and legislative debates during the period of 2009 to 2010, and then beyond the actual enactment of the Patient Protection and Affordable Care Act (PPACA) in 2013, and yet continuing, well past the election cycle of 2016?

Meanwhile, after the Madison Square Garden addresses, democratic progressivists organized rallies in 45 cities, and labor unions condemned the delays in the Ways and Means Committee; but the King Anderson Bill eventually failed by a 52-48 margin. This prelude-to-Medicare bill was a watered down version of a previously failed Forand bill, which would have provided health insurance to all Social Security beneficiaries. Perhaps President Kennedy was a bit overconfident too early in his very popular career and failed to appreciate the impact of the Viet Nam War – Police Action on the American people. Perhaps rushing the healthcare delivery agenda through without a thorough reading upset a now forgotten paradigm of righteous due-diligence values among the constituents of elected legislative representatives, which perhaps also included the mores of the American people at that time. Or, perhaps an "omnibus" bill was not the way to proceed with **Healthcare Reform**, because the progress of liberal progressivism is historically most effective when taken one small step at a time.

President Kennedy was also placed in an unpopular corner because his constituent majority also championed the 1960 Kerr-Mills-Act or "Medical Assistance for the Aged Law", a potential **Healthcare Reform** which provided voluntary healthcare insurance for "medically needy elderly" – people over 65 who existed in an economic sector that did not qualify for public assistance yet still were unable to pay for medical expenses. This overwhelming popular Kerr-Mills Act had passed the Senate by a margin of 91-2 in 1960 and gave the states the authority to determine which citizens were in need of financial assistance, assistance aided by federal matching funds.

Post-war migratory economic prosperity, the beginning of an affluent society, ended with the end of the Dwight D. Eisenhower administration. In the way of **Healthcare Reform**, President Eisenhower had proposed a reimbursement to insurance corporations should they have losses from providing coverage to the uninsured, but the President's $25 Million "reinsurance" fund found itself presented and proclaimed dead on arrival. The now forgotten political line of the 1960's was transforming to the "poverty line", and both sides of the isle hated it. Politically profiling people, be they citizens or legislators, simply and rashly as a "Republican" or "Democrat" is an ignorant harsh insult to the complexity of sincere varied emotions and honored-protected equal-opportunity migratory economics that constitute the wonderful American way of life. It really was not true that if you wound up an Eisenhower doll, all it would do is stand still for eight years. Republican President Eisenhower, after signing the Civil Rights Act of 1957, the first civil rights act since the Civil War and an act hotly opposed by the Southern Democrats because it protected the right to vote for all Americans, then followed up his Republican integration policy by ordering federal troops to safeguard nine children integrating Central High School in Littlerock, Kentucky. The honored former five-star General, President Eisenhower, then warned all Americans of the political and migratory economic dangers inherent in a military-industrial complex. The migratory economics of a **Healthcare Reform** medical-industrial complex were yet too nascent to notice.

Political profiling also hides the many merits of Democratic President John F. Kennedy. The left or liberal profiling of this popular president, seemingly just because he presented himself as a social liberal, obscures some of his greatest achievements. President Kennedy acted as possibly the strictest fiscal, military and religious conservative ever to have been elected to the presidency. He immediately took up the presidential gauntlet to turn things around and save the American economy. By "sequestering" the dynamics of capital flow with two enormous decreases in federal taxes, one for business and one for personal income, President Kennedy indeed proved himself more than able to "get the country moving again". With a migratory supply side economic policy that was more energetic than anything the Laffer-Friedman-Reagan team would eventually dream up, President Kennedy accomplished a drastic increase in economic growth, a bona fide fulfillment of a repeated promise made during his presidential campaign.

Under the guidance of an old, clever, and very balding President Lynden B. Johnson, 1965 bore witness to a political resurrection of a bill from the dead bill graveyard. That previously defeated King Anderson Bill was reintroduced and finally passed; and progressivism marched on during a period which began with a robust conservative economy in the spirit of a President Kennedy legacy. President Johnson also formally signed Medicare and Medicaid (California Medi-Cal) into federal law as part of his "great society" socio-economic vision. Former President Truman was noticeably present and smiling at the signing ceremony. "Medicare is just one result of a continual dynamic migratory economic force in America that defines and redefines capitalistic production and value in terms of evolving societal norms for health and the art of living."

Medicare and Medicaid Services proved to be an evolutionary Healthcare Reforming watershed event. Healthcare Reform through migratory medical ecolo-nomics again changed the course of healthcare delivery: Hospital costs had doubled over a ten-year period and there was a perceived medical manpower need for increasing medical school enrollment, both to provide for an increased number of needed physicians and to provide for dynamic competition in pricing among those physicians. However, the over-all combined liberal economic policies of President Johnson turned the fiscally conservative tax-cut Kennedy financial boom into a migratory economic bust. President Johnson was not able to concomitantly fund his progressive vision of a "Great Society" along with what was required to pay for the very expensive Viet Nam warlike "police action". (Massive federal borrowing along with a continually increasing national debt was absolutely unthinkable at that time, even among the most progressive liberals.)

In 1970, the Kennedy Griffiths Health Security Act failed to create a giant national healthcare insurance system. In addition to a new AMA spin of "socialized Medicine", labor unions were dissatisfied with the total provisions, and the United States Congress was afraid to incur the obligatory federal debt. Money talked.

Then along came President Richard Milhous Nixon with a completely new idea for the Money problem….

Republican President Richard M. Nixon, after opening diplomatic relationships with China, hoped that his very progressive liberal legacy would be the enactment of a national healthcare delivery plan, but first another war or police action had to end. In 1973, President Nixon approved start-up federal funding and legislation to give governmental protection and a dynamic competitive marketing advantage to new pre-paid organizations managing large groups of patients as previously advised by the original CCMC in 1927. Health Maintenance Organizations (HMOs) then began their rise to prominence during the second overlapping medical ecolo-nomic generation (1970-1990). President Nixon hoped and planned for much more. Quoting from his campaign, "I shall propose a sweeping new program that will assure comprehensive health insurance protection to millions of Americans who cannot now obtain or afford it, with vastly improved protection against catastrophic illness." That proposed President Nixon administration national health plan formed the basis for a future President Clinton and then President Obama administration health plan. The corporate practice of Medicine was drooling on the Whitehouse steps in anxious expectation. The concept of a Kaiser-type of HMO was well fixed in the President's mind years before he was elected to the Office of U.S. President, and now that same migratory economic **Healthcare Reform** concept was pounding on his White House Doors. [90] However, there was also a softer conservative knock on those

---

[90] Interview with citizen Richard M. Nixon, June, 1967

Let me relate to you the events that transpired during the evening of my medical school graduation:

After reaching for my M.D. diploma and tossing my tasseled graduation cap into the air, I joked and fumbled about with my fellow classmates while we marched into a dining hall for an expected boring commencement speech and a commencement dinner. The dean of our medical school along with various and sundry distinguished faculty ceremoniously led our famous keynote speaker into the great dining hall. "This Guy", the infamous commencement speaker, had just lost -- came in second place -- in the race for governor of California. His political career seemed over and done. He was, therefore, on the "available list" for the national graduation speakers' circuit in June of 1967. I managed to sit myself down at a long table across from a vacant space, and then carefully postured or positioned my body into a presumed attentive listening appearance, to assimilate all the carefully crafted words of wisdom naturally expected from our keynote speaker (tedious and boring was what I expected). After delivering his corny canned commencement speech, "This Guy" walked down from the podium, and bypassed the specially name-tagged seat reserved for him at the medical school faculty table. "This Guy" somehow serendipitously chose to sit down in the student section, right in the vacant seat across from little ole me. Abruptly following a firm and brisk handshake which accompanied terse introductions, "This Guy" arose a bit from his seat and leaned forward across that long dining table, stared intensely and directly into my eyes, and commented with evident assured authority, "Some of "You Guys" will never in your lifetimes know as much about what really goes on in Medicine as you know today". Then, holding firm to that brisk authoritarian facial expression, he continued to further project that straight, stark stare, from his eyeballs directly into mine, accompanied now by an increasingly uncomfortable still and silent pause that seemed to want to go on and torture me for an eternity. I found myself physically floundering for a proper and hopefully intelligent or at least intelligible vocal response; and then capitulated, hopelessly suckered into gesturing with an awkward and prolonged repetitiously redundant head nodding up and down. My head continued along in its bobbling motion, but my eyes stayed drawn and fixed in a direct line with "This Guy's" mesmerizing stare. I felt disturbed and insecure for having provided such a hopelessly meek and totally inadequate acquiescence to "This Guy's" fine and timely advice or predictive admonition about the totality of my future professional life. I wasn't sure of the legitimacy in my response, and quite apparently showed my insecurity by means of my clumsy and inadequate physical demeanor. Observing my primping, fidgeting, squirming about and reactive diminutive body posturing with absolute perfect timing, "This Guy" slyly grinned, leaned even father on forward across the dining table, and whispered loud enough for others to hear, but presumably for my ears only,

same doors that politely demanded to be heard. The person knocking was a Mr. Boyd Thompson, from the San Joaquin Foundation for Medical Care (SJFMC or SJMF): [91]

During the first half of the 20th Century, the overwhelming majority of private practice physicians throughout the state of California organized Medical Service Bureaus. These bureaus sought to limit the expansion of pre-pay and closed panel health plans and later developed into local county medical societies and exclusively restricted the sale of low cost malpractice insurance exclusively to their membership. As previously described, pre-pay or employed physicians were neither welcomed nor accepted into the membership of the Los Angeles County Medical Society (LACMA) until Dr. H. Clifford Loos successfully reversed the LACMA policy. Growth in pre-pay organized healthcare delivery organizations, however, continued on at a steady pace through all the migratory economic-related **Healthcare Reform** conflicts.

Some fee-for-service physicians in the four-county area surrounding San Joaquin County in Northern California had on "good rumor" become suspicious and worried that the Kaiser Foundation Health Plan (KFHP) organization might penetrate inland to the port of Stockton. During the first years of the first medical ecolo-nomic generation of overlapping change in organized healthcare delivery

---

"After today, some other, a few other, of "You Guys" will never know as little". Well I was, of course, stung by a sage and clever bee; but I strangely and immensely enjoyed that sharp sting, and actually brain-buzzed from the effect of its venom penetrating into my consciousness. The rest of a rather lively dinner conversation turned to topics about the future of healthcare delivery in the United States, and what was in store for "You Guys"-- again meaning little ole me. The conversation after desert and coffee took the form of a debate that stretched out well into the evening hours. "This Guy" teased me with a line from Cole Porter, "Be a doctor and people will greet you with dread." In retort, and knowing that "this guy" had been a Republican candidate, I feebly attempted a political taunt, praising the intentions of the Democratic Party and their interest in financing healthcare reform, and how the Democratic party coffers in Providence had provided an academic-based scholarship to help pay for my undergraduate Ivy League education, as well as the fact that my father, a Democrat, was the first Italian-American elected to the state senate in Rhode Island; but "This Guy's" superb swan song missed not a single beat. I became totally confused regarding his political affiliation; he seemed more progressive liberal than constitutional conservative; he had me going to the far left and then back to the far right with every other spoken sentence. His overwhelming persona chased my well-developed team debating defenses into a corner from which there was no escape. My tasseled graduation cap, the one that I had tossed so highly to the sky, must have landed in a healthcare delivery political no-holds-barred boxing ring and "This Guy" was pulling those tassels apart, fiber by fiber. Then it came upon me like lightening, an epiphany, I suddenly realized that I was serendipitously immersed in a once in a lifetime experience; I was encountering a force of character and personality that would prove to be a watershed event or directional point in my life. At that time, I had no idea that I was actually immersed in a free-for-all unhampered healthcare delivery interview with "THE GUY" who would one day be President of the United States of America. I have interviewed Many fine people since, but that night's discussion about healthcare delivery proved to be the penultimate interview of my career, and the starting point for my lifetime interest in the politics and the medical ecolo-nomics of healthcare delivery and healthcare reform.

[91] Interview with Boyd Thompson, October 25, 2000.

(1950-1970), those local fee-for-service physicians took proactive action to forestall that perceived potential significant financial impact upon their fee-for-service payer risk pool private practices in San Joaquin County, California. To wit: The International Longshoremen's and Warehouseman's Union (ILWU) in Stockton had been Romancing the Kaiser Foundation Health Plan and offered to make a financial commitment involving partial use of ILWU trust funds. The above-mentioned local fee-for-service physicians became even more greatly concerned. An additional unfounded and unsubstantiated rumor gave them more anguish and probable cause to worry; prevailing gossip insinuated that the Kaiser organization was about to float a hospital ship up river to Stockton and start some variety of pre-pay healthcare delivery service. ILWU leaders were determined to find some pre-pay organization for ILWU members, and there seemed to be no competition for the Kaiser medical organization in the local medical ecolo-nomic marketplace. A migratory economic window of opportunity opened for niche medical ecolo-nomic practice development and migratory economic **Healthcare Reform**. Ready-made dynamic competitive advantage anxiously awaited the solution, patiently waiting in the flapping carrier pigeon wings for some other type of organized healthcare delivery system; but no message arrived. The Kaiser organization, in fact, was not terribly anxious to develop an up-stream enterprise at that particular moment in time; but, repeatedly, the Kaiser organization did not respond to multiple queries; KFHP refused to neither confirm nor to deny that potential possibility and thereby immediately put to an end the feared rumor. The time was perfectly ripe for entrepreneurial insight, and a visionary physician-administrator combo at a local medical association provided a clear view to that window of opportunity:

The physician, Doctor Donald C. Harrington, happily enjoyed a financially and emotionally successful ob-gyn surgical practice. He had been born in Brazil while his father, a Methodist minister, performed missionary work. After medical training at the University of California, he settled in the port area of Stockton and formed a medical practice partnership with Doctor Nicholas Demas and Doctor Larry Heston. The trio became locally known as the "stork club" and delivered babies for 90% of the doctors' wives in San Joaquin County. Doctor Harrington earned the utmost respect and trust from all the physicians in the area, and became the leader of the county medical society. He was not only a local visionary leader, but also an entrepreneurial salesman and marketer *par excellence* for his future organized healthcare delivery product in Sacramento and then other cities in the state of California.

The administrator, Mr. Boyd Thompson, son of a local MD father and RN mother, had been pursuing a career in higher academics, working on a doctorate in education while temporarily assigned as director of athletics for the University of the Pacific. Dr. Harrington hired Mr. Thompson to administrate the San Joaquin Medical Association (SJMA) in 1952. Agencies used by SJMA physicians for collection of accounts receivable proved themselves unsatisfactory; they were perceived as uncompassionate, many patients could not immediately pay costly medical bills because of intrinsic family problems and alcoholism. Mr. Thompson formed a more compassionate, for-profit corporation, the "Bureau of Medical Economics" within the SJMA to help in collection of the physician members' accounts receivable. Hire and fire of social workers and other staff quickly gave Mr. Thompson a working education in medical management. In 1953, the local Red Cross opted out of the local blood bank business. Mr. Thompson designed a non-profit corporation for SJMA to rescue the blood bank. Management of the collections bureau and the blood bank corporation proceeded quite well, and the entities remained economically feasible.

Following the passage of the Wagner National Labor Relations Act (NLRA) in 1935, the Taft-Hartley Act of 1947 additionally drilled down to detail the rights and responsibilities of unions and provided for a collectively-bargained Taft-Hartley Trust Plan through which a Labor-Management Board of Trustees, a Third Party Administrator (TPA), could legally manage healthcare delivery and pension funds contributed by employees for their union members. This federally-sanctioned migratory economic opportunity legally opened the door or window of opportunity for several other **Healthcare Reform** Third Party Administrator (TPA) types to connect doctor payments with various patient coverage arrangements:

Mr. Thompson set up weekly meetings with Doctor Harrington, and when word of the aforementioned longshoremen's' supposed intentions was made known, a very special luncheon meeting was held at Russo's Italian restaurant in Stockton. By the end of the luncheon, the three ob-gyn doctors (Drs. Harrington, Demas, and Heston) and Mr. Thompson produced a working idea and a name for a brand new organized healthcare delivery product for **Healthcare Reform**. A non-profit corporation -- The San Joaquin Foundation for Medical Care (SJFMC) had been conceived, and a very profitable Third Party Administrator (TPA) function would soon be born. Being a trusted and honorable friend to the local medical community, Doctor Harrington quickly and completely sold the concept to local practicing physicians. Mr. Thompson likewise rapidly became a respected entrepreneurial businessman and readily sold the concept to various patient and union groups. He also selected out reliable underwriters; he assured the SJFMC that the chosen insurers would also meet a strict set of standards.

On March 1, 1954, a non-profit corporation, the SJFMC, sent out those birth announcements. The SJFMC began as a preferred physician panel pre-pay healthcare delivery organization that was modeled after the 1942 Permanente Foundation. The SJFMC attempted to offer a broader set of benefits than were offered by the Kaiser Foundation Health Plan of the first medical ecolo-nomic generation (1950-1970). Third medical ecolo-nomic generation (1990-2010) historians would have categorized the healthcare delivery system as containing contractual elements of both a Preferred Provider Organization (PPO) and an Independent Provider Association (IPA). Contracted SJFMC doctors agreed to a fundamental migratory economic **Healthcare Reform** measure -- to collectively negotiate a fee structure equivalent to 75% of their usual and customary fee.

The needs and rational desires of the healthcare delivery marketplace were economically dynamic and had to be met, reset, and met again for future success. The SJFMC strategy grew from a sustainable migratory economic concept that Mr. Boyd Thompson had learned from study of the 1928 American Gas Company public relations program. "Identify your own needs and desires. Identify the needs and desires of your customers. Communicate with your customers and mutually select desires that are truly worthy. Develop programs to meet the selected needs and desires with permission from your customers to change what was necessary to achieve common goals."[92] Mr. Thompson dissected the essentials of the Kaiser Foundation Health Plan and envisioned specific dynamic competitive advantages for the SJFMC. Local hospital contracting and the ability to have patients visit their own physicians in a private office were the sweetened pot additives offered in the dish to the longshoremen. Sensing a new and delicious epicurean aroma, ILWU leaders lost their appetite for the elusive Kaiser organization and hungered to taste that new Foundation dish. Mr. Thompson negotiated an at-risk pool contract (third medical ecolo-nomic generation Independent Practice Association -- IPA) and all parties signed on the pretty little dotted lines at the end of the contract pages for the SJFMC.

Soon after the Longshoremen signed on, teachers, school districts and county employees became enticed to come on-board. The Foundation also needed to grow or wither on the migratory medical economic vine. Just as Permanente Medical Group founder, Dr. Sidney Garfield, had discovered back in 1942, the Foundation

---

[92] Boyd Thompson, personal communication and interview.

realized that dynamic strategies were essential to compete in the changing medical ecolo-nomic marketplace. Efficiency also had to be improved. There had to be some separation between the medical treatment and business management entities. Mr. Thompson was convinced that he had "a bear by the tail."[93] Service insurance companies entered the California medical ecolo-nomic marketplace to compete with Blue Cross and Blue Shield. After six years, 16 different insurance companies sponsored Foundations for Medical Care (FMC) throughout California and the states of Hawaii, Oregon, Utah, New Mexico, Colorado, Minnesota, Wisconsin, Ohio, Massachusetts, Florida, Illinois, Kansas, Georgia, and Iowa.

In 1953, SJFMC launched a successful charitable program to provide medical care for migrant workers. The Foundation's blood donation vans were utilized as mobile treatment units. The project became a successfully repeated community outreach program. Local physicians temporarily cut their billings by 50% and local hospitals provided facilities during under-used after-hour night and weekend time. (The more stressed the vine, the sweeter the wine.) Migrant workers received needed healthcare and the Foundation Health Care system gained additional respect.

The Foundation defined and serviced an additional medical ecolo-nomic niche risk payer pool for the "mud trades" -- hod carriers, latherers, and plasterers – tradesmen who could not afford the traditional Foundation pre-pay rate. Mr. Thompson established a coverage adaptation to include a lower rate in 1954. Continental Casualty underwrote the contract. This particular migratory economic **Healthcare Reform** experiment was not totally successful. Several of the local doctors sought to recover extra payments by employing the tactic of over-utilization. Continental Casualty advised the Foundation to review claims and identify outlier physician practices. Mr. Thompson established a utilization review system through the third party claims administration (TPCA) to control outlier physician costs. He standardized the utilization review program, and it quickly developed to become the eventual prototype for the federal Physician Services Review Organization (PSRO) and a later federal Professional Standards Review Organization (PRO). The SJMF's concept of pre-evaluation for admission to hospital led to other Foundations developing the Certified Hospital Admission Program (CHAP), later to be copied statewide for all hospitals as the California Medical Review Incorporated (CMRI).

---

[93] Boyd Thompson, personal communication and interview.

Upon hearing a speech by George Johns, then head of the American Federation of Labor and Congress of Industrial Organizations (AFL-CIO), Mr. Thompson became quite concerned about one particular sentence: "We have to do something about health insurance; the insurance is insuring doctors' incomes, not the cost of healthcare."[94]

A typical problematic scenario began with a lament from a patient who was either assured by a slick insurance salesperson or simply yet falsely "assumed" that indemnity insurance carried no co-pay. The patient would naturally become annoyed and frustrated when asked by a physician to pay an additional amount for some medical procedure. First, doctors asked for additional payments just to supplement the discounted fee and to meet the usual and customary amount ("balance billing"). Patients balked. Doctors responded by temporarily pricing the total charge beyond their traditional "usual", for this new and higher "usual and customary fee" to be recorded in the indemnity insurer's physician profile. Doctors then hoped that the maneuver would eliminate any need for patient co-pays to make up the difference in the balance and thus eliminate the complaints engendered from the practice of "balance billing". Doctors quickly realized that patients would not object because a well-established insurance hazard -- an invisible third party with apparently unlimited funds from some magical money tree incapable of personal retribution -- was serendipitously paying the medical bill. The total listed charge stayed well beyond what a concurrent negotiated cash payment (a truer cost of actual direct healthcare delivery) rendered from a cash-paying patient would normally have been. Quite natural to follow from the new and higher physician cost profile, an eventual higher premium cost to the patient came trailing along. Insurance salespersons then sold these updated (more expensive and more profitably commissioned) policies. Except for the interests of general patient pool, the entire cost-spiral migratory economic process benefited all administrative and practicing entities, progressively repeating itself without dynamic competitive medical ecolo-nomic justification. The entire cyclic and usurious migratory economic process obviously demanded a desperately needed dynamically competitive adjustment to the **Healthcare Reform.**

In order to end this corrupt practice that the AFL-CIO labeled as "insuring doctors", the San Joaquin Foundation for Medical Care offered "certainty of full coverage" for its enrollees on a year-to-year basis starting in 1955. No increasing of fees, minimum standards of appropriate care, and a 75% cap on the doctors' true (cash-accepted) usual and customary fee became mandatory requirements.

---

[94] Boyd Thompson, personal communications and interview.

Coverage included well baby care from the time of birth and outpatient diagnostic work ups. By withholding 30% of the physician payments for the first three years, a created physician risk pool "retention fund" assured the sustainability of future physician payments. Mr. Thompson negotiated a new contract containing these provisions with the ILWU, underwritten by New York Life. **This remarkable type of migratory economic Healthcare Reform healthcare delivery contracting agreement stayed in force for 40 years.**

At the beginning of the second medical ecolo-nomic generation (1970-1990), Mr. Thompson devised a formal national networking for his product. He founded the American Association of Foundations for Medical Care (AAFMC) in 1971. Sacramento, Stockton, and San Joaquin were all contracted together as one Foundation Health Plan. Mr. Thompson, the executive director, made a personal practice of purchasing small "out of California" state flags to dress up the luncheon table for every out-of-state AAFMC administrator visiting his local Foundation. Before the end of the second overlapping medical ecolo-nomic generation in reforming healthcare delivery, Boyd Thompson had collected a total of 41 decorative little state flags.[95]

In 1978, Foundation Health Plan became the very first health plan in the United States of America to be officially licensed as an HMO under the Knox-Keene Act, an accomplishment credited to the Nixon Administration.

1982 shined as a landmark year for **Healthcare Reform** in California healthcare delivery. Entitled Medi-Cal contracting, a legislative genetic mutation of Medicaid, insidiously reared its unintended legislative consequences. At first, this contracting mutation allowed the State of California Medi-Cal (federal Medicaid) to bargain for the cheapest hospital rate on a hospital to hospital basis. Medi-Cal next bargained with physicians and physician groups for their cheapest possible healthcare delivery rates. A new migratory economic dynamic competition entered into the healthcare marketplace. Medi-Cal contracting was indeed a medical ecolo-nomic necessity for the near to pro-bono patient risk pool served. Because Medi-Cal contracting glowed with that semi-charitable aura, the passage of the legislation flowed smoothly along, handled with kid gloves and not given substantial thought for opposition. However, physicians later recognized that this migratory economic's unintended, unwanted and unexpected consequence, this now legal direct selective contracting dynamic end game would be akin to the

---

[95] Boyd Thompson, personal communications and interview.

introduction of a bad rotten apple into a fermenting private physician fee-for-service apple cider barrel.

The true devil was, as always, in the details. Actually a second "companion bill" was really the unwanted insidious bacteria that changed that fermenting apple cider into apple......compost. Unbeknownst to most lobbyists in Capitol City, Sacramento, "private corporate insurer organizations" throughout the state were also, concomitantly, being given that legislated right to "selectively contract" with hospitals and (regrettably for fee-for-service) also with individual physicians. This new private insurer strategic migratory economic advantage in **Healthcare Reform** severely hurt the previous private physician dynamic competitive advantage. Physicians and hospitals vehemently opposed the measure because hospitals and physicians permanently lost their former significant individual dynamic economic competitive advantage that was through group-only contracting for the healthcare dollar. (Nothing anti-union new under the sun, Divide and Conquer" comes from the old tried and true Latin-Roman strategy – "Divide et Impera".) Post facto, some select hospitals, physicians and physician groups voiced their objections to the California state legislature, but all that combined whimpering and whining were again too little and too late to affect small step by small step progressive **Healthcare Reform.**

Private insurance selective contracting was not simply a discounting mechanism forced upon the fee-for-service world -- Kaiser Foundation Health Plan (KFHP) may have been the temporary greater loser of competitive advantage. KFHP was well on its way to being the national model for organized healthcare delivery and was more than secretly hoping that if and when the final medical ecolo-nomic survivor was proclaimed, that the one and only surviving national plan would be KFHP. There existed no significant dynamic competition from any other fully integrated plan at the time when the selective contracting bill was passed. The extremely large volume of insured lives contracted to the KFHP triad of health plan, hospital, and dependent closed panel medical group exclusively at that time remained unique to Kaiser. The new 1982 selective discounting process gave lifeblood to two new species of dynamically competing healthcare delivery organizations. Preferred Provider Organizations (PPOs) were given a second wind and sailed out to venture in deeper waters. Next, HMOs and hospital service organizations (HSOs) vertically integrated and became indistinguishable. The new organizations reduced physicians to the role of sub-contracted agents, and shifted healthcare delivery profits to the general contractors -- to the Money collecting hierarchy, to the health plan level. Large insurance companies bought out multiple HMO entities and merged with partially and totally integrated forms to produce a newer yet species of healthcare delivery organization; the Health Keeper Organization (HKO) was evolved in the third 20-year medical ecolo-nomic era (1990-2010). These newly-formed HKOs were then, and only then, able to confront, with head to head competition, the former California lonely giant -- Kaiser Foundation Health Plan. But, contrary to fairy tale ideology, giants are not always dull and awkward; Money giants cleverly survive to become bigger giants that may seem to stumble but usually don't fall from a tall beanstalk somewhere above the clouds so easily; or they might not fall at all and instead not only build a network of even more beautiful and grandiose castles, but also vertically expand into the basic nature of Medicine's research and personnel development.....

Lacking oversight of the 1982 California state lobbyists, which led to selective contracting, may have been KFHP's second or perhaps third dynamic competitive advantage miscalculation. The first miscalculation occurred 10 years earlier, before a congressional committee at the federal level. When the Nixon Administration was developing the HMO concept in 1972, Kaiser stood alone as the idealized model, near to a certainty for emulation; and perhaps more aggressive marketing at that time would have cinched and clinched the national healthcare market for Kaiser. Perhaps Kaiser miscalculated dynamic competitive advantage even earlier, in 1952. Perhaps, in 1953, The Kaiser Hospital Foundation should have been less elusive and vehemently and conclusively denied those rumors of a hospital ship floating up river to Stockton. Dr. Harrington and Mr. Thompson would have had no incentive to form the first IPA-TPA in the state of California. The developmental course of managed care would have drastically changed. Then there would have been no Foundation Health and no Mr. Thompson to go to Washington and testify before the congressional committees of the Nixon Administration in 1972. That testimony, in opposition to the Kaiser contracting plan as the sole and unique national healthcare delivery model, favored an IPA-TPA contracting plan as an HMO model. What if? Could have. Would have. Should have. -- Only speculative food for thought and/or topics for term papers, debates, or some stimulating seminars in medical ecolo-nomics! (Teaching made fun, 101.)

The Foundation system received especial national recognition when the United States Congress used the San Joaquin Foundation Medical Clinic (SJFMC) professional standards review program as a blueprint for the Professional Standards Review Organization (PSRO) Act. Congress also set the minimum size of a PSRO at 350 physician members because the SJFMC program just happened to be then functioning well with that seemingly magic 350 number. Mr. Thompson was named the executive director for the American Association of PSROs, which became part of the American Association of Health Plans.

"Be fruitful and multiply" were the biblical words given to the **Healthcare Reforming** HMOs in the second medical ecolo-nomic generation (1970-1990). The dynamic healthcare delivery marketplace demanded investiture of more and more Money. It took Money to make Money, and the quickest and most obvious way to raise capital was to convert a non-profit organization into a for-profit organization. In 1984, Foundation Health Plan became a for-profit plan and aligned itself with Americare Healthcare Corporation (AHC), a public holding company. AHC legally stored away or hid the profit from their for-profit holdings in a discretionary fund. Physicians immediately lost control of their previously agreed to set-aside risk-pooled funds, and they became arrogantly outraged to no avail. The impotent physicians, including all their vindictive lawyers with their bulging briefcases filled to the brim with lawsuits, were at once both powerless and ineffective because, along with Money, the for-profit shift handed the reins of control up the Money chain, up to the health plan level. (The golden rule of business is that the guy with the gold makes the rules.) Corporate policy and corporate decision-making took full command. That command reduced physicians to de facto employees, facilitators of insured lives in the organized healthcare delivery process. In accordance with the Knox-Keene Act, the conversion to a for-profit required the creation of a charitable foundation; thus, AHC gave birth to the Sierra Health Foundation. The migratory economics of the KFHP medical ecolo-nomic evolution from 1950-1955 repeated itself like a bad movie some 30 years later within this new corporate health plan take-over, carefully and sequentially staged like a plagiarized step-by-step video copy of the KFHP historic migratory economic events. Physicians expressed rhetoric and revealed miscomprehensions in an amazingly identical sequence. Senseless and powerless physician demands, groundless demands that once again arose from collective frustration, were once again brushed aside by amused corporate boards. Physicians who blinded themselves and did not learn the lessons of dynamic competitive advantage survival from medical ecolo-nomic history were not unexpectently bound to......

Then came along a basically good physician-inspired idea for a **Healthcare Reform** billing mechanism, a formula that for political reasons unfortunately turned into a billing fiasco for the well-intentioned but self-oriented physician-centric scheme: The first attempt to bring transparency or at least some communal understanding into physician billing practices marketed itself under the title of "relative value". A simple formula set to a multiplier scale for the first time in American history mathematically compared and contrasted the billing of one physician versus another throughout the entire nation and then calculated the relative value of physicians' Money value of services. This well-intentioned scheme received the worst press possible. Then came the law suits -- Relative Value book-publishing physician organizations, several physician practice groups and individual physicians collectively and individually, all being sued for the "collective" and proclaimed "illegal" development of a "minimum" relative value scale (RVS). After all the fuss and dust settled down, the concept of a fiscally capped RBRVS (Resource Based Relative Value Scale) for the calculation of "maximum" payments to physicians evolved to be perfectly fine for the government gander of Medicare and Medicaid, but the old physician-published RVS schedule apparently appeared as too golden a goose for the physicians to possess and possibly manipulate to lay monopolized golden eggs. Relative value schedules were initially spun as prejudicial "price fixing manuals", even if that relatively calculated fixed price verifiably totaled to be lower than the average on-going rate and actually saved patients Money – like the judicially admitted below average fee RVS Manual printed by the Foundation for Medical Care at Mariposa Arizona. That Foundation was singled out (scapegoated) and successfully railroaded then sued for "price fixing". The relative value of the fixed price mattered not. A keystone then fractured, loosened and fell, collapsing an important supporting arch in the Foundation Healthcare delivery concept.

Unfunded healthcare delivery mandates and reduced fee schedules would eventually lead to bankruptcies for a number of legitimate solo healthcare delivery groups and individual healthcare practitioners that yet attempted to do business without hope for parity in a medical ecolo-nomic dynamic competitive arena. The new migratory economic tossed Foundation/AHC into a new milieu of buyouts and mergers along with horizontal and vertical integrations, which eventually added to the creation of the aforementioned Health Keeper Organizations (HKOs) of the third medical ecolo-nomic generation. AmeriCare contracts were bought out in 1986 after only two years of existence. The purchase price was a cheap $140 Million. In 1988, Foundation Health Plan won the contract for the federal Civilian Health and Medical Program – CHAMPUS (later known as TRICARE). In the third medical ecolo-nomic generation (1990-2010), a significant restructuring of the Foundation Health Plans became urgently necessary; Foundation Health Corporation (FHC) re-formed under a new publicly traded ownership.

The rapid national growth of the original Foundation Health Plans (FHP) evolved for the most part through IPA-TPA contracts. A great number of IPAs failed in the third medical ecolo-nomic generation. The tight administrative structure of the San Joaquin Foundation, with third party claims administration (TPA) and utilization review for standards of healthcare delivery, did not always play as a typical tune for other Foundation Health Plans. Financial reserves (retention funds) were always difficult to accumulate for other TPA's. Therefore, several FHPs suffered lost licenses; they were sacrificed at the feet of the mandated financial requirements in the Knox-Keene Act. Local, state and national marketing of the FHP brand name product also suffered because FHP was no longer branded as a consistent reproducible business franchise, a sure economic death sentence for any "brand". The public mindset grew to not trust the national franchise. Finally, taking the liberty to paraphrase Boyd Thompson, "Many foundations failed to recognize what originally gave them their dynamic competitive edge -- the willingness and ableness to respond quickly, directly, and compassionately to medical ecolo-nomic patient needs and wants".

The year 2000 again called for changes and patient-provider migratory economic migrations in the world of medical ecolo-nomics. Boyd Thompson spoke with renewed foresight: "Capitation is dead.... The PPO window is larger and more open to the physician than it ever has been..... The gatekeeper's gate is swinging open to the specialist physician for direct access and follow-up of specialty problems..... What we have unfortunately come to see lately is an automobile (healthcare delivery system) with no steering wheel and a physician in the back seat."[96] Mr. Thompson's quote was especially interesting when compared to a contemporary quote from orthopedic surgeon Dr. David Lawrence, the CEO of KFHP at that time. Dr. Lawrence's perspective was that the problematic healthcare delivery automobile had "no chassis".

1998 gave birth to the National Foundation for Medical Care. A National "templating" of standards of care and unification of credentialing processes were among the "new" goals. These new-found goals appeared to have been copied from the 1953 physicians' handbook of the original San Joaquin Foundation for Medical Care in. Nonetheless, a good thing was certainly worth repeating. Practice did not make perfect, only perfect practice did, and Mr. Thompson was especially bent on perfection this time round. The California Foundation for Medical Care (CFMC) functioned as a statewide network, offering bids to physicians and physician organizations with guarantee payments in competitive alignment with the new and approved Resource Based Relative Value Scale (RBRVS). Several county medical associations, such as LACMA, sponsored the project and developed TPA's. Vertical integration of pharmacy, optical, dental, and mental health added dynamic competitive advantage. One stop shopping was

---

[96] Boyd Thompson, multiple personal communications and interviews.

what the payer risk pool wanted and received. CFMC was yet a Cub Scout on the HKO trail, but the organization possessed an experienced Eagle Scout's heart and dedication -- the courage and lifelong guiding light of an original Foundation founder -- Mr. Boyd Thompson.

Hope and desire -- Republican President Nixon originally hoped that the HMO legislation would be a two-part plan, ending with mandated, employer-paid national health insurance. Hopes and clout for part two of his plan got lost in the shuffle when President Nixon suddenly resigned from office after the Watergate scandal, but there were other of his progressive liberal accomplishments that are indeed remembered: "It was Nixon, after all, who initiated the first Federal Affirmative Action programs and signed the creation of the EPA (Environmental Protection Agency) and OSHA (Occupational Safety and Health Administration) into law." -- (Barack Obama, The Audacity of Hope, pp. 28)

Looking back to 1974, the federal Kennedy-Mills Healthcare Bill copied the healthcare delivery idealism of the Nixon plan, but really sidetracked and entertained the American public interest by featuring instead, a Fannie Fox sex scandal to distracted attention, far and away from ever seriously considering national **Healthcare Reform**. Fanny, the infamous "Argentine firecracker" and beltway stripper had an illicit affair with Congressman Wilbur Mills. President Nixon's emphasis (much like the 2010 Patient Protection and Accountable Care Act (PPACA)) turned to private insurance industry partnerships for support, while Kennedy had favored a simpler government-run single payer system much like the suddenly scuttled "Common Plan" -- the Obama administration's feeble or half-hearted administrative attempt at enacting a single payer federal system.

There was a basic disturbance with the foundations of the U.S. economy during the late sixties, post war and on into the seventies. The widespread disgusting societal disrespect for returning Viet Nam War veterans in the late 60's, advanced by a degrading of: capitalistic culture, protectionism of world democracies and any imperialistic intent through musical lyrics such as "all you need is love" (Beetles). The contributing factors all morphed into a social paradigm of decreased societal productivity accompanied by progressive lonely and depressive psychological musical lyrics such as those declaring "life goin' nowhere, help me, yeah" "just stayin' alive" -- (Bee Gees). Unlike the vigorous, assertive and defiant Zoot Suit era of the 40's, or the pegged pants, DA haircut and ruffian motor cycle black leather jackets of the late 50's, a 70's passive culture, a culture of leisure, eventually highlighted by disco music with its accompanying formal one-piece jump-like "Leisure Suit" castrated the aggressiveness of the U.S. economy and left a permanent disabling scar. Haircuts for men and women became indistinguishable. The university-bred free love "flower-girl" of the 60's shared no love for supporting the American Military-Industrial complex and evolved into a 70's woman. That new college-girl paradigm -- more highly skilled and educated for an unfortunately declining industrial job market, but decidedly much more lonely, more inwardly depressed and less entrepreneurial or productive, burdened with no explanation for a humiliating average Scholastic Aptitude Test (SAT) score 25% lower than her sixties sister – unfortunately also possessed a failure-feared psychological unwillingness to partake in a beginning evolution, an explosion of transformative / disruptive technologies in the USA.

The 1970 era's migratory economics for **Healthcare Reform** shouted out, "Retire early, live longer than anyone else in the world if you can, make it past 70 on government handouts, and spend even more on healthcare delivery". Wrongfully thought to be temporizing public safety measures, public welfare, entitlements, and food stamps induced a significant proportion of the American populous to into a migratory economic paradigm, a tract of multi-generational poverty as an apparently accepted normal way of life for one to inherit and pass on to one's heirs. Far greater than the lack of health insurance, simple acceptance of poverty as an acceptable way of life is the most detrimental ingredient to individual health and the health of a productive nation. This "less work" societal attitude spilled over onto **Healthcare Reform**. A change in technology altered the methodology for delivering healthcare and drastically changed a physician's idealized life style. Work contracts became developed, negotiated and signed to formally link a physician's employment with a hospital's viability. Mutual financial alignment of otherwise competing parties tends to accommodate (lower) mutual expectations in favor of profit versus quality, politically correctly spoken and expressed as "cost-effectiveness". SWAG, a "scientific wild ass guess" for policy direction to accommodate the new-formed alliance's migratory economics, can often be accredited to purposely overlooking various degrees of evidence-based policies and procedures that might threaten their mutual profit.

The naissance of the first physician residency program in "Emergency Medicine" took place at the LA-County USC hospital. Working a set numbered-hour shift, and then passing forward the patient-care responsibility like a baton in a relay race quickly became increasingly popular. All "after work" responsibilities, stress and worries then were laid upon someone else. Physicians gladly and willingly traded non-contractual professional autonomy for contractual non-professional autonomy with no residual work related stress during free time activities. So Many, too many physicians abandoned the sacrosanct doctor-patient relationship somewhere in the small-fine print hidden on so many typical employer-employee contracts.

Decadence arose while the devastating 70's non-productive entitlement migratory economic paradigm prevailed. Healthcare delivery costs insidiously stayed about 3% ahead of inflation from 1950 to 1975. Healthcare delivery took a wrong turn among the poorer inter-city neighborhoods. The traditional intra-city work for next to no profit till you drop dedicated doctor departed for the good life in the suburbs or began to enlist as an employee for a healthcare delivery corporation. The abandoned intra-city facilities that formerly catered to residences of patients without the means for transportation increased social degradation. The abandoned constituents became forced to find methods to travel longer distances or forgo formalized healthcare delivery. Pockets of unavailable healthcare delivery burned like spilled acid in the very midst of large American city neighborhoods. Dependence on future Social Security became obvious; the federal government sought the use of a temporary Band-Aid by indexing Social Security to national inflation. Popular MD-novelists like Michael Crichton offhandedly referred to a new sloppy generation of "Dumber Doctors" as productive efficiency decreased in all sectors of the economy.

The Nixon administration's migratory economic policies also continued to be hotly debated. The issue again was moderation of individual freedom and international strength of the dollar. Margaret Thatcher diligently attempted to dig the British out from a Keynesian dilemma by investing in a Milton Friedman type of free market capitalism while she concomitantly praised economist Friedrich Von Hayek for the enlightenment gained from his Road to Serfdom, which would result from any excessively big central government's rules and regulations. The Prime Minister sought a "laissez-faire" approach to economics for her Brits; but to the contrary, Republican President Nixon instituted more "Anti-Republican" or "Anti-Conservative" progressive government interventions with wage and price controls followed by the creation of a fiat monetary system by finally and forever totally and completely going off any remnant of a partial gold standard. The lack of a common national and international standard may have been a temporary good in easing restrictions in government spending at home and abroad; but once on a fiat monetary standard, always on that standard; there is no easy or economically acceptable going back. Economists considered this additional Nixon administration rise in progressivism to have dealt an insidious great blow to conservative and upper middle class stability. In his posthumous *History of Economic Analysis*, Joseph Schumpeter characterized the gold standard as "both the badge and guarantee of bourgeois freedom". Also, as previously admonished even by Democratic President Johnson in 1968 (who had previously stopped the minting of silver coins due to inflation), the Nixon administration's floating of the U.S. dollar to initially make USA international debt repayment easier inevitably would lead to an uncontrolled inflation. From that point onward, U.S. citizens relied on and accepted the value of their paper dollars to be maintained by the future good word and considered preservative actions of their federal governments' administrations to come. Good luck with that!

But 'Tricky Dicky from Yorba Linda" as Country Joe McDonald's song went, never did operate in a vacuum. President Nixon cleverly cut a 1970 deal with Saudi Aribia and OPEC: In return for American protection, the greenback United States Dollars would be the unique official global reserve currency for crude oil transactions anywhere in the world. Allowing the USA to print extra dollars almost at will, this American dollar hegemony persisted into the 21st Century, as evidenced by 80 percent of all international trade still utilizing those good old greenbacks. This power of hegemony allowed the 21st Century issue of excessive debt rising faster than economic output in America to become casually swept aside, even when the interest on the debt appeared as unpayable, even with a growing "Big Brother" governmental hand reaching out for more and more tax revenue. Many sceptics and economists of acclaim predicted an eventual dollar crisis and the return of "stagflation", often quoting the timing of debt cancellation "Jubilee" from Leviticus 25:8-55 – the tenth day of the seventh month in the fiftieth year after seven times seven years of debt. President Nixon's deal also held the Chinese Yuan in abeyance for nearly half a century, as his managed paper currency migratory economic paradigm has successfully and sustainably persisted to this very day, even though every possible relationship among American greenbacks, paper notes or official international trade agreements ceased to be in any way valued or redeemed through or in metallic gold ever since 1976.

The "official" USA "gold standard", the guaranteed conversion of issued paper notes into metallic gold, ended in 1933, thus applying some brakes to a depleting outflow of U.S. gold nationally/internationally and allowing the U.S. to horde or "nationalize" its metallic gold reserve. Even with this slowing rate of depletion, the U.S. continued to exchange paper for gold in certain approved and official international transactions, again in an attempt to maintain parity of gold with prevailing migratory economic foreign exchange mechanisms. By 1967, this international coverage migratory economic of a "partial gold standard" had its brake pedal pushed to the metal and finally slid to a screeching halt "officially" ended by federal banking officials proclaiming a final and unrecoverable crash in 1976. However, in actual and historical monitory practice, there never existed sufficient gold reserves to cover global banking services. The "golden Rule" of mercantile and other adventures in life states that, "The party with the gold makes the rules." Thus, gold reserves function and allow bidding and bragging rights for a nation or a kingdom. That particular gold-rich parcel of earth is then acclaimed and recognized as an exclusive controller of credit allocations and granted additional dynamic competitive advantaged mercantile power that may at times be for sale. The variable negotiated sale price for every morsel of power is further influenced and sustained by the actual extent of the gold reserves. Similar to the greater export-trading partner being advantaged over others in a free-trade agreement, obvious opportunities for complete or partial hegemony become apparent for the more powerful/bountiful gold hoarders over those hoarding less. Moreover, it is too often overlooked that the migratory economic scope, amount and duration of power and control must be carefully titrated for the mutual sustainable benefit of Man and his ecological environment accomplished through a balancing of his economic systems – ecolo-nomics.

But as for that attractive and addicting pretty yellow bling-bling, greed for "Gold Money" and tales of a "Midas touch" have always been associated with Man and Medicine. From *The Canterbury Tales*: Prologue, lines 444-446: (The Physician)
"He kepte that he wan in pestilence.
For gold in phisik is a cordial,
Therfore he lovede gold in special".
"The commerce and industry of the country, however, it must be acknowledged, though they may be somewhat augmented [by paper Money], cannot be altogether so secure, when they are thus, as it were, suspended upon the Daedalian wings of paper Money, as when they travel about upon the solid ground of gold and silver."
-- Adam Smith, Wealth of Nations, pp. 262
"Gold has worked down from Alexander's time…. When something holds good for two thousand years I do not believe it can be so because of prejudice or mistaken theory.   -- Bernard Baruch (1870-1965)
"Gold still represents the ultimate form of payment in the world. Fiat Money in extremis is accepted by nobody. Gold is always accepted."
-- Alan Greenspan, May 20, 1999

The future is sure to disruptively design a distinctly new migratory economic model operated via a new accompanying process for sustainable mercantile support. A futuristic time migratory economic computerized monitory exchange system housed in a heavenly Internet cloud may become the accepted and designated reserve for monitory storage to finally replace metallic gold. New myths of "justice" to equilibrate social advantages will naturally accompany the migratory economic paradigm and be touted as a higher "laws" of economics.

The aforementioned supposedly short-term good but questionably and debatably long-term bad "off gold" economic policy was for a time made worse when President Carter's administration enacted stricter Keynesian policies, à la pre WWII. Even with Keynesian-like governmental spending, spending like a drunken sailor, the Carter administration could not halt his administration's impending economic crisis which finally created an economic state of "stagflation", during which interest rates and unemployment percentages arose together as wantonly evil fiscal-forecasting twins for the first time in U.S. economic history. Increasing the Money supply at that time unfortunately only put out a brightly waving red flag indicating a dangerous future inflationary spiral just ahead. Therefore, consumer prices and wages arose in anticipation to meet that future expectation of inflation, forcing total employment to fall and that unemployment percentage to rise even further. As a direct result of the aforementioned stagflation, medical school tuitions inflated beyond the reach of loan-free family assistance for the average medical student's family to bear; and the future economic production of a fiscally sustainable doctor supply side necessary to serve the ever increasing demand side of healthcare delivery for American citizens began to be (finally) seriously questioned by economists on both sides of the political aisle; but **Healthcare Reform in medical education** was not on the table, on the stove, or on the congressional pantry shelf. In addition to his stern objections to the prejudicial Congressional limiting of health insurance to intrastate rather than interstate commerce (McCarran-Ferguson Act of 1945), Milton Friedman advocated **Healthcare Reform** with the elimination of the continuing restrictive physician state by state licensing policy and hinted at national examinations to foster the elimination of all state-by-state regulated regimented training prerequisites for licensing a physician or any other type of medical practitioner, all as an effort to promote universal healthcare delivery competition, reduce costs and sustain free-market capitalistic economy.

After President Carter won the electorate in 1976, he also joined the long list of his presidential predecessors who, once they changed their seating position, failed to stand up for or live up to a highly publicized campaign "promise" to deliver national healthcare delivery insurance. However, his ineffectual administration, a period that is primarily remembered for stagflation's increased prices in the face of decreased economic output, did manage to propose **Healthcare Reform** legislation for hospital cost containment. Albeit perhaps too little and too late in 1979 and not to give the total Carter Administration too bad a rap, there was a concerted effort to tackle that stagflation problem of declining jobs and increasing inflation by appointing a new federal reserve director, Paul Volker, who sought to raise the federal funds rate, which eventually lowered inflation from a peak of 13.5 in 1981 to 3.2% by 1983. Of course, this marvelous magical recovery happened during the years of the President Reagan Administration, so.......

In 1977, Alain Enthoven introduced the **Healthcare Reform** concept of "Managed Competition", but the U.S. Congress could not see competition in healthcare delivery as something that could be managed. After much debate and opposition from various hospital groups, the U.S. Congress agreed upon a plan for voluntary self-control of hospital revenues. Alain Enthoven, Paul Ellwood, MD, and others at Jackson Hole, Wyoming continued debating market-based **Healthcare Reform**, but the weather got colder up in those Grand Teton mountains and they became stranded, snow-bound in all the piles of political snow drifts; the frozen fundamental issue of "national healthcare" dropped from their conversations and from the ears of the American public. Yet still, the American public was, albeit ever so slowly, learning about the migratory economics debated for **Healthcare Reform**. When the first introduction of a "prudent consumer" concept occurred in 1979, the consumer or patient-healthkeeper cultural era or paradigm started on its merry and confusing way.

Monetarism, as a guiding light to economic practices in the very late 1970's, successfully met and conquered the challenge of battling economic stagflation. Milton Friedman and others envisioned economic growth to be dynamically proportional to the amount of active Money in "robust" circulation. The monetarists declared that decreasing the Money circulation decreased the interest rate while increasing the Money circulation increased inflation. As head of the Federal Reserve, Alan Greenspan had the ability to decrease the Money supply or interest rate and thereby lower inflation. That realized expectation also demonstrated that a couple of points of increased GDP percentage would decrease the unemployment rate one percentage point. The President Ronald Reagan supply side migratory economic program went on to totally vanquish stagflation with a President John Kennedy-like conservative fiscal policy that was openly acknowledged by President Reagan. The program utilized specific tax cuts to bolstered business confidence by lowering barriers to production, thus allowing a supply side of wealth to trickle down and promote a general economic growth in all sectors of the economy. In direct opposition and in contradistinction to a Marxian philosophy which admonished that benefiting the few would naturally result in the exploitation of the many, President Ronald Reagan adhered to a strict Milton Friedman-like doctrine that placed free markets and private ownership in a sacrosanct position from which prosperity would naturally flow for all. His cabinet was more concerned about where they were on the "Art Laffer's Curve" (taxation and government revenue) then they were about negative economic analogies affecting trust from a lower class in society such as the infamous story of the "Horse and Sparrow". Perhaps there was also some concern about where they were in the graphic "Phillips Curve" (inflation supposedly increasing employment), and the dynamic concept of a worker's wage-demand being dependent on elevating or lowering a worker's life expectations. Earned public confidence in the leadership and administrative management abilities of a very popular President proved to be the key factor, and therefore, recovery and prosperity did ensue. The 1960's civil rights agenda got the ball rolling for the special rights that should be afforded to the disabled as a concept of **Healthcare Reform.** That ball was picked up by Republican Richard Nixon administration's passage of Section 504 of the 1973 Rehabilitation Act. The migratory economic baseball was next thrown overhead and forward with Republican Ronald Reagan Administration's initial introduction of a first draft of the Americans with Disabilities Act (ADA) in 1988, and finally tagged into law under the penned signature of Republican President George H. W. Bush on that ADA act. Good baseball – from Nixon to Reagan to Bush.

In 1982 the AMA and all other types of Medical Societies were dealt a near-fatal blow when they were adjudicated to be trade organizations resulting from *Goldfarb v. Virginia State Bar,* 421 U.S. 773 (1975). The U.S. Supreme Court adjudicated mandatory AMA membership as a precondition for hospital privileges to be illegal; and thus effectively ended the practical authority and influence of an "organized physician" lobby by eliminating the enforced revenue that had resulted from mandatory medical society membership for practicing physicians. **Healthcare Reform,** enacted by the Supreme Court, demanded that the "Profession" of "Private Practice" must be adjudicated to a "Trade" of fee-for-service "Unaffiliated Practice" in which individual physicians interacted in a "professional" manner, thus demonstrating their concerned "professionalism". Organized physician membership rolls, influence and prestige were remanded to take a huge step down from their high societal standing onto a precarious foothold, which was set to insidiously slide down a slippery slope directly downhill in prestige and influence. An employee is set apart from an employer with much the same set of basic human economic reactionary responses as acting with professionalism is economically set apart from acting as a true professional. Future physician migratory economic patterns for **Healthcare Reform** and pay-rated patient healthcare delivery satisfaction surveys more than proved the point.

President Ronald Reagan's administration proposed **Healthcare Reform** by limiting the employer exemption for healthcare delivery to an agreed-upon dollar amount below the usual and customary health plan charge so that the consumer could assume more responsibility and small businesses could better survive. That proposal never reached the floor of Congress. President Reagan next modified the Consolidated Omnibus Budget Reconciliation Act (COBRA) to include an Emergency Medical Transport and Active Labor Act (EMTALA) provision that granted and mandated emergency medical services to anyone entering any hospital emergency room in the United States without regard for the individual's citizenship or ability to pay. This **EMTALA**, was the **very first federal universal access healthcare delivery provision** ever proposed then actually enacted in and by the Congress and Senate of the USA. However, access to sustainable healthcare delivery after stabilization in an emergency room was not solved by President Reagan's EMTALA. Both timely access to quality healthcare delivery before emergency stabilization in an emergency room and timely access to quality follow-up and referral healthcare delivery after the emergency room visit had to be what universal healthcare delivery was to be all about. Furthermore, since any providing hospital in the USA was not allowed to enquire about patient payment or insurance coverage until after the presenting "emergent" condition was medically stabilized, the providing hospital emergency room rapidly became the home base for non-emergent and routine healthcare delivery for many people who could neither ever hope to pay nor have any agency successfully collect on their medical bill (and happened to be permanently or temporarily dwelling in the USA). Several fiscally worried hospitals responded by simply permanently closing their emergency rooms to all-comers; cash payment, insured payment, EMTALA or not made no difference for gaining patient access for emergency care once those hospital emergency room doors were slammed and bolted closed.

Medicare, especially initially, was rapidly becoming much too expensive for the federal government. Patients were running-up enormous medical tabs for slews of extensive and comprehensive medical work-ups that were repeated by even more slews of physician specialists as second, third, and fourth opinions, often miles apart and often in different states. President Reagan took this federal fiscal-depleting matter to hand and initiated a **Healthcare Reform** with the Diagnostic Related Group (DRG) payment system that permitted federal payment one time and only one time for a single diagnosis while under active treatment, thus saving Medicare from an unexpected consequence of immediate bankruptcy and other insurance entities billions of dollars from what would have been unpayable Medicare accounts receivable. **The DRG migratory economic payment system also proved to be an evolutionary Healthcare Reforming watershed event.**

In 1989, Senator Chaffee from Vermont introduced the concept of a single federal payer to the U.S. Senate. The ecolo-nomics of the pacific coast had traveled across the USA to reach to the shores of the Atlantic. However, both legislative bodies remained silent and enacted nothing in the way of **Healthcare Reform** that year.

President Nixon's HMOs were destined to insidiously evolve as a progressive progression in medical ecolo-nomics. As previously described, a new species, physically and interactively larger with greatly expanded vertical and horizontal integrated components compared to the smaller species of HMOs, a species or evolved healthcare delivery enterprise previously termed here as Health Keeper Organizations (HKOs) arose to prominence, bankrupted the smaller HMOs, and then dynamically competed against one another to determine who would be the last HKO standing during the third overlapping medical ecolo-nomic generation (1990-2010) and beyond.

Meanwhile, healthcare delivery costs continued to rise beyond the rate of inflation and created a new critical economic crisis. Several contributing factors have been implicated, such as:
. Increased longevity of the general population;
. Better, and more expensive drugs, technology and procedures;
. Supply side provider demand;
. Demand side user demand;
. Increased medical-legal risks and expensive malpractice premiums;
. Defensive and expensive medical-legal practices by physicians;
. A shortage of competition among a shortage of physician specialists; and
. An insatiable demand for physician-centered healthcare delivery rendered by primary care physicians in a continuing exclusive non-competitive marketplace.

California again took the **Healthcare Reform** lead in 1991 when the California Insurance Commissioner, John Garamendi, proposed a Health Insurance Purchasing Corporation (HIPC). The proposed HIPCs would combine the resources of governmental entities, employers, and consumers to dynamically manage competition and thus motivate efficiency among health plans. It was generally acknowledged that HIPCs would need three incentive-conscious payment methods that could fulfill three **Healthcare Reform** functions in order to sustainably survive:
First, HIPC health plans must be motivated to search continually for better methods/mechanisms of service delivery; the HIPC should not pay more to

selected health plans that experience higher costs due to their individual inefficiency.

Second, HIPC health plans must be discouraged from selectively enrolling healthy individuals and avoiding the chronically ill (cherry-picking); the HIPC should make larger payments to those plans serving a proven high-risk population and to those plans serving a documented population with pre-existing diseases.

Third, HIPC health plans must be motivated to evaluate the cost-effectiveness of new technologies and procedures and then appropriately **ration** them; the HIPC should rigorously negotiate health plan requests for premium increases over time.

An important lesson about **Healthcare Reform** might be learned by a brief review of resultant HIPC problems: The Garamendi proposal utilized a single payer plan to restructure existing corporate organized healthcare delivery systems. His HIPC concept hoped to be financed through payroll tax deductions and patient co-pays. Therefore, the HIPC concept unfortunately and unintendedly went down to defeat during the years of 1993 to 2006 with yearly repeated quick one-two punches:

1. Being not comprehensive enough to account for and attract the millions of healthy uninsured in the state, HIPIC became a magnet for the more expensive to treat unhealthy and otherwise uninsurable patients; and

2. The HIPC lacked sufficient grass root support; premiums for an increasingly unhealthy payer pool arose too far above existing open market levels for healthy patients, forcing profit-based bottom-line corporate insurers to eventually drop out. There was no provision for a government based reserve or retention fund to save those initially good-intentioned corporate insurers, and Californians were also really reticent about increasing state taxes for the purpose of furthering the profits of a corporate insurance industry with a bailout. Corporate bailout financial support was not popular at that particular migratory ecolo-nomic time.

As HIPC failed, the Jackson Hole Group again shouted from the top of their mountain, "Managed Competition", but nobody in the plains, valleys or ocean-sides listened; and Jackson Hole just got too darn cold to hold or sponsor argument and therefore froze and packed away as ice cubes any and all planned debates. Managed competition died and was buried with the (viewed by millions on TV but never produced) Clinton national health credit card. A migratory economic of **Healthcare Reform** had fallen to its knees; "HillaryCare", the Health Security Act of 1993, would never rise to stand again. Fearing a return of unpopular opinion from a repeated federal bureaucratic attempt to regulate HMOs during the rest of his first and throughout his second term, President Clinton never reintroduced the topic of national healthcare insurance. Instead, he signed into law the Health Insurance Portability and Accountability Act (HIPPA) (PL104-191,1996) and the

State Children's Health Insurance Plan (SCHIP). Both passed as politically correct and popular – HIPAA outlined standards for uniform health-related data transmission, the privacy requirements for the transfer of said data, and additionally assured continuing access to existing group health insurance when switching jobs ("What I may see or hear in the course of the treatment or even outside of the treatment in regard to the life of men, which on no account one must spread abroad, I will keep to myself, holding such things shameful to be spoken about."). SCHIP provided federal aid for children in working families just above the then Medicaid means-tested level.

Nationally, sound bites of talk, just talk, talking debates and debaters all portrayed a global plan for corporate national health, promised to be financed by payroll taxes. But who or what corporation or agency was to administer such a program? Gossip whispered that either state-run healthcare delivery agencies would be created for administration of corporate interests (The Bob Kerry Plan), or administrative functions would be performed directly by corporate interests without the state agencies (CHA-Catholic Health Association Plan). A lot larger than any small tin can to kick forward, the looming issue of single payer national health insurance, that 500-pound gorilla always in the debating room that actually weighed closer to half a ton, was again ignored and left to wander and wonder for another legislative day....

MIGRATORY ECONOMIC
FACTORS & PATTERNS
EVOLVING
MAN, MONEY & MEDICINE

PART FIVE

THE PROGRESSIVE RISE OF LIBERALISM:
MIGRATORY CULTURAL MORES

The third overlapping medical ecolo-nomic generation from 1990 to 2010 was a cost-driven equalization era of healthcare delivery and Healthcare Reform. The previous regulation and reduction of insurance payments by means of Diagnostic Related Groups (DRGs) hallmarked a five-year-old Healthcare Reform watershed event that finally became fully expressed.

The cultural ecology of an epoch, the socio-economics of political culture, and the moral-ethical character paradigm of people residing in any particular region are all expressed in contemporary territorial design – all art as well as the arts of migratory economics and healing are also so designed.

-- Ralzak

Yes, everyone knew quite well that if and when the lessons of history are not thoroughly researched in their total environmental-cultural context and appropriately appreciated and learned, then unfortunate unanticipated consequences of that history are determined and destined to repeat themselves. So it was with the infamous HEALTHCARE REFORM debates......

Vilfredo Pareto's purely economic term "Ophelimity", "Utility" can translate as a common migratory economic term meaning broadly-based happiness or satisfaction, the amount of pleasurable outcome resulting from consuming a good or service benefit, often measured and adjusted according to moral and political paradigms peculiar to a set place and time-definite. "A continual dynamic migratory economic force in America defines and redefines capitalistic production and value in terms of evolving societal norms for health and the art of living." Some might inconclusively argue that for the individual, public-provided utilities, modalities for gas, electric and fire-fighting services, are not included in that definition. In governmental terms, a "public utility" is a very highly and strictly regulated, vitally necessary and useful commodity, firm or service that is transmitted or distributed directly to benefit the public, usually through a private corporation. The cost of the "public utility" is partially subsidized to citizens at a certain poverty level through general tax revenues: but the "public utility" cost to an individual should rise exponentially, and become much more expensive according to an individual's personal usage beyond a certain reasonable basic benefit level. The basic public utility benefits all citizens equally regardless of potential differential increased individual usage risk when said vitally necessary usage variances result from expected and/or uncontrollable economic outliers due to unfortunate individual circumstance; for example, basic housing, climate, or remote geographic location. That's all pretty straightforward, clear and easy to understand; and that's what Americans want and in fact do receive from their government-controlled and privately owned utility modalities. No fuss, screaming, cranking or crying about that – but, in the first part of the 20th Century, when the commodity of healthcare delivery was added to that list of "public utilities" for the USA...... there suddenly followed public outrage and public concern of consequence -- a hundred-year-long **Healthcare Reform** political war had ensued.

Perhaps the structure of healthcare delivery in the United States during the 20th Century represented an anomaly on the world stage. Perhaps that structure stood out as an odd anachronism to other nations. Perhaps that structure stood as the temporary product of negative push-pull polling spin and political propaganda crippled by national methodological imperatives and practices. Nowhere else in the world could a proposal to offer "group health" ever be considered against the national pride of a country and characterized with negative national terms such as "un-American."

Perhaps American corporate structures gained oligopolistic influence and simply nudged organized healthcare delivery practices to suit their business needs. Perhaps when big business' capitalistic spin no longer effectively controlled the public mindset concerning organized healthcare delivery, corporate America simply took over direct control and spun any old tall tale to credit and guarantee the mechanism to deliver anything that the gullible public wanted to hear. Perhaps physicians were duped or were merely blinded pawns, manipulated on an economically-driven evolving dynamic competitive game board -- never really asserting control nor truly understanding the rules or consequences of play.

Perhaps healthkeepers in the United States simply got out of step with the rest of the world, and the short hundred years or so of the 20th Century lasted as a period of adjustment, a time warp that brought American healthkeepers back in step. Perhaps managed care arose as an epiphany. Perhaps managed care's associated problems and solutions hopefully awoke the general public to the reality and essential nature of organized healthcare delivery.

Perhaps a Machiavellian philosophy put survival of the state (the right to healthcare delivery as a pursuit of happiness) above some personal liberties (physician autonomy and unlimited personalized treatments). Perhaps the entire process remains as a historical document or footnote, a Plato-scripted questioning search for medical ecolo-nomic justice. Perhaps physician-centric healthcare delivery and the traditional doctor-patient relationship needed to be sacrificed in order to accomplish a greater good for a greater number of patients. Perhaps a new and deeper doctor-patient relationship could possibly emerge and offer quality healthcare delivery along with personal professional satisfaction for physicians.

There are so many "perhaps" possibilities…..

Late in the 20th Century, a 40-cent United States airmail stamp featured the portrait of Philip Mazzei, an American patriot. Mazzei's best known quote, "All men are by nature equally free and independent" – politically interpreted and then forever coined as "created equal", became the motto to summarize the guided behavior of Americans as well as the individual American as a concerned and caring human being. Medical practice autonomy and healthcare delivery autonomy, therefore, at first followed as natural and desired states of being American, which arose from having been born free with a love and hunger for independence, or "created equal". The gradual loss of autonomy among physicians throughout the 20th Century subsequently became regarded as an unnatural event to most practicing physicians. A minority of physicians saw the process as an evolving natural liberal progressiveness. A minority of physicians viewed loss of autonomy equal to un-American bonds of enslavement. The greater majority of physicians never bothered to contemplate their migratory medical practice (business) autonomy, or their loss of healthcare delivery (professional) autonomy, until the time and place for such an action to be effective were far and away, much too late to alter because of an ultimate natural and evolving course of migratory medical ecolo-nomic events. Fear not or worry more, for progressive social determinism would more than have its way beginning in the 21st Century.

But back then, the overt and necessary migratory economics of the day, as always, stood in direct conflict with various politico-social forces: In 1961, the AMA officially formed an American Medical Political Action Committee to act as a separate arm to directly represented Physician/Patient healthcare political interests. However, an AMA consensus to defeat any comprehensive national health insurance bill was nothing new; in 1932 The AMA championed a campaign altering a Social Security take-away from President Roosevelt, in 1949 the AMA lobby defeated the Murray-Wagner-Dingell bill and in 1962 the AMA overtly killed President Kennedy's King Anderson bill. The migratory economics of health insurance had evolved to the point where all contenders obviously agreed that the poor, elderly, and chronically disabled were in desperate need of insurance, but the degree and source of healthcare funding remained in hot debate. The AMA was concerned about retrieving payments for physician services; the political conservatives in DC did not want health services funding to be linked to a welfare system; the liberals wanted all healthcare services universally linked to social security (as was previously proposed then withdrawn by President Roosevelt in order to allow a successful launch of Social Security in 1932). Medical bankruptcy from unexpected costs became a menacing reality, especially among the elderly; but Congress was against increasing taxes, and the AMA was against decreasing doctors' income. The political climate was not proper for President Kennedy's King Anderson bill, but the weather forecast changed and incrementally became pleasant for President Johnson with his newly elected Democratic majority in the Congress. Medicare's Part A – hospital insurance for the elderly not being linked to a poverty level restriction – satisfied the liberals; and Part B – outpatient healthcare not linked to a poverty level restriction -- satisfied the AMA and the conservatives. Medicaid (an un-named Part C) offered exclusive healthcare to the state-defined eligible poor from an independent scope-amount-duration benefit system administered by the states, with diverse provisions in conjunction with their state public assistance programs. Approval for Medicaid snuck in under the political wire as the program offered a possible correction for the failing productivity and payments then offered by the means and asset tested Kerr-Mills legislation for poor families and those unfortunate blind and disabled citizens. The Medicaid program enrollment would grow from an initial 10 million nationally to over 14 million in California alone. If Medicaid's future growth could have been foreseen, the AMA would have surely lobbied to ditch the program – but that was back in the 60's when the AMA was not dependent upon the federal government for fiscal stability. Man, Money and Medicine -- the ecologically evolving weave of migratory economics entangles **Healthcare Reform** in so many varied ways and means.

Presidents Kennedy and Clinton both failed to get any comprehensive/universal omnibus **Healthcare Reform** package passed by Congress. Three lessons learned from those attempts should or might have been:

First, do not create a clandestine plan without buy-in from all interested parties during the time of its creation.

Second, do not suddenly offer an omnibus plan to a federal legislature that has not had the time to mull over and digest its contents after a thorough reading.

Third, small incremental migratory economic changes towards a defined goal usually slide by until it becomes too late and requires too much effort to reverse them.

Better still, the 1975 words of systematics writer and pediatrician Dr. John Gall emphatically stated that a complex system functions well only if and when it has evolved from a simple system, and to begin with complexity is to invite disaster. Nevertheless, yes, political planning had gone and will repeatedly go astray, like President Clinton's buried healthcare delivery credit card imprinted with bold letters – "Health Security", the "United States of America": In 1994, President William Jefferson Clinton's Health Security Act introduced the idea of a national healthcare delivery (health security) for the United States of America, featuring a credit card which, if ever used, combined individual mandated and employer mandated coverage along with a subsidized mandate for the poor and unemployed. Advocates boasted free choice of physician, free choice of plan, free choice of continuous coverage whether changing jobs or unemployed, and a 25% reduction in administrative costs. The Clintons believed that HKOs would surely compete nationally with other HKOs in the corporate healthcare marketplace for patient-shopped funding based on corporate performance dashboard scorecards. However, albeit for some politically propagated reasons, managed competition was not then a valid, workable concept in the public mindset, primarily because of the late-to-arrive patient-healthkeeper and poor political planning within the Clinton Administration, which seemed to be a recurrent error, as was the scandalous Paula Jones affair and subsequent "wink as good as a nod" untruthfulness to a federal grand jury about the matter (and not his DNA diagnostic semen stain on Monica Lewinsky's infamous blue dress), which ultimately led to President Clinton's impeachment sanction.

In addition to political spin backfire, the Clinton **Healthcare Reform** vehicle lacked sincerity in the minds of the American people. Instead of offering to fix what was agreed to be broken in the sturdy old American healthcare delivery truck, which reportedly failed to make deliveries to 40 million uninsured Americans, the Clinton spin attempted to sell expensive brand-new "Edsels" to 240 million Americans. The true Clinton legislative legacy became (ironically perhaps for a Democratic administration) his fiscally conservative migratory economic reduction of the capital gains tax, a temporary migratory economic factor which fueled a bear stock market and gave rise to a hysteric investor-driven, non-value rated IPO buying craze. Except for a few niche market-driven groups, only large corporate oligopolistic HKO plans became sustainable; small emerging corporate HKO plan survival was strenuous and not unusually brief.

Meanwhile glancing at the migratory economics transpiring on the physician fee fraction front, the Balanced Budget Act of 1997 amended Section 1848(f) of the Social Security Act -- the Medicare Sustainable Growth Rate (SGR) replaced the previous method, the Medicare Volume Performance Standard (MVPS), which CMS used to control costs and hopefully might have eased patients into managed care healthcare delivery plans. The SGR scheme was not created to simply rob Peter to pay Paul; albeit poorly formulated and never totally understood, the SGR was actually a truly valid attempt to enact **Healthcare Reform**: Looking again at the migratory economics, Medicare is a defined benefit program and Medicare Advantage for managed care plans is a defined cost program. As an inevitable demand for more and more Medicare benefits increase, there is no way to control eventual costs without rationing healthcare delivery or rationing payments according to public income status or public age for plan commencement. Redefining of benefits does not bode well in an already defined benefit plan. Any attempt in that direction cannot be politically or efficaciously accomplished without a tremendous senior-voter backlash. There arises too great of a politically tenuous situation if and where said benefits have already been defined. This is why the present form of Medicare will eventually implode and destroy itself if not drastically changed. However, in a defined cost program, such as Medicare Advantage, benefits can more easily be "restructured" (politically correct cold potato word for the hot potato word "rationed") to fit a current fixed or adjusted allotment of available funds. The U. S. Congress truly hoped that this new SGR formula could prevent the traditional yearly increased expense per Medicare beneficiary from exceeding first the yearly and then the 10-year average growth in GDP. Another justifiable Congressional worry and concern predicted that private practicing physicians simply would not agree to diagnose and treat Medicare patients if their somewhat substantial physician income did not exceed physician expenses. Therefore, the recidivist yearly threatening of a SGR mandated decrease in physician payment percentage became predictably suspended or adjusted (a "doc fix") by a panicked bi-partisan Congress on that same yearly basis ever since its conception. After more than a dozen years, very early in the year of 2014, in bicameral agreement, the SGR formula was permanently fixed or maybe just altered by basically adopting an anti M. Le Grendre "laissez-nous faire" economic course, again with wage and price freezes and the introduction of pay-for-performance requirements. Even though migratory economic policies engendered by free markets have consistently proven to be the most successful and sustainable, the bizarre and strange mind of a politician can, at will, dismiss any and all migratory economic strategy for **Healthcare Reform** as a failed myth from somewhere in the past. "Morbleu", at least extend a personal pardon to the very valid economic teachings of Vincent de Gournay and Francois Quesnay.

Y2K naturally saw healthcare costs on the rise once again. Politicians suddenly and accurately viewed Medicare and the entire employer-based insurance system to be unsustainable in the not so distant future. Cost-conscious physicians privately enacted a point-of-delivery **Healthcare Reform** by allowing their expanding responsibility for primary care to overflow into the laps of nurses and physician assistants, but cost containment still remained an unsolvable migratory economic conundrum. Healthkeepers of every type rationed healthcare delivery costs by rationing the smaller physician expense fractional piece of the total medical-economic pie. Pundits providing for the politically vocal few again deprived the silent many. The mistakes of the past were not recognized, and therefore repeated; good judgment based on experience and future dynamic economic planning did not prevail. A chunk of hot potato healthcare "cost rationing" dropped off the table and its hot butter topping oozed through the cracks of increasingly expensive and inappropriate middle-man corporate-organized healthcare delivery systems.

On December 8, 2003, after a close but positive vote in Congress, President George W. Bush, signed into law the Medicare Prescription Drug Improvement and Modernization Act, better known as the Medicare Modernization Act (MMA). By establishing an entitlement benefit for prescription drugs by means of tax breaks and subsidies, the MMA produced the largest **Healthcare Reform** of Medicare in the public health program's 38-year history. Economic balance, the greatest problem, of course and as always, remained unsolved, and the details for funding this expensive program in the face of ongoing fiscal shortages elsewhere became an unintended consequence that required federal borrowing from the future. Thus a precedent to accept a large federal debt without any proposed mechanism for repayment, as all worthy politically progressives yearn to do, was officially established as acceptable federal migratory economic policy by a Republican administration. Although severely criticized by candidate Obama, this economic concept and subsequent further federal indebtedness was soon to be magnified many fold during the President Obama administration.

Healthcare Reform once again shouted out politically as a buzzword during the year 2004 Presidential campaign. The voting public wanted improvements in their corporate organized healthcare delivery systems that would give them greater choice and coverage. Improvements via **Healthcare Reforms** had to be balanced with an equality of benefits to all groups, not just the small percentage of already insured voting public at that time. A realistic, new look at the cost-benefit analysis revealed fewer and fewer opportunities to reduce cost without restricting (rationing) healthcare delivery options. An economic reappraisal, prudently undertaken to determine what percentage of the national budget could be or would be "acceptable" to spend on healthcare delivery left progressive push-pull pollsters pondering, but unable to interpret the data. Push–pull progressive phrasing propaganda prospered. The economic chance probability perception from a polled presentation of medical opinion is always better when positive rather than negative advantages are not only emphasized but also scribed in "ABC" words versus boldly portrayed by "123" numbers. For example, even though the simple calculated odds are exactly the same, "9 out of ten are doing well" is perceived by the easily-manipulated and habitually-compelled human brain as a far better consequence than "one out of 10 died". Consensus did surely tell that if all the migratory economic healthcare statisticians and pollsters in America were lined up, shoulder-to-shoulder, across the great and wondrous land of the USA, they still could never probably or possibly hope to reach a valid and sustainable ecolo-nomic healthcare delivery conclusion.

President George W. Bush's administration introduced a patient bill of rights -- a convenient rug to lift then sweep under and hide the dirty business of true **Healthcare Reform**. Patients were given a limited right to sue their corporate HKOs, but the lawyers were capped at $1.5 million. Post 911, most federal funding went diverted into national defense efforts. The AMA prescription drug benefit was put on hold until 2006. The Center for Medicare and Medicaid Services (CMS) reduced physician payments by 5.7%. Several doctors opted out – super-specialty fee-for-service private practice and concierge primary practice became more lucrative without "80% -- pay Medicaid" or 100% of Medicare's newly reduced payment schedule. Also in 2006, Governor Mitt Romney, a future unsuccessful republican candidate for President of the USA, created a near-to-universal mandatory state-run insurance plan for Massachusetts.

In 2008, the last year of President Bush's administration, the United States became burdened with the start of a great jobless recession that was brought on by the unintended consequences of current and previous federal legislation. A 19th Century Carlo Ponzi scheme of economics, a sizzling 2/28 mortgage with a mandatory to stay solvent repeated re-fi every two years finally boiled, bubbled then burst. Walter Bagehot's "Dictum" from his writing, *Lombard Street*, back in 1873 very clearly and precisely stated that especially in times of financial crisis, banks should restrict the lending of Money to highly qualified borrowers possessing substantiated collateral back–up assets and set rates higher, purposely so to further restrict or ration borrowing to those "most worthy" among the very needy. Bagehot also previously admonished, in *Physics and Politics* that once a nation has firmly and determinedly established itself as a world power through constitutional conformity and military might, then that time and place is unfortunately ripe for progressive liberalism to gain a foothold, falsely disguised as diversity and freedom. A bit later in the 1800's, John Stuart Mill, in his treatise *On Liberty*, additionally enforced Bagehot's economic warning concerning progressive liberalism by writing, "unmeasured vituperation, employed on the side of prevailing opinion, really does deter people from expressing contrary opinions, and from listening to those who express them".

In the first half of the Twentieth Century, economist Joseph Schumpeter clearly described the internal evolutionary collapse of a capitalistic society into a demise of socialism when the entrepreneurial spirit of a nation is crushed by over-regulation. He described a group of academically-oriented elite intellectuals which others have referred to as "statists". They arise from the unfortunately highly over-educated, multiply-degreed and unemployed or unfulfilled-employed in a society where their talents are not essential for sustaining the economic equilibrium. A subset of this group or particular class of individuals becomes increasingly jealous of, then offended by, the growing wealth of entrepreneurial corporate interests and enterprises that they cannot possibly join nor financially benefit from. They thrive and achieve notoriety by openly critiquing and morally degrading the economically successful in order to gain approval from and then politically represent the supposedly downtrodden masses of society. They exploit a "rich versus poor" income and wealth differential by implying and suggesting hardship and calamity, but without actually defining "poor" as some level or subset of human existence. It is one thing to define "poor and poverty" in underdeveloped countries where starvation is culling an otherwise growing population; but it is quite another to use the exact same terminology (and therefore inferences) to equate income differences in the USA where some "poor" welfare recipients are awarded with an array of beneficiary products and services, including smartphones with unlimited data. The supposed elite intellectuals hide behind an expressed hateful subversive propaganda of diversity that also exploits racial and ethnic dissimilarities as fearful and feared inequalities. Rather than promoting pleasure in encountering the thrilling diversity among people and communities of people, they seek to divide and spoil the unity of people within a nation, a nation that has gone on a dire blood-borne record as tolerant and indivisible, with the expressed and carefully written fundamental concepts of liberty and justice for all as a prerequisite for its sustained survival. With the uncanny yet insidiously functional leadership process of the elitists in place, this select group of societal disruptors then take the impudence to exert the ultimate gall by holding themselves aloof from both -- the causes of and personal involvements in -- their invented miseries and sufferings within a thusly provoked jealous mass segment of society. Their malignant agenda is to create and continually sustain a growing powerful political majority to which these spiteful elite could never truly belong except as cocky shameless leaders. Starting as agitators at the community level, the elitists organize growing resentful protests of societal discontent and induce an increasingly malignant societal unrest that eventually unbalances the dynamically stabilized organized chaos of Schumpeter's Walrasian economic equilibrium. This smug and insolent elite intellectual class strives to poison, divide and turn a capitalistic society against itself, to discredit formerly honored constitutional roots and to destroy the forever politically threatened middle class and upper middle class of American society through a left wing extremist to socialistic progressive redistribution of wealth and resultant decline in entrepreneurship interest. These intermittent goals they best accomplish with gradual but persistent increases in wealth redistribution by first abusing the altruistic legalities of differential taxation and regulation. However, these supposedly concerned for the "underclass" intellectuals never relieve or even seek to cure their insidious and despicable induced societal unrest of inequality or promote a means for the supposed "underclass" to rise up on the social scale. Such a seemingly reasonable goal would, of course, threaten and eventually eliminate the elitist need, purpose and very existence. Rather, their malignant, devious and constantly induced undertone to divide society into segments with intermittent overt recidivistic unrest is of utmost importance and indeed, painfully essential for their continued and sustainable political existence. As with any political force -- once in power, the essential end goal becomes staying in power. Their end justifies their means – the statists simply let the chips fall where they may.

The mythological "American Dream" for the masses may have actually existed during part of the 1950's and the 1960's. The typical blue-collar worker was able to purchase an individual home complete with a car, TV and often a white picket fence. Weekends were spent mowing the front lawn and conversing with one's neighbor as to the timing of the next neighborhood barbeque. That epoch or paradigm arose quickly and disappeared just as fast. Globalization vanquished the dynamic competitive advantage of the American worker. Staying a step ahead of the rest of the world demanded job market concessions to entrepreneurial business enterprises.

In the late sixties, LIFE magazine raised the price of a single issue, almost doubled it, from 25 cents to 40 cents. In the December 20, 1968 issue, LIFE examined the plight of what were politically lump-thought to be wealthy Americans; but this popularized segment of the population, as the "Life Magazine" investigation readily discovered, predominantly grouped upper middle class Americans. The truly wealthy actually comprised and still comprise just the top 0.5% or less. Political speak about the "two percenters" or the "one percenters" (especially when expressed by Schumpeter's elite) links the upper middle class of working income earners to the much wealthier multi-multi-millionaire and billionaire class, and seeks ultimately, intentionally or not, to destroy solely that fragile upper middle class. (The same segment of society that the General Secretary of the Central Committee of the Communist Party of the Soviet Union, Joseph Vissarionovich Stalin sought to exterminate by execution.) Dollar numbers adjusted for the place and time of the 1960's, here is a quote from that article in LIFE: "Prosperity brings its miseries. To investigate this paradox – the sad state of affluence – LIFE interviewed six families from various parts of the country whose incomes all hover around $20,000, a salary that only 2% of Americans can claim. None felt prosperous, most in fact felt poor. The cost of living has risen about 4.5% this year, the biggest jump in nearly two decades. Besides, by the time the six finish paying for the simple necessities, like a self-cleaning oven, and jaunts like a weekend at Disneyland with the kids, there is simply nothing left over for plain fun. No, $20,000 isn't *anything* even though most of us go around with a fuzzy notion that once, a long time ago, twenty thou stood for wealth. Herewith, some glum disclosures about what it means to "succeed" in an affluent society."

Nonetheless, something significant began to happen to the bell-bottom pant-suit and disco-dancing U.S. economy during the 1970's. An insidious ecolo-nomic conglomeration was destined to eventually create a migratory economic monster that fattened its pockets at the cost of increasing an income inequality gap. Domestic debt was rising along with non-banking industry debt, such as household debt. New technologies in the business sector were increasing product productivity; but wages remained relatively flat, excluding employees from sharing in the good times ahead. Capital gains in the banking industry featured politically influential Shylock corporations playing and winning big in the "no product for society" Money/credit game of giving little to the lenders/depositors and charging a lot to the spenders/borrowers. The stock dividend game along with the non-productive "buy low and sell high" Wall Street "bear and bull" games were both increasingly popular and getting red hot for the gambling players. The thrown migratory economic dice were rolling and when they stopped against the far green cushion on the ecolo-nomic table, all could suddenly see that there had been a positional rearrangement of the stratified influential power structure in the economy and American life.

Income gap inequality (which does not necessarily denote but in political popularity does connote a sub-standard of human existence) continued to steadily expand in the USA. The upper middle class $20,000 range of the sixties grew to the $100,000 range in the eighties, but the overall dynamic remained the same. An ever-widening gap between the 0.5% and the rest of the population became a dynamic statistical fact. Therefore, in an attempt to build public confidence, the President Ronald Reagan administration of 1980 passed the Depository Institutions Deregulation and Monetary Control Act for average Americans to increase savings in commercial banks by increasing federal deposit insurance from $40 K to $100 K and allowing new "Savings and Loan" firms to offer interest rates without a cap. 1982 saw the passage of the Garn -- St. Germain Depository Institutions Act, an unsuccessful attempt to rescue thrift institutions which contained in title VII, the Alternate Mortgage Transactions Parity Act (AMTPA). Federal Law preempted any State Law that had previously restricted commercial banks from writing mortgages beyond a conventional fixed rate of amortization.

Federal regulatory lessening or de-control of the banking industry entrepreneurially introduced an adjustable mortgage rate that could be written by federally-chartered housing creditors. This initial migratory economic was actually a good bet as long as real estate values were increasing and the housing could be readily re-financed by a legitimately qualified borrower. However, there were other quite valid concerns – the unequal bargaining power of labor versus management, business technology demanding skilled and trained workers versus unskilled lower income labor, reduced inflation expectations and the possible overall reduced aggregate economic demand from income hoarding – all valid concerns that highlighted and fostered resultant functional wage stagnations, a dire and ominous migratory economic state in the evolving U.S. economy.

There exists a great difference between "income inequalities" versus "wealth inequalities": Income can be defined as dollars earned plus job supplements and various governmental rebates/allocations/ – rent, food, healthcare, child support, transportation, cellphones, welfare, and tax write-offs. When all of the above items are considered in the formula, the difference in income inequality between the very poor and the middle class or upper middle class tends to shrink severely.

This loss of stratification becomes a source of perverse incentives which promulgate a generational acceptance of a welfare state of existence. The mores of the American people would never accept a blazing economy that is built at the expense of a class structure as exists in China or Brazil. Taxes and federal control of interest rates may help to spark the U.S. economy, but good jobs for middle class workers that pay enough for the middle class to pursue that mythical American dream is the true heart and soul of the American economy. The upper one tenth of the upper one-percenters either generate no income at all or generate (as opposed to "earn" which denotes the sweat of one's brow and elbow grease metaphors) an income vastly out of proportion to 90 percent of the upper one-percenters. On the other hand, wealth inequality is quite a different matter. In a lagging economy, the opportunity for the upper middle class to obtain fiscal wealth is diminished and the opportunity for people working in the middle class to stay one step above the lower class in fiscal wealth is near to eliminated. Thus, the fiscal wealth gap continually widens and becomes near to impossible to cross. This widening gap also affects the societal physical-mental wealth gap by adding increasing amounts of physical inflammation and mental depression, otherwise known as medical treatment and job loss expenses to the economy caused by disease and dissatisfaction. Again, the linkage of Man, Money and Medicine.

Income inequality, when considered alone in isolation is a moral-ethical issue, not a national economic stability issue. In a Democracy, election to political power is accomplished by majority vote of the constituent electorate. Prudent political action carelessly succumbed into predictable reflex political reaction positions without regard for determining or deterring long term unintended consequences. Thus were negligently sowed the seeds that would blossom in a future great economic crisis. Nonetheless, the first Community Reinvestment act (CRA) of President Carter's administration stood as a wise migratory economic policy to decrease a perceived lending discrimination policy in the banking industry. Lower-income citizens with good and honorable credit histories were better able to finance private family homes – an established American ideal. Again, no good deed goes unpunished.

Rather than adjust and stratify the society, a progressive political agenda pandered to that equalizing lowering standard for all, did not increase vulnerable middle class income and promised a better day to follow by not acting or planning, but just "thinking about tomorrow". A popular conjured myth of justice that portrayed a destiny for Man to live in a global environment with equal opportunity and equal happiness for all regardless of global geographic location or painfully obvious genetic/cultural/racial/individual/national/sexual/intellectual or physical/biological differences.

Thousands of banks went belly up during the Great American Depression. Therefore, ever since 1933, the Glass-Steagall Act had quite successfully limited the vertical investment or line of business interaction between commercial banks and investment security firms otherwise known as investment "banks" by specifying a lower limit of quality on allowed commodity interaction. Commercial banks insured the hard-earned savings of common people and investment "banks" were reserved for high-end speculators to take monetary risks; but in 1999, the Democratic Clinton Administration sought "modernization" and deemed the act to be unworkable. The Gramm-Leach-Biley Act repealed the Glass-Steagall Act. The de-regulation problem progressed to the point in 2004, when the banks were now able to and indeed unilaterally decided to reduce capital holdings in relation to debt from around 1:12 to about 1:30. A future unsuccessful Democratic primary candidate (Bernie Sanders) would admonish and advise that the original 1933 legislation be reinstated to prevent unbalances leveraging, such as a miniscule 4% to 5% put away reserve fund for banks denoted as "too big to fail". There was also concern about the guaranteeing or underwriting-insuring of "Bad Bet Debt" by the "non-banks" or "shadow banks" such as AIG, Lehman Brothers, Bear Stearns and others. Bernie Sanders depicted Wall Street as a fraudulent out-of-control, economic modality acting contrary to the interests of the vast American public sector. He further insisted on capping much more than a simple lid on the "illegitimately" incurred debt. (A portion of his wishes came true when President Donald Trump reinstated a revised version of the Glass-Steagall Act.)

Those many forms of carelessly scattered seeds leading to the eventual 2008 recession began to germinate two years earlier, in 1977, when under the Clinton Administration, a revised Community Reinvestment Act (CRA) further eased loan credit history restrictions for home loans to low income families. Those new and unwise revisions became the basic too heavy load that could not tolerate the straw that broke the housing investment camel's back. A new type of "moral hazard" introduced itself to the American economy. Inferring from various Clinton Administration political pressures, commercial banks now additionally felt a confidently protected politico-financial need to respond to the non-creditworthy demands of organizations such as the Association of Community Organizations for Reform Now (AORN) in order to hopefully, in return, receive dynamic competitive advantage for governmental approval when attempting to expand or when entering into mergers. A documented and proven further reduction in lending standards offered these commercial banks an opportunity for obtaining a quick governmental wink of approval rather than suffer the risk of burdensome investigations and possible sanctions. This progressive liberal thinking along with a conservative moral/ethical attitude of the time both envisioned a mythical human condition where Man, living in a very modern and rich nation, was yet not able to enjoy a very significantly higher standard of living, a standard that a productive nation should morally/ethically provide for its citizenry. Offering the opportunity of individual home ownership to fill an income inequality gap for low wage earners who were otherwise unable to save required an unobtainable means -- a down payment and the ability to produce the necessary credit rating to secure a conventional mortgage. Eliminating these requirements seemed to be a progressive liberal rightly "end" to justify a totally unexamined, if not blinded, "means".

Ever since civilization began about 5000 years ago, one Man's garbage has been another Man's desire/treasure, and that has kept numerous national economies up, running and vibrant. Ideally, when one Man saves Money, another Man sees an opportunity to borrow Money. Through entrepreneurial innovation, the second Man hopefully finds a profitable investment for those funds and a cyclic capitalistic cycle rolls round. If the investment is not profitable, then the borrower loses Money and starts saving to pay off the incurred debt until it is possible to start borrowing again. To maximize profits and minimize debt through the monitory policies of the federal banking system, the interest rate can be proportionally adjusted to reflect the number of borrowers. If the borrower cannot save due to national poverty, then a serious disruption of the cycle will inoculate a contagious national depression epidemic as occurred in the USA in 1913 and 1929. Historical origin values within a nation's population vied against progressive governmental actions bolstered by media propaganda to redefine a republic's rules and regulations. Furthermore, the public asks no questions when the minds of the masses are properly filled with lies.....

According to Ralzak, there are three fundamental requirements for Man to achieve socio-economic success: He has to possess and exhibit a combination of abilities best characterized by Albert Einstein, Tom Sawyer, and a United States Marine. Then there must be a gut-driven persistence and willingness to accept repeated failures without loss of an alpha wolf's drive-motivation or lupine-like goal-orientation. It is not necessary for Man to be totally Einstein bright, potentially fiscally successful Man must just have an above average in IQ. A United States Marine is respected for dependability in arriving on time and getting the job done effectively, a "semper fi" to trusted followers. Tom Sawyer had the social ability to manipulate others to the point of paying Tom for the "privilege" of painting his aunt Bessie's fence, an annoying chore that she had already assigned to Tom. Having satisfied those pre-requisite individual characteristics for financial success, three known mechanisms for the expression of those traits present themselves to Man as traditional pathways, trails for wealth accumulation. Trail number one is to be the very first innovator; trail number two is a path through mercantilism -- to be the most proficient maker, marketer or performer; trail number three, unfortunately is a yielding to corruption, to become the smartest and most devious criminal or self-aggrandizing politician. These three pathways are expressed in the decadent entertainment industry as writer, producer/artist, and crooked/criminal under-the-table contractor. Looking at the technological development sector, the three pathway categories are the first innovator-developer, the best marketer-seller, and the most proficient international pirate-drug-gun runner. House builder, mortgage lender and fraudulently over-rated bundled junk bond salesperson also seem to fit the general pattern as observed in the "bubbles" that burst in 2008:

The financial markets are relatively new inventions of mercantile Man to deal with "various forms of his Money". It was always important and still is important to have a fixed set of rules on how "various forms of his Money" could be and can be manipulated. Such a system naturally has its ups and downs, but generally works fairly smoothly with minor adjustments over time. When these rules of engagement are suddenly and drastically changed by federal government decree, then, with the help of an "innovative" few, those "various forms of his Money" can, and most likely will take on a new life on their own. One can blame the "various forms of his Money" for a financial disaster, but that is akin to blaming a bomb for tragic mass destruction rather than the process and decision of a government in creating and delivering that weapon to some specified target.

In Man's historical financial marketplace, there is really nothing new under the sun concerning the concept of "Derivatives". Derivatives are as old as basic bargaining for Man. Historically, derivatives have contracted two points of interest that are private, balanced, transparent, well considered and not affecting the interests of others. They have been like a variant of insurance, an even-sided gamble for some type of remuneration depending on the chance that something will or will not happen in the future. Investment entities, sometimes referred to as investment "banks" have participated in well-formatted derivative trades for the past two centuries. Such trading was regulated by the "Commodity Exchange Act" of 1936, which defined "safety and soundness" established centrally-cleared standards and limited derivative trades as liquid and standardized "futures", security interactions between "sophisticated parties" under federal law. In July of 1998, Alan Greenspan appeared before the U.S. Congress and stated, "Regulation of derivatives transactions that are privately negotiated by professionals is unnecessary." The expresses policy of the Clinton Administration was to eliminate government regulation in derivative trades and swaps. On December 21, 2000, president William Clinton officially signed the "Commodity Futures Modernization Act" into federal law and thus limited the "functional regulation" power of the "Commodity Futures Trading Commission".

With change comes opportunity for wealth-accumulation pathway number one – innovation: Lew Ranieri, among others on Wall Street, invented a "securitization" processing for toxic asset home loans by packaging them in bundles for sale to various investment banks locally and internationally. Suddenly, new trading entities, Over-The-Counter (OTC) derivatives appeared on the fiscal horizon and were not subject to participation in a formal exchange network or an intermediary. They could be non-transparent, risky, without standards, and not limited to "sophisticated parties", and they certainly were all of that and then some – traded and privately negotiated exotic options such as forward rate agreements, lock or option products more popularly known as lifetime "Swaps" and short term "Interest Rate Caps".

There was also nothing new about wealth-accumulation pathway number two -- the concept of Commodity Swaps. Such trades were looked upon as commonplace since the mid 1970's, as a simple contract to exchange a potential future cash flow or interest rate change for a spot price offering with the risk of future profit or loss as an effort to hedge spot commodity prices; but the regulatory rules, clearing houses and trading methodologies were drastically changed if not totally eliminated by that "Commodity Futures Modernization Act" of Y2K. Not unexpectedly, the un-blazed trail for Credit Exchange Swaps and Collateralized Debt Obligations led directly to Pathway Number Three for wealth accumulation: Exponential growth of investment banking interests began immediately to the point where, by 2015, five supposedly "too-big-to-fail" institutions – JP Morgan, Chase, Bank of America, Wells Fargo, Citigroup and U.S. Bancorp -- controlled $15.3 Trillion or about half of total investment industry assets.

In between the lines, there is a Man, Money and Medicine/Wealth Health story to be told of what strange things Man finds to do with Man's Money. As a result of this "innovative" Y2K deregulation linked with obvious moral hazard, Wall Street began to sing a tune first popularized in 1918: "I'm forever blowing bubbles, pretty bubbles in the air. They fly so high, nearly reach the sky," but those in the "making Money using other people's Money" business somehow forgot the last part of that tune's rhyme: "Then like my dreams, they fade and die." "Pay or Die" time would arrive, pop that bubble, ring the bell at the world-wide investment banking doors for a quickly retreating "Ding Dong Dash", and leave those investments banks hopelessly trying to stamp out paper bags on fire that were filled with dog crap as their only asset. Belly up-disaster prone, this bubble would have much greater consequences than the collapse of the housing market in the USA; this bubble would pop the roof off of the investment banking industries and resultant economies throughout the entire planet. David Oddsson, Iceland's prime minister and central bank governor, was put to shame for placing his country into intolerable debt from a macroeconomic meltdown.

Then came the supposed recovery; but first, to appropriately appreciate and succulently savor this total operatic production and all its supporting cast, it is necessary to digress, turn aside and wander through the created mire of muck:

As noted in the above overview, Schumpeter-admonished political pandering during the President Clinton administration apparently "coerced" the naturally greed-oriented commercial banks and other mortgage lending institutions to make uninvestigated fiscal-means loans to formerly unqualified borrowers, innumerable borrowers with absolutely no collateral back-up assets at all. Why not anyway – the commercial banks and lenders were now by federal governmental decree just the originators of bad debt loans whose consequences would not be felt until a future time and place; and these mortgage brokers profited by way of multiple transaction costs and, furthermore, would surely not end up holding those horribly-written mortgages in the end. As a matter of fact, nearly 50% of that unknown fraudulently over-rated bad debt would eventually be purchased globally on the foreign exchange. These hustled deals amounted to far-advanced slipperier and slicker scams than anything old Schumpeter could have possibly imagined.

American workers with stagnated wages envisioned borrowing for a home that had traditionally increased in asset value as a fantastic window of opportunity to maintain their standard of living. In 1989, directly contrary to the teachings of economist Bagehot, a Home Mortgage Act disrupted prudent lending a bit further and offered sub-prime loans to an even greater number of unqualified borrowers at the insistence of that ever so heavy persistent hand of federal government. Once again migratory economic policy took that short step leading to an imminent deep abyss, a miniscule step and hop from political correctness onto political pandering. The ill-advised and unexamined migratory economic process continued even when American workers had difficulties making mortgage payments, but still held hope that the increasing monetary value of a real estate asset would eventually save their butts, hopefully during some miraculous day to come. A risk-taking culture became the norm for the red-blooded American public and also flowed throughout the circulation system of federal bodies. The average workers' bargaining power with management in the public sector and their functional public-sourced income was increasing, but their bargaining power with management in the private-sourced sector and with functional private-sourced income was decreasing.

Also under the President Clinton administration in 1992, a Housing and Community Development Act (HUDA) instructed the federal department of Housing and Urban Development (HUD) to require a migratory economic commitment from the Federal National Mortgage Association (Fannie Mae) and the Federal Home Loan Mortgage Corporation (Freddie Mac). 30% of federal loan purchases had to be listed as affordable housing. (This requirement would be raised to 56% during the President Bush administration despite the president's vain attempts to convince a Democratic-majority legislature to place regulation controls over Fannie May and Freddie Mac.) These federal actions, highly acclaimed by politically active (vote-influencing) constituent groups such as The National Council of La Raza (NCLR) (La Raza, The Race) and the Association of Community Organizations for Reform Now (ACORN), naturally added to further relaxing of banking credit standards.

In 1995, the already existing fiscally unjustifiable loan repayment problem became compounded when some of those formerly mentioned but not specifically named elitist community organizers legally represented agencies such as ACORN. These well-educated organizers, with law degrees from places like Harvard and seeking a political future, offered a politically progressive legal defense for a dual standard in judging the actions of non-profit/progressive lobby agencies. The legal justification granted to those agencies drastically lowered the already lowered standards for loan rating methodology to the point of virtually ignoring borrower qualifications and offering 100% loan financing. To wit, ACORN approved "liar loans", the low-or-no documentation mortgages that took puppet borrowers at their word (as advised by the puppet-master ACORN) without checking their pay stubs or W-2s and depended on some sort of joyful paean to the mystical gods of imaginary magical Money trees for future loan repayment. ACORN was eventually taken to task, proven guilty of encouraging otherwise not interested and grossly unqualified borrowers to take out and take on poorly structured loans. By the time this horrid situation finally became painfully apparent and disturbingly obvious, all too many "bad loans" were floating about the American economy.

Congress, feeling themselves put into a politically self-created tight spot between a rock and a hard place, or more likely feeling like that the possible execution spot was "Tra San Marco e Leone", blindly jumped into the mire and fatally forced the publicly-traded Fannie Mae and Freddie Mac to buy up the resultant irresolvable debt. That was at best a feeble attempt to divert a catastrophe; and of course, no good deed goes unpunished – a moral hazard pitfall loomed over Man and his Money. Investment banks felt overly confident that the federal government would always come galloping in on a white horse to rescue them, even if they were tied to the railroad tracks with a screeching locomotive approaching. The banks neither saw nor envisioned shame. In spite of obvious poor lending policies, they would have the frank and unmitigated gall to ask for even more Money, openly expressing that they were "too big to fail".

With the heavy and quite visible hand of federal agencies now holding and supposedly guaranteeing all these absolutely proven "bad notes", New York Stock Exchange insurance groups such as American International Group, Inc. (AIG) rapidly, knowingly and intentionally covered these essentially federally-guaranteed Mortgage Backed Securities (MBS = "much bad stuff"), at substantially discounted rates during 1996. In turn, 1997 saw the Federal Reserve being assuaged or actually forced to issue funding to back-up the failing federal Fannie and Freddie agencies. The Federal Reserve, through the efforts of Alan Greenspan in 2001, cut the interest rate nine times; in turn, the commercial banks lent out even more unrepayable funds. Home loans became cheaper and more delicious with initial low "teaser" rates being offered at that time. Such "predatory lending" was not limited to residential properties; consumer real estate borrowers also, like hungry trout, jumped to swallow the tasty bait and got snagged before they even had the opportunity to gulp it down. Bubble number one (the residential housing market) expanded by joining with bubble number two (the commercial real estate market). There were already Billions of Dollars invested in sub-prime loans. Big banks went one step further by pooling these mortgages so that the cheap paper could be marketed to investors of various types. To help accomplish these sales, Wall Street entrepreneurs created residential mortgage-backed securities (RMBS), some very clever and quite entrepreneurial bundles of asset-backed securities in discrete packages that could either be issued by Fannie May and Freddie Mac, or under a private label constructed by investment banks. The banks then acted as middle-management gambling bet stakeholders for the flow of payments from mortgage holders to the risk-liable investors.

Investors were at first reluctant to take on the inherent contracted risk. The perceived need of Man and Money greed being two mothers of invention, young and intelligent "financial engineers", people like Charles Prince and Robert Rubin, envisioned a unique window of opportunity to convert the residential mortgage based (RMBS) into a potentially higher level of profit which included a higher level of risk to the investor. In order to disguise this newly increased risk, the investment Gurus cleverly found low-rated, high-risk securities, mainly consisting of bad mortgages, and then converted them into same nominal value high-rated, "low-risk" AAA--rated "synthetic" securities, quite attractively engineered investment modalities formed by overly enthusiastic calculations made with flexible and fumbling rubber numbers. The process supposedly overlooked a vital requirement, picking securities from varied distant geographical locations, and in addition eventually proved mathematically impossible – to the point of being considered criminal fraud by some in retrospect. Quite simply put, the investment engineering geniuses gathered up C and D rated securities and then bundled them into such entities as collateralized debt obligations (CDOs) or credit default swaps (CDSs), both with higher ratings stamped with approval from such agencies as Standard and Poor's (S&P). (The Dodd-Frank Wall Street Reform and Consumer Protection Act requiring sellers to take on a portion of the buyer's economic risk would not become federal law until 2010, may have overly regulated and was eventually replaced by something more akin to the Glass-Steagall Act during the President Trump administration.)   Duped investors arrived from all over the world, especially China, rich with surplus export fund profits. These funds were termed "savings gluts" and effectively functioned to push capital into the USA, but there was also a higher rate of local consumption which aided in pulling more capital into the local U.S. market. All too many of these "low-risk" securities eventually turned out to be absolutely worthless.

Meanwhile, American workers depleted their private savings by investing more Money into the Ponzi scheme known as the housing market. Asset inflation had been an established reality in the American economy for the past 20 years and there was no indication, no warning issued or revealed to the average American uneducated investor that real estate net worth growth would ever stop.

When still more Money seemed to be needed, primarily to pay down an increasing debt from a war in Iraq, the federal government simply turned on their Money-making ink-presses and printed more dollars. Instead of correcting the on-going progressive problem, the Bush administration enacted additional non-specific, across-the-board tax cuts that did not encourage the average American to spend more in the general non-housing general economy or sufficiently provide for specifically increasing incentives for supply side production. The upper echelon of society did not create more jobs because they did not trust the direction of the economy -- President Bush lacked the ability to project an economic confidence to the general public as President Ronald Reagan had successfully accomplished. The progressively liberal structure of the President Bush tax cuts actually added to the deepening recession by forcing the feds to lower the interest rates.   True

Reaganomics and conservative Milton Friedman's fact-based or "what is" positive economics, value-based economics, had disappeared, totally gone from governmental view or vision. Those conservative-valued philosophy of economics were quietly and simply ignored once again by the current Republican Administration. Rather than a free market complexity of stabilization policy, a hopeful, wishful and wanting semi-Keynesian federal policy took hold. The growing migratory economic housing bubble was quietly set aside so as to be ignored by the media. The traditional conservative cyclic concept of economic death and subsequent rebirth/reorganization from the spoils in a vibrant capitalistic environment became too horribly frightful for President Bush's staff of progressive-oriented economists to acknowledge or even envision. The then Democratic house and Democratic senate acted in accord. Normative judgments sought out hopeful/wishful goals of what ought to happen, relying too heavily on irrelevant past occurrences to predict future events.

There was the interaction of Man and Money, but President Bush's administration did not forget about the third "M" – It was known as the "Medicare Drug Benefit". Medicine prices in the USA were high to start and made sustainably higher by a codicil in the drug benefit agreement that prohibited Medicare from negotiating with the pharmaceutical industry for lower drug prices.

Because of the huge governmental bailouts, Banks and entities such as Goldman Sachs found themselves under the umbrella of a no risk moral hazard. Morality and business ethics were silently abandoned; Wall Street took no personal responsibility to look after Main Street. They simply looked forward to grow their oligopolistic power and influence into frankly illegal monopolistic control of the American economy in direct violation of the spirit of Sherman Anti-Trust. The federal government had the power to disperse them into smaller functioning units, but this possible solution was never even hinted to be on the agenda. The Wall Street agenda turned out to be a badly played baseball game for the American public:

One, two, three strikes and you are out! Shenanigans within the innovative bank home mortgage loan programs progressed to innovative shenanigans within the bond market.

The first strike let a low and inside fast ball slip by the corner of the strike zone in 1970. Lending banks pooled reliable and safe "AAA" mortgages from a mixture of geographic locations, combined or bundled them into one "mortgage backed security", known as a MBS. Federal government controlled agencies -- "Ginnie

Mae", "Freddie Mac" and "Fannie Mae" -- issued the MBS's to support the mortgage market and offered a fairly secure set of yields inversely proportionate to the perceived credit reliability.

Strike two came next with a cleverly thrown curve ball. – As the housing bubble grew in size during the early turn of the century years, the government bolstered the oncoming bubble by creating more and more MBS's (now named CDO's – collateralized debt obligations); but this time the bond pool contained mostly unreliable mortgages, sub-prime adjustable home mortgages, often originating in single geographic locations. Unfortunately, Standard & Poor's rating scale as well as the fraudulent favorable rating scales of other firms such as Moody's blessed these CDO's with an unjustified 90% A-ratings when about 65% really deserved something nearer to a F-rating. That old perverse golden rule again – the firms with the Money (investment banks) make the rules for payment; and, of course, Moody's and Standard & Poor's sorely wanted to get paid......

The housing market went on to accept increased risk, yielding to Man's primal greed by turning a fast buck – lending multiple mortgages on a single property and lending to borrowers with multiple properties rented out to cover a perceived temporary gap of low or no interest payments or in some cases actually purposely defaulting in the determined expectation that a future re-financing could and would easily be accomplished down the spiraling inflationary house value road. Why not – house values had been increasing, were increasing and were naturally expected to continue to increase in the future, when that big balloon payment would become due....... or not!

Then sizzling through the air came the pitch of a hot fast ball, delivered to the high and outside corner of the zone, and inducing the batter to swing and sorely miss, for strike three – the creation of "Synthetics" CDS's. The investment banks pasted together a bundle of already bad CDO's to form the CDS's. As concisely yet figuratively expressed in the movie, "The Big Short", "Dog shit was wrapped in cat shit." Fraudulently again labeled with A-ratings from a variety of firms, over-confident investment banks such as Goldman Sachs, Bear-Stearns, Countywide, Morgan Chase and Deutsche Bank– just to name a few, bought and sold the CDS's, perhaps in expectation that the bubble would never burst, or perhaps because they already knew that the government would eventually save their butts with a bail-out in the end. Due to the previously governmental ordered tear down of regulatory walls that once securely separated insured commercial banking and risky investment banking, an artificial investment bank confidence level grew so strong that these banks were even willing to sell "short" to investors who would be obliged to pay more should the CDS bond value increase, but would be paid more generously should the CDS bond value decrease. Even when it was becoming obvious that the housing bubble would burst, these banking firms managed to keep the ratings on their CDS and CDO bond instruments at a painfully obvious fraudulent high level, ironically (or worse) while these same investment banks frantically attempted to sell off what they could to unsuspecting clients in a vain attempt to remain solvent. Meanwhile, those "credit default swaps" shorted about 1.3 Billion dollars, eventually paying those clairvoyant clever investors who bought "short" a 10 to 1 return on their gambled greenbacks. The world economy took a giant hit, not one out of the ball park, but definitely one to the sustainable standard of living of their citizens. In the USA, 8 million citizens lost their jobs; and 6 million lost their homes.

The Bush Administration's solution resorted to incurring those large budgetary deficits and propagandizing a myth of inflation looming on the horizon, both strategies hoping and praying to absorb private sector hoarding. The American people were not reassured by the President's words. The make-believe Keynesian ploy fell short of its mark. The upper class bought more high end toys and trinkets; luxury item sales were way up. The middle class, the societal class structure that historically was always responsible for leading a bloody revolution, bought into the ominous migratory economic big time, way over their financial heads. Investment in real estate and house "flipping" was at an all-time high. As long as the increased value pricing in the real estate market was dependably improving, borrowing and spending increased, while personal savings decreased. Americans purchased and "flipped" multiples of "track homes" before completion of the building project and in some cases before ground had been broken for additional track projects. They acted like happy campfire girls carefully toasting marshmallows for "s'mores" over an open fire, giggling away until the marshmallows suddenly caught on fire. 60% of housing investment went into private residences. Average Americans could close on a house mortgage deal and then plan to default on the payments in hope that an increased market evaluation would allow future sale of the property at a profit, even after sizeable penalty adjustments for the non-payment of the incurred debt. The price of the average home increased over 100% in the ten-year period before 2006. All of the above offered a temporary migratory economic monitory acceleration to the lower class, a greater opportunity for jobs producing excess exhaust Money from employment that that could help maintain their monthly mortgage payments, fight wage stagnation and possibly start up a high-powered engine for demand growth to loudly rumble and race through the American economy with the muscle-car force and power of a big-block L-71 550 horsepower engine hotly roaring under a tri-2-

carb Holley carburetor, all encased in a shining-bright flashing-red 1967 Corvette Sting Ray fastback sporting an accommodative hood elevation and vented side exhausts. Instead, the U.S. government entered into a child's race of "all around the mulberry bush", then…..

Pop went the bubble!! During the years of 2006-2007, investors, uncles and aunts all lost their shirts, plus their pants. Too too many wishing and wanting citizens were totally dependent on continued low interest rates in that Adjustable Rate Mortgage (ARM) Ponzi scheme. Suddenly things changed. Interest rates rose higher and higher in an attempt to adjust to that severe drop in housing prices. Investors now lacked the means to re-finance; defaults and foreclosures ran ramped, appeared everywhere; and debt was simply ubiquitous. The public debt load in the housing market rapidly grew to be significantly greater than the actual real value of the real estate. Prices dropped even further as newly-built homes found no buyers, as they were impossible to sell in the glutted real estate market. CDOs and CDSs turned into worthless pieces of "Wall" paper. "CRISIS" rang out as the word of the day all about planet earth.

There was no Ludwig Ehard on that horizon. Consequently, calendar year 2008 headlined the collapse of Lehman-Sachs and especially the insurance arm of AIG, who had taken on a credit risk of nearly half a trillion dollars – the thirty-year-old housing market bubble finally had burst and Americans were forced to face the reality of an oncoming prolonged financial recession. There was no prudent governmental wizard hiding behind a curtain; Americans finally removed their rose-tainted fiscal blinders to suddenly discover that they actually were not living in the land of OZ.

Employment figures were about to fall in spite of an attempted stabilization with federally-induced low inflation. Investment would naturally halt, and growth would then be crippled in a financially unstable economy. Without wage growth, further income stagnation would increase, resulting in more debt, more income inequality; and as for continued asset price inflation, well that was left first sagging then totally assassinated in the process. All of the above migratory economic circumstances also jeopardized then murdered demand growth. The time and moment suddenly demanded a protective and rescuing federal government to saddle up and ride, gallop directly into this fiscal disaster zone and miraculously find something that could be done to correct the situation.

Supposedly conservative Republican President Bush then laid down the ground work, a foundation for a most extremely liberal and left wing progressive response to the oncoming crisis in 2008. The previous prediction of President Nixon, "We are all Keynesians now", resounded again in the Whitehouse. The Bush administration responded with a "too big to fail" savior-prayer (similar to, but not really faithful to the spirit of true/responsible pay-back progressive Keynesian corporate bail-out economic policies). The Bush administration depended on a fiscal gamble to solve the national problem of a great homeless and jobless recession. Soon floundering Merrill Lynch found itself added to the list of those entities that had to be "saved", and the feds forced Bank of America to buy the investment company. Then there appeared in suit the "non-bank" bankers such as Lehman Brothers and Bear Stearns who had bought into those non-renewing sale and purchase agreements, those "swaps" for which they were suddenly offering up all their frozen asset cards, possibly for a now ready ripe take-over. GM and Chrysler soon followed suit in a growing queue of selected enterprises for bail-outs like Goldman Sacks and Morgan Stanley, all in an orderly sheep herd line to shed their discontented winter wool and be financially "fed from the fed", from that seemingly endless and overflowing federal governmental trough. Capitalistic corporations oddly dressed themselves in finely tailored "save me" anti-capitalistic, progressive-inspired stylish brand-new but tatter-torn suits. Too big to fail also meant too big to jail. No company person or company policy was ever held responsible for criminal action. The feds tossed aside any entrepreneurial notion for recovery including any consideration of Schumpeter's endogenous capitalistic creative destruction and rebirth cycle. The inevitable tide of progressivism could be seen rising, but was yet to crest. Socrates could never have imagined a tide that selectively raised all yachts. The feds had not done their homework and failed to comprehend the lessons learned from France's John Law bankrupt bank debacle that resulted from buying up Mississippi Company stock in America at the beginning of the 18th century......

Giant corporations and major banks were deemed too big to fail; and individual American homeowners were too small to bail, while the jobless recession prevailed to sting society like endless heavy hail.

2006 also had witnessed the election of a new Democratic Party liberal majority both in the U.S. Congress and in the U.S. Senate; but all those supposedly aggressive and "dedicated to change" hot to trot newly-elected progressive left-wing legislators filled old and tired progressive liberal cold shoes and quickly developed a new case of cold feet long before 2008. They all, quietly but anxiously, awaited a new President to take up the progressive liberal cause once more. Both parties acknowledged that the migratory economics for a sustainable Medicare, Medicaid and Social Security were not in place, and something in the way of **Healthcare Reform** had to be done to solve the problem of further cost increases and increasing debt both in the individual's pocket book and in federal systems. More progressive liberalism in federal spending and incurred debt was not especially attractive, but…..

The ecological dilemma for migratory economics evolving **Healthcare Reform** has always rested in determining to what degree a society is willing and able to afford to provide for its constituents. The basic philosophical question always boils down to one's psychological justification of one's admitted and realized short mortal existence within a society. There are many "raisons d'être" and any chosen scenario is perfectly appropriate for any individual believer or any society. Moreover, all organizational-grouping scenarios touting varied fundamental reasons for existence are at least temporarily workable under the proper set of migratory economic cultural conditions. These various arrangements include a long list of concepts such as: living for equality and freedom in a democracy ordered by the concept of one-man-one-vote (Ancient Greek), swearing allegiance to a free-expression republic with criteria for citizens to vote (the Roman Republic), degrading a representative democracy through decadence resulting in a totalitarian pantheistic governmental state (The Imperial Roman Empire), worshiping to the absolute extremist letter the words of a totalitarian religious culture that envisions itself as a conquering nation ordained by God in which there is absolutely no separation of church and state (Islam with Sharia Law or the Holy Catholic Roman Empire), existing in a republic with the personal freedom of equal God-given inalienable opportunity for all to choose and work towards an individual reason for existence (American Democratic Republic), toiling only for the benefit of others and rejecting disruptive innovative technology to ease that toil because such invention is against the collective belief of the majority (*Anthem*), and for one last shot, yielding to the absolute rule of an all-knowing "big brother" (*1984*). There are also multitudes of individuals within and outside of all such cultures that for whatever reason direct their lives to exist solely to reward their own personal egos. Then that original fundamental philosophical question must also beg an answer to the conundrum of offering healthcare delivery from a moral feeling of altruistic brotherly love – must it be that one cannot love only self or family but rather must firstly or secondly love society, religion or nation; or must that extended type of brotherly love be primarily earned to variable degrees beyond a simple passive right of birth? So finally there must painfully arise the recalcitrant offending question as to the moral/ethical-political direction to be taken in the migratory economics of **Healthcare Reform**. The problem or supreme gift for Man's rationality is and always has been simply that evolved human cognitive reasoning has genetically condemned Mankind to continually explore the supposed known and the great unknown, very often in direct violation of belief systems or "raisons d'être" set forth and scripted in individual morality or in various organized societal rules and regulations. The audacity of hope had sprung eternal....

By 2009 the stock market had decreased in value almost 50%; and President Obama did not wait for one minute or even pretend to ponder; he quickly adopted the exact same basic liberal progressive fiscal economic recovery plan first laid out by his continually accused and maligned presidential predecessor. His American Recovery and Reinvestment Act provided for $787 Billion marked as "stimulus funds", compared to the $168 Billion allotted for "stimulus funds" by the administration of President Bush. Following precisely in President Bush's personally-condemned footsteps, President Obama plagiarized the process and enormously expanded the previous President Bush liberal progressive policy. Moral hazard "Bail-Outs" with neither the promise for repayment nor penalties or proposed punishments for individuals and entities whose bad and often knowingly improper decisions were responsible for huge manipulative investment failures along with Bail-Outs for corporate entities without penalties or guarantees for pay-backs continued as the recession trickled down and then up the economic strata, pretty much at the same time. That huge non-repayable "stimulus package" increased the national U.S. debt from $10 Trillion in 2008 to $16.1 Trillion in 2012, beyond what had ever been imagined in the history of America; but like President Roosevelt's and President Bush's efforts, the problem and dilemma of joblessness for the American people was not solved. On top of all this bailout federal financing, President Obama simultaneously proposed huge further increases in financing for **Healthcare Reform**.

In reference to *Capitalism, Socialism, and Democracy* (1942), Joseph Schumpeter's "gale" depicted and predicted a cycle of both expected and vitally necessary capitalistic "creative destruction", which allowed for economic innovation to repeatedly accumulate wealth after a predicted evolutionary periodic collapse of an economic enterprise. In considering the housing loan dilemma, the Bush and Obama administrations, both administrations with progressive liberal Democratic legislative majorities, blocked the natural completion of that cyclic gale with the heavy hand of federal governmental decrees. Rather than reconfigure a migratory economic order through a known capitalistic process, the Obama administration simply dug deeper into the federal debt hole of rising liberal progressivism that was initiated by the Bush administration. At first, presidential administrative policy hoped and prayed that at least a new and successful strong and sturdy foundation would be dug for **Healthcare Reform,** a

250

foundation that would result in the unearthing of a lasting treasure, the final American arrival at just one and only one, just one **National Single Federal Payer Socialized Healthcare Delivery System**. Moreover, the vitally necessary death and "creative destruction" of the presently existing inefficient and overly expensive capitalistic multiple third-party state-regulated healthcare delivery system, that necessary capitalistic energetic rebirth from the clearing of dead and decaying wood to provide for the desperately needed, more efficient and productive growth of a new nationally regulated healthcare delivery system was also, and perhaps unfortunately, finally thwarted. The best of both worlds for **Healthcare Reform** were put in a coffin and buried in a common grave. The tried and true creative forces of capitalistic entrepreneurship and dynamic competitive advantage in Turgot's classic "laissez faire, laissez passer" economy were put to rest in favor of a subsequent ill-prepared but comprehensive third-party embellished **Healthcare Reform** package.

President Barrack Obama's administration introduced another "omnibus" **Healthcare Reform** bill that certainly did initially include an innovative single-payer federal government-run public option "Common Plan" and a "co-op option plan". Multiple bipartisan bills in opposition to "universal coverage" were hotly debated because of falsely assumed increased cost and the obviously real rationing possibilities that are natural albeit perhaps accepted unintended consequences of "universal access". Once again America had the wonderful opportunity to witness and enjoy a young, handsome and dynamic speaker as its President. He addressed and pleaded to a joint session of the federal legislature and the American public via TV coverage on all four major networks (ABC, CBS, NBC, and FOX). He then made almost more than daily speeches that were also covered nationally, while downplaying his troop escalation for a war-police action in Afghanistan. This time round, the AMA offered not one hint of opposition to any federal health plan initiative. By now, diminished enrollment and dwindling funds from physician member dues provided insufficient funding for the AMA to adequately function; the AMA existed totally dependent on millions of dollars in federal funding to produce medical coding-billing books each year. Again, the golden rule of economics -- the party with the Money makes the rules, and the recipient better follow those rules.

Universal bipartisan agreement decried and disallowed rescissions or dropping coverage after a disease has been discovered by corporate insurance carriers, and sought divergent ways to magically allow affordable private corporate insurance coverage for pre-existing conditions. Likewise, there was little argument about eliminating a cap on coverage, but unfortunately, for the pleasure of private insurers, desperately little discussion about the cost of eliminating the cap or the selling of private corporate healthcare delivery insurance at reduced rates across state lines. The cost of malpractice insurance, excessive malpractice penalties and "cover your butt" excessive medical testing all added up to an insidious implicit inflationary tax that raised the cost of healthcare delivery premiums to the general public while offering absolutely no increased value, quality or efficiency to **Healthcare Reform**. However, the topic of reducing "implicit taxes" seemed to be taboo.....

In his book, *"Reinventing American Health Care"*, Ezekiel J. Emanuel reported on the political conviction of his brother Rahm, the white house chief of staff during the period of crafting the ACA: **"Shut the f— up! We are not doing malpractice. Period. Every time the AMA comes in here, they don't talk about malpractice." Their first, second and third priority, he said, was the formula used by Medicare to determine doctors' pay. "We don't need to do malpractice for the doctors, and I am not alienating the president's base for nothing," he barked. "Stop it."** Both sides of the political isle did finally at least, albeit in a low breath, admit that tort reform would drastically reduce costs, especially after a public reading of a Congressional business office report which stated unequivocally that tort reform, as a significant piece of **Healthcare Reform** would and could in fact drastically reduce costs. Progressive Liberal Democrats dogged the bullet and made no effort to pursue this **Healthcare Reform** tactic, and the forever shy and timid Conservative Republicans did not bother, and thus lost their prime opportunity to speak up. (Public confidence in the old-boy Republican leadership base dwindled, as would become ever so painfully evident in the subsequent re-election cycles.) K-street remained victorious as always; the overwhelming majority of Congress remained loyal to their trial lawyer lobbyists and failed to pen in a single word concerning tort reform in medical practice or in **Healthcare Reform**.

Rather than true economic concerns, most points of argument concerning **Healthcare Reform** centered about the emotional concerns of various voting sectors; abortion, right to life, same sex marriage, the ill-defined possibly federally-run single-payer healthcare public option "Common Plan", and especially the individual American citizen's mandated purchase of healthcare delivery insurance. Inflated and deflated cost estimates for the **Healthcare Reform** program ran so far to opposite extremes on each side of the political aisle that it became difficult for the public to understand or believe one single word spoken by any of the legislators. Everyone agreed, however, that a great slamming "Thor's Hammer", in the form of a cash crisis in healthcare delivery,

was ready, set, willing and at the point of breaking the government's bank, making urgent **Healthcare Reform** absolutely necessary:
Most everyone agreed that there now culturally existed in America some moral obligation to pay for the healthcare delivery of those good people who truly and honestly could not afford the price;
Many agreed that everyone must share some cost burden; and
Some agreed to accept the possibility of increased personal cost without increased personal benefits;
Few agreed, however, that everyone should have mandated costly enrollment or decreased personal medical benefits for the common good, regardless of price -- the old hot potato of rationing never did go away.

To completely avoid discussion of that politically unpopular latter hot-potato, the Obama administration, without the proper aid of 20-20 hindsight, thought that a better strategy or deception would be to have the **Healthcare Reform** plan cleverly and obscurely originate in the legislature overtly without a provision for a "common plan" or "public option", and then be presented back to the President for his approval and signature and administrative control that could change the rules of the healthcare delivery game back to something like the "common plan" sometime in the future. For the time being, since the omnibus plan remained clandestine and essentially formed by the same network of people that crafted the Clinton plan, the legislation did not offer any opportunity for early contributions (emotional bonding) from all interested parties that could have offered refinements, consensus and the essential buy-ins from both sides of the political aisle. Without an overt personal involvement in the actual creation of the plan, the President perhaps purposely placed himself at a devastating disadvantage when delivering his almost daily addresses to the nation on why his federal legislature-produced **Healthcare Reform** plan stood above all the rest as the absolute best, the one and only final singular omnibus plan that the country needed and deserved. President Obama forced himself into a position where he (at first) was neither able to correctly "calibrate" nor accurately comment about keeping an existing plan or existing physician when delivering his commentary of remarks on specific details of the different **Healthcare Reform** plans being offered by the Senate or the House. The President had unfortunately allowed and encouraged the Democrats in the Senate to set the unexamined agenda that unfortunately unjustly inhibited the President from taking an accurate initial stand on the scope of the bill. The President cornered himself to speak in generalities and platitudes about the "framework" of "our plan" without any specific entire endorsement of a particular specific **Healthcare Reform** plan. His eloquent speeches could not and did not really give the answer to many direct questions that the American people demanded to know and understand in detail. There were also statistical and factual inconsistencies: Rhetoric changed from "You can keep your present insurance" to "You will not be required to change your present insurance" to "you will be offered an alternate "better" (???) Insurance Plan" and the number of supposed needy uninsured changed from 47 million to 30 million. The public was never informed that the alternative insurance would be more expensive for the middle class or that there would be increased co-pays and deductibles, and, of course, carve-outs for congress and special interest groups. Financial failure might result in a manipulation of one sixth of the USA economy that was certainly "too big to fail" and that would require further federal borrowing and future federal debt for a "bail-out" followed by further federal income tax increases. The overall plan was an administrative political error perhaps, or perhaps the overt obscureness and obfuscation amounted to outright and deliberate "PD" "probable deniability" -- the political bullet-proof cloak of invisibility that would be readily available for the President or Democratic legislators to don and protectively wear. Perhaps there were top-secret politically progressive marching orders that could and would not ever be openly stated: "Distract, beguile and do do whatever it takes to eliminate the economically advantaged from continuing to enjoy their choice-driven healthcare delivery system."

A third error in swaying public opinion may have been that the Obama administration-directed plan was again an omnibus plan, an all or none plan and a one size fits all plan. Being all-inclusive, anybody's or any political party's omnibus legislation is forced to address all aspects of healthcare delivery decision-making that could reasonably and potentially present to the American people in the future. Omnibus **Healthcare Reform** plans are, therefore by their defined nature, not able to adequately address extremely strong emotional feelings and persistent differing fundamental beliefs among the American people – which did not and do not necessarily follow along any political lines or owe to any political loyalties. Rather than let sleeping dogs lie, an omnibus plan awakens deep rooted feelings and beliefs to the floor of debate.

A few of these hotly debated beliefs concerning omnibus **Healthcare Reform** amounted to a "do or die" fight-for long-standing fundamental rights in the mindset of many Americans:
Ever since 1976, women's rights aside, Americans have generally agreed that public funds should not pay for elective abortions or contraception. Instances of rape or where there would be serious health consequences to the mother, of course, explicitly stood as blatant exceptions to that general rule. The Federal House made no mention of abortion until the Deb Amendment specified that

funds could be put aside for abortions. The yearly-proposed Hyde Amendment which stated that no public funds would ever be used for abortion had to be added before a deciding vote could be taken. The Senate bill made no mention of abortion, and in not doing so, opened the door for a future judicial decision that could possibly, by decree of law, forge the way for federal funds to cover elective abortion expenses. The majority of the House, including both sides of the isle, saw this as an unacceptable possibility, while other legislators openly welcomed the possibility. As one can readily see and understand, these extremely strong and differing beliefs could not and cannot rapidly or adequately be reconciled for passage in any political party's omnibus **Healthcare Reform** bill.

The turmoil in America over allowing administrative healthcare decision-makers to prescribe, by giving legal permission for the right to die versus the right to live, stood as another long standing issue that had divided the states and baffled the feds for years. This issue had evolved to become generally accepted as a matter of concern in the realm of states' rights. Incorporating any part of this issue into an omnibus federal **Healthcare Reform** bill unfortunately transformed the debate of right to die onto national rights, because although state constitutions stand-alone and are unique, they can be superseded by federal legislation. Again, there is no "right" or 'wrong" or political party partisan belief here. Remember that per economist Jacques Turgot, an ephemeral general consensus of beliefs determines the medical mores of a culture; a medical ecology of cultural mores determines medical ethics; and an evolving ecology of medical ethics determines medical economic priorities. That process has here been termed medical ecolo-nomics.

One can readily look to one set of medical ethics, and then say that to totally accept autonomy in patient decision-making with a justice that requires all cases to be treated alike -- with alike compassion and alike openness of decision-making -- then one might perhaps determine that competent and terminally ill patients are by nature and nature's God allowed to hasten their death by treatment refusal. However, when well-meaning, politically appointed administrative panels get involved and attempt to define exactly what nature's God can and cannot do, tempers do tend to flare. Hot on the burner in 1976, the liberal California legislature passed the "California Natural Death Act", the nation's first right to die act, which gave legal status to living wills and protected physicians from malpractice law suits in failing to treat in an attempt to cure incurable disease conditions. Although personal privacy laws were already afforded to the citizens of California, laws that prevented prosecution of the terminally ill who happen to elect a suicide to end their lives, the California-licensed physicians were never legally protected. The California Penal Code adopted by the California Legislature in 1874 declared that anyone who "deliberately aids, or advises, or encourages another to commit suicide" is guilty of a felony. That legal admonition, a "littera scripta manet", included California-licensed physicians who might wish to "assist in dying" (to be politically-spun correct).

Moving this reasoning process one giant progressively liberal step further along, the state of Oregon formally accepted and has stayed vehemently and officially pro on the issue of physician-assisted suicide since 1998. The Oregon battle for this state right began in 1994, when in a general election, Oregon voters narrowly approved measure 16, a "Death with Dignity" act. In October of 1997, Oregon successfully enacted the Death with Dignity Act, finally permitting self-termination with physician-assisted prescription drugs.

On the other and definitely more conservative hand, those possessing and advocating for the opposing or con-belief in physician-assisted suicide quickly cited ethical and moral values concerning the sanctity of humanity and life itself, the potential for abuse of physician-assisted suicide due to vague ties in determining passive versus active distinctions as well as the propensity for mental coercion, the fallibility of professional integrity and the questionable integrity of any Man who is not God.

A U.S. district court slowed the Death with Dignity" acceptance process down. A physician, Dr. Harold Glucksberg, with four other physicians and three terminally-ill patients, along with a 501(c) – "Compassion in Dying", sued claiming that physician-assisted suicide was protected under the "Due Process" clause in the fourteenth amendment to the U.S. Constitution. In *Washington v. Glucksberg, (521 U.S. 702; 1997)*, the U.S. Supreme court ruled that physician-assisted suicide is not a "fundamental liberty interest", and therefore not federally protected under the 14th Amendment. As previously decided in *Moore v. City of East Cleveland, (431 U.S. 494; 1977)* liberty interests not "deeply rooted in the nation's history" do not qualify as being a federal protected liberty, and yet further, that the decision regarding physician-assisted suicide should be that of the individual states. There was no constitutional right to euthanasia, but its final acceptance was left to be determined by a "Laboratory of the States". In 2006, the U.S. Supreme court defeated a challenge to the Oregon "Death with Dignity" law in *Gonzales vs. Oregon.*

Since there was also no known right to physician-assisted suicide (patient self-termination with method/means previously supplied by a physician) by the "Due Process" clause in the U.S. Constitution, in New York State Dr. Timothy Quill and three terminally ill patients sued for their right to be afforded physician-assisted suicide under the "Equal Protection" clause in the same 14th Amendment to the United States constitution. In 1997, *"Vacco versus Quill"* resulted in a landmark decision, 9-0 against Quill and for "Life over Death" by declaring that there is no amended federal constitutional right to assisting in letting one die. There was no "right to die" defined by pro-euthanasia activists as the establishment of suicide as a "civil right".

Neighboring Washington State argued the concepts of physician-assisted suicide, and a "death over life" argument initially went down to defeat in spite of efforts from Dr. Robert Pearlman, the notorious author of a 52-page pamphlet, "Your Life, Your Choices" which became known as the "VA Death Book". Dr. Derek Humphry, one of the founders of the "Companion and Care" or the "Hemlock Society" wrote in his book, <u>Final Exit</u>: "What can those of us who sympathize with a justified suicide by a handicapped person do to help?" Then in chapter 20, he went a bit further and crossed a well-drawn mores line in the sand by possibly redefining a lovers' leap to death for the sick and elderly: "Some couples choose to die together regardless of whether both are in poor health or only one….That the couple would wish to die together is a tribute to the strength of a loving relationship." In 2008, a "Death with Dignity" ballot measure passed in Washington State; and in 2009, the law took effect. Also in *Baxter vs. Montana (2009),* a state Supreme Court allowed for physician-assisted suicide in cases of the mentally competent / terminally ill.

It should have been painfully obvious to foresee and appreciate that when an omnibus Congressional bill suggested that physicians must be paid at regular mandated intervals to offer end of life alternatives to the elderly, the aforesaid conflicting emotions and beliefs of so many Americans would certainly be aroused and confused. Making physician-assisted suicide an impersonal event may have eased the psyche, but did not truly relieve responsibility for or justify the act in any legal or moral way. Patients have and will most certainly share drugs with loved ones and quite possibly with friends or others who are near death. Inappropriate use of prescription drugs and overdoses associated with the taking of various drugs are responsible for more deaths per year than traffic accidents. The proposed laws also carefully avoided answering the unsolvable question of life expectancy; "How near to death is "near to death""? There was already a reported case in Oregon where a patient was mistakenly given a less than lethal dose of a supposedly fatal drug and awoke to cry out that he was glad that the drug did not work because he really did not want to die after all sorts of familial and societal coercion was said and done. In an attempt to relieve the psyche of physicians, a "**Healthcare Reform**" bill nearly passed that would have allowed physicians to write a prescription for a fatal drug dose and not be present at the time of the patient's suicide. Such a proposed preposterous passive prescription practice could have been the slimy start atop a slippery slope slide that might someday see 95+ year olds sacrificing themselves on a Logan's Run carrousel to avoid over-population of the unproductive aged and the future societal expense of an aged population; yet just wait till you hear the actual age suggested by the ethics professor at the University of Pennsylvania…..

Intimidating and onerous language from both sides of the political aisle hit and splashed in the press, on television, and across the Internet. The American public bombarded itself with horrific imaginary and undocumented reports of future government-run "Death Panels", politically appointed administrators playing God, gross lack of a moral code, and then quoted with u-tube videos as sustaining proof – videos of government administrative officials declaring that they were "God's Partners". From the other ever-rising progressively liberal side came charges of selfish discrimination, distortion of the truth, organized disruption, anarchy, and mob rule. All of the above were actually quite natural and expected reactions to any interference with anyone's deep moral and ethical beliefs. A somewhat engineered evolution of a public mind-set induced a state of turmoil because there was no consensus on "Principles for Allocation of Scarce Medical Interventions" as advocated by Presidential advisor ethics professor Ezekiel Emanuel, brother of Rahm Emanuel, President Obama's then White House Chief of Staff. In 2014, professor Emanuel went a bit further beyond his already crossed line in the sand concerning tests and curative treatments for the elderly in an article entitled, "Why I Hope to Die at 75" -- "For many reasons, **75** is a pretty good **age** to aim to **stop**." Any liberal or progressive discussion of "Quality Adjusted Life Years" or "Disability Adjusted Life Years" quickly became totally unaccepted by a significant percentage of the more conservative American public. Therefore, federal triage healthcare, Public Options, Public Plans, Public buy-in Programs, Government Sponsored plans, and governmental Purchasing Co-Ops became unfortunately demonized in the chaotic mix and stood out as horrific elements of fear in the initially proposed but never passed "Common Public Option Plan" for **Healthcare Reform**. Fear brokering won out over reasoning and logic on both sides of the political aisle. The viable concept of incorporating a public option, a unified federally run single payer healthcare delivery program for the USA seemed to vanish into thin air.

Interesting to note: a national, government-run, public option insurance plan may not have been consistent with traditional AMA principles of pluralism, freedom of choice, freedom of practice, and universal access for patients, and the AMA stamp of approval certainly did not assure political sustainability, but the AMA felt a political-economic need, desperate financial need to and, therefore, adamantly followed the leading progressive liberal political agenda and went on to favor and publicly support President Obama's failed attempt to sell a "Common Plan". Rulemaking 101 – the guy with the gold.....

In November of 1998, "60 Minutes" aired a tape on TV of Dr. Jack Kevorkian administering a lethal injection. His patient, a 52-year old Thomas Youk, suffered from Amyotrophic Lateral Sclerosis (ALS), also known as Lou Gehrig's Disease. As a result of the showing, Dr. Kevorkian was subsequently tried for first degree murder in Oakland County, Michigan. Prosecutors argued that, in giving the injection, Dr. Kevorkian stepped over the line of physician-assisted suicide, into the dark realm of pro-active euthanasia, and that his actions amounted to murder. The court convicted Dr. Kevorkian of second degree murder and then sentenced him to a 10 to 25-year prison term. After serving two years of the sentence, the court released him on parole in Oregon, where he died some ten years later.

As stated by Daniel Callahan in *Issues in Law and* Medicine: "An ancient but evergreen practice with controversial political and ethical issues is to manipulate ideas and language, spinning them to serve one's ends......The advocates for physician-assisted suicide made use of a favorite method from the spin tool box, that of obfuscation, defined in dictionaries as an effort to render something unclear, evasive, or confusing. I believe that in recent years, many advocates of euthanasia and physician-assisted suicide have used organized obfuscation as a political tactic." "The problem with determining basic health care services lies in society's inability to draw a discernable line in the sand that won't be blown away by lobbied legislative action." (Ralzak) Admitting that there is a scarce resource, an altruistic guarantee of paid basic reasonably medically necessary healthcare services for a society, quickly transforms into accepting the impossible fiscal task of providing all possible healthcare services for everyone. Alternative ethical paths have been suggested such as allowing access to suicide or access to basic healthcare delivery determined by a quantitative and qualitative evaluation of the personal "worthiness", unfortunately defined as the ability of a human life to benefit a society. Ezekiel Emanuel, as reflected in a Hastings Center Report (1996) 26:12, almost may have suggested such an evaluation rolled into a simple coin flip to determine the ethical basis for basic public-funded healthcare delivery. Spending public funds for saving/sacrificing human life might also possibly apply by the same ethical reasoning process: "(Basic Healthcare) services that promote the continuation of the policy – those that ensure healthy future generations, practical reasoning skills, and full participation in public deliberations – are to be socially guaranteed (paid) as basic. Conversely, services to individuals who are irreversibly prevented from being or becoming participating citizens (treating dementia or neuropsychological services for children with permanent learning disabilities) are not basic, and should not be (paid) guaranteed." -- Heads up, society pays; tails, you die – a dire migratory economic goal for determining future medical treatment.

Forget about heads versus tails, and now to investigate another possible migratory economic goal in the thin circumference of the spinning life-death coin flip: Licensed physician involvement in the timing of a patient's death, through administrative edict, has become an insidious accepted mores and ethic in the 21st Century. However, the extent – scope, amount and duration -- of legal ramifications associated with that legally assigned involvement remains in question. On a strictly independent and totally voluntary basis of decision making to end one's life, any person, even a cancer patient that is bedridden, can commit a very personal and uninvolved peaceful suicide by simply not eating, not drinking, overdosing on over-the-counter medications or alcohol, refusing to take or overdosing on saved-up prescribed medications, or suicide by various somewhat violent means that do not endanger anyone else. Life insurance policies would probably refuse to pay, and there would be no legal or financial ramifications directed toward physicians. A patient-physician conversation prior to the act implies advice and/or implicit permission to end one's life. The medical malpractice liability associated with this interaction has never been established. The next level of physician involvement would be mutually agreed withholding or withdrawing treatment or overtreatment of the patient's symptoms. This level of involvement could be with or without ongoing or previously established valid informed and cognizant active or passive patient permission/consent. A higher phase of this physician involvement level would be the administration of continuous deep sedation for an undetermined time until the final point of patient death. The highest level of physician involvement, short of overt euthanasia, would be to provide active or passive support and the actual chemical or mechanical means to aid the patient in dying. Much if not all of the aforementioned end of life discussions, advice and permission could very easily and effectively be just as well administered by non-physicians such as lawyers or administrators, but for legal and yet untested retaliation considerations, administration agencies have traditionally, actively and eagerly passed that "hot potato or buck" of dire responsibility exclusively onto officially licensed physicians. For painfully obvious similar reasons, physicians have traditionally objected to accept such dire responsibility with its associated unintended financial/moral consequences. While losing autonomy over traditional physician prescribed medical services and procedures, most physicians concurrently have deemed it inappropriate and coercive to be forcibly and administratively placed in the position of unique sole prescriptive responsibility, authority and unique autonomy to accomplish the termination of a human life.

Nevertheless, late in 2015, the California legislator passed a bill to legally permit limited physician-assisted end-of-life or right-to-die suicide. Above his signature on the legislation, former seminarian and Catholic governor Jerry Brown commented, "I do not know what I would do if I were **dying in prolonged and excruciating pain**, I am certain, however, that it would be a comfort to be able to consider the options afforded by this bill." Political legislative history has always run along a course of "more always being better than less"—if the legislation gives a little, it will eventually be replaced with legislation that gives a lot. Along this slippery-slope line of thought, The Society for Old Age Rational Suicide (SOARS) in England presently reflect the aforementioned death wish of Professor Ezekiel Emanuel for his 75th birthday – The society advocates legally approved suicide for those **"suffering unbearably" from various health problems which are not necessarily physically painful or terminal**. "Better to go too far than not far enough" -- Joseph Vissarionovich Stalin

Enough is enough -- Now back to the interim pre-ACA migratory economic tale of national **Healthcare Reform**: That old devil was and is always in the details, and details within an omnibus reform system offended all too many personal beliefs. The majority of Americans concluded that new-age liberal progressive reasoning may have gone a bit too far. Individual states complained that they did not have the funds to match federally mandated increased enrollment in Medicaid programs once the federal subsides ran out. Mandated citizen-paid enrollment into private insurance health care insurance corporations was decried. Through marches on Washington, Town Hall Meetings, letters, faxes, and e-mails, the majority of tax-paying Americans petitioned their elective representatives to answer a few simple questions:
--Why not just fix, with one well thought out step at a time, the 80% public-approved healthcare delivery system that the USA already has running in a cash-poor state of financing rather than scrap the system that seems to work well for the majority in favor of a new and yet unproven payment-only system that might not cater as well to all.
--If a new system could indeed be financed by audits and investigations bringing to an end the spending of billions of dollars in multiple excesses from within the present system, why not immediately correct for those excesses and use that Money to pay for those advertised 30 million uninsured and fixing the present

system right now ...and

--What have you representatives in the various levels of American legislatures been waiting for, and why are you still just aimlessly twirling your thumbs, mumbling and waiting right now instead of correcting an agreed on-going urgent problem?

-- If we want to cover everybody, why not just keep the present administrative system to expand Medicare or Medicaid and avoid an expensive additional governmental bureaucratic boondoggle before it blossoms?

Those questions were obviously never answered with any degree of transparency. The progressive brainwashed mindset hoped and prayed for a bureaucratic boondoggle that would evolve into national single payer healthcare delivery system. Facts and figures never did matter to alter any political idealism.

"We the people" clearly saw that a limited budget generates a difficult balance. An individual's right to healthcare measured against a population group's right to healthcare became an unpleasant sight to behold and an oppressing thought to harbor, and as "we the public" carefully watched the balancing act between taxes and benefits, there always remained an unstable three-legged stool to balance among payee cost, patient access and quality healthcare delivery service. It is and was a difficult process to clearly understand, but in the end, the cost and the benefit loss to the presently insured individual for sustaining the organized healthcare delivery system became tantamount in a tax-paying voter's mindset and in a politician's chances for re-election from a politically gerrymandered district. The conservative-liberal isle widened to form a political nightmare moat filled with vicious term-ending crocodiles. An omnibus plan with mandated purchase of healthcare delivery for all that emphatically initially included a start at "government-care for all" was not a good political solution for private healthcare insurance corporations. Alternatively and ultimately, something sweet, added for the insurance corporations' consumption, was the only possible political solution. Fear mongering yet madly reigned. Insurance corporation pundits pushed the thought that an unintended consequence of a partially federally-run program could evolve into a national government-run "Triage to Nowhere Ville".

"Triage" is sorting, sifting, selecting and assigning. That seems a pretty clear-cut concept, but Americans should and do have a great deal of trouble when it comes to the mathematical expansion of this simple fractal concept from micro-economic emergency medical decision making to macro-economic planned medical services rationing. The American public might, and in fact did, question that basic expansion assumption to be a false assumption – there may not be a simple fractal expansion because outlier variables and strange attractors inevitably get introduced along the way and disturb any direct and orderly reasoning process. Fractal expansion itself into exponential Mathematica also produces unexpected and strange new novel outliers. Triage can have many connotations and denotations. The term may indicate allocation of limited space, allocation of priority, or allocation of "assumed" available services, if and when said services are or become available. Triage also takes on different meanings when referring to different settings, such as on a battle field, in an emergency room, dealing with a mass disaster, assigning elective lists for treatment, and in national **Healthcare Reform** planning or implementation thereof. The point here is to not to fall into the trap of "assuming" that appropriate services are in fact available or ever can be functionally available at some other poorly defined location. Efficiency, order, and priority are big important parts of triage, as are considerations of insufficient immediate or delayed resources. Assigning a patient to a healthcare network that does not have the personnel (healthkeepers) to provide a full scope of coverage inevitably seeks disaster and ultimately finds what it seeks. Distribution decisions are made by the balancing of various factors, but the relative importance of each of those factors in relation to each other is often in great dispute. Therefore, the basic assumptions behind triage algorithms are often and naturally questioned. The basic goal of triage is to maximize the number of survivors, but the criteria to achieve this goal and to exactly define the term "survivor" and the essence of "survival" for a patient seeking healthcare evoked way too many emotionally-charged debates.

Most of those past debates boiled down to migratory economic ethical considerations of resources and funds. When debating that migratory economic resources were not and would not be available, the reason why availability was absent became the penultimate driver to raise the eyebrows of the general public, the debaters' audience. In the "good old days" there were most often no known treatments and/or no known cures for most diseases. Once a medical diagnosis was made, prayer and compassion with the gradual passing of time were valid and accepted alternatives. But by the 21st Century, providers of healthcare delivery had both the means and knowledge to affect technologically expensive cures as well as to relieve pain and suffering that were never before imagined possible, making delays in treatment and rationing of known benefits emotionally and morally unacceptable, although often economically unavoidable. Urgency and need of medical care then sought a new basis for denial. Whereas formally unethical to base denial of care on the absence of funding, in the Twenty-first Century, changing mores apparently found public policy unethical if funding was not included as a factor for denial of treatment. Right to life evolved to be questioned and then debated against the many social and migratory economic costs of "survival".

The relevancies of cost and cost-effectiveness were further expanded when 21st Century Man personally considered the migratory economic cost to whom on a one-to-one basis, then on to a family, community, state or federal basis. The importance of having one's "skin in the game" and of "dollar-one coverage" suddenly became important discretionary ethical factors. Discretionary healthcare delivery was pitted against non-discretionary healthcare delivery. The personal doctor-patient relationship in Medicine or the doctor holding on to being an advocate for his personal patient was placed in conflict with a doctor's duty to a greater and morally confused societal contract. Migratory economic factors had evolved most of all practicing physicians into medical practices economically dependent on third party payers. (Remember the golden rule of economics – the party with the Money...) In the political arena, the importance of the act of "doctoring" beyond prescribed computer algorithms became universally and unfortunately ignored. Individual patient safety and privacy battled against stipulated reporting for regulatory and public safety purposes. Cures and prolongation of life economically vied against the American public's excessively expensive perceived need for pain and suffering relief. The concept of a compassionate and all-inclusive Medical Home became politically transformed into a much more cost-effective Medical Orphanage. Individualized healthcare delivery evolved into a faceless, non-physician-centric diagnostic group protocol for mass healthcare delivery.

As these health and economic issues rise and fall like an ebbing tide so do the accompanying political issues in the total ecolo-nomic ocean of American life. The surprising multiple primary victories of two anti-establishment candidates, Donald Trump and Bernie Sanders, revealed that there were probably four distinct political parties in the USA rather than the traditional two. "Old Guard" Republicans were forced to define exactly who the voting majority of people in their party preferred to align with. There suddenly appeared an obvious physiological disconnect from the traditional Washington beltway pseudo-intellectual right wingers, who's publically perceived failed policies and political programs painfully exhibited weakness, loss of vision and a feckless lacking in strength of character. Since the time of President Bush, USA citizens newly defined to be in "poverty" rose 10 Million; people utilizing food stamps rose 12.4 Million; and the national debt rose from $9 Trillion to $21 Trillion. The GDP of the USA remained at 3.5 or below for 8 years, the longest period of time in U.S. history – The sustainable capitalistic economy high-wire walking act on that tightrope balancing GDP against welfare seemed to be unbalanced; 50 Million Americans were now on welfare. So it all boiled down to jobs. The Donald Trump candidacy approach promised more jobs and bringing back jobs by rigorously controlling immigration, ending common core and NAFTA, and increasing the military strength of the USA. On the other side of the isle, Democrats were likewise forced to draw an obvious boundary line between perceived traditional non-fulfilled Democratic party-line statist propaganda and promises versus a new Social-Democratic or a frankly and overtly youthful-popular Socialistic idealism that also revolved around jobs. The Bernie Sanders candidacy also focused on creating jobs, especially for the rapidly registering-to-vote millennial population. Average household income was down $2000 per family. The job market for college graduates was perceived to have collapsed. So-called "ladders of opportunity" were not at all evident. Cronyism and political corruption became hated and despised scapegoats. Wall Street and deregulation of economic modalities became demonized. The individual mandate for millennials to pay or be fined and expected double digit rise in the cost of health insurance through the ACA became popular rallying points. An apparent propagandized increased note of jealousy for the "rich" and an accused closed conspiracy of corporate interests suggested that the wealth of the nation could be better distributed. Student debt overshadowed credit card debt and would remain an unpayable debt. The dollar cost for a traditional on-campus college education had skyrocketed beyond economic comprehension; a popular notion arose that higher education should be a fiscally-free American right; and the Accountable Care Act simply did not provide for a promised practical and feasible single-payer universal healthcare system. The odds of any two individuals becoming the final candidates rolled with the dice in Las Vegas casinos. The traditionalists seemed to have it all tucked away from the very start, but as time went on, things changed radically. Perhaps the Bernie Sanders campaign just entered the Democratic race a bit too late....

Again, progressivism works most successfully when advancing at a snail's pace, and the President Obama administration moved forward a bit too swiftly, especially by ignoring federal legislative bodies when placing "Presidential Signature" bills into American law. A no-longer voiceless one-ton gorilla previously hidden in the corner suddenly appeared; and it also became painfully obvious that the American political will was divided into four interest groups -- the old guard republican, the old guard democratic, the new mixed "democratic and republican" working small business class and the new "socialistic–democratic" millennium movement. Getting down to brass tacks, the only "republican" that Hillary Clinton could possibly defeat was Donald Trump, and the only "democrat" that Donald Trump could possibly defeat was Hillary Clinton. The U.S. presidential election of 2016 proved to be a vote-map military conquest, a political civil war waged between the previously unacknowledged miseries of working class citizens living in rural America versus the minority intra-city welfare populations and the more "sophisticated" city dwellers. Domestic issues such as same sex toilets in public schools rose to be debated as important Presidential-decreed national issues as a political insider Washington–Beltway elitist vied against a Billionaire political-outsider. All the push-pull polling right up to Election Day ignored a social desirability bias that would not reveal itself until a citizen could be offered the privacy of the election booth.

The final "democratic" candidate, painted and perceived by the private working class as a narcissistically arrogant radical leftist extremist, a secular progressive elitist who, forsaking her own childhood religion, refused to acknowledge radical Islamic extremist goals, third term abortion restrictions, and especially a crude "unsophisticated" migratory economic, the stumbling voice of rural middle American "common" people. That "basket of deplorables", middle class workers who were abhorred at the prospect of permanently losing jobs to an immense migration of non-citizens by means of a U.S. federal government accepting a forever open and unvested border-crossing policy and a continually increasing national debt, those millions of Americans who had just lost their homes and their jobs but were too proud to accept welfare, those who honored the American ideal of letting the ballot box rule acted affirmatively to assure a Hillary Clinton losing her bid for the U.S. Presidency in 2016.

The "I must experience a woman president during my lifetime" group of Hillary Clinton supporters, sadly and unfortunately with shattered hopes, acutely suffered from a self-inflicted pestilence. Having been self-constrained in a constrictive cage of meaningless mind weaves by means of mesmerizing methodological mechanisms, they suddenly found that their methods, means and opportunity had not only horribly failed them, but also exposed them to a post-election world of jeopardy. The serenity of harmonic but myopic "cognitive consonance", which had psychologically impaired them from ever thinking "out of the box" and constricted their overwhelming political motivations by fostering a federal-dependent consistency in their mental processing, had to awaken to the ultimate reality of a loss, a loss of the election and a loss of the artificially perceived protectionist political environment. A frightful "cognitive dissonance" loomed about and intensified their abandonment and disenfranchised feelings. Therefore, the weepy-whiny, namby-pamby "break the glass ceiling or bust" group of election losers had to enter into a natural and important period of mourning, quite typical of the five psychological processed phases of grief: First, DENIAL overtook the entire group. Seeking a natural and healthy physical action-activity relief from mental frustration, they wandered mindlessly throughout the big city streets in the USA, peaceful protests unfortunately infiltrated by non-voting rioters that spoiled their legal and proper protest marches with the rotten stench and ugly aura of anarchy. Second, ANGER, accusation and the placing of guilt onto just about any person, place or thing that could have made the failed political campaign a winner rather than a loser, also was essential for their grieving process. Third in order came BARGAINING for republicans to accept various bits and pieces of the failed democratic agenda. Ideological trades or swaps of legislative alternatives were considered "peace offerings". (They included parts of the AAACL that republicans had already posted on a reform agenda and the possibility of a new and revised Glass-Steagall Act that would appeal to Bernie Sanders' supporters.) The forth grieving process depicted a DEPRESSION that varied according to the one's previously committed cathexis. Fifth, and as is always, the begrudged party after any type of contest loss must eventually admit, like it or not, "you won and we lost"; that ultimately final grieving process mechanism was and is ACCEPTANCE.

The "selected from a primary group of seventeen" "republican" candidate, equally narcissistically arrogant and also ostensibly bold and brash, sharp-tongued, loose-lipped and flippant at unpredictable odd moments, continually stayed in tune to the misunderstood frustration and frank anger within the middle class working common people, successfully adapted a seemingly natural psychological "affective attunement" to the common people in his "no honey-coated" presentations to inner city and rural citizens such as restoring industries to the "rust belt", openly embracing a Judeo-Christian ethic, and promising to bring back well-paying jobs by closing the U.S. boarders and through re-negotiating global trade and security agreements while strengthening the U.S. military, police and public safety. The new mixed "republican" victorious base generally despise the media, the Washington D.C. establishment and multiple big governmental rules and regulations; they are anxious and excited to find new jobs through projected approvals of such infrastructure projects as the Keystone Oil Pipeline.

Donald Trump, the newly elected 45th U.S. President, has yet to prove what his campaign promised goals will actually accomplish, especially in uniting all Americans to a common National purpose to reestablish the USA as the absolute superior combat-ready dominant military-industrial power on planet earth. That purpose would include ending domestic fears and hatreds by adapting policies with a bipartisan constructed consensus to eliminate the progressive liberal core of angst. Those policies would necessarily include accepting the rights and family structures of progressive liberal groups such as LGBT's and fearfully upset selective minorities in the American citizenry. Corporate incentives would bring jobs to the depressed inner city populations. Reduction in the size of the federal government would be accomplished by attrition, starting with a federal hiring freeze and a two for one swap of existing regulations for every new federal regulation. Term limits would eventually "drain the swamp" of corruptive crony legislators owing unto K-street. Following the course of President Obama, "Reconciliation" would eliminate Obamacare. **Healthcare Reform** would first encourage free-market privatization, eliminate the mandated tax requirement, encourage the purchase of catastrophic care for all and keep intact provisions that would allow for coverage of those with previous health conditions as well as provisions for dependent coverage to the age of 26. Health Savings Accounts would encourage high deductibles and more patient-centered healthcare with no limitation on lifetime coverage. To successfully accomplish these goals, insurance corporations must sell policies interstate and be subjected to the Sherman Anti-Trust Act provisions; tort reform must be passed by the federal legislature to effectively bring down healthcare costs, and **the laying on of human hands** should be encouraged for all types of healthkeepers rendering medical treatments.

So just where did federal responsibility, personal responsibility and physician healthkeeper responsibility begin and end? What was the rest of the story about the ecologic changing of healthcare delivery through migratory economic factors and patterns evolving **Healthcare Reform** in the USA? Assuring everyone can get to see an imaginary doctor where a physician shortage already exists by mandating everyone to buy healthcare delivery insurance that does not adequately pay an inadequate number of existing doctors is of the same type of irrational logic as assuring total relief from world hunger by simply mandating that everyone buy or be dispensed food stamps where an inadequate amount of food is available. Paying for a gate-key pass for universal access into a parking lot where all the spaces are already taken does not portray itself to be a prudent or wise investment. From somewhere there shall eventually come, the coin of the realm and the continually mutating migratory economic supply chain of actual deliverable merchandise for meaningful **Healthcare Reform**. A basic change in the pattern and mechanisms of healthcare delivery along with a rebuilt infrastructure for the foundation of healthcare delivery just had to be skipping along on its merry way......

MIGRATORY ECONOMIC FACTORS & PATTERNS EVOLVING MAN, MONEY & MEDICINE

PART SIX

COMPETITION IN A GLOBAL ECONOMY: PHARMA PHYSICIAN UNIONISM HEALTHKEEPERS CAN DO, EVEN IN KATMANDU

The fourth overlapping medical ecolo-nomic generation from 2010 to 2030 highlights an ecologically evolved migratory economic paradigm, a patient-driven enlightenment era of medical practice and healthcare delivery. Globalization of Universal Healthcare Delivery ecolo-nomics hallmarks the era's Healthcare Reform watershed event.

"History is a pack of lies about events that never happened told by people who weren't there......
Those who do not remember the past are condemned to repeat it."
-- George Santayana
"Remember the future"
-- Ralzak, the Fisherwolf

There have obviously been many relentless unyielding and uncompromising conflicts of interest among various healthkeepers -- economic, political and moral -- intertwined in the development of a unified national health insurance plan for the USA. Additionally, all have taken sides and then switched to various other sides on the healthcare delivery issue, and all have been subjected to wear a pair of tunnel-vision blinders imposed by the constraining forces of "methodological nationalism". **Welcome to the 21st Century.** The administrative and judicial framework of the Nation-State can no longer be the unique and only relevant migratory ecolo-nomic boundary for determining both the methodology and delivery systems necessary for high quality and cost-effective healthcare maintenance as well as direct healthcare delivery. When all sides of the healthcare delivery debate are no longer subjected to those blinders of "methodological nationalism", a truer understanding of the total scope in global migratory ecolo-nomic relations to achieve healthcare policy goals become untangled, undistorted and appropriately balanced. Ultimate globalization of healthcare delivery introduces a worldwide interdependence and strips away those previously fixed-premised blinders. Constitutional principles of federalism will still play a most important role, but should ultimately be viewed from a multi-level perspective of both analysis and governance on a world-wide stage.

A government has a duty to its people. A nation that does not tend to the basic fundamental healthcare of its residents is both foolish and doomed. Eradication of infectious diseases and epidemics, and disease prevention, including control of traumatic injuries and medical preparedness for possible bioterrorism or natural disasters, are vital and essential prerequisites. No doubt, there was always a non-partisan momentum flowing and speaking through American byways and airways to advocate for a change in American healthcare delivery systems. Was this momentum gathering a chorus of voices that were now calling in a synchronized fashion to develop a defined program, or was the momentum just a lot more of hot air buzzing to storm about in a vociferous heat-accelerated but confused or randomized Brownian motion?

By Y2K, America really had an overwhelming consensus that there was a healthcare crisis and a need for more people to have access to healthcare delivery, perhaps through some sort of federally subsidized private Universal Healthcare Insurance versus Universal Healthcare Assurance versus a federal government-run national triage, versus a federal single payer health plan, versus segmental reform of the existing system on a national or state by state basis. So, hopefully beginning with the end in mind, one would hope to first discover the federal government's versus the people's goal, and one might wonder if each clearly saw or imagined some visionary end point or end game. Specifically, one might inquire as to what degree of healthcare delivery the people considered acceptable as a minimal essential benefit, and exactly for whom, as well as exactly what the people desired to be contained in a most basic benefit package. The perennial unsolved conundrum of what the people versus the government were willing and able to accept in the way of benefit restrictions and cost ceilings in the total package also had to be addressed. What did they consider to be the essence of essential healthcare delivery service in any type of **Healthcare Reform**? Just exactly what were they really aiming for? Did they ever really stop to look and see or even think to see a clear target, or any target at all? Go figure, "Cicale Cicale", everybody was talking, but nobody really knew.

Certainly one would expect that the federal government must be able to eventually provide a comprehensive **"reasonable and medically necessary standard"** healthcare delivery mechanism, a very basic federal program for at least four unique groups of American residents:
For the truly poor,
For the chronically disabled,
For those whose medical condition puts them near to the end of their lives, and
For those in the precious early years of life

In general political terms, the federal government must provide for America's "tired, poor, homeless, tempest-tossed, wretched refuse"….. "all those yearning to breathe free." In ecological migratory economic terms, those who are yearning include groups of Americans who try and fail to otherwise purchase healthcare: due to their known insurance hazard, due to existing cherry picking of enrollees in select corporate competitive markets, and due to a multitude of cleverly constructed techniques and policy exclusions that purposely aim to avoid any adverse selection process and willingly leaves millions of Americans uninsured or underinsured – irrespective of whether pre-existing conditions are considered covered or not. Not included in the above previously mentioned groupings are those vast numbers of uninsured Americans who could very well pay for health insurance but choose by their own free will not to accept sponsored coverage enrollment or to purchase insurance on their own. Only about a quarter or so out of the supposed 47 or 30 million previously uninsured absolutely needed financial help from the federal government to finance their healthcare delivery insurance. Many of the rest had made a personal choice, a hopefully rational risk-balanced choice about what to do with their beloved hard-earned dollars, and had chosen to spend their old wrinkled greenbacks and new "marine-green backs" elsewhere. Questions then naturally arise concerning what to do for or about this economic risk-seeking segment of population when they are in desperate need of healthcare delivery, have been allowed a choice in spite of an unenforceable mandate, and already have spent all and any funds needed to cover the expenses generated by their medically necessary healthcare delivery services. Supposed mandatory tax penalties were too low to fund the gap. Would they now be considered future unproductive citizens and "guided" to be put into a special category, just as the followers of Professor Emanuel's teachings had grouped the "over 75 years old"? Certainly not in the USA of today.

A healthy and productive population reinforces a healthy and productive government, and vice versa. When a well indoctrinated and firmly established delivery mechanism of any type is known to be insufficient and deficient, it cannot be cured of its inadequacy by simply throwing more and more Money at it. AADD, Aged American Disability and Depression as well as chronic disease continued to grow like a plague across the American continent during the steadily advancing 21st Century, and there were set aside neither sufficient sustainable federal funding nor adequate federal reserves to overtly care for the United States' increasingly aged population. The federal government had issued a promised duty to Medicare, which gradually became inadequately funded to continue as originally promised in 1964. No private corporate insurance carrier would have allowed its health insurance coverage to remain an actuarially stagnant without benefit adjustment for a population whose average survival increased from 65 to 80 years over a period of half a century, since 1965. Yes, Medicare was well funded to begin coverage at the age of 65 in 1965, but will eventually become bankrupt if it continues in its present form of universal coverage beginning at age 65. However, no type of mandate to or from the federal government ever existed, neither direct nor implied, that at any time demanded or guaranteed payment of the complete and uncensored totaled bill resulting from unrestricted but valid direct healthcare delivery fees charged to each and every American resident. Such an on-demand system would not only quickly bankrupt the government, but would also insult a person's pride, honor, and personal freedom by removing every sense of personal responsibility – or not? Had personal responsibility in the USA taken a permanent back seat?

One is required to take a drivers' test to get a drivers' license; should one have to take a healthcare test to obtain further healthcare? A right in the American republic was traditionally and constitutionally defined as a right to be able to act, to do, to produce. The purpose of childhood healthcare delivery and the mass education of American children is to ensure a future healthy and productive population. People have the right to act politically by way of voting. Through that productive process, people can demand that their democratically elected representatives enact a specific healthcare delivery-financing and delivery-mechanism systems of their choosing into the law of the land. Before that legislative action occurs, the people should have had a chance, a right, to voice their specific will through the democratic voting process. If the people do not want Universal Healthcare Delivery Coverage, or if the people are not willing to pay for an ill-defined "basic" coverage that would be blown away in a sandstorm of political pandering, then that serious conundrum should have needed to be publicly debated and solved first, solved and accepted by the people before mostly uninformed and a few unconcerned legislators would inevitably bring about another undesired and/or unrealistic solution; hopefully not another solution with unanticipated harmful consequences from a bill that the legislature had neither adequately digested nor even read, or not -- real life can be stranger than a scripted imaginary plot. Personal healthcare choices that did not impact one's neighbor were among American fundamental rights to personal choice and personal liberty – or not? Apparently there is a SCOTUS judged federal right to bond or fine a citizen for non-payment of a federally mandated purchase to a privatized service not utilized. Would a rebirth of a debtor's prison system be next? – Certainly not in the USA of today.

American Medical Societies have stated that patient care in any healthcare delivery system must ideally focus on individual patient need, administered by practicing physicians through a sacrosanct, physician-centric doctor-patient relationship and allow for an artful and legitimate process known as "doctoring". According to the physician-led Medical Societies, any attempt at **Healthcare Reform** should ideally seek to facilitate and enhance that doctor-patient relationship. Can this concept in any way possibly retain validity if there are not enough doctors? Then why over all these many years has the too often fallible heavy hand of the U. S. federal government repeatedly acted against a laissez-faire migratory economic factor and severely limited the production of American-trained doctors, actually for over a century in time? Furthermore and cheaper yet, allied professional healthkeepers have continually been restricted in their scope of practice. On what planet were the medical societies residing? – Perhaps their millennium-and-a-half old or ancient thoughts were just coming into light on planet earth from far away Kepler-452b. Is it not painfully obvious to anyone who has not repeated third grade more than three times that changing the mechanisms and fundamental requirements for advanced technological healthcare delivery could and would serve more for less? Remember the logically reasoned CCMC report of 1923.

Government financing must also "ideally" be driven by "reasonably" medically necessary patient need, and that financing must "ideally" adequately satisfy individualized patient-centric care -- at that "ideal" level of service. Further financing beyond the "ideal" level, for instance, medical homes for additional layers of healthcare delivery services should "ideally" be readily available, affordable and subject to the discretion of the individual patient. Benefits should "ideally" keep pace with advancing technological treatments and cures. Catastrophic healthcare delivery insurance is certainly necessary and "ideally" should be a part of any general program. Routine maintenance of one's health was and is "ideally" best accomplished on a pay-as-you-go basis for all Americans except for those aforementioned four special groups of American residents. But that assumes personal responsibility, an "ideal" fading away in the contemporary

American ethic.

The word "ideal" was purposely inserted to be irritating and redundant to the reader in the previous paragraph, poetic license to induce an emotional response. Mick and the Stones sang out, "You can't always get what you want", but was anyone really taking those lyrics to heart? One may search for nirvana, but no one lives in an ideal or utopian world. Unfortunately and sadly, the federal government's politically presumed premise is completely sold, hook, line and sinker, to both themselves and to the public on the hope and prayer that there are and will be enough available high quality cutting edge medical services at a price that a country can afford to spend on its population in an equally distributed manor without some severe form of benefit rationing. Americans have never, do not, and without immediate delivery mechanism change, most likely never will live in such a world. It is not currently politically prudent to advise severe rationing of healthcare delivery services, but that hot-potato ethic will also naturally evolve.

So what about the immediate here and now in the 21st Century? With limited and really not enough sustainable long-term Money reserves in the present system, tax credits and tax deductions to inspire various healthcare delivery incentives might help, but those incentives would not be enough to adequately remunerate for all the potential healthcare delivery to be given in a universally covered system. Bureaucratic processing entanglements, red tape, and layers upon layers of administrative interference due to legislators continually yielding to special interest K-street middle-man politics shrink the percentage of the healthcare dollar that is available and actually goes into migratory economic reimbursement for point-of-service hands-on healthcare delivery. The undue cost attributable to medical-legal defensive practice patterns -- extra tests and procedures -- has to be eliminated by meaningful tort reform. There has to be an end to insurance schemes that result in insidious restricted access to tests and procedures along with delays, down coding, and denials, done to enhance profits of unnecessary middle-man corporate health plan stock investors or the needless continued growth and equity-based expansion of the corporate insurance plans themselves. Land and real estate holding such as can be found in Los Angeles on Wilshire Boulevard's "miracle mile" represent a portion of such hidden corporate profits. The basic mechanism for healthcare delivery in America must change and will evolve as migratory economic factors induce **Healthcare Reform**. Needless to say, true transparency in billing practices and in defining benefits must be achieved by all types of hcalthkeepers.

Balance billing or the right to individual contracting was and would again be essential, but the popular political trend continues to ignore add-on private contracting both for the doctor and for the patient. An appeal to the highest court to reverse lower court judicial decisions is of high priority and must be accomplished as soon as possible. Private individual contracting can assure and increase all types of provider participation and future provider development, thereby increasing the sustainability of both present and future mechanisms of healthcare delivery. A sustainable and growing funding source for adequate remuneration is a sine qua non prerequisite for any governmental program. A sales tax increase or an income tax increase is ultimately necessary to support naturally expected increasing costs in basic universal coverage. This cost could be held to a minimum if **Healthcare Reform** is directed to cut out the administrative middle-man corporate fat and preserve the point-of service lean. The right to private contracting beyond or in place of or at least in addition to Medicare and Medicaid could save their impending financial collapse.

Mandates are worse than simply useless. Mandates are proven historically to be ultimately counterproductive, and they also increase cost while they devolve to become unenforceable and unfulfilled. Coercion was and is an infringement upon personal liberty. All legislated mandates should be allowed to expire or sunset after a fixed period of time and then be re-evaluated for their continuance. It must also be clearly understood by the legislature as it is well understood by much of the public that any basic healthcare delivery coverage with a basic benefit package cannot and will not satisfy every patient's desire to optimize personal health on an individual basis.

Health insurance is actually only one of so many ways to finance healthcare delivery. Financing to optimize a patient's functional capacity has historically come from many sources other than insurance corporations, such as direct out-of-pocket pay from patients, patient pre-funded health savings and loans, government programs, tax-free corporate grants, business employment, philanthropy, and individual or collective physician charity. Americans should not forget to utilize the Health Savings Account (HSA) as a proven financing mechanism for not all but a greater percentage of people every day. An ideal health insurance program would be comprehensive in benefit, transparent, and portable interstate without restrictions or rescission clauses for changing medical conditions or changing medical need and specify dedicated dollars for non-contracted and point-of-service healthcare delivery. Who else but the federal government can ultimately legislate and provide this? There should and will be sufficient federal funding to fiscally assist the coverage for those citizens with expensive-to-treat pre-existing medical conditions. Increased costs for increased benefits, such as healthcare insurance sold in the face of pre-existing medical conditions currently is subsidized for those who cannot afford the cost; as pre-existing conditions are now mandated to the collective population, they become a legally justifiable incentive for non-transparent unnecessary middle-man insurance carriers to overly raise rates to the general populace. Beware to accept that that a federal mandate's unintended consequence most often hides the differential accounting data and eventually unduly inflates costs for everyone.

Ideally, (again) the contracting and payment-reimbursement structure should be contracted directly with the patient, but this will most likely never happen. A patient has the ultimate power to best control healthcare delivery expenses. Transparency in comparative total disclosure of physician billings, fees, and physician coverage availability is essential for a patient to make an informed decision regarding healthcare delivery. Unfortunately, the great majority of physicians in active medical practice have neither concept and/or concern regarding what medical fees are being offered to the American populace on their behalf. Rates and fees in their ordered corporate-organized medical practice in the 21st Century are simply not the bailiwick of an employee physician. Risk bearing organizations also need to be transparent in their benefit packages and physician network offerings, but this has never happened. Patients must be given freedom, this inalienable American right to act on their own behalf with adequate available autonomy through transparency, but first there has to be transparency. In a guaranteed free market insurance segment, if a tired and weary mechanism of healthcare delivery is allowed to continue to exist, all types and all levels of insurance can be offered, and people can have the ultimately confusing opportunity for choice, to pick and choose the price and benefit package that may or may not best suit their individual needs, all without a true understanding of the risks and/or benefits – and costs, well…..

Speaking of costs, the ginormous cost of pharmaceuticals far outweighs the cost of physician services in any functioning health insurance plan. One cannot even begin to consider enactment of migratory economic **Healthcare Reform** policies without an understanding and appreciation of **PHARMA** – the migratory economics of the pharmaceutical industry that is truly unique to the United States:

Health spending as a percentage of Gross Domestic Product (GDP) continually increased from 8.9% in 1980 to 13.7% in 2000 to 17.9% in 2011[97]. According to

---

[97] World Health Organization (WHO).

the National Income and Product Accounts, table 13.2014, the USA spent in 2014, $1,920,300,000,000.00 on healthcare, of which physician services were less than 20%. $384 Billion was spent on pharmaceuticals in 2013.   Much of this increase was due to new technologies and the cost of drugs. The remainder of the increase was due to increased volume of sales, new medications, and an increase in the use of existing products.[98] Heavily advertised drugs were responsible for nearly half of all pharmaceutical profit.   Therefore and quite naturally expected, Pharma spends more on advertising than on research and development of new products. "Profit" from sales in the drug industry represented over 90% of all healthcare delivery "profit". The price of drugs is not set in any relationship to the total cost of healthcare delivery; the price is a balanced bargain, a migratory economic subtly negotiated with the federal government so that Pharma will continue to produce and stay in business within the confines of the USA. Rather than meeting and replacing an established pharmaceutical need, new drugs are created in research centers to establish new and different needs – a grant-required pre-demand migratory economic inducement. There is also no positive incentive for Pharma to research generics compared to brand name drugs. Drug cost alone has increased as much as 17% per year. In 1985, the pharmaceutical industry spent $4 billion on research and development and released 28 new drugs. 1995 saw $15.2 billion spent and again 28 new drugs released. In 1999, drug companies spent $24 billion.[99] The Food and Drug Administration (FDA) approved only 20 new drugs in 2007. Pharmaceutical manufacturing is strictly business, not a non-beastly humanistic enterprise. Motivated primarily by a lucrative bottom profit line, Pharma really has no practical altruistic incentive nor innate desire to produce non-profitable drugs that might or might not prolong or cure disease states (without federal exception incentives).

All drug companies differ in their exact business plans, but their combined philosophies roughly divide them into two general categories, as they also refer to themselves: "Big Pharma" and "Developing Pharma", or "BP" and "DP". Much of Big Pharma is simply the day-to-day business of selling and distributing drugs rather than manufacturing.   For an expensive manufacturing process to commence, the final product has to be favorably evaluated as a future cost benefit -- something medically needed and able to turn a substantial profit for a huge investment and risk of time and especially Money. Just like the HKOs, drug companies practice a brand of risk-avoidance and cherry picking. Just like the doctors and their new technologies, the drug companies create demand

---

[98] "Health Affairs", californiahealthline.org, 12/13/00.
[99] "Worth", March 2000, p.102

inducement. All of the above drive up total cost of healthcare to the public at large.

Negative spin commercials directed at other types of healthkeepers helps to legitimize the huge profits for Pharma. The CBS Sunday night TV movie on 2/17/02 featured a fictitious patient character that resented his healthcare delivery encounter and complained that his "Managed Care Doctor" was only interested in collecting his co-pay and then advising some over-the-counter (OTC) drug. Drug company propaganda immediately arose to the occasion and insinuated that doctors advising OTC medications must be selfish, motivated by a yearly bonus from their HKO for under-prescribing. What people really needed for acid-reflux was the purple prescription pill, not something OTC – that was until the little purple pill became popular enough to hold its own in the bigger OTC marketplace. Drug companies then spun a pharmacist-patient relationship as apparently more honest, caring and sincere than a new-age physician-patient relationship. All accomplished for the universal no-surprise economic secret, to reap a profitable investment.....Perception, perception, and perception thrice, a three-peat win again.

The pharmaceutical industry required substantial tangible proof of probable potential increased volume of sales before agreeing to any rebate program with a hospital or dispensing pharmacy. In response, hospital or HKO plan pharmacies reduced the variety of drugs and employed formularies and generic equivalents wherever possible. Direct to consumer and direct to physician extender advertising, along with encouraged prescribing for off-label indications, more than made up for any hospital formulary-induced savings. The cost of drugs is now not only more than the cost of physician services on HKO budget sheets; the cost of drugs is also the preeminent cost factor in all of healthcare delivery. If Pharma and HKOs determine value by the difference of revenue less expense divided by hassle, then are formulary "hassle" controls also ignoring the special needs of individual patients? Is not this "prescribed economic" de facto practicing Medicine without a state-validated license to do so?

Developing and bringing a completely new drug up to market for that aforementioned substantial profit is really quite an expensive undertaking, more than Developing Pharma (DP) can afford. The average cost for the entire process is usually over $500 million, with a minimum cost of $50 million. Generics can be brought up to market for $20-$50 million. The average time needed to bring a completely new and different drug up to market is 11.2 years, while a generic takes around 4 years. So Pharma does indeed have a great economic burden to carry on its shoulders as well as a critical time factor to capture a competitive market niche before obtaining final approval from the FDA.

BP is concerned with three things: discovery (by offering grants and research seminars to universities throughout the world), manufacturing "big ticket" drugs, and marketing and distribution sales of Pharmaceuticals. BP does very little in-house manufacturing on its own for small product lines. DP via a private 501(c) or university-affiliated program also starts out with a huge expense and too many usual and customary functional payoffs. For example, a good start would be a grant from the NIH for around $20 million. Of that amount, $6-8 million goes to pay off the university, $4 million is allocated for doctorial and staff salaries, and about 6% of the $20 million goes to pay off the professional free-lance consultant firm that was hired pending a successful write up of the grant proposal in the first place. The rest, less than half the original cash, can then be dedicated to the actual research. That's life and times in the USA university environment – love it or leave it, it is eventually gonna cost ya.

DP enjoys a symbiotic modus operandi, a migratory economic paradigm that eats off the huge plate of BP: DP does the legwork to find precursors for new drugs, often sells out to BP early-on to avoid investment expenses, and then acts as a subsidiary to manufacture the same drug for a brand name BP label. DP rarely acquires pharmaceuticals from a late testing phase in development, and DP also produces competing generic products. Aside from the secret side deals made between DP and BP to keep the initial generic price high, the lack of competition among the generic manufacturers decrease the ready availability of genetics and naturally raises the price of those generics which remain available. When DP begins to look like a profitable competitor in a future market, DP is silently, proficiently and quickly "acquired" by BP. This purchase is for no small dollar amount, and when BP sets a price that is supposedly justified by research and development, the big bucks paid out for the DP acquisition are listed in Big Pharma's overall R&D ticket.

New drug applications contain a simple procedural outline:

The Federal Drug Administration (FDA) sets four distinct human testing "Phases" of pharmaceutical development for an investigational new drug (IND). ("Pre-Phase" development involves species testing in other than the human species.)

Phase 1 offers proof of no human toxicity. Twelve to fifty "normal" random volunteer humans take ten to one hundred times the therapeutic range of a drug and hopefully survive the experiment.

Phase 2 is a dose ranging study. The study is blinded with placebo medication, which offers some ethical conflicts for physicians administering the drugs. One such ethical dilemma example is the administration of a placebo control for a life threatening condition such as Infant Respiratory Distress Syndrome, which carries a mortality rate of 80% if left untreated. "Selected" volunteers might be patients with some disease state which DP or BP hoped would be "alleviated", but the process is really designed to collect data, not to treat, heal, or cure human suffering. Therefore, Phase 2 drugs are allotted to physicians by contract research organizations (CRO), thus blinding the physician to the production lot number and not permitting the physician the ability to determine whether or not the pill is a placebo or the real thing. Physicians hate being removed from the equation, so Pharma constantly seeks to blind them with a variety of confusing tactics. But physicians are not as stupid as the drug companies would like to believe; after observing very few clinical results (and doing some simple side-testing such as tasting, smelling, and dissolving), physicians can often figure out which groups of pills are, in fact, placebos. When such a discovery is made, the study is at once un-blinded, and the caring physician cannot and does not ethically give a sugar pill to a sick kid when there is something in the other bottle that might possibly make the kid well. Drug companies hate this unscientific emotionalism and are often forced to hide, throw out, or modify conclusions in their studies.

This "arrogant attitude" on the part of truly dedicated physicians is nothing new: Doctor Paul Ehrlich disagreed with a standardized sweat bath treatment for Syphilis and was fired by an equally arrogant hospital administrator. The good doctor went to work at a research institute, gained some prominence in developing a staining technique for Tuberculosis, and then discovered the nature of antibodies in the blood. He developed an experimental serum to cure Diphtheria, and was invited back to that very same hospital from which he was previously fired to try to curb a devastating epidemic that was killing hundreds of children. When told that for "scientific" reasons, he would only be allowed to treat half of the afflicted children, he immediately agreed to the hospital administrator's terms. However, as soon as the snotty administrator left the pediatric sick ward, Doctor Ehrlich administered the serum to all the children that were afflicted with Diphtheria. Such hubris! He was again swiftly fired from the same hospital; but when the local and national newspapers announced that all of the sick children were miraculously cured of Diphtheria, the government took great interest in his research and awarded him with a grant to develop a chemical injection "magic bullet" into the human body that could possibly treat Syphilis. That government

Money soon ran out and Doctor Ehrlich had then to beg for private funding. Arrogance and persistence triumphed again. After 606 clinical trials, he finally developed a functional treatment compound. In the meantime, he won the Nobel Prize for Medicine. Again, such hubris!

A totally different ethical conflict arises when the actual research doctor with the inside scoop has personally invested a huge number of hard-earned sea-green dead presidents into the research drug project. Risk of monetary loss and greed for monetary gain continue to be a common motive in countless crimes. Such an unacceptable conflict of interest cannot help but eschew validity in the end results of a pharmaceutical study.

People routinely hate to part with a single penny to pay for healthcare delivery when they feel fairly healthy, but when they are really ill, they have no problem digging down deep into their pockets to spend their last penny on their healthcare delivery. That is why the public has such conflicting emotion towards the medical profession: doctors in general are thought of as being Money-greedy, egotistical, and uncaring, but the patient's personal doctor that cures some significant illness is always the best, the most altruistic, and the most compassionate physician of all.

Phase 3 offers a fixed dosage regimen measured against a fixed endpoint. This is a "pivotal" BP IND trial for Pharma. This dependent Phase is what "is" really is. This Phase is where dollar value is added, where the Money is, and where Developing Pharma often sells out to Big Pharma. A drug in Phase 3 has a 20% chance of getting to market, where a drug in Phase 1 has only a 1% chance of getting to market. Phase 3 employs a "clinical endpoint" of validity, which is supposed to be a tangible, meaningful, measured and monitored metric that yields a measurable effect. Huge and expensive clinical trials are necessary to glean a statistically significant measurable effect, such as: "Improving personal function and quality of life, as well as enhancing ability to participate in social activity". This above quoted "Quality of Medicine" statement, generally accepted to validate treatment protocols, is an elusive and ill-defined "standard", therefore, other criteria often become a "standard". Pharma found a more efficient and a more lucrative means to accomplish the same "clinical endpoint" with biochemical surrogate markers. "Chemists and Physicians", who may or may not be competent to issue an unbiased independent decision, then review the course of a surrogate biochemical marker, traced through a supposed pathological pharmacological pathway of a given disease state. Thus, they, BP and DP, document a tangible, measurable effect, a "Significantly Significant Standard" outcome effect. This type of measurable effect experiment with a localized biochemical study is dirt-cheap when compared to a huge Phase 3 clinical trial, yet the surrogate marker study satisfies published FDA protocol and requirements.

Phase 4 is a labeling study. At this point, Pharma starts to make paper Money out of chemical powder Medicine. Protocols demand standardization of insert information: "to be appropriate and make no unethical claims." The FDA issues an approval letter, an authorization to launch the IND for sale while reserving the right to refuse final approval pending Phase 4 completion. Once approved, however, stopping drug distribution requires a FDA recall. Issuing a recall is a complicated and not a really practical process. A drug has to be horribly bad or be questionable and get bad media press to be recalled.

As an inducement for Pharma to produce needed yet less profitable drugs, the IND application process has three legally accepted shortcuts or exclusivity loopholes -- orphan drug designation, pediatric use designation, and generic drug production (Thanks to the Hatch-Waxman Act).

Hatch and Waxman, a republican and a democrat, working finally for a common public purpose, gave Developing Pharma a great incentive to produce generic drugs by granting six months of exclusivity in sales for the first generic to actually come to market. The DP's are locked and loaded, ready to market the drug on the very day that BP's exclusive patent expires. Before that time, DP produces, packages, and stores away the pharmaceutical product during every wakened second that they are not engaged in continual harassing law suits with Big Pharma, usually futile attempts to invalidate or shorten BP's exclusive patent rights. Needless to say, lawyers were, are and will be the instigators and the only victors in such schemes. Due to that beastly subsuming human need for greed, the American litigious society sued and continues to sue concerning collective patients' needs and finances, and thereby incurs huge legal litigation costs. Pharma also passes on those unnecessary legal costs right back to the litigious public in the pricing of their pharmaceutical product. Also, foreign to the spirit of the Hatch and Waxman Act but technically legal, Developing Pharma conspires with Big Pharma to keep the price of the generic pharmaceutical high during those first six months of genetic drug exclusivity so that the brand name drug can continue to sell in competition with an artificially high-priced generic drug. Cost to consumer does not go down appreciably for either product until after those additional six months of exclusivity have expired. At that time of expiration, a free and open market determines true competitive pricing, and Big Pharma rapidly seeks to introduce a new "more effective" prescription product. A "newer and improved" product comes into vogue and the whole process is self-started up all over again. Surprise, that new product gets a media blitz, becomes beloved by the American public, and, surprise, surprise, costs more. Prices go up and stay up, way up.

The FDA could approve a drug in Phase 2 if there is either some compelling medical need for a niche or "orphan" population of less than 2000 patients (people who suffer from an ailment that offers little financial incentive for drug production), or if the drug is designated for exclusive pediatric use. If there is also no competitive medical or surgical treatment available for a designated Disease State, then the FDA can also assign the drug an "orphan" designation. These exclusivity designations, pediatric and orphan, remove a half million-dollar investigational new drug (IND) application fee and allow a corridor for quick FDA approval after only 50 to 100 patient trials. The average time for an IND to pass from Phase 1 to Phase 3 is nine years. With an exclusivity designation, Pharma files an Abbreviated New Drug Application (ANDA) which passes through the same stages of testing in an average of two years. A pediatric designation, loophole number one, also grants an additional one-year of exclusivity in the market place. Pharma continually strives with determined delight to apply for pediatric designations post Phase 3, to use the IND data to satisfy an ANDA, and then hopefully to do the major marketing after approval -- with an "off label" indication that would deliver a very popular sales item to a much larger consumer group, a greater payer pool.

The smell and taste of profit in the air is so thick around the smokestacks of pharmaceutical corporations that it blurs the vision of any air pollution. "Doing great, feeling fine, as everything at Pharma is coming up roses", that familiar tune rings out regularly at the pharmaceutical products cash registers. The lyrics often include a repeated refrain, "Please don't throw the solution into the political arena." (Translation: Please don't throw tar baby Br'er Rabbit into that awful briar patch.) Gee, what industry might have a very effective K-street lobby set up to deliver propaganda to the U.S. Congress? The melody in that old familiar tune is an often repeated popular refrain -- a political process with healthcare overtones. Yes, a repeated musical and what a new "hit" (multiple translations left to the reader).

How about that "off label" end run? That is some a kind of a loophole. Shortly after Pharma gets an orphan drug through on an ANDA with seven years of exclusivity in a market place designated to treat a 2,000 niche population for say a specific type of anemia, Pharma could and would suddenly discover that, "lo and behold", the drug could also be used to treat other types of anemia. This outstanding "discovery" is then relayed on to physicians, pharmacists, nurse practitioners, and physician assistants through personal contacts, often over lavish evening meal-seminars with "physician" drug company representatives presenting continuing education power-point presentations of ghost-written "research" papers. Practicing physicians are encouraged to prescribe the drug product for an indication not included in the drug brochure, on a "off label" basis. Occasionally, Pharma reapplies to the FDA to get approval for the extended indications. Pharma could go directly into Phase 3 and Phase 4 with their application because toxicity and dose-ranging have already been approved by the FDA. Now, as in any sport, timing is of utmost importance. The extended indication application is best made towards the time that orphan exclusivity is about to run out. That way, the exclusivity period (increased pricing) can also be extended for the "new" indication – new and innovative migratory economic games in healthcare delivery that people and corporations do routinely play are always on the way.

Pharma has even more clever tricks up its sleeve to extend exclusivity/increased pricing. The Pharma con game is a present-day version of the old-time familiar buckboard-hocking snake oil salesman who offered a "new and improved" product that did the same job, but never before in a different colored bottle. Pharma unscrupulously manipulates the market to control market share and gain an additional 9 years of exclusivity by producing isomers of existing drugs. "PEGylation" is the chemical process whereby a biochemical moiety is attached to an existing drug in order to extend the half-life or duration/action of the drug in the human body. After PEGylation, you can take a pill, syrup, capsule, ointment or spray once a day rather than twice a day. People no longer use buckboards, so freeway billboards and the mass media/Internet do the hocking. Naturally, the public will be expected to pay more for that added convenience of once a day drug usage – uninformed patients will pay the price actuarially calculated for a completely new drug that has painfully progressed through Phases 1 to 4 of FDA approval even though that process never ever happened with the PEGylated, longer-acting product.

Why do we Americans whimper, whine and complain that drugs are cheaper in Europe and Canada? Look at all the hoops that we require Pharma to jump through in America. Pharma doesn't have to do that in Europe and Canada, but that is not what makes the drugs cheaper outside of the USA. Remember news headlines about expensive patent-pending legality infighting between Big Pharma and Developing Pharma over drug exclusivity rights and drug copyrights? Well, on a practical basis of impossible policing, the rest of the world doesn't have to honor USA copyrights. Drugs could be easily produced outside of the USA that are cheaper and retain sufficient quality for safe patient use, but this illegal anti-copyright manufacturing and sales, for the most part, does not happen. Why not? Drugs are cheaper in Canada, Europe and Asia because Pharma makes side deals with countries like China outside of the USA. That difference from lowered cost of drugs outside of the USA is like Mafia inspired protection Money paid out to foreign governments to assure that pharmaceutical copyrights will not be violated on a world-wide basis. That type of governmental Organized Crime pay-off to lower costs in a socialized healthcare delivery system is per RICO (Racketeer Influenced and Corrupt Organizations Act) illegal in the USA, at least so far.....

Still, the United States remains the only free market for legitimate drug production and distribution in the entire world. All those other nations, countries that we Americans drug slaves seem to so jealously envy, with cheaper prescription drug cost to their public, rigidly control, and that means ration, harshly ration their prescription drug marketplace. (One might insert a Libertarian political argument here, that the mere idea/concept to transfer personal individual responsibility to a government-sanctioned authorized "prescription" in order to supposedly protect and safeguard the public interest is for the most part ludicrous, as has been absolutely proven, by a tried and tested non-prescription free open market for drugs in Portugal.)

A LACMA LA City District newsletter ran some interesting op-eds written by its President in 2005 -- such as: "Medicare prescription drug benefits should be based on therapeutic outcome benefit." What about the American house of Medicine -- The American Medical Association? After seeing how well the Harvard debating flunkies at the New England Journal of Medicine botched their investigative report interview about publishing ghost-written pharmaceutical research reports, The Journal of the American Medical Association suddenly changed their publication policy to require registration in a public trials registry as a prerequisite for clinical studies involving human patients before the journal could or would consider publication of any "report" concerning patient treatment medications. Wow, if that's how the AMA really felt, then for sure we must all have been duped for years. But wait, there is more. The AMA House of Delegates passed resolutions directed to eliminate bias in the design of and selective publication of drug research studies, and the AMA campaigned to eliminate the use of covenants and clauses that might interfere with scientific communication in agreements between pharmaceutical companies and research physicians. Gee, somebody must have been aware of what was going on. These AMA efforts resulted in the FDA passing an Amendments Act to evaluate publication bias and require Pharma to report all basic results data, pro and con, from clinical trials. That incriminated selective data reporting, which may or may not have been supportive of a product, was too often not published at all. The Pharmaceutical industry juggernaut of regulation, publication, and suppression must eventually bow to a religion of transparency. How come one never hears much popular press about this kind of great stuff from the AMA? Are they hiding all their good plans and just releasing scandals to the press?

To tell the other side of the story, what about Pharma's rebuttal?

Pharma offered considerations that were apparently being overlooked, such as physicians justly prescribing many medications for treatments that were off-formulary. That is to say, physicians "found" valid and effective indications not listed after the drugs underwent stepwise FDA trials and were initially released for use on the general public. (?)(!) How did busy prescribing physicians "find" these things? The tale of a sale of a bridge from New York City to Brooklyn now comes to mind. Remarkable, but without being told precisely where to look, physicians serendipitously "found" or discovered hidden details concerning the secret testing of a drug. (Subjecting already available drugs to new sets of FDA trials and regulations to prove efficacy for new indications is not especially cost effective.) Clinical usage in the general population is the eventual, final, and most critical test, and those off-formulary drugs have already passed that exam.

Pharma also insisted that the long-term savings afforded by drug therapies are being ignored: If expensive knee injections with hyaluronate-formulated drugs slow down the course of arthritis, then the consequences of that effect need to be examined on a community population basis. By slowing down the course of arthritis, more expensive knee replacement surgeries are postponed. If the postponement is sufficient to allow patients to die of other causes before the surgeries are necessary, then significant savings accrue from not performing the surgeries. These future savings have to be included as a factor in the initial cost effectiveness of a new drug. (However, Pharma has nothing to say when, in 2013, the New England Journal of Medicine published an article scientifically rejecting the notion that "viscosupplementation" prolonged the time interval to total joint surgery). Likewise, if a drug or procedure postponed even more expensive cardiac surgery to the point of patient base attrition (death), then that cost saving of postponement merits consideration as a drug benefit factor. (Fortunately, cigarette manufacturers did not pursue this line of reasoning to prove the long-term healthcare cost efficacy of their tobacco product – eliminating the huge cost of elder care.) However, one must eventually kowtow and ultimately admit that due to pharmaceuticals, Americans are living longer and eventually need those more expensive therapies anyway. Alas, Man is ultimately compelled to spend his Money on Medicine. All Americans must finally realize that healthcare delivery and especially pharmaceuticals are not cost-effective commodities, but well worth the price, every single salty copper penny of it, for a healthy quality of life along with increased longevity is priceless. Time, quality time, is the penultimate gift to Mankind.

Under absolutely no circumstances does Pharma ever want or wish for a medically necessary drug to be sold over-the-counter (OTC) unless there is some specific dynamic competitive advantage for the "brand" to compete in that consumer-driven market; but fortunately when consumers finally decide and tell what they "want" to Mick and the Stones, the public "gets" sung back the aforementioned reality answer. As long as a HKO or government agency pays for a drug, a patient never realizes or attempts to evaluate the true drug cost, thus making it difficult for the consumer to make a OTC cost-effective decision. According to economic statistician and politically conservative Milton Friedman, "The fallacy that it is feasible and possible "to do good" with other people's Money has two flaws. If I'm going "to do good" with other people's Money, one first has to take it (that Money) away from them. Secondly, very few people spend other people's Money as carefully as they spend their own." OTC drugs are direct out of pocket expenses for patients. Once that true competitive cost is realized, demand decreases due to patient-payer decision making in the absence of the third party insurance hazard. Pharma considers encouraging such a scenario a particularly bad strategic business practice. On an apologetic tongue-in-cheek lighter note, Pharma and medical device corporations have spent more R&D dollars on investigating and selling things like Viagra and breast implants than they have on Alzheimer's disease R&D. Does this mean that Americans are going to produce a vast aged generation consisting of hobbling-about centenarians with perky breasts and hard penises, a mentally confused and conflicted Alzheimer's generation that won't have the slightest inkling of an idea of what to do with either one of those body parts?

But seriously, as a matter of obvious observation, the pharmaceutical industry is ultimately a friend, an exceedingly rich friend, but nonetheless a true and highly valued friend. They admittedly do have to overcome their so many weaknesses, obstacles and threats from so many government's rules and regulations, from their shareholders expected bottom line, and from technological-biological limitations. The uniquely American ever-pulling consumer demand for ever newer and more expensive drugs to treat every possible ailment regardless of cost cannot be ignored. Those drug treatments, albeit quite expensive healthcare remedies, have significantly prolonged the lifespan for all Americans; many Americans and most elderly Americans simply cannot continue to live from day-to-day without them. Competition among the Big Pharma corporations has been limited because of excessive regulation and mandates from an American FDA that has been more and more responsive to lobbies and political influence and in such tremendous fear of lawsuits that the simple evaluation, certification, and reporting of patient safety statistics is not given proper priority. It would be unrealistic to believe that any contemporary American could get elected to public legislative office on a platform that rationed drugs according to excessive production cost or demanded degree of usage. **Healthcare Reform** -- tort reform for the pharmaceutical industry with an acceptance and granted immunity by the courts for active and transparent post-release Phase IV testing could bring back dynamic competition into the pharmaceutical marketplace, increase the development of breakthrough pharmaceutical remedies, and radically reduce drug costs to the American public. American basic drug research is now stymied in Big Pharma USA. In the United States, Big Pharma is primarily in the business of advertising and distributing drugs produced elsewhere, often overseas by overseas Big Pharma; and America may be entering into an era of retarding new pharmaceutical technological development.

In considering **Healthcare Reform**, universal access to actually staffed ready, willing and able healthcare delivery systems is what should be assured, not universal access to waiting lists that are so often reshuffled and restacked due to inadequate availability of physician providers. Infrastructure and migrating economic mechanisms of healthcare delivery must receive paramount attention. Total Information Technology should add transparency to the authorized release of patient medical records through the internet. HIPPA privacy restrictions should be severely lessened. Community healthcare delivery safety nets are vitally essential, life-saving and cannot be abandoned by chronic underfunding.

The migratory economic of simply throwing more federal Money at the Veterans Administration Hospitals will not solve the problem with their long wait lists. The cause of wait list problem immediately presented itself when the elected heavy hand of government, the Clinton Administration, approved treatment and total financial coverage for veterans with non-service-related conditions in VA Hospitals. This very popular politically-directed Presidential edict never did take into consideration any due diligent research regarding the resultant migratory economic consequences of an offering for services that did not previously exist. The necessary physical hospital-clinic and human staffing infrastructures for the obvious consequential increased-patient demand capacity was not present at that time of the edict. Nor was there designated dollars – Money for Medicine --

allocated for essential infrastructure planned to be in place, not one thin dime for adequately improved veterans' healthcare delivery. Sufficient quality and quantity of operating rooms, for expensive operations such as total joint replacement surgeries and births/obstetrical care, urgently needed to be built before the federal government's instigated crisis could subside. Present day funding is desperately trying to catch up to years of fiscal neglect by the federal government.

USA democracy responds to American cultural ecology, which is determined by American mores and ethics. There is also a natural evolution with an ebb and flow gradually changing those mores and ethical values. It is important to guard against migratory economic detrimental drift. Americans, as citizens of the greatest and most powerful nation on this beloved planet, cannot allow their American culture to putrefy, decay, and undergo a destructive evolution of dissolution as did the super power of the ancient Roman world. Americans must resist the compulsion to worship only "bread and circus" – fast foods and television/mass entertainment -- and thus abandon the importance of great and fundamental American ideals and concepts of freedom. A couple of definitions are in order here: The great American passive pastime of sport entertainment – the new and improved games copied from the ancient Circus Maximus and Coliseum, sporting events of Ancient Rome, now are readily recognized as capitalistic-derived American sport commodities (TEAMS): a grouping of mercenary soldier-like individual athletes possessing short-term leases, contractual and tradable leases owned by sports corporations, mandating each individual athlete by contractual obligation to dynamically compete against other similarly contracted athletes by way of their uniformly structured corporate-interest commodities (TEAMS), which are cleverly registered and easily identified by the general public with the names of varied and variable temporary geographic base-location cities. A "SPORTS FAN": an individual with an overpowering and unique cathexis who has formed an unbelievably strong imaginary or mythical allegiance to a corporate entertainment commodity (TEAM) whose temporary geographic base-location city happens to be at or near the said sports fan's present or past home living/working area. They are the infamous American Gladiator Teams – Hear the hypnotic sound and music of the media broadcasting the weekend afternoon to weekly night CORPORATE BUSINESS cry echoing through the great American landscape. As once shouted from the Emperor's deck in ancient Roman coliseums – "Let the games begin".

National migratory economic policies have been, are, and will be thusly directed to respond to an evolving cultural ecology in the USA. That ecolo-nomic foretells the USA to beware and be forewarned; it is very possible for the federal government to engineer the changing course of American mores and ethics, especially when citizens are under great migratory economic stress. During such times, it might seem tempting or make sense to surrender American traditional values, only to have them readjusted by an internalization of a more established set of dysfunctional globalized norms. The USA is, after all, well into the Globalization Era. It might at times look like quickly accepting multinational or transnational concepts of migratory economics, **Healthcare Reform** and moral values could save the USA's debt-ridden migratory economic economy, but watch out fellow Americans:

To act in such a rash manor and embrace an internalization of global norms without thoroughly thinking and digesting possible unwanted or unintended outcomes would be contrary to American constitutional concepts of personal liberties, the unencumbered ability to act freely and unimpaired by needless central governmental controls. Those principles have separated Americans from the rest of the world's citizens and made the great USA the most envious of world super powers. On the other hand, American personal liberties might need adjustment to provide for the concept of increased entitlement rights that many of America's citizenry demand in the 21st Century. Heed the ancient words of Cicero – "Beware of the compulsion to slip from active political engagement in a vibrant Republic and slide into a passivity and indifference" -- that would make America a Republic in name only. Acknowledge also Cicero's second admonition – "Laws are inversely related to justice -- the more laws, the less justice". Let not the American Republic decay into a centrally controlled Democracy that will inevitably evolve to further political degeneration. The American colonial banner, "give me liberty or give me death" once formed an impossible to pass, an impenetrable line in the sand that is now blown and distorted by the winds of fortune; and American eyes, inflamed by those same particles of sand, might occasionally be blurred into not seeing a detrimental progression of political policies all too clearly.

Political pundits preach an absurd, pompous, superior-moralisic and non-evidenced based hubris conviction that the best way to achieve better public health is through increased federal insurance funding for tertiary prevention -- direct healthcare delivery for more and more people. Their fundamental basic premise is unsubstantiated yet never questioned by the mass media. As concluded in *The Oregon Experiment — Effects of Medicaid on Clinical Outcomes,* New England Journal of Medicine, 2013; 368:1713-1722, statistical evidence suggests that overall health and increased federal health insurance funding for direct healthcare delivery do not share a direct relationship in improving the Public's Health. There is also a reluctance by the above pundits to admit that health "insurance" is not necessarily health "assurance", and no guarantee of adequate access to healthcare is ever sold with any policy. In fact, abiding solely by fiscal policy benefits scripted in a minimal coverage subsitized insurance policy (Bronze level federal insurance exchange) could be not only quite restrictive in obtaining healthcare but also may be harmful to one's health. What is actually insured, as demonstrated in the "Oregon Experiment", is not "health" but one's personal "wealth"; and with that subsidized coverage in place, the insured individual makes more inappropriate but questionably less-costly healthcare visits, has more cash on hand, feels less depressed, less stressed and actually worries less, especially about healthcare bills. There is nothing new to that conclusion, which simply restates a typical scenario of "insurance hazzard".

A view from outside of the proverbial "Box" is interesting and somewhat incredulous. The politically brainwashed voting public too readily accepts at face value that painfully obvious misnomer –"Healh Insurance". As far as most people would be willing to admit to, **no Man-made institution or any existing Human Being can actually insure one's vibrant health.** The only "Being" possibly able to perform that heavenly miracle does not reside on planet earth and that "Supreme Being" sells nothing, but does offer faith and hope to Mankind. What an insurance corporation or government sells to an individual is actually "Wealth Assurance", the ability to pay routine medical bills and remain solvent if and when catastrophic medical bills threaten bankruptcy. National "Health Insurance" would, therefore, really be insuring a nation's economy or to be actually better put, "National Wealth Assurance."

Americans express only a passive wish to maintain their present albeit imperfect yet fine system of governance over healthcare delivery; or, because of obvious inequities and costs, Americans gradually abandon their wish and drift ever closer to a socialistic state of "National Wealth Assurance" redistribution. Americans will truly eventually get whatever they don't actively wish for. After Americans abandon their imperfect but fine system of healthcare delivery, they will drift ever closer to a single payer socialized government-run national healthcare system of triage only after experimenting with overly-expensive middle-man mechanisms of healthcare delivery. The American voting public has proven itself too naïve to independently seek out the vital education necessary to control their basic health needs. Yes, healthcare delivery expenses must be controlled, that is painfully obvious; but let not the tail wag the dog, and let the American public be prepared to move forward ever so cautiously and at a step-by-step calculated pace, so that each and every American can beware of and avoid stepping into tragic unanticipated and unintended consequences. "Nota Bene", the commodity of "Healthcare" has steadily evolved along to be redistributed and sold with a newly written business plan and through an administratively "value-based" business model. The lucrative success of this business plan is no longer based on the volume of medically necessary services rendered, but rather on a cost-quality-access curve that administratively adjusted to accept an overall optimum degree of medical quality that could reasonably be attained for "reasonably" medically necessary "qualifying" conditions, rather than striving for the very best quality that could be attainable through modern science and technology. A subtle variation in controlled or allowed access proved to be the secret ingredient to set this migratory economic of **Healthcare Reform** in motion. Politically motivated "Wordsmithing" can be devastating; for instance, take the word "activity". The apparent politically progressive migratory economic business model word-shift still rewards with calculated payment according to volume of "activity", but the evolved definition of "activity" or work-productivity is now not the "number of things" (tests, procedures, consults, etc.) "totally provided" per patient, but rather the new "activity" financial reward is calculated and dispersed according to the "number of patients" "partially served" per pay-reimbursement-rated diagnosis.

From the 2002 movie, John Q: "You got an HMO, right? There's your answer. HMO's pay their doctors not to test. Their way of keeping costs down. Let's say Mike needed additional testing, insurance says they won't cover them. The doctor keeps his mouth shut and no one's the wiser. Little Mike falls through the cracks, and come Christmas, the HMO sends the doc a big, fat bonus check".

Politically correct verbiage included such dynamic pronouncements as "coordinated care", "collaborative care", "standardized care", "optimized care" and "re-directed care". The alphabet soup boiled down to accomplish a cost-effective elimination of "wasteful spending" and "un-necessary work" by accepting a slightly lower but administratively "adequate" level of medical quality and service, a politically successful propaganda campaign that greatly lowered both public and provider expectations. The yearly history and physical exam has been put aside, and an adequate physical examination requiring an hours-worth of medical practitioner time has been reduced to less than ten minutes. Forget about a high quality medical examination – any "adequate" medical examination is impossible to perform in that limited time span. The ultimate goal is to deliver administratively determined "optimum quality" or a redo of the proverbial "right care" at the "right time" to the "right patient" at the "right place" from the "right provider". Of course, the variable meaning and significance of word "right" is administratively defined per individual administrator at some obscure space and time coordinate that may not be accessible on planet earth. Does an average good result mean that 50% of the time the result is bad?

Chronic disease states are orderly arranged and placed in Algorithmetric groupings to determine the duration and extent of their medical management through administratively determined population-based protocols. The chronic disease-grouped patients are rendered medical care from various levels of medical providers at established places or settings for provider-patient encounters such as large public classrooms. Payment denials for all medical tests and procedures, including the inexpensive and the more expensive, such as MRI's and cancer treatment modalities, are issued based on computerized "acceptance" rejections from standard deviation outcome mappings simplified into algorithms.

Early end-of-life decision-making becomes based on a similar computerized set of "quality life predictors". The consideration and psychological adjustment to an older chronological age as a percent of live U.S. citizens within general societal mores becomes of even greater consequence when administratively determining justification for those increased number of elderly citizens demanding medically necessary healthcare delivery. When the economic boils down to approvals for passing out sea-greenback dollars for expensive technology, an increased need for funding that would not "significantly" (administratively-determined) extend one's life span, medical intelligence (an oxymoron?) sought to encourage the involved population to shout out aloud as possible at the top of their lung capacity, as in a Madison Avenue engineered new product branding-release, "I don't want it!"; but that declarative simply did not satisfy Man's primitive ego that demanded and compelled its prime directive to immediately and spontaneously translate that hopeful governmental propaganda slogan into "You can't have it!"...... "I don't want to play in your yard; I don't like you anymore". On the other hand, how could any type of universal health delivery system hope to fiscally sustain its existence in the face of medically necessary and absolutely proven effective technology that sees no cost barrier to production? For example, the starting medical bill receipt, just for administration of two doses of a drug admittedly proven to cure Cancer (Blincyto), is a whopping $178,000.00. That is just the start. One can expect newer individual or genetically-designed remedies to be ten times that price – it is just a simple prestidigitation, within the wink of an eye, a switch of a decimal point over one cipher to the right.

Man's primal instinct also drove a changing paradigm in psychological affect rendered to the medical practice ethics of company-employed practitioners of

Medicine as evidenced in their resultant economic patterns of healthcare delivery. Fewer tests are now ordered, and the rejected payment rate for ordered tests is decreased from past rates; but that result is accompanied by an opposing economic, a concomitant decrease in multi-level healthkeeper productivity. Parkinson's Law of inefficiency, the natural human expansion of work to fit an allotted or available time for completion, seemed to have turned around and upside down. The increased volume of those easily processed, repeatedly recycled patients insidiously fit the allotted time in order to preserve a dynamic competitive advantage of leisure time. Former persistent entrepreneurial-driven attention to detail in quality and continuity of care as well as drilled downed detailed shift debriefings and dedication to the root cause of patient advocacy for quality and timeliness were all traded for an increased pursuit of individual healthcare practitioner happiness in partaking of leisure time productive and non-productive activities. Adequate after-hours, weekend, and holiday leisure access time availability for a highly trained and conscientious physician who is willing to take on and thoroughly care for an expanding volume of patients with severe and complicated medical problems is a near to impossible to obtain or attain; actually leisure time under those circumstances becomes a hardy ho-ho whimsical wish. Therefore, physician recycling combined with cherry picking of low-stress easy-to-care-for patients became a constant problem for the contracting medical corporations paying their salaries. All sorts of cost-saving economic maneuvers have an opposite and opposing economic effect when dealing with the productive life cycle of an independent cognitive reasoning human. Time clocks were monitored; patient care seemed to be a chess match with a bell that rang every ten to twelve minutes. In response, what could have been accomplished during the totally inadequate ten-minute encounter was reduced to what could be inadequately accomplished in a five-minute encounter. Leisure time proved to be quite dear and the ticking clock proved to be no match for intuitive gaming of the corporate healthcare delivery system by the physicians.

"'Repent, Harlequin!' Said the Ticktockman"

In panicked response, corporate entities developed emergency programs directed to curb physician "burn out", unknowingly causing a resultant revolt of non-compliant "disruptive" physicians ordering too many expensive medical tests. The remaining physicians then coupled their newly-found resistance to higher productivity stress levels with corporate-obligated high-priced and longer-duration pension debt by initiating a rash of early physician retirements, thereby costing the corporate entities to additionally fund the cash reserves in those previously agreed-to and quite substantial pension programs. These resultant devious migratory economics derived from unintended consequences of **Healthcare Reform** forgot to consider the patient. The once sacrosanct doctor-patient relationship of trust and empathy hopelessly found itself bloodedly sacrificed upon a corporate business alter, permitting physician-patient centric medical practice to exsanguinate, to pale away into an organizational oblivion.

The physicians obviously needed some help to get their scalps out from the corner turnbuckles on the economic survival ring that the corporations "unfortunately and unintentionally" had beaten and subjected them into. The healthcare practitioner world kept spinning dizzily around; the physicians missed the dynamic competitive economic advantage that they once possessed, but if one missed one revolution in the **Healthcare Reform** world, most assuredly there would shortly come another; and never forget that Man is the only animal that can both realize his ephemeral existence and eventual demise and yet see beyond that depression into a future life vision powered by his endless imagination. Formerly repressed cognitive awareness of migratory economic realities and possibilities becomes strangely and suddenly revived by the circumstance of the day. Physicians searched for a substantial and sustainable economic survival in a formerly taboo-forbidden direction. They now drilled down a bit more deeply from another migratory economic angle or perspective in **Healthcare Reform**, and with more apparent overt enthusiasm about being "all together for the greater good":

That visionary talk of the day evolved to debating consequences of work environment relationships, such as those concerning national and international dynamic competitive business advantage, which more frequently than not found a catchy summation in two old and very familiar words -- "Quality Assurance". Albeit a business deliverable goal that is defined with some difficulty because so many myriad metrics function to fulfill that goal, quality assurance becomes an over-riding human metric that not only stands out among the rest, but additionally persists and prevails above all others......Furthermore, person or workplace production groups that are at ease, satisfied with their job at hand and share a common goal readily exhibit both happier and more productive attitudes towards fulfilling that idealized goal of "Quality Assurance". A congenial economically-invested workplace atmosphere creates the ideal WIN -- WIN scenario, both for the employee and the employer, and is the penultimate assurance for any sustainable business success, including the business of healthcare delivery..... To achieve sustainable "Quality Assurance".

This ideal business dynamic competitive advantage migratory economic has a traditional grass-root of origin at the worksite and can be best accomplished when and where there exists a pleasant invested-in business environment that fosters and produces an equal footing, level playing field, an opportunity for face-to-face conversation concerning mutual desires, needs and goals between and among management and workers. These ultimately amiable conversations are not just about pay or productivity rankings or pay for performance; they accomplish a much greater productive purpose: Unhappy workers are poor with work-flow, and unhappy managers are poor producers of a sustainable bottom profit line. By outlining the totality of everyone's concerns, productive business goals can then be jointly met with enthusiastic reliance on mutual needs and with mutual respect. Albert Camus's 1942 conclusions that, "struggle itself towards the heights is enough to fill Man's heart" aside, a bare and repetitious "Sisyphean task" simply need not dwell in a milieu of hopelessness and futileness if the meaning and motivation expectations of the task participant are properly "adjusted". Numerous migratory economic lab experiments have shown that workers strive to do more and better, actually work harder where and when the workers' attitudes are adjusted to see a bigger picture attributed to by their laborious efforts, as per the economic philosophy of Richard Taylor. Increased self-esteem leads to increased self-actualization. Workers will then go the extra mile to help others with un-assigned tasks, and managers will then also take the extra steps to show that they are more appreciative of their employees; and all will be naturally and mutually more compliant to the others' physical, mental, and safety needs. A family-like atmosphere, a sense of affectionate relationships, a business ethic of acknowledged and desired mutual dependency and belonging can then prevail no matter what size the business organization choses to become. This type of workplace produces a reliable and respected culture which in turn produces the fundamental basis for continuing successful industrial relations and success. A sustainable happy productive atmosphere within a workplace environment is the most powerful dynamic competitive advantage that one economic firm or business organization can have over another; it is the essential workable goal toward which **Healthcare Reform** should drive healthcare delivery.

In order to accomplish such a utopian and sustainable business partnership, there has to be a mechanism and a site for the aforementioned original and primary face-to-face employer-employee conversations to take place. That precise site, the site for such discussions and negotiations had been traditionally referred to as a "collective bargaining table". Needless to say, the unfortunate sound or connotation of that term immediately conjures historical visions of rioting trade unionism versus solidarity for depressed workers working for uncaring conglomerates. Such visions are not something pleasant or comfortable for the eyes or ears of the traditional providers of healthcare delivery. Indeed, the old connoted "dirty" word "unionism" was historically rejected by medical societies.

However, shortly into the 21st Century, the financial role of the majority of practicing physicians was rapidly transforming into that of a "W2" standardized employee who suddenly needed the support of group bargaining; and many physicians were finding the aforementioned essential business and work place harmonic relationship readily achievable and mutually enjoyable through unionism. The expression, "Money talks and wimpy whiners walk" became obvious to those 21st Century employee physicians. They quickly and quietly found out why the overall tried and true union mechanism of sustainable solidarity was so important for their collective healthcare delivery unions to properly function. Institutional financial stability to assure a continued and increased employment of future workers is also an essential "double win" component of successful unionism and solidarity negotiations. Both sides had to be strong, forthwith in responsiveness, willing to negotiate and respectful. New models of healthcare delivery thusly derived in and through such a collaborative manor are championed rather than challenged by physicians, even when the derived algorithms are obviously less "physician–centric". On the other hand, a financially weakened union position at the bargaining table does not readily accomplish a fostering of relationships between physician employees and employers of the corporations that hold the patient beneficiary recipient's dues payments. With a weakened union position, that old golden rule of business, (the party possessing the gold making the rules) becomes all too painfully obvious as does the formation of bad rules with unintended consequences. Moreover, "Quality Assurance" will eventually suffer as the unintended consequence of such a one-sided arrangement. The dynamic competitive advantage of the entire healthcare delivery business enterprise would then be lost, and needless to comment, the all so vitally important factor for sustainability, the business bottom line would be horridly hurt; and LOSE -- LOSE would unfortunately be the scenario, a dirge sadly sung by all the unhappily involved parties.

Although many physicians felt devastated by healthcare delivery legislation, there was some light at the end of a tunnel. The following whimsical dialogue, written by two former medical school fraternity house roommates, outlines the threat to the doctor-patient relationship as a consequence of these legislative changes and suggests three things physicians could do and did do to protect that relationship:

What Hippocrates Said to Achilles (with apologies to Lewis Carroll)

The Tortoise comes upon his friend, Achilles,
who is painfully limping slowly down the road.

Tortoise: Hello, Mr. A! What's the matter with your foot?

Achilles: It's my heel acting up again. It will be the death of me!

Tortoise: Have you seen your doctor about it?

Achilles: Indeed. I just came from Hippocrates' office and he literally gave me a mouthful.

Tortoise: How so?

Achilles: He thinks I should see an orthopedic surgeon, but is having great deal of trouble booking an appointment for me.

Tortoise: What's the problem?

Achilles: It seems that none of the medical or surgical specialists are seeing new patients since the passage of that damnable **Healthcare Reform** bill.

Tortoise: I thought the bill was supposed to reform healthcare, whatever that means.

Achilles: So did I, but Hippocrates says it is just the beginning of widespread rationing. He says a number of his specialty colleagues would rather leave medical practice than work under such a system.

Tortoise: That seems a rather radical response!

Achilles: I agree. I'd kick them in the butt, but my heel hurts too much.

Tortoise: Does Hippocrates offer any solutions to the problem?

Achilles: In fact, he does. He thinks there are three things doctors can do to improve the quality and cost of care while strengthening the confidentiality of the doctor-patient relationship. Hippocrates holds this to be one of the central ethical tenets of the profession. As he put it, "I will follow that method of treatment which, according to my ability and judgment, I consider for the benefit of my patients, and abstain from whatever is deleterious and mischievous."

Tortoise: It's a little preachy, but I get the idea. How does he suggest protecting the doctor-patient relationship?

Achilles: The first thing he recommends is that doctors start converting their practices over to something he calls "direct care."

Tortoise: Are they currently providing "indirect care"?

Achilles: Very funny! Direct care doctors do much more than perform consultations or operations. They are really patient advocates -- just like the family doctors that cared for your parent's decades ago. But unlike the family doctor, they are skilled also in providing the best of modern healthcare delivery.

Tortoise: What does that entail?

Achilles: A limited patient population, transparency in pricing of all costs of medical care, including the publishing of all patient fees, and opting out of the third party payment system.

Tortoise: How does Hippocrates accomplish this?

Achilles: The direct care doctor works closely with patients like us, taking the necessary time to hear and determine what we really need. All the studies and data prove that patients who pay for their care directly truly get the value based healthcare that they want and deserve.

Tortoise: How about patient privacy?

Achilles: Hippocrates says, "What I may see or hear in the course of the treatment or even outside of the treatment in regard to the life of men, which on no account one must spread abroad, I will keep to myself, holding such things shameful to be spoken about."

Tortoise: Can you give me an example of how this direct care works?

Achilles: Suppose you are unfortunate enough to wind up in an emergency room at 3 am. You do not have to rely on a total stranger to provide your care. Your direct care physician, whom you know and who knows you, will immediately be on your case and most possibly at your side to represent your medical interests and coordinate all aspects of your healthcare.

Tortoise: But what if two patients need the same doctor at the same time?

Achilles: I certainly wouldn't want to be shunted off to some unknown on-call person if my personal physician was busy with someone else; and as Hippocrates explained it, that probably wouldn't happen. The total number of patients served is limited and the time devoted to each is expanded.

Tortoise: What about their ancillary support staff?

Achilles: These doctors also have good, knowledgeable and reliable staffs, truly concerned staff people who get to know all their patients well. When you call in, it is like talking to an old friend.

Tortoise: Does this save time and add quality?

Achilles: Time is efficiently managed so that everybody gets excellent care and all the one-on one time they need.

Tortoise: Could you give me a specific example?

Achilles: OK, here's one. Your direct care physician sees you in the hospital and personally confers with all of your consultants so that your care is truly coordinated, not just on paper, and then every indication, risk, and alternative is personally explained to you in detail. There are no omissions or cracks left for you to fall through -- something particularly important to me given my current infirmity. You can rest assured with peace of mind. It is really great!

Tortoise: Is this compatible with the new health care reforms that are all the rage? Who pays for this personalized service? Won't this simply add an additional cost (the annual "direct care" fee) to an already overblown and inflated system?

Achilles: Slow down, Mr. T. Let's take things one at a time. The current legislation actually allows for patients to purchase an additional direct care policy that is less expensive than their basic insurance. In the long run, it saves Money and patient time by delivering more efficient healthcare.

Tortoise: Do we patients have to do an actuarial analysis before the government can understand the intended consequences in dollars saved?

Achilles: Probably not, but it turns out to be a wonderful opportunity to pay reasonably for needed healthcare access.

Tortoise: Won't the new law guarantee healthcare anyway for everyone?

Achilles: Sadly no, it won't even be close, nor should it attempt to. Remember, when something is "free" there's never enough of it.

Tortoise: What about cost?

Achilles: Yes, there's a small price to be paid, but the cost is well worth the value.

Tortoise: What will happen to us if we do not use some ancillary system like direct contracting or direct care?

Achilles: Millions of us will eventually be deprived of the trust and understanding we have come to expect from American doctors. That essential relationship will erode even further under the future single payer government proposed managed care model.

Tortoise: Well, hadn't we better do something about this, and I mean pronto?

Achilles: Indeed. Hippocrates thinks the current "reform" legislation represents only the first step toward a national, government-run single-payer system healthcare triage/rationing system that will make getting specialty health care even harder to get. I don't want to get too political here, but this expansive vision has been at the top of the "to-do" list among social progressives for decades.

Tortoise: Let's not get into that right now.

Achilles: You can ignore politics, Mr. T, but you can't avoid it!

Tortoise: I'll just have to take my chances. What else does Hippocrates recommend?

Achilles: Pro-active legislation. According to Hippocrates, the only hope for sustainable future medical practice may be to drastically modify or to repeal and rewrite the **Healthcare Reform** law.

Tortoise: Is that realistic?

Achilles: He acknowledges that's out of his direct control. The best he and his colleagues can do is to educate and persuade patients such as you and me to vote for political candidates that hold the best interest of the patient above cost-cap rationing.

Tortoise: What about the current system?

Achilles: Under the current system, the patient gives Money to an insurer or the government which, after taking their cut, they pay the doctor as they see fit. And so they both say everyone now has just a little bit more of a lot less healthcare.

Tortoise: Are you saying that patients should decide about their basic health needs and then what to do with their own Money?

Achilles: Healthcare costs must be controlled, but we should not let the tail wag the dog, and we should be prepared to move at a calculated pace to avoid tragic unintended consequences.

Tortoise: OK, OK! Step down off your soapbox. Be very careful about your injured heel and tell me how on earth this pro-active legislation can become a reality.

Achilles: Yes, if patients kept the Money that they are forced to pay to the government in health care taxes for basic health care that they can manage for themselves and instead use the funds to find and pay a doctor of their choice, the patient and the doctor would control medical care and lowering costs. The government and insurance corporations would not be telling you what to do, what not to do, how much something should cost etc, etc, etc.

Tortoise: So under the current circumstances of Healthcare Reform, what could or should physicians do?

Achilles: Hippocrates says doctors should begin organizing into unions. Under present governmental rules and regulations, a union is the only mechanism that would allow them to engage in collective bargaining both for themselves and their patients.

Tortoise: Unions?! Not to get political again, but aren't they the darlings of the progressives you so often malign?

Achilles: It's totally consistent with Hippocrates' ethical philosophy, by which he has sworn "To hold him who has taught me this art as equal to my parents and to live my life in partnership with him..." A union is a doctor-partnership.

Tortoise: Philosophy is one thing, but are you saying that real-world practicality is another.

Achilles: This is the real-world! In order to successfully play the game, you have to know and abide by the rules. Why should government or insurance corporations be in the middle of the relationship between physicians and their patients? If you could take government and insurance corporations out of the equation, then unions and collective bargaining would become irrelevant.

Tortoise: Why not just collectively bargain when necessary without a union?

Achilles: Physicians have been excluded from collective bargaining for decades, ever since a cabal of lawyers was found guilty of price fixing. Since then, the law of the land was extended to all other "learned professions", including physicians engaged in the practice of Medicine.

Tortoise: That was quite a while ago. Has anyone tried to change that law?

Achilles: Yes, but so far the attempts have been unsuccessful. It's very hard to un-pass a law.

Tortoise: Hard but not impossible. What can be done?

Achilles: Hippocrates also thinks that physicians should get directly involved in the legislative process and sponsor specific legislation that clarifies their position and rights as income-earning citizens as well as the inalienable rights of patients to act freely and unencumbered in America's free society. This right to unencumbered private contracting between a doctor and a patient and a patient and a doctor should be legislatively chiseled in stone. Hippocrates insists that no future law shall or should be passed that would interfere with a person's right to pay directly for lawful medical services and that no future law shall or should be passed that restricts a person's freedom of choice.

Tortoise: Doesn't the new healthcare legislation address some of this?

Achilles: No way! Hippocrates says that all patients, physicians, and insurers must be granted the right to privately contract among one another and not be legally restricted in this contracting by some superficially attractive financing scheme, cleverly disguised as just a small government-run "cooperative". I call it a Trojan horse.

Tortoise: Never heard of such a horse.

Achilles: That's because we Greeks won't unveil this weapon for a few years yet. Anyway, Hippocrates thinks physicians should unionize to combat this specious government-run universal healthcare scheme and assure quality healthcare for their patients, then advertise their own fair fees and compete in a transparent free global market. That's the three legs of Hippocrates' platform of ethical reform.

Tortoise: Had you not better be quick about it, or the game will be over and the opposite will be your lot?

Achilles: Hippocrates is both a futurist and an optimist. He says we now live in an era of dynamic global competition. American healthcare delivery's future road of travel will be a definite part of a medical ecologic and economic or "ecolo-nomic" evolution played on a world-wide global stage.

Tortoise: Yes, Atlas keeps on shrugging and the world keeps on changing, and so must we not adapt a wider perspective?

Achilles: Sure, but don't forget, at the home front, appeal of oppressive anti-trust legislation would also allow for empowerment of physician unions to engage in more effective collective bargaining.

Tortoise: And when is the best time for this action?

Achilles: According to Hippocrates, now, right now, the time is ripe for a choice that is clear and demands immediate legislative action -- the time has come to draw the penultimate line in the sand that time cannot erase and from which physicians shall never retreat.

Tortoise: Do you mean that in order to ensure the legality and permanence of that line in the sand, physicians must proceed through the political process of legislative action?

Achilles: Physicians must write and promote a legislative bill that clarifies their position and rights as income-earning American citizens as well as the inalienable rights of American patients to act freely and unencumbered in the uniquely American free society. The right to unencumbered individual contracting between a doctor and a patient and a patient and a doctor should be legislatively chiseled in stone.

Tortoise: *Are you saying that **Physicians must insist that no law shall exist that would interfere with a person's right to pay directly for independent medical services and that no future law shall be passed that restricts a person's freedom of choice** -- to choose independent physician healthcare delivery unencumbered by rules, regulations and fines?*

Achilles: Yes, all patients, physicians, and insurers must be granted the right to privately contract among one another and not be legally restricted in this contracting by any present type or any future type of mandatory percent participation in some governmental program.

Tortoise: So, apart from becoming directly and actively involved in the legislative process, what are three positive things that a physician can do to help correct the situation and partially restore dignity to their profession in the wake of this horrible healthcare delivery law?

Achilles: You mean like one, two, three things?

Tortoise: Yes, in addition to the aforementioned legislation, what must be done for physicians to survive and have their patients continue to reap the rewards of the finest quality and overall best individualized medical and surgical practice in the world?

Achilles: Physicians must:
    1. Develop direct care medical practices.
    2. Support physician unionization.
    3. Advertise and publish fair fees and compete in a transparent open market both here and abroad.
Tortoise: A three-legged race for the cure...I like it! Speaking of races, how about reconsidering an attempt to race me precisely halfway home?
Achilles: I would but I'm just not up to it......my foot at the heel, you know. Anyway, I'm supposed to meet up with a fellow warrior for some fancy archery practice. See you soon, Mr. T!

A short time thereafter, Hippocrates met over lunch with some representatives of various union, society, academy, and association physician organizations. They agreed to seek immediate legal and legislative council and begin to work together to unify their organizational philosophical perspectives towards a common goal of attaining antitrust relief and independent patient contracting for all patients and physicians. Meanwhile, Achilles underwent excision of a bone spur and is recovering nicely with his ankle and heel temporarily protected in a plaster cast.

References
1. Carroll L. "What the tortoise said to Achilles", Mind 1895;4:278-80. Available at: http://www.ditext.com/carroll/tortise.html
2. Zeno's "Paradox of the Tortoise and Achilles", Available at: http://www.mathacademy.com/pr/prime/articles/zeno_tort/index.asp
3. DiLibero RJ, Diamond GA. "ObamaCare", Am J Cardiol 2010;105:900.

What about this "UNIONISM"?

Without the consent or buy-in of physicians, a California hospital group converted itself into a Nixon Administration type of HMO. The physicians were abhorred. Therefore, general surgeon Dr. Sanford A. Marcus founded the Union of American Physicians and Dentists (UAPD) in 1972. The UAPD began promotion of physician unionism with a local tumult and stormy national rejection. However, local private practice physicians, especially those in Independent Practice Associations (IPA's), dug immediately into their wallets and sent Dr. Marcus on a union-organizer lecture tour locally and nationally. The AMA and medical societies overtly and overwhelmingly rejected unionism for physicians at that time. George Meany, President of the AFL-CIO responded with "I can't help you now. But come back in ten years. Most of you will have become employees. Then we will be able to talk."[100]

During the 1970's, over two dozen doctor unions fearlessly formed alliances throughout the United States, but alas they yet remained as "toothless declawed tigers"; and their numbers became reduced to only a few after thirty dreary years of fighting for survival. Dr. Marcus's UAPD was one of those exceptional unions whose membership steadily grew after winning many important dollar-amount labor contracts for its members. 1974 saw many county-employed physicians added to the UAPD union rolls. In 1975, the healthcare division of the California State Employees Association enrolled into the UAPD as the State Employed Physicians Association (SEPA). In 1982, California State Universities' student health physicians came on board, and the UAPD joined with the legislative lobbying efforts of the California Medical Association to defeat expanding scope of practice bills involving psychologists and nurse specialists. A 1986 lawsuit settlement for failing to pay prevailing wages returned fifteen million dollars to union doctors.

Dr. Marcus continued to spread the word of physician unionism by delivering speeches and quotations across America:
"There are no dinosaurs left, simply because they were unable to adapt to the changing environmental conditions. We doctors are now faced with the greatest revolution in the allocation of medical care since the time of Hippocrates, yet we too, are presently milling about ponderously, waiting for the old watering holes to refill. They never will....."
"We stand a much better chance of preserving our professionalism through the process of becoming unionized workers – admittedly a terribly unprofessional thing to do, by my own estimation, just a few short years ago. But then, that is just the sort of adaptation those now extinct dinosaurs were incapable of making, isn't it?..."
"With the cash flow of the health care industry now coming under almost total control of a new class of managers, a trade union offers the only vehicle that doctors, as the de facto employees of those managers, can use to develop effective negotiating power given the new market conditions under which they must now serve."
"Physicians have been drawn to us because the AMA and the state societies have done nothing but retreat and wring their hands... (They are) the toothless fogies who clutter up the socioeconomic battlefield"[101]

[100] *The Union for Doctors, UAPD,* Gary Robinson, 2012, www.uapd.com.

After nineteen years of serving and defending the rights of physicians and dentists in California, Dr. Marcus retired.

A private practice neurologist and a member of CMA's Workers' Compensation Committee, Dr. Robert L. Weinmann, took over the presidential reins of the UAPD in 1990. Under his direction, the UAPD resisted privatization, anti-collective bargaining and pay cut initiatives, imposed by California Governor Pete Wilson, legislation that would have affected physicians, podiatrists and dentists employed in the state's prison system. The UAPD then expanded its scope to review contracts for doctors involved in HMOs, PPOs and TPAs.

After authoring a newspaper article that severely criticized the UAPD for violating anti-trust laws, a flip-flopping AMA stumbled then fell on its face. A three-million-dollar attempt to organize its own national AMA doctor union abruptly failed. A Federal Trade Commission (FTC) investigation into the affairs of the UAPD found no evidence of that trumped up anti-trust law violation, offered compliance with the UAPD's practice and efforts in negotiation with PPO's and HMO's, and opened the door for other sub groups of private practice physicians who treated certain allowed percentages of enrolled patients to do the same. The UAPD next formed a 501(c) Independent Practice Association (IPA) for private practice group collective bargaining. In 1997, the UAPD gained national identity and status by formally joining with a national affiliate, the American Federation of State County, and Municipal Employees (AFSCME) under an agreement with the AFL-CIO. After 25 years, the 1972 words of George Meany finally rang true.

By the time of Y2K, a UAPD "Medical Defense Fund" established in the 1980's was able to easily support over one hundred thousand dollars per year in contributions to local and state of California ballot initiatives and political candidates. A successful bill sponsored by UAPD assured patient enrollees assignment of a primary care physician upon enrollment into any HMO; and another bill rescued retirement benefits for doctors in major metropolitan areas by mandating that a California County of over three million residents could not remove an existing healthcare benefit. The year of 2003 pronounced the UAPD successful in defeating a President G. W. Bush administration plan that would have eliminated the national physician work force of disability evaluators for the Department of Social Services (DSS).

---

[101] *The Union for Doctors, UAPD,* Gary Robinson, 2012, www.uapd.com.

After 17 years of dedicated service, Dr. Robert L. Weinmann retired as UAPD President, but he still had a lot to say:
"Unless physicians immediately apply collective bargaining techniques to their demands, they'll continue to be marginalized and at first picked off one by one, then little group by little group, next big group by big group, until they're all finally herded into the same confining corral from which their only last resort for sustained professional survival will be to choose collective barking."[102] He further stated, "Doctors who don't organize into effective bargaining units will become the chips with which other organizations bargain."[103]

In 2006, Stuart Bussey, JD MD, a medical consultant for the California Department of Social Services (DSS) and a primary care private practice practitioner, arose to the post of UAPD President. He immediately declared, "To level the playing field, doctors need the right to negotiate with payers and an organization that can make it happen. The UAPD is that organization."[104] As to the future of physician unionism and the evolution of medical practice and **Healthcare Reform**, in late November of 2013 Dr. Bussey added, "As more and more physicians turn to public and private employment it is inevitable that they seek protection of their income, credibility licensure and livelihood. Unions historically remain the most effective and politically galvanizing means of achieving these goals. It is time for doctors to honestly admit to themselves that their position on the American healthcare system is no longer preeminent. It is time to join a doctors' union."[105]

As with any vibrant and growing organization, a successful and sustainable doctor's union required indoctrination – unionism equals solidarity, but cannot exist without an efficient and workable recruiting policy for new members, "spell it out – u-n-i – and stop right there". UAPD practiced the tried and true initial first five steps of organizing unionism activation through one-on-one communication with potential members by rote:
1. Introduction – express a case for urgency to get one's attention with "affective attunement" directed to the prospective member.
2. Get the story – discover what the potential member really wants and what can be reasonably changed to achieve a desired satisfactory goal.
3. Share the UAPD union vision – demonstrate an urgent and critical need to "stand together" right now.

---

[102] Personal communication
[103] Personal communication
[104] *The Union for Doctors, UAPD,* Gary Robinson, 2012, www.uapd.com.
[105] Personal communication

4. Assess support and move to action – change a potential member into a certified UAPD union member, and "sign-up" on the AFL-CIO card.

5. Inoculate fear of further non-productive and often punitive supervisory mandates and/or attacks – support the new member in encouraging healthcare co-workers to join the UAPD union, and become united "people-people" to stop further healthcare employer attacks and/or unjust mandates – not me or WIIFM, but WIIFUS -- what is in it for "US".

The next indoctrination/activation step was for the UAPD to gain further political influence and favor. The path to a legislative ear to enact **Healthcare Reform** became obvious. The Union had to grow their vitally necessary potent persuasive political power from within. UAPD physician members were therefore elected to the state legislative assembly/senate and appointed to the state medical licensing board. In addition to horizontal expansion in negotiating contracts and representing member grievances, the union expanded further vertically by creating a state practitioner license accredited continuing education program and a Legal Defense Fund for physician and dentist employment-related lawsuits. By 2015, UAPD was set for a new round of state and national expansion. Additionally, UAPD inducted ancillary healthkeepers, such as Pharmacists, into the expanding union.

The transition from 2016 to 2017 found UAPD successfully negotiating interstate with various physician groups. Private practice physicians on the medical staff of Auburn Medical Center (AMC) at Tacoma, Washington joined the UAPD. This unionization of the medical staff permitted the practicing physicians to utilize the protections of the National Labor Relations Act (NLRA) and legally negotiate with MultiCare, a healthcare delivery organization that had previously prevented their doctors from discussing wages and working conditions. The future of UAPD seems destined for further interstate expansion, with current interest being expressed across the USA, from New Orleans to Washington D.C.. A new era in physician unionization was well on its way.

At the start of the 21st Century, a great medical ecolo-nomic wrecking ball swung and demolished the bricks and mortar of the American hospital system, leaving only an infrastructure of foundations to build upon. From that rubble, a re-vitalized foundation built with new-aged architectural plans created a place in a continually evolving **Healthcare Reform** paradigm that no longer looked to the concept or model of hospital-centric healthcare delivery. The new hospital emerged as a highly technical life-saving treatment center that provided specific medical-surgical sub-specialty center of excellence healthcare that could not be

308

safely or reasonably performed at any other location. The hospital's hub evolved to become the operating room, whose wings provided for specific acute and emergent medical procedural entities and acute intensive medical care units. Sub-acute care and former non-life-saving emergency room services were furnished elsewhere – at ancillary community clinics, skilled nursing facilities, free-standing outpatient facilities and hospital-owned emergency treatment centers -- all financially incentivized to deliver the patient to the original home environment ASAP, where organized home-environment managed care delivery systems could complete the patient's discharge into independent life. This very important and essential final segment, getting the patient to live independently in the community, required a medical service goal of self-directed healthcare accomplished by a social worker, a medical case-management team and extensive home care services in a patient care algorithm.[106]

So finally, the unveiled ultimate semi or more likely quarter-final **Healthcare Reform** goal became revealed to the private insurance corporations -- all would be required and economically mandated to do more with less:
National Socialized Healthcare, with legal authority for approvals and denials dictated by big government bureaucrat agencies that mandated patient and physician participation while offering decreased services from all types of providers looked to be on its way to becoming the proposed norm in a not too distant future. There must and therefore would be decreased payments and "bundled payments" to providers of all types -- practitioners, labs and vendors alike; there would be less of everything to go around, but everything would be shared by and through hotly negotiated settlements involving all interested parties in competition with each other. The words "Accountable Care" flew through the air, but these words were interpreted quite differently on a variety of special interest radar screens.

According to traditionally acclaimed economist extraordinaire Adam Smith, payment for professional services would be enhanced by and directly proportionate to:
The expense of time and education necessary to attain the high professional position, and the number of people that had tried and had been unsuccessful in attaining the position. As an example, Adam Smith used top-paid litigator lawyers practicing in Great Britain during his century. Two centuries later, the introduction of the "computer" and then the "cloud" as an infinite-sized storehouse of medical information downgraded the prided and honored necessity for relatively high IQ

---

[106] per Olmstead v. L.C., 527 U.S. 581, 119 S.Ct. 2176 (1999)

physician decision making, thus opening wide and deep the immense field of medical practice to and for those many more individuals possessing a lower IQ and simultaneously decreasing the total time, extraordinary dedicated competitive effort and huge expense necessary to train a medical practitioner while increasing the number of successfully trained, trained or educated to questionable new lower standards for a "qualified" "medical provider" "job" position. Consider this quote from a top-selling 2003 novel that was eventually made into a movie: "The best people weren't going into Medicine anymore, not with the HMOs running everything. This kid might be one of the **new breed of dumb doctor**." – (Dr.) Michael Crichton, MD -- <u>Prey</u>. The practicing physician healthkeeper demonstrated a variety of reactions to that worrisome predicted course of action or migratory ecolo-nomic strategy for **Healthcare Reform**:

On June 15, 2009, physicians listened to an admonishing speech from President Obama at the AMA House of Delegates and then quickly adopted, without dissent, amended AMA Resolution # 203:
"That our American Medical Association include in its top advocacy priorities (1) the enactment of federal legislation that ensures and protects the fundamental right of patients to privately contract with physicians without penalties for doing so and regardless of payer within the framework of free market principles with the goal of accomplishing this by 2010; and (2) the restoration of fairness to the current healthcare marketplace through changes in statutes and regulations so that physicians are able to negotiate (individually and as defined groups) fair contracts with the private sector and public sector health plans".

Perhaps someone there happened to read, hear about or knew the authors of the aforementioned discussion concerning unionism between Achilles and the Tortoise? Actually yes, but it mattered not, because those formally resolved, near to unanimous and suddenly reactive by the delegates to the convention AMA goals have not been accomplished, and no future AMA leadership or designated policy committee will have the courage to demand that they ever be accomplished. With the AMA livelihood directly dependent on federal funding of code books, that old golden rule of economics once again prevails. Meanwhile, the Middle-Man or third-party reduced payment grinding machines in corporate insurance firms already had their motors oiled and running. With slippery salty saliva drooling from the far corners of their lips and then dripping in long strands from the edges of their chins, they anxiously waited in anticipation of migratory economic pleasure. Those third-party payment reduction grinders also created an immense dirty cloud of dust and smog by gleefully tearing apart the "Common Plan" proposed support from an AMA that had totally lost its credible independent

310

political clout since becoming dependent upon government financing. The political payoff to the insurance industry stood out as painfully obvious: as long as the Obama administration's "Common Plan" remained buried in a political grave, private third party insurers felt perfectly safe. A word of caution and admonition to all in the future -- never trust an agreement made with blackmail within its intent.

The basic overall **Healthcare Reform** soup underwent reduction by boiling off the glamorous sauce of choice, value and quality, and simmered down to a thickened, condensed essential gravy in migratory ecolo-nomic concept: to force the various providers to coordinate their segment of healthcare delivery by "integrating" the delivery of healthcare services with an average low-ball payment for the complete and "bundled payment" covering the total medical-surgical service. The federal administrators hoped that this "integrated service" delivery model would reduce disparities and costs while improving transitions in healthcare delivery and maintaining quality. Of course, all medical policy was near completely subject to political whim; and legislative edicts continued to spill into and spice up that simmering integrated budget originating from a waterfall of repayment debt, the inevitable pay-off consequence of special interest group campaign financing.

Physicians were not very careful about what they wished for; there never was and is no free lunch, especially with the gift of technology such as physician-designed telehealth and telemedicine programs: Rite-Aid pharmacy announced that physician consultation via telephone would be available at their locations at the rate of $45 for ten minutes. The physician fee cut remained undisclosed, but most likely something like 9 to 14 percent of the $270 per hour charge. Thinking globally, the exact world geographic physical location of this unseen physician also remained unknown; and that global location may have actually been not one, but many, in multiple spots about planet earth. Can do, but not only in Katmandu; and that was A-OK with Rite-Aid and their migratory economic payer pool of "clients" or "patients", as the two words became increasingly and confusingly intertwined. Not to be undone, Walmart jumped into the telemedicine fray and soon Target would have small Kaiser medical advice clinics and a partially prescribing pharmacy run by the CVS – Walgreens drugstore chain. But shut up and "foahgetaboutit", forget about Rite-Aid and all the retail market commercialism of sacrosanct medical consultation and primary care at the drugstore or anywhere else – there eventually would be no need to travel to any fixed market geographical location at all, when one could get the same questionable medical advice 365/24/7 right on a handy cell phone by just pressing a finger (any finger grandma) or waving a wand over one of the many telemedicine apps.

Evidence based psychological studies prove that throwing a frog into boiling water will induce the frog to immediately jump out of the pot; but gently placing a frog into cool water and then gradually heating the pot, slowly bit by bit, results in the unsuspecting amphibian merrily swimming about until it is completely and thoroughly boiled to death. Slowly boiling a physician-frog, that is by gradually adding on, bit by bit, more work and less pay for a physician employee, thus allowing the employee to enter and enroll into an elite group of those "working smarter" (or perhaps as others have noted working dumb, numb and dumber) in an increasingly resource-poor setting can actually be accomplished without too much complaint and result in the boiling to death of all and any physician autonomy and decision making. By the way, thinking globally, there are an awful lot of physician-frogs jumping about on this planet earth and they are incredibly quite easy to net and then relocate to or stay put and "Telework" in the USA marketplace.

That psychological slow boil with marinated ingredients added has historically worked well with an assumed outward appearance for political posturing during the Roman Republic. It always helps psychologically to be "properly" or "appropriately" dressed for an occasion today, but there is an inherent psychological fear of mistrust if one appears too "sparkling". In Ancient Rome, one had to wear maroon sandals, gold rings, and a broad bright purple stripe across a brilliantly gleaming white toga if you happened to be a patrician senator seeking one of the two top positions of "Chief Consul of Rome". Cicero's winning oration, the "Oratio in Toga Candida" (white toga, from which is derived "political candidate") denounced the clothing of other runners-up and implied that they also possessed hidden evil powers of injustice, a thought allowed to grow and fester in the senatorial electorate. Make note the next time an American politico takes off his jacket and rolls up his sleeves to psychologically show nothing to hide when making a campaign or presidential speech.

Markedly more insidious are the classical political campaigning maneuvers of "deceit, treachery and betrayal" first scribed in Latin by an ancient Roman, Quintus Tullius Cicero, the lesser known brother of Marcus Tullius Cicero. According to the writings of Quintus, a successful politician must be a constant chameleon and smear all his opponents at every opportunity, while offering threats and fear, which work more effectively than actual litigation. Quintus quite graciously acknowledged that the populous are moved more by appearances than reality, and that the deliverance of favors, hope and supposed personal political attachment, when coupled with political promises of everything possible made to everybody, would certainly bring an easily swayed populous to favor any specific political offering and gain many more allies as a bonus in so doing. Quintus further advised any ambitious politician or politico to first offer hope and promises, to offer help, dynamic competitive mercantile and political advantage as well as monitory savings to everyone, to place others in political debt for personal favors, and to also be personally in everyone's debt for political favors. Then subsequent to that said politician's "fait accompli", (election to office or passage of legislation) to simply back out of all the promised obligations by claiming that although the successful candidate and now office holder so dearly still wanted "to help if only he could", "circumstances" beyond the political office control were unfortunately preventing such action.....Nice guy was this Quintus?......(Hint, he never came in last.)

"The moving finger writes and having writ moves on. Nor all thy piety nor wit shall lure it back to cancel half a line. Nor all thy tears wash out a word of it." Loose lips, "moving lips" are writ on digital script that neither time nor circumstance can or dare delete. But why should routinely repeated political shenanigans, political business-as-usual, be so shocking anyway? Hoax, fraudulent contract or tricky dealings coupled with a firm documented belief in the "stupidity of the American voter" as a factor in designing federal legislation may be a window into the thinking-justification mechanism within a liberal-progressive mind, fitting well and in accord with that potent political advice formally scripted by Quintus Tullius Cicero. Perhaps the Clinton Administration Healthcare Reform attempt stymied, thwarted and then foiled because the basic concept was so widely debated without true knowledge of its contents. The Patient Protection and Accountable Care Act (PPACA) would likely fall victim to that same poorly-planned and non-transparent process. It was tragic enough that the Obama Administration's "common plan" alternative failed by one cold day in December's vote (Senator Lieberman) to be an injected provision into the Federal Healthcare Exchanges. Chicanery, not Mighty Mouse, would prove to be better than the fantasy cartoon absolutely necessary to save the day for the PPACA.

The Patient Protection and Accountable Care Act (PPACA) was designed and written by basically the same progressive democratic-backed "equal sharing of less' think-tank crowd that had previously conjured republican-backed "RomneyCare" for Massachusetts. Loose-lipped and digitally scripted on moving lips, progressive political pundits, including President Obama, often quoted Jonathan Gruber, referencing him as one of the main architects of the PPACA.

Then unexpectedly more moving lips, recorded in high dimensional digital script, first depicted Gruber boldly bragging that he, through deception, had been cleverly able and willing to move over $400 Million in federal funds to be unknowingly used in the RomneyCare program. Gruber went significantly further in his loose-lipped "Honest Man" confession – Knowing well in advance that the financial number crunching did not add up or compute to be politically digestible, Gruber admitted that transparency was purposely avoided in the PPACA document; the necessary wealth distribution enrollment of the entire American populous was quasi legally disguised as a well-understood illegal reference to legitimacy, covered by the "commerce clause" rather than presented as an actual mandated federal tax. An admitted tax would certainly not have been so popular with and so easily have successfully duped the apparently illiterate U.S. Senate and U.S. House of Representatives. Moreover, Gruber subsequently, offhandedly and yet on more than four distinctly recorded videos, further pontificated on digital script that the accomplished PPACA task (fait accompli) also depended on the "stupidity of the American voting public" not to notice or realize that there was real wealth-insurance redistribution. If still alive about 2000 years after his birth, Quintus Tullius Cicero would surely have been so proud and honored to be an active part of the migratory economics evolving **Healthcare Reform** in the PPACA.

On March 23, 2010, President Barack Obama signed the infamously passed but yet unread Patient Protection and Accountable Care Act (PPACA) into law. In an inspiring and exquisitely-delivered speech touting the still unread **Healthcare Reform** at the University of Iowa two days later, he triumphantly exclaimed and proclaimed, "From this day forward, all of the cynics, all the naysayers — they're going to have to confront the reality of what this reform is and what it isn't. ... They'll see that if Americans like their doctor, they'll be keeping their doctor. You like your plan? You'll be keeping your plan. No one is taking that away from you. ... It wasn't Armageddon." "If you already have insurance, this reform will make it more secure and more affordable. ... Costs will come down for families, and businesses and the federal government, reducing our deficit by more than $1 trillion over the next two decades. That's what reform is going to do." – Thank you, Quintus.

Moving on to late 2013 and early 2014, Americans anxiously awaited the primary elements of the PPACA to become a reality; formerly supporting PPACA mass media headlines began to change as a trail of markedly meaningful measured and monitored milestones of completely opposite events to those previously promised by President Obama began to surface. Formerly supporting employee unions demanded a carve-out exception to the legislation, just like the exception that was given to the U.S. Congress and many other groups. The enforcement of the individual mandate to buy private insurance was unsuccessfully postponed, but the big business mandate to buy coverage for 50 or greater employees was questioned and successfully postponed. Very few small business provisions were postponed. Moreover, gradually peeling back the multi-layered skins on the tear-evoking onion known as the PPACA produced mournful and tearful cries whimpering that:

It was not true that if "Americans like their doctor, they'll keep their doctor." The Congressional Budget Office predicted a minimum of 7 million Americans to lose their employer-provided coverage because of the PPACA. Many of these cancelled insurance policies were group insurance policies issued to families, placing the actual number of citizens affected by the loss at a much greater number. One of the least-known provisions was a "community standards" requirement, that as of Jan. 1, 2014 mandated -- by federal law -- health insurers to cover a broad range of treatments and services — much more than John Q. Public's typical policy. More than 98 percent of existing policies did not qualify and many Americans could no longer keep their doctor or their existing insurance coverage. This is also why it was not correctly stated that insurance would be "more secure" for those who already had it. The presidential claim that insurance will be "more affordable" was also not correctly stated for the vast majority of middle-class Americans who could not obtain governmental monetary assistance in the form of subsidies.

During the year of 2009, President Obama made over three dozen public appearances in which he essentially stated, "Under our proposals, if you like your doctor, you keep your doctor. If you like your current insurance, you keep that insurance. Period! End of story." Because the PPACA mandated a sharp increase in what health insurance policies must cover, such as previously existing medical conditions and maternity benefits, many studies found that less than 2 percent of the existing health plans met the law's "community standards." In turn, the mandated broader coverage increased the cost of the insurance policy and eventually forced cancellations of nearly 10 million existing insurance policies. Therefore, on 11/14/13, President Obama half-heartedly apologized to the nation for "circumstances beyond his control" (a direct quote from the scripted teachings of Quintus Tullius Cicero) by suggesting a possible yet improbable "fix" for the problem -- (the federal government) "isn't going to get in the way" of insurance companies offering plans to existing customers in the individual insurance market that don't meet minimum coverage requirements."

The fines were far cheaper than the mandated premiums; even those who did flunk third grade three times could figure that out. Since under the PPACA, insurers could not reject someone because of pre-existing conditions, the relatively healthy public majority quickly realized that it might be far cheaper to wait until you are sick or injured before starting to pay insurance premiums. These uninsured "free riders", on the backs of the government, hospitals and those who did pay for coverage, forced the price of insurance premiums up another notch. Employers also utilized their own unintended "free rider" incentive by paying the temporally-posted minimal fines rather than offering broad work-provided insurance coverage.

Nor was it true that health insurance "costs will come down" for businesses. Therefore, businesses shifted philosophies and hired more part-time workers to counteract the increased healthcare insurance costs. From January 2012 to January 2013, 200,000 retail jobs were added in the U.S., but the total number of retail hours worked went down. "We can cut the average family's premium by about $2,500 a year" and the idea that health insurance "costs will come down" for the federal government were also sadly disproven. In February of 2013, the Congressional Budget Office (CBO) estimated that over its first 10 years, there would be no clear path to Trillion-dollar savings. Quite the opposite path -- the CBO estimated PPACA costs would account for $1.3 trillion in additional spending, costs far beyond what the U.S. was presently spending on health insurance programs. The most definitive California study, by a Milliman analysis, forecasted a 22.2 percent increase in premium costs. The most credible national study, by the Society of Actuaries, forecasted a 32 percent increase. It was then predicted that the national debt would also increase beyond the previously set legislative limit or debt ceiling. The Obama administration shut down the government's federal expenditures in an effort to get a Republican majority U.S. Congress to comply. Some called this magical reversal of policy technique prestidigitation ("quick fingers") or "léger de main" because during the Bush Administration, then candidate Senator Obama had this to say, **"The fact that we are here today to debate raising America's debt limit is a sign of leadership failure. It is a sign that the U.S. government can't pay its own bills. ... I therefore intend to oppose the effort to increase America's debt limit." – Barak Obama, 3/16/2006.**
"It wasn't Armageddon," or was it?

Was it then, "*The Audacity of Hope*" that prayed, "Uva Uvam Vivendo Varia Fit" – a continually changing and adapting vine eventually becomes the final living vine, or some other audacious hope that another translation might suffice -- Different and diverse varietals of grapes, through time, grow together. Yes, that was and is a tried and true principal of political reality. The Obama administration remained implacable because the PPACA was truly believed to be that unique varietal of ultimately sustainable grape, a very confusing or amusing and yet unproven pleasure-averse (for the upper middle class) "Heterodox Economic Theory" for **Healthcare Reform**:

If 15 million to 30 million "previously uninsured" people suddenly became truly financially "insured" from incurring medical bill debt and were truly offered ready access to medical care, the current American healthcare delivery system mechanism would have soon been overwhelmed, forcing referral delays, treatment delays as well as inevitable implicit taxes and rationing in one hidden form or another in spite of the purposely overlooked consequences of higher deductibles, increased co-pays and stricter prescription formularies. Yes, about 26 million Americans were eligible for financial subsidies, and manyAmericans saved lots or spent less mullah from what they might or might not have potentially spent out-of-pocket, but vastly more Americans were not eligible for federal financial subsidies, and by in large would have to pay considerably more mullah for their private or federal/state exchange insurance if they chose not to pay a lesser fine for non-coverage. The simple non-heterodox rational economic self-interest choice between the two mullah alternatives became much too painfully obvious, especially for the young and healthy.

The Society of Actuaries concluded that the cost of adding so many people would "overwhelm" the savings that were supposed to "bend the curve", resulting in that 32 percent increase in the cost of underlying health insurance claims nationally by the year 2017. (Bronze plan deductibles rose to over $12,000.00, and Silver plan premiums rose to an average of 17% in 2017.) The purposely unforeseen and purposely hidden unaccountable consequences of President Obama's **Healthcare Reform** intentions that mandated a huge increase in government-subsidized healthcare delivery costs were purely political and not deficit-reduction economic strategies. The ultimate goal was always wealth-redistribution directed towards a federally-run socialistic single payer plan like his unfortunately withdrawn "Common Plan", and many progressive liberals could not imagine why that direction towards single payer national health was not immediately railroaded through at a time when both the U.S. House and the U.S. Senate held unstoppable democratic majority voting rights, during the first two years of the Obama Administration. (They also wondered why immigration amnesty was not legally granted by and through that same liberal-progressive legislative body.) The unintended consequences in the PPACA resulting from that aforesaid political collusion with private healthcare insurance corporations tightly knit and bound those progressive liberal intentions in a very secure and not so easily unwound Gordian knot; on the immediate horizon, there was no son of Zeus named Alexander to draw his sword and slice that political knot apart. But stormy political climates, given sufficient time to bathe in some sunshine, do evolve…..

To take some heat off the supposed "stupidity" of the voter segment of John Q. Public, when it came time, at the end of 2014, to put your Money where your mouth had been vomiting, a pathetic "cry baby cry" whimpering and whining echoed in vain throughout the great halls of supposedly "not stupid" Academia. What was politically praised to be good sauce for the gander apparently was not so good for the Ivy League gobbledygook goose whose personal "goose" would also be cooked in time. John Harvard's elite had previously praised the provisions of the PPACA, but when that gibberish drooling dog came back to bite its masters, the Faculty of Arts and Sciences unanimously passed a motion, "That for 2015, the Faculty President and Fellows be asked to replace the currently proposed health care benefit plan with an appropriately adjusted version of the 2014 health benefit package, maintaining the 2014 plan design." Although the faculty had applauded the provisions in the PPACA for the general public, the academicians expected to be excluded (like Congress) and were abhorred with the prospect of additional personal liabilities amounting to $1,500 per person and up to $4,500 a year for families of three or more just to cover co-pays, drugs, deductibles, and coinsurance. That sky-high ivory tower belonging to the academic elitists was quite frightfully no longer safely insulated and protected from the real world; and guess what, the general public frankly didn't and doesn't give a damn. Gee, a successful surprise kick in the butt from their beloved federal government, a deceptive and evasive pay cut in the disguise of health insurance, slipped right by or simply got sloppily schlepped out to beguile the boastful brainiest guys and gals in the nation -- who ever would ever have thunk?

A few previously supportive democratic U.S. Senators woefully misunderstood the true political course for the PPACA, and quoted the program to be "headed for a train wreck". They could not envision what the temperance of time and a few corrective surgical procedures could do to gain pubic acceptance. They yet yearned for the semi-final migratory economic **Healthcare Reform** paradigm -- universal single payer federally funded and federally administered healthcare delivery – which had not yet arrived. With hope springing eternal, progressive liberals kept the faith and prayed that a faint distant locomotive whistle could be heard and a subtle rumbling sensation could be felt on train tracks directly under their feet, hoping both welcoming omens would be signaling that that the really big **Healthcare Reform** engine and all its freight in so many cargo cars existed somewhere, secure and inevitably well on its way, and that such a healthcare-freight train might shortly arrive like Mighty Mouse -- in time to save the day.

In contemplation of those railroad rumblings, one might take a peek, a snapshot from an outside-the-box perspective. Perhaps this insidious but inspirational "formed to fail" or "born to beguile" omnibus insurance fiasco actually and quite cleverly implanted a diabolical yet methodical mindset, a magnificent method manifested within its manufactured mayhem and madness:

There are four (or hopefully not five) migratory economic consequences of evolved ecolo-nomics for **Healthcare Reform that might be accomplished by the ACA** that could accomplish the vitally necessary set of conditions necessary for the General Public's future approval/acceptance of Single Federal Payer National Health Insurance:

1. The General Public's acceptance of rationing down to basic benefit healthcare delivery coverage for all. (A lowering of expectations so that a relatively minor advancement can be readily cheered.)

2. The General Public's acceptance of redistribution of wealth to pay for those who will not otherwise afford and/or willingly pay for the insurance. (In accordance with the progressive concept of the United States globally redistributing industrial power.)

3. The General Public's acceptance of receiving the majority of their healthcare delivery and all their primary care from non-MD practitioners. (With lower costs consistent with scope, duration and amount controls along with lower payment rates as mandated by Medicare and Medicaid code tables.)

4. The General Public's acceptance of receiving healthcare delivery controlled by the federal government. (With less face-to-face healthkeeper time per patient visit.)

5........Perhaps the general public suffers or shares some shades of Holden Caulfield's migratory economic psychosis or neurosis in thinking that, "....how do you know what you are going to do until you do it"? With unfortunate admonishment, there is a stand-alone fifth migratory economic condition that would immediately signal Single Federal Payer National Health Insurance; but hopefully every American prays that such a horrific event will never happen -- A pandemic with an agent such as Ebola or an artificially manufactured mega virus would immediately activate that migratory economic; the Department Of Defense (DOD) would immediately initiate that very technologically possible but hopefully never-to-happen pandemic-reaction **Healthcare Reform** event.

Before the enactment of the PPACA, about 80% of multiply polled Americans were apparently not unsatisfied with their healthcare insurance system, which might be considered a baseline of status-quo public acceptance of a system albeit a system destined for future financial failure. Starting from that very temporary reality as ground zero, those above listed four economic conditions are very difficult to politically evolve; but with an imminent gross failure of a third-party-directed national omnibus health insurance program insidiously eking along in extreme distress and pushed directly into the public's purview to constantly view, the push-pull political transition to evolved acceptance of "federal single payer" might not be or have been so great a task. Per that old trickster Quintus, political "circumstances beyond one's control" would eventually foster that migratory ecolo-nomic paradigm for **Healthcare Reform**.

Then surely would follow suit, the enormous and politically treacherous task of effectively dealing with that one-ton gorilla, that political biggie, boldly staring right into the face and eyes of the federal government, that taunting, lobby-rich K-Street giant political monster forming and presenting the greatest migratory economic challenge to federally-directed single-payer **Healthcare Reform.** The task of finding a political sword strong and sharp enough to slice that aforesaid politically-tied Gordian knot of corporate collusion and to get those private healthcare insurer corporations in line would require serious dynamic strategic planning.

A great hidden strategy might have been to do something that might make the general public trust a federal plan more than a private plan. How about really annoying the American public by encouraging big businesses to become uncomfortable with providing private insurance coverage for their employees, many of whom were being laid-off; or by incentivizing small businesses, by way of a very small fine, to partially avoid that insurance responsibility, or to completely skirt around the law through an unwritten policy of hiring only part-time workers. When a President openly declares to a vast American media audience (by decree albeit illegal) that private corporate insurers should reinstate their previously cancelled insurance policies in order to free so many millions of dear suffering Americans from: the need to worry about higher co-pays, higher deductible limits, less portability to specialty care, the inability to see a previous doctor, the inability to find service available at a top specialty hospital and an overall increased cost to the middle class – well that sort of gobble de gook just must be spun and then naturally perceived as the fault of the private corporate insurance industry for not complying with that federal or Presidential "order" and furthermore, those faceless private corporate insurers must have been causing all that trouble with lay-offs, part-time employment and insurance cancellations in the first place. (Yes, Quintus, smear the opponent at every possible opportunity.)

The private corporate insurance industries' expected rebuttal of "we were just following government orders" is, was and always will be a long remembered horrid inexcusable excuse that never could hold any potable water or claim anything else of moral or ethical validity. (Remember the 1947 Nuremberg trials.)

Finally, remember the adage of keeping the end in mind. What could any omnibus PPACA, alias ObamaCare, have ever possibly accomplished in the first place for the 30% of the American public that were uninsured? If that group of uninsured broke down to 25% Medicaid eligible, 45% non-citizens and 30% truly eligible, then reaching only 15% of a healthcare exchange enrollment goal really meant that the program was actually half way there. 30% enrollment in exchanges (excluding Medicaid) filled the bank, but unfortunately did not provide or hope to produce enough funds to pay for the total PPACA program. There just logically had to be a much greater intent in ObamaCare, and although opaque rather than transparent, anyone who had not just recently fallen from a turnip truck could clearly see or had to at least envision that the PPACA had to eventual reach out to include all USA residents, including illegal immigrants. Tort reform and transparency would have to lick their wounds and savor a chance comeback for some future day.

Meanwhile, damned if you do and damned if you don't -- practicing physicians, especially fee-for-service physicians were again caught in a "Catch 22" situation: Rather than own up to the practical reality of ever expanding and advancing, albeit expensive, medical diagnostic and treatment technologies that offered vastly improved quality outcomes, politically cost-effective extremists, **Healthcare Reform** advocates like Ezekiel Emanuel, focused on restricting then eliminating such items as "Perverse Physician Incentives" in the American healthcare delivery system. Rather than seeking to improve quality, these progressive pundits sought to regulate the American healthcare delivery practice and payment system by directly reducing physician payments according to a negative and reverse incentive formula for arguable total bundled costs -- the greater the total bundled costs for a diagnosis and treatment, the less percentage the physician would be paid. Simultaneously, lobbyists for the vendors of these expensive diagnostic and treatment modalities swayed legislators to legally approve and sanction huge numbers of various modalities as "medically necessary" measures that could be grounds for a malpractice law suit if not promptly ordered by a physician. If ordered routinely or too often according to behind-door employer review, even though "medically necessary", then the doctors pay would be cut by some corporate health plan. (Remember the quote from the movie -- "John Q.")   In responsive inebriated celebration, the already-buzzed physician had been effectively coerced and already rehearsed to drink up more and more administrative intoxicants at the federal governmental trough, to gulp, chug-a-lug and swallow more and more of that good ole governmental malarkey, to lift up a chin and pour one down with a "Cin Cin". That Kickapoo Joy Juice induced non-logical administrative pandering; it was like pouring a big gulp of administration poison directly down into the dear doctors' gut to get the old doc truly unruly and deeply drunk. Alias, then to let it all pass by with unabashed forgetfulness of the entire event, just like back when, in the good old university times, like in a former pre-med life, like being back at the aftermath of a good ole Dartmouth College boys' fraternity hijinks.

MIGRATORY ECONOMIC
FACTORS & PATTERNS
EVOLVING
MAN, MONEY & MEDICINE

PART SEVEN

NATIONAL HEALTHCARE DELIVERY:
ANTI-TRUST, P-4-P & BALANCE BILLING
CHARITY AND THE PHYSICIAN

The physician medical societies were in an uproar, and they indeed roared:

"Those aforementioned sandy winds of fortune need to be addressed. Now, right now, the time is ripe for a choice that is clear and demands immediate legislative action -- the time has come to draw a penultimate line in the sand that time cannot erase and from which we shall never retreat. To ensure the legality and permanence of this line, we must proceed through the political process of legislative action."

*"**We must write and promote a legislative bill that clarifies our position as American citizens and the inalienable rights of patients to act freely and unencumbered in our free society. The right to unencumbered private contracting between a doctor and a patient and a patient and a doctor should be legislatively chiseled in stone.**"*

"We must insist that no law shall be passed that would interfere with a person's right to pay directly for lawful medical services and no law shall be passed that restricts a person's freedom of choice -- to choose or not to choose independent private physician healthcare delivery. All patients, physicians, and insurers must be granted the right to privately contract among one another and not be legally restricted in this contracting by any present type or any future type of Trojan horse financing sting that might be cleverly introduced as just a small government-run "public plan" or "government-run cooperative."

The Democratic majority of the United States Congress held to a different point of view:
"We have to pass the bill (PPACA) so that you can find out what is in it"
– House majority leader Nancy Pelosi, 3/9/10.

Congressional due diligence and legal responsibility on behalf of the American public had apparently reached a point of such decadence that the work of reading and understanding legislation was so difficult that it simply had to be passed on to the Supreme Court of the United States (SCOTUS).

Justices on the Supreme Court of The United States (SCOTUS) also had their say:
"Generally speaking, when confronting a constitutional flaw in a statute, justices try to limit the solution to the problem." -- Justice Sandra Day O'Connor 2006
Chief Justice Roberts further stipulated in 2012: "It is not our job to protect the people from the consequences of their political choices."
Justice Scalia stated in 2015, "Rather than rewriting the law under the pretense of interpreting it, the Court should have left it to Congress to decide.... insistence on making a choice that should be made by Congress both aggrandizes judicial power and encourages congressional lassitude...... We should start calling this law SCOTUScare".

Third party and governmental forces advancing and evolving along the migratory economic trail of **Healthcare Reform** trot in tandem on a trail of economically reforming physician concerns which influence changing attitudes regarding such physician-centric matters as image, autonomy and charity......

Image, like politics, is based on perception, not reality -- or perhaps perception is truly the reality of the moment. Image is an art form of prejudices, fears, and desires expressed as public opinion. Image is related to medical science in a similar manner as spin is related to political science. Throughout the first half of the 20th Century, the patients' image of the doctor, and the doctors' image of the patient were both of high esteem. In the late 1920's, mutual trust in the doctor-patient relationship reached an all-time high mark, as did individual doctor concern for charity healthcare delivery. The Norman Rockwell poster of the "watchful wait" portrayed such imagery. A concerned doctor sitting by the bedside of a sick patient denoted sincerity, respect and mutual trust. The ability to practice Medicine and the receiving of medical care were considered mutual privileges; and for the favor of privilege and trust, doctors felt a deep indebtedness to their patients, especially the poor and illiterate. A doctor married the practice of Medicine, for richer or poorer, for a lifetime -- till death. Stephen Paget characterized Medicine as a "divine vocation". As that positive image of the physician negatively changed with time, the perception of healthcare delivery became even more imaginary. The classical image of the doctor became the idealized wish and dream of the patient, further positively transformed by the reality of life-long unwavering dedication to medical practice. The demographics of medical school graduates during that era accurately reflected that popular physician image. An overwhelming predominance of males with a North European ancestry dominated the field of Medicine. Women medical school graduates were uncommon, and women surgeons were especially rare. The pictorial magazine image of the idealized doctor depicted a well-dressed, exhausted and occasionally disheveled from work, white male. "That he is underpaid and overworked; that he has but little time for study and less for recreation -- these are the blows that give finer temper to his steel, and bring out the nobler elements of his character."[107]

The inspiring and altruistic doctor force of charity concern, the non-reimbursed propensity to help and serve the sick and injured, regardless of personal leisure or financial risk did vigorously flourish. Physicians practiced in that light of an unspoken honor and privilege. For the first half of the 20th Century, individual practicing physicians proudly and quietly did just that; then a new and evolving ecology and migratory economics arrived to produce **Healthcare Reform**. "Organized Medicine" before 1950 generally existed in the form of medical societies and associations, but the actual healthcare delivery system was not yet truly organized. As previously noted, the life-long course of medical practice was considered a continuous learning experience, and personal practice experience became the basis for most critical medical judgment decisions. Older physicians were honored mentors for younger physicians, both in private practice and in the emerging organized group delivery systems. Financial risk-taking and legal liability were recognized entities, but neither dictated nor influenced the delivery of medical care. Results from healthcare delivery were not critically analyzed, yet believed to be generally good; but those results were often quite variable.

In 1947, the course of medical experimentation heard a verdict round the world originating from a judicial hammer swung in Nuremberg; there was now and forever a "Code" for "permissible medical experiments". That old boy network of older to younger for the transfer of medical knowledge came to an abrupt end. A paradigm of nepotism in medical education would soon follow, but only for a brief period of time.

As the second half of the 20th Century began, the image of the American physician as an honorable, self-sacrificing gentleman remained fixed in the eyes of patients

---

[107] Bean, R., Sir William Osler Aphorisms, C.C.Tomas, Illinois, 1961, p.56.

until the predominance of entitlement philosophies came into vogue, culminated with enactment of the 1965 Medicare/Medicaid legislation. "Doctor Hudson's Secret Journal", a popular radio program, portrayed an imaginary physician as a detective who investigated the multiple mysteries of Medicine for the benefit of his patients. The post Y2K television series of "House, MD" with an abrasive, addictive yet honorable personality would have been horribly abhorred at that time. Rising TV sales first gave the American public a lovable young "Doctor Kildare"; then a "Father Knows Best" TV character underwent psychological transference to a "Doctor Knows Best". The role of "Doctor Marcus Welby" became the idealized model for a primary care physician to emulate. The arrogance of correctness and authoritative power, often expressed by surgeons, became portrayed and emulated with the acceptance of "Ben Casey", a surgeon whose necessary arrogance and patient advocacy moved all obstacles to save patient lives. The MD was considered the only "real doctor", therefore, when doctors of osteopathic Medicine were given the opportunity to abandon their trade and become MDs by California state decree in the early 1960's, few failed to respond. State government decree closed all California osteopathic hospitals or converted them to MD hospitals. The art of osteopathic Medicine, especially manipulation, was unfortunately lost to the residents of the state of California. That loss created a significant gap of niche practice opportunity in the continuity of patient care which was quickly filled by then insufficiently trained professions. Those non-physician professions, predominantly Chiropractic practitioners, soon realized their weaknesses, and educated themselves to gain substantive and accredited footing in the migratory economics of the dynamically competitive medical practice business arena.

The golden era of healthcare delivery was literally just that – gold for one era only, and very few of those yellow gold nuggets were mined by way of elbow grease in the process of delivering medically necessary primary care healthcare before or after that era. However, during that "golden era of medical practice" the primary care doctors who graciously earned the gold were generous in return. Individual physicians and groups of physicians still felt a societal duty and personal responsibility to deliver charity pro bono healthcare. Physicians regularly donated their time and skills to the care of the poor and elderly. However and partly due to improved medical technologies, the number of poor-elderly began increasing at a rate that rationed their access and placed increased financial pressure on community-sponsored healthcare delivery programs. Still, many poor-elderly patients remained treated for free in private fee–for-service offices. A multitude of physicians also donated their time, equipment, and medications to screening clinics sponsored by schools, religious organizations, charitable organizations, and community service organizations. Educating doctors who were in training and further teachings in the art of Medicine to fellow doctors in active medical practice were also considered charitable functions, "without fee or stipulation"[108] in the doctor's life. Regarding "his offspring on the same footing as my brothers",[109] fees were not charged when treating family members of other physicians; the practice was considered an honorable undertaking termed "Professional Courtesy". County hospital and university hospital staffs overflowed with voluntary attending staff physicians. Doctors vied for those honorable and charitable tasks and joyfully worked the extra hours.

Meanwhile, something termed "innovative disruptive medical technology" was blasting off on a rocket ship; Watson and Crick described DNA and Salk developed a polio vaccine while kidney transplants and open heart surgeries saw their way into hospital operating rooms – shocking and eye opening at first, but medical technological creative destruction was just in its infancy.

There was no questioning of physicians' decisions concerning appropriateness or necessity of care. Physician group consensus only slightly restricted individual physician autonomy. Medical technology was just beginning that exponential growth in new procedures, tests, and in costs, and the profession of Medicine continued to self-regulate healthcare delivery as the longevity of the American populace continued to increase. Technical and ethical standards were simple and easy to define, but the quality of healthcare delivery issue was much more complex. Payola was the scandal of the record industry and fee-splitting became a physician-centric medical scandal. In an effort to legitimize the payback for referrals, a General Practitioner (GP) (later termed primary care (PC) or Family Medicine (FM) practitioner) would briefly appear in an operating room to generate a paper trail for fee-splitting payments, routinely paid without question by indemnity insurance companies. Those few "ghost surgeons" severely hurt the esteem of honest practicing physicians. The bad press engendered by those few stuck like a dirty blight on the bright white coats of the many.

Allocation of physician responsibility became a popular trend. The separation of doctor duties from enhanced assistant duties was at first thought to bolster the stately physician image. By the time physicians realized that excessive allocation of responsibility had become detrimental to future medical practice autonomy, the remaining opportunity in time available was just too little and too late to reverse

---

[108] The Oath of Hippocrates
[109] The Oath of Hippocrates

the process. The image of a physician then mutated from the fatherly doctor to a professional health provider on a team that organized and delivered healthcare – a healthkeeper team. Stripped of brass rankings and busted to just a subordinate crew officer on a large healthkeeper battleship, the formerly all-knowing, fatherly "captain of the ship" physician lost stature as the primary sacrosanct keeper of health. The surgeon still stood as captain of a personal yacht when in the operating room, but even that captain's importance waned with the increasing complexity of computerized monitoring and homeostatic devices, manned and operated by various certified technicians. Honest physicians also suffered from an ever-present hostile government-administered progressive biased press. Much more than a few selected sensational reports in city news media cited shortcomings of previously undetected and government-financed fly-by-night abortion mills as well as fraudulent Medicare-Medicaid billings. The media, nonchalantly and without a single ounce of pity, portrayed and poured the excesses of a minority of physicians onto the good deeds of the majority. The few again disgraced the many.

The public's societal hierarchy ranking scale for physicians fell from a highest in respect and honor to a decidedly diminished level. Physicians endured a sad, slippery and splintering slide downward from the unselfish-trusted totem pole top, while desperately clinging onto imaginary control and healthkeeper leadership with painful splintered and splintering fingers. Doctors became the brunt of jokes concerning medical economics and medical financing. The sacrosanct, first half of the 20th Century, public taboo concerning the intellectual privacy of a fatherly physician disappeared -- vanished forever. Worse was yet to come; as Sigmund Freud's tabooed totem, the American physician was about to be feasted upon -- eaten alive by third party and Middle-Man interests:

Too many new hospitals had been built as a result of the Hill-Burton hospital expansion legislation of the first medical ecolo-nomic generation (1950-1970). An unnecessary number of available hospital beds were being over-utilized just because they were available and thereby could be over-utilized. This unjustified medical ecolo-nomic opportunity for increased profit did not go unnoticed by high-utilization physicians nor by the ever searching eyes of greedy hospital administrators. The U.S. hospital occupancy rate rose to an all-time high in 1975 and would never again be equaled (as a percentage of the United States population actually hospitalized). Under the President Gerald Ford administration, the federal government sought to stop this unwarranted hospital expansion with a **Healthcare Reform** mechanism to reduce excessive healthcare delivery costs. A new division of government, the Health Services Agency (HSA) reviewed any perceived need for increasing any number of hospital beds and thereby slowed down the growth of hospitals. The basic idea was to "control cost by limiting capacity". Apparently no thought or serious consideration was given to the future general public's right to access to an increasing supply of diverse medical care due to disruptive technological advancements. A government-engineered national achievement goal set a limitation of four hospital beds per thousand residents in densely populated areas. The HSA drafted legislation with a methodology that drastically reduced the prestige of physicians. The physician-healthkeeper fraternity had to drop all of its exclusion clauses: HSAs formed panels composed of all possible affected and interested parties and mandated all interested parties to strictly align themselves with one of two medical ecolo-nomic groups. To this end, at the HSA hearings, an imaginary line drawn across the conference rooms separated interested parties into two distinct groups – those who would not receive funds or benefit from conflict of interest favor from hospital-based healthcare delivery versus all those who might in any way profit, benefit, or gain favor from that modality of healthcare delivery. That second group included vendors of equipment, hospital staff, physicians, and hospital workers, such as laundry workers. Governmental administrative-speak added new vocabulary words to the mix: When an MD arose to speak at the hearing, no mention of title such as "doctor" or physician" was ever allowed to prejudice the physician's remarks. Not only was the word "physician" or "doctor" forbidden usage, but a physician was also required to verbally identify himself as a "provider" (i.e. "John Doe – provider" rather than John Doe – doctor, physician, or MD) each and every time he spoke. This obvious administrative "put-down" foretold and directed an ominous omen of humbling forces to come. The functional need for the HSAs ended in 1982 when a "selective contracting" migratory ecolo-nomic decreased the need for hospital beds, even before the era of the Diagnostic Related Groups (DRGs). In 1983, financial risk formally became a part of hospital business. However, resentment concerning the term "provider" slowly stewed-on in a disgruntled physician crock-pot. Nearly 20 years later, in the year 2000, Blue Cross of California offered up a feeble crumb-like concession to physicians by agreeing to change the term "provider" to "physician" on an Internet screen used for the tracking of unpaid claims.[110] By that time, however, migratory governmental-decreed ecolo-nomics complicated the lingo by commonly accepting the term "physician" to also include several non-physician or better put, non-MD medical service provider groups.

---

[110] Leonard D. Schaeffer, CEO, Wellpoint, address to CMA Leadership conference, 10/16/00

In 1974, the federal Professional Standards Review Organization (PSRO) or Peer Review Organization (PRO) began to review hospital charts for "appropriateness" of in-patient services and care. The practice of hospitalizing patients the night before an early morning surgery ended abruptly. "Same day surgery" became a new catch phrase. Elderly patients from distant locations registered with their own non-reimbursable funds at near-by motels for a pre-admission night's stay. All laboratory tests and procedures that were required before the time of admission cost-shifted their billings to the outpatient sector. Outpatient surgeries in "Surgi-Centers" came into vogue. Patients admitted for hospital stays now came from a different risk payer pool. Patients in this new higher-risk pool were sicker, demanded more care, cost more direct hospital expenditure, yet stayed in-house for shorter periods of time. Hospital financing hovered at the hurt level, and the progression of circumstances seemed destined to get much worse. PSROs also offered physician compliance education: Physicians first were taught rules for writing "appropriate" chart notes and key government-speak words to be used in "valid documentation" of procedures. When the name PSRO changed to PRO, "standards of care" arose up front as the major issue. Historical standards such as past education, learned-life experience, and community practice became lost in translation and then were deemed obsolete. A national standard, based on the supposed "best possible" or "nationally optimal" healthcare delivery, became the universal goal. Albeit difficult to define then and worse later under the burden of price-controls, the final government-speak term, "best practice", reared its letters high to crop up as a landmark on the migratory medical ecolo-nomic landscape.

Physicians had traditionally donated "doctor time" to care for the poor and uninsured in "free clinics", like for the media-popularized early 1960's free love generation medical clinics. Those youthful poor, in valid need of charitable healthcare, eventually became unfortunately viewed as psychotic "homeless people", lined up for a free meal at a poorhouse. Thanks to Medicare, the "over 65" poor and formerly uninsured suddenly found better places for healthcare delivery. That new Medicare-financed crowd abandoned the free clinics and county hospitals for private Medicare facilities and services. Individual and fee-for-service charity patient cases still existed, but the poor were apparently more numerous and definitely more organized. With a new philosophy and actual entitlements in hand, the public mind-set was also anxious and willing to accept the former charity healthcare delivery in a more organized fashion. The migratory economic of Medicaid changed the way physicians' charitable consciousness viewed the poor and the way the poor then viewed physicians. The amount and complexity level of healthcare demanded and needed by the organized poor increased to more than what society deemed necessary or satisfactory five years later during the second medical ecolo-nomic generation (1970-1990). As older physicians became more negative concerning former medical practice ideals, they tended to shy away from medically oriented charitable functions. Since they were already paying for charity care through federal taxation for entitlements, many physicians felt no further inner need or innate propensity to individually contribute. Physicians no longer enthusiastically supported hospital charity fundraisers for indigent patient care. The common charitable plank, that once bound physician and hospital, fractured and then permanently displaced; there was never again to be satisfactory realignment nor solid fixation/healing to reunite physicians and hospitals on a charitable basis.

Autonomy faded alongside charity, but at and for one brief moment in earth-time, this is how relationships still stood: Of all the health professionals recognized by California law, only physicians and surgeons were granted a plenary license. Specifically, the license granted to physicians gave them an unrestricted authority to practice Medicine and surgery, "to use drugs or devices in or upon human beings and to sever and penetrate the tissues of human beings and to use any and all other methods in the treatment of diseases, injuries, deformities, and other physical and mental conditions."[111] To assure the quality of healthcare delivery and by right of law based upon the aforesaid plenary license, only physicians had the unilateral authority to have overall responsibility for the medical care of hospitalized patients that necessarily involved the application of judgment and "diagnostic" skills. The California Medical Practice Act defined "diagnosis" as "any undertaking by any method, device or procedure whatsoever, and whether gratuitous or not, to ascertain or establish whether the person is suffering from any physical or mental disorder."[112] Moreover, only physicians, by virtue of their state-authenticated and granted license, along with their training and experience, were as a practical and legal matter qualified to undertake this "diagnostic" evaluation independently. As stated by the California Attorney General: "We must not lose sight of the fact that the patient involved in a diagnostic study is the physician's patient" -- (not the health plan's or the government's patient). "It is the physician who must ascertain the relevant facts about the case, it is the physician who must interpret the results and make a diagnosis, and it is the physician who is responsible for the patient and on whose professional judgment the patient's well-being depends."[113] In 1937, the State of California Business & Professions Code (the corporate bar on the practice of Medicine) assured that only a state licensed physician could hire and have as an employee, another state

---

[111] California Business & Professions Code §2051
[112] California Business & Professions Code §2038
[113] 66 Ops.Cal.Atty.Gen. 428, 434 (1983)

licensed physician. Physicians admonished other physicians that violation of the Business & Professions Code would create a socialistic practice of Medicine with the "specter" of corporations, unions, or governmental agencies controlling healthcare delivery. Physician medical practice autonomy would be destroyed in such an evolving migratory medical ecolo-nomic world. Exceptions to the Business and Professions Code included County Hospitals and Clinics as well as medical schools. Exceptions always allowed for legislative creep and crawl to find social and legal migratory ecolo-nomic logic for more exceptions; and in the first medical ecolo-nomic generation (1950-1970), the State of California allowed a further exception -- the HMO. Federal HMO legislation mandated the state to provide that additional loophole. The loophole to the corporate practice of Medicine proved to promulgate a loose stitch in the fabric of fee-for-service healthcare delivery. Before the end of the second migratory medical ecolo-nomic generation (1970-1990), that very stitch unraveled the tight knit fabric of private medical practice. That garment was never again to be restored to its Sunday best condition. Rag tag employee doctors stepped blindly into the third migratory medical ecolo-nomic generation (1990-2010), grasping for a guide rail from newer healthkeeper corporate edifices.

The proudest profession went to war, a war against a former friend and now new-found foe -- the proudest professionals. The image of the physician-healthkeeper changed from a professional health provider to that of a health plan employee. The patient's image of his or her doctor began to become confused, while the same patient's image of "doctors" as a group sunk even lower. The HMO physician's position at first hugged the lowest rung in a social scale hierarchy, but those poor rankings were soon to be somewhat elevated via lowered patient expectations. Patients soon regarded themselves as patients of the health plans rather than as patients of individual physicians, readily speaking such phrases as "My HMO gave me a shot and some pills." In 1996, American medical schools graduated 16,000 doctors, and an additional 7,000 foreign-trained doctors were licensed to practice in the USA.[114] This new, fresh out of medical school doctor knew that there existed some vague document known as Hippocratic Oath; but the average, novice new-age physician had never pondered any meaning or purpose in attesting to or even reading that ancient document. The migrating economic factors inducing **Healthcare Reform** now swore an oath to technological expansion, not to Apollo; disruptive innovations such as computer-driven protocols and exquisitely trained assistive personnel drained the medical doctor of his formerly prized intellectual storehouse property. That cranial-stored data and the physician

---

[114] The Medical Racket, Martin L. Gross, Avon Books, New York, 1998, p.202.

bodies that possessed intellectual knowledge were seemingly no longer necessary or needed. Per Saint John Baptist de la Salle, the patron saint of teachers -- their hearts seemed to know what their minds could never understand.

Even Hollywood (at first, before the general acceptance of lowered expectations in a progressive liberal environment took a firmer hold) -- Even Hollywood objected to the inherent rationing required in a HMO system, as evidenced by the punch line delivered by Helen Hunt in the movie "As Good As It Gets" – Those "HMO bastards, pieces of shit".

Therefore, Health Keeper Organizations (HKOs) next felt the need to project images of caring, culturally diverse, and well-educated "Ivy League" medical school type doctors in their media ads. In actual practice, these physicians were and are few and far between. The majority of physicians in California would soon be foreign-trained. The media campaigns assured a perception that a visit to their particular plan would actually include a visit not only to a real doctor, but also to a unique idealized doctor, specially selected and exquisitely trained and draped in ivy to meet any patients' individual needs. The impatient outpatient public first felt cheated when they arrived at the clinics and were immediately assigned to a Physician Assistant (PA); but again, a gradual persistent sophisticated lowering of patient expectations gradually ended that problem. That art of slowly heating a cold kettle of frogs to boil was well known and marvelously practiced in healthcare delivery business migratory ecolo-nomic circles.

The evolutionary inept conclusion that only physicians were able to be responsible for the overall medical care of a patient was further complicated by a consideration of multiple scope of practice statutes authorizing a myriad of limited license practitioners to diagnose various unrelated ailments. The California Legislature granted limited licenses to other allied health professionals to perform tasks "previously within the exclusive province of the physician", but recognized that physicians must be responsible for the overall medical care of a patient (for a time not definite). Also, "in the absence of some statutory exception," someone who was not exclusively licensed to practice Medicine could not provide any services that were "medical or surgical in character."[115] While there may have been some "overlap" in functions, unless there was explicit legislative authority that directly authorized the activity, only physicians had the legally-sanctioned plenary authority to provide overall medical care for patients, at least for the brief time being.

---

[115] *Magit v. Board of Medical Examiners* (1961) 57 Cal.2d 74

This above set of conditions persisted as a uniquely American medical practice anachronism -- that is how things had stood for almost an entire century; but all things must ultimately change, and what goes around most often comes around. First, scopes of practice for non-physicians expanded to include just about anything done by a physician as long as those things were done under the "direct supervision" of a physician. Then that "direct" supervision definition changed to a "proximity" allowance and then again to a vague "availability" range that did not define any distance at all. Next, limited prescribing, limited diagnosing and minor procedures became legislatively allowed, totally independent of any physician involvement. Finally, legally sanctioned licensed independent practice for the ancillary healthkeepers put an end to the percent of physician financial profits arising from huge portions of former exclusively primary care physician medical services.

Financial forces developed beyond the control of an individual physician as the corporate control of the Money migratory ecolo-nomics of Medicine flourished with insurance company mergers, acquisitions and consolidations, all diminishing the ability of physicians both to protect their patients' welfare and to ensure their own economic viability. To fully develop, all of these evolutionary changes took a period time after a specific action or event. Economic consequences of evolving antitrust regulation played the heaviest mover-shaker role. Federal antitrust legislation and regulations created an un-leveled playing field, allowing corporations to have virtual oligopolies, which resulted in physicians being relegated to a relatively powerless role in negotiating within the legally approved American migratory economic processes. Some individual physicians tried to compete as a group in the marketplace by using various strategies, such as "third-party messenger models" and "super groups", but restrictive federal regulatory oversight and/or sanctions severely limited these efforts. Physician unionism lurked just around the corner and became more and more attractive day by day.

Unfair, or less emotionally put, unbalanced anti-competitive advantages did not suddenly come into fruition. Big business, well trained in the process of following the Money, kept close track on cost control, as a dynamic competitive healthcare market advantage. Corporate boards successfully hid and then ignored a simple truth: Healthcare delivery can never be considered an industry completely subject to the antitrust rules that allow for the fair running of a free market economy. Unlike participants in other industries that are not enormously conflicted with moral dilemmas, physicians – thankfully – are never willing to refuse to deliver life or death services to those unfortunate who are unable to pay or to any one else for that matter. An understanding of the evolved insurance corporations' dynamic competitive advantages over physicians begins with an understanding of the migratory economic history of monopolies and antitrust:

In 1624, the English government passed The Statute of Monopolies to protect small businesses and prevent rich consolidated business interests from paying the Crown for a trade advantage, the status of "monopoly". A freely competitive business society has always been seen as the best protection for general consumer welfare.

In the late 1800's, American small business expressed a great deal of economic concern that large business monopolies would totally control interstate commerce and therefore stifle competition from small business enterprises. At that time, healthcare delivery existed as a small cottage industry controlled by solo and small group practicing physicians. There was no such thing as a physician who earned a living through administration of medical services or by the fruits of the labors of other physicians. Physicians paid no concern to unintended consequence -- that corporations might someday grow to exert oligopolistic migratory medical ecolo-nomic control and then transform legal and medical systems with no regard for their existing sacrosanct doctor-patient relationship. The "lay practice of Medicine", functioning as a viable, cost effective method to bring medical care to the masses, had neither been invented nor yet debated in the great halls of Washington, D.C..

Republican Senator John Sherman, brother of American Civil War's infamous William Tecumseh Sherman, drafted an antitrust bill that made monopoly business practice a misdemeanor punishable by a $1000 fine. In 1890, President Benjamin Harrison signed the Sherman Anti-Trust Act to protect small, cottage industry businesses. Physicians and lawyers were not even considered in the legislation because they were "learned professions" and absolutely not considered true businesses or any sort of trade. Insurance companies were likewise not considered in the legislation because they were not yet deemed to be a type of commerce. Union organizations and state and federal governments were also not considered to be part of the legislation. Physicians had no reason to believe that they would ever need to bargain collectively, and if they had desired to do so, collective bargaining at that time would not have been illegal.

In 1914, the Clayton Antitrust Act grew some biting front teeth on terms the Sherman Antitrust Act by establishing three times the total combined penalty for each individual involved in the conspiracy of antitrust. Restraining or monopolizing free trade and reducing competition escalated from a misdemeanor to a felony. The Act, specifically to the letter of the law, defined price fixing, restraint of trade, and restriction of competition as "per se" unlawful felony violations. The "learned professions" such as Medicine and law continued to stay immune to the legislation because those professions still were specifically considered neither a "trade" nor a type of "commerce" at that time.

Quoting from United States vs. South-Eastern Underwriters, 332 U.S. 533 (1944): "In 1904 and again in 1905, President Roosevelt urged that the Congress carefully consider whether the power of the Bureau of Corporations cannot constitutionally be extended to cover interstate transactions in Insurance. The District court pointed out that the offences charged by the indictment are a conspiracy to fix arbitrary and non-competitive premium rates on fire insurance sold in many states, and by means of that conspiracy to restrain and to monopolize trade and commerce in fire insurance in those states. The whole case, therefore, depends upon the question as to whether or not the business of insurance is interstate trade or commerce, and, if so, whether the insurance transactions alleged in the indictment indeed constitute interstate commerce. The doctrine that the insurance business is not commerce always had been criticized as unrealistic, illogical, and inconsistent with the holdings of the Court." A plurality of the Court agreed that the interstate "commerce" of insurance should not be exempt from the Sherman Antitrust Act.

The insurance corporations had dire need to immediately respond and seek a loophole, and that they did: K street lights burned throughout the night. Under the influence of powerful insurance corporation lobby interests, Congress quickly passed The McCarran–Ferguson Act of 1945. This infamous Act explicitly assigned insurance regulation and taxation to the intrastate-protected state commerce level thus avoiding any future charge and possible violation of interstate commerce and Sherman anti-trust violation. Unintended by some and insidiously intended by others, the Act further enhanced the individual state market power of insurance companies albeit on an intrastate, statewide-allowable collaborative level. The Act relieved insurance corporations from interstate antitrust restraints and allowed those corporations to successfully lobby individual intrastate agencies for rights of outright collusion to "price fix" (a "per se" unlawful felony violation in the Sherman Act) medical service payments to physicians. Insurance rates and payment schedules continue with wide variation from state to state today. Legislative efforts to reverse the Act have all fallen short – another win for K Street.

336

Less face-to-face individual identification, less income, and less free leisure time all negatively impacted the "force of doctor concerns" regarding charity; but charity yet survived in the hearts of many physicians as an obligatory social concept. That charitable honor finally turned into a horror show and went on its rocky way; paid public service, by some "mind-warp" process, sold itself as charitable service. Perhaps a feeling of inadequacy in the ability to adequately respond to unfunded government mandates, increasing underpayments and uncollected post-due accounts payable, cleansed the soul and cleared the physicians' conscience of the slightest remnant of social guilt as more and more physicians refused to render pro-bono services and remained inwardly forever forgiven, the psychological quintessence of a spotless soul. Those ever-increasing mandated governmental programs concomitantly forgave that former obligatory social need for charity. Nonetheless, some few physicians denied financial reality and refused to consider how or when to draw a line on charity in the medical ecolo-nomic sand. Some other physicians falsely assumed that they could defeat financial losses by increasing volume. Third grade arithmetic -- one procedure times zero profit equaled one hundred procedures times zero profit. The products were equal, but the production cost became bankrupting. Even when a tornado took their primary care medical practices swirling in sewage counter-clockwise per Corialis's hot air in the northern hemisphere and anticipating a huge ending flush, a few physicians still remained charitable. When medical businesses finally failed, all their charitable guilt totally disappeared right along with their business assets and capability for future private medical practice. For many physicians, neither ever returned, and (like poor old Charlie on the MTA) their fate remained unknown.

As medical migratory ecolo-nomics evolved prior to 1975, so did healthcare delivery systems. With the advent of third party payers, some physicians formed medical practice groups, financial buying groups, and various medical society groups. Limited collective bargaining by one physician on behalf of any group of physicians sharing assets from the same financial payment pool became rather commonplace. Such collective bargaining practices violated neither the letter nor the spirit of existing antitrust laws, but that would also soon change:

When on June 16 in 1975, the U.S. Supreme Court found a group of lawyers guilty of price fixing for their professional services, the Goldfarb v. the Virginia State Bar decision went on to invalidate the assumed legal notion of any "learned profession". The Sherman Anti-Trust Act then crunched down on the medical profession with back molars which did not include any wisdom teeth. The scenario: A Virginia County Bar established a rigid fixed minimum price floor fee for its member lawyers to charge as a standard fee to validate title insurance, a necessary requirement for an individual to purchase a home. The Virginia State Bar went one step further; the Bar also threatened disciplinary action against member lawyers who charged less than that minimum fixed price. When a husband and wife, the Goldfarbs, wished to buy a house in Virginia, a member of the "learned profession", a lawyer, agreed to exchange his services for the minimum rigidly fixed price of $200, as published in County Bar Association minimum fee schedule, thus price fixing and restricting competition in a free market, a "per se" felony violation of antitrust. The Goldfarbs refused to pay such a "fixed price". In light of those events, the U.S. Supreme Court defined the transaction as "anticompetitive" and the exchange of Money for the legal service as "commerce" as practiced by a commercial trade.

The U.S. Supreme Court then lifted a leg up to stirrup, saddled-up, loosened the reigns and proceeded one trot-step further on a high horse by extending the Sherman Anti-Trust Act to include all the "learned professions", including the semi-organized profession of medical practice. The legislated status downward from a profession to a "trade" deprived independently practicing physicians' collective bargaining and collusion rights that were generally reserved for formal trade unions (and also the great American pastime of baseball). Double whammy -- remember also that in The Federal Trade Commission vs. the American Medical Association (1975) the Court denied the AMA any right to hold its physician members accountable by enforcement and organizational mechanisms in regard to advertising, solicitations, and contract practice, a decision that nearly destroyed the AMA.

Foundations for Medical Care (FMC), a medical insurance concept that originated with the San Joaquin County Medical Association in California, became quite popular throughout the United States in the late 1970s. Lobbied by legally collaborating-conspiring state-protected health insurance corporations, the state of Arizona filed a complaint against two Arizona county medical associations that organized and ran two such Foundations for Medical Care, albeit indirectly via medical association owned Third Party Administration services (TPAs). Participating FMC physicians had agreed to a price ceiling on their usual and customary fees, but were free to charge less if they so desired. Was this practice that enabled more cost-effective medical care to the general public really to the letter and spirit of the antitrust law's "per se" price fixing to reduce competition?

Partial summary judgments were sought in the District Court and the Arizona Court of Appeals, but both motions were denied. The matter was then brought to the Supreme Court, 457 U.S. 332 (1982), Arizona v. Maricopa Foundation for Medical Care and Pima Foundation for Medical care. The published fee schedules that limited the amount that a physician could charge for a rendered medical service were found to be "per se" price fixing violations of the Sherman Anti-Trust Act by Justice Stevens and the majority of Justices (5-2-0). Justice Blackmun and Justice O'Connor took no part in the decision. The chief Justice, Justice Powell, and Justice Rehnquist rendered dissenting opinions. These justices stated that the **SCOTUS "rule of reason"** was abandoned in that fixing a maximum price is actually pro-competitive in the spirit of the law, and the "per se" rule should not apply. They further stated that the Sherman Act was a law to benefit consumers, and this case of maximum price fixing benefited consumers and the public good, with physicians bearing the economic risk of essentially a new and different competitive insurance product. All very reasonable arguments, but alas no cigar; spewing and coifing within a cloudy puff of smoky justice, the doctors lost the verdict. Control of migratory medical ecolo-nomics continued to evolve along a one-way street in a direction away from doctors' offices and into the power-hungry hands of oligopolistic insurance-healthcare corporations:

In 1982, Congress passed the Antitrust Equal Enforcement Act, which defined consequences for litigating aspects of the Sherman Anti-Trust Act, but failed to make any exception for the practice of Medicine. Physicians lobbied an exemption bill through Congress, but lost support in the K-street lobbied Senate. The legislation provided for severe penalties: jail sentences, loss of citizenship, lifetime business restrictions and fines up to $100,000 with corporate fines up to $1 million per count. There yet existed one slight exception that continued to be legally accepted: Collective bargaining by one physician on behalf of a limited group of physicians sharing income from a common pool of, not patients, but pooled economic receipts.

Many physicians expressed that their evolved and less-honored place in society was not worth the price now being demanded – being equivalent to an indentured worker for life. Additionally, the average future student graduate choosing to go into a general primary care medical practice would not be able to pay off an average medical school loan, purchase an upper middle class home, raise/educate a family of two or more, and achieve sustainable financial independence during an average working career. Financial independence generated from medical practice, an American physician's dream, was no longer a given consequence of life-long medical practice. After finishing medical school, the once coveted "doctor" degree no longer functioned as a magic skeleton key to unlock the doors of financial security, obtain an unsecured start-up business loan, and reward its owner with the joy and satisfaction of primary care medical practice. The new American family structure would require an additional breadwinner for hoping to attain enduring independent financial security. Rediscovering their political outrage, some physicians forgot their personal petty differences and banded together. The Union of American Physicians and Dentists (UAPD) gained increasing membership as physicians sought to be more pro-active in defining healthcare delivery management policies. Interns and residents, as full-time employees, were allowed to unionize and collectively bargain to achieve better working conditions, less working hours per week, and regular working hours. That necessarily induced migratory economic set an employee-physician mentality pattern for their future life-work ethic. The traditional burning hellfire in a future medical practitioner's gut to achieve a medical degree and professional advancement at any personal pleasure cost became smothered and put out by the new migratory medical ecolo-nomics. The new physician no longer projected an aura of a proud and elegant Flamenco dancer, spotlighted at center stage, whose commanding rhythmic feet set the beat for the pace of healthcare delivery and **Healthcare Reform**. The new physician of the third migratory medical ecolo-nomic generation (1990-2010) possessed and accepted an image now demoted to a chorus line extra who danced on demand to the monotonous beat of a HKO's drum. As to the traditional repetitious dream of physicians past -- to have their children follow in their entrepreneurial footsteps -- that dream ended abruptly, as if cleanly and sharply sliced, swiftly beheaded by a migratory economic guillotine.

The original antitrust act to protect small businesses, such as a private doctor's office business, now inversely protected oligopolistic and monopolistic healthcare delivery corporations by denying physicians the right to collectively bargain. Instead, individual private practice primary care physicians were now forced to sign non-negotiable "take it or leave it" contracts on an individual basis or risk losing 50% or more of their patient payer pool base. Before 1982, physicians agreed to utilize a great variety of health insurance companies on a non-contractual assignment basis. Collective bargaining was not really necessary because a physician could pick and choose among many non-contracted insurance plans and then charge the balance of a fair and reasonable fee to the patient. The practice was known as "Balance-Billing", but that migratory economic also changed. Medi-Cal or Medicaid independent contracting came along as a good thing for the poor and was readily accepted by physicians, but a hidden rider to that good deed punished physicians by allowing independent contracting privileges for all healthcare insurer corporations. Devil in the details -- Direct independent contracting eventually created an additional and unquestioned imbalance of power in favor of insurance companies and to the detriment of primary care physicians, patients, and the quality of Medicine.

Antitrust problems for physicians also emerged on the local level. Between 1985 and 1999, over two thirds of medical antitrust issues involved physicians versus hospitals. These disputes usually involved the hospitals' exclusive care contracting physicians vs. non-contracted but independent private practicing staff physicians. The non-contracted staff physicians contended that they were not being duly elected to medical staff executive committees because a typical hospital Board of Directors directly appointed their own and relatively controlled contracted physicians to these ruling and rule-making executive committees.

California-elected U.S. Congress Representative Thomas J. Campbell introduced a federal **Healthcare Reform** bill to give competing private practice physicians the right to collectively bargain with health plans under the National Labor Relations Act (NLRA). This Quality Health Care Coalition Act of 1999 (QHCCA) passed the U.S. House of Representatives as H.R.1304, and would have restored independently practicing physicians with that right to collectively bargain, without conferring any right to participate in any collective cessation of services to patients; but the bill failed passage in the United States Senate. The minority of Senators in favor of the Act stated that allowing physicians to negotiate collectively with overly powerful corporate healthcare plans would and will not change the physician's ethical duty to continue to provide medically necessary care to their patients. Offering opinion to the contrary, the dissenting majority of Senators insisted that antitrust labor laws were designed to protect and allow workers (not entrepreneurial private practice physicians, W2ers vs 1099ers) to obtain better wages and working conditions. Furthermore, they contended that the antitrust laws were not designed to improve the quality of patient care or the quality of any goods produced in the free market. These Senators warned and cautioned that passage of QHCCA would result in higher costs for healthcare delivery, higher insurance premiums, higher patient out-of-pocket expenses, reduction in Medicare and Medicaid services while increasing budget demands with an increase in the number of uninsured Americans. Interesting to note is that all of their horrid precaution predictions actually came to be accurate and true, but without passage of QHCCA or any change in antitrust legislation that would have in any way aided physicians in their battle with corporate insurance carriers.

Physicians interviewed[116] after Y2K admitted that actively encouraging their own children to become physicians would result in everlasting parental guilt; such advice was possibly and probably bad and harmful parental advice; and they were therefore reluctant to even offer to give it. Changes in healthcare delivery modalities and migrating economic mechanisms were interacting and occurring at such a rapid rate that any advice about the future practice of Medicine was most likely unsubstantiated gossip.

Most young doctors[117] entering into new medical practices had lowered financial expectations for their careers. many expressed no sense of a marriage to medical practice. They often considered their "doctor" degree a stepping-stone to other forms of business enterprises. A lifetime of practice in one loving, family-oriented, "Leave it to Beaver" community was not the current set ideal. The young doctor really sought a "job", not a "practice". The start-up costs for primary care private medical practice became more than any bank or savings institution was willing to lend, and educational loans yet remained unpaid. The percent of women graduating from medical schools became equal to and soon surpassed the percentage of men. The percentage of non-white minority nationalities, especially Asian and Indian, likewise increased. The most common image of the new doctor painted a thin young female of some political-social minority. Unfortunately, that feminine mystique also carried a perceived but unjustified devaluation in the worth for services rendered. Hispanic physicians were in high demand and aggressively recruited by HKOs to comply with the demographics of California's population base. Women physicians polled concerning the whys and wherefores of their joining a HKO generally responded by saying, "I need the job until I start my family, and then I'll be a part-timer, share a full time job with two other women, or be completely out for about 15 years". Yet, all of this may not have been so totally "bad". New applicants to medical schools may have had more of a "calling" (in the religious seminarian sense) for the practice of Medicine, and this might be considered "good". Therefore, one could at least hope and pray that some good entropy might have come out of all the evolved and unfortunate chaos; perhaps a hidden Phoenix might take flight.

Entropy or not, the constant pairing of Money and Medicine continually evolved new ethical standards for the practice of Medicine. Bad versus good became replaced by quick and cost effective versus prolonged and inefficient, or was it

---

[116] Interview by Author
[117] Interview by Author

vice versa? The formula for mass physician education would undergo drastic modification in the first quarter of the 21st Century. That aforementioned standard of academic group learning accompanied by a strong background in the sciences as a pre-requisite for a higher level of experimental-derived medical school education envisioned over a century ago by Abraham Flexner was finally put to rest. The Money and Medicine conspiracy marched onward. A new-age three dimensional MD printing machine first reduced the timeline from four to three years and eventually envisioned a two year course of clinical-centric study to proclaim once worthy and honored of the title Doctor of Medicine. The century-old apprentice system that was banished by the Flexner report sprung anew like that mythological phoenix, reborn from the ashes of academic institutions. Kaiser Foundation Health Plan had once again taken the innovative lead in 2019, establishing a Kaiser Permanente School of Medicine which offered clinical training from enrollment day one and an eventual shortened time to clinical practice after doctorial graduation.

On the legality side of Money and Medicine, health never was or could ever be a "take it or leave it" commodity strictly ruled and regulated by the "letter" of antitrust or any other legislation. The American nation's health is and always was a vital necessity, a fundamental service that should never be judged solely by the "spirit" of antitrust law. On the other hand, healthcare is not always a matter of free market choice; healthcare need is most often an urgent necessity. The persuasion propaganda for control of medical necessity advanced by insurance corporations was often insidiously planned, prepared with false inspiration and projected fear, and proselytized from a bully pulpit that portrayed a false perception of validity in matters of healthcare delivery. Physicians know well that treating only the symptoms of a pathological process will allow a disease to fester and eventually produce even more debilitating symptoms. If not treating the cause of the American healthcare delivery problem, then American patients risked suffering from a greater number, more severe and potentially fatal healthcare delivery symptoms......

"Praestat cautela quam medela", that is to say, prevention is better than cure according to some old Roman doc, or Cicero, or Sir Edward Coke. Primary preventive care is not a new concept, or better put by wise old doctor Hippocrates, "If we could give every individual the right amount of nourishment and exercise, not too little and not too much, we would have found the safest way to health". Taking and acting upon individual responsibility in primary preventive health maintenance had to be up and coming, as one of many **Healthcare Reform** mechanisms to save the USA's healthcare delivery system.

Meanwhile, physicians tried but failed to reestablish collegiality among themselves, with their hospitals and with formerly philanthropic patients. The antiquated American hospital that once functioned as the social center of a doctor's life evolved to be regarded by physicians as a horrid and feared indentured workplace. Medical societies tried but failed to work hand in hand with hospitals towards recruiting doctors for a common goal of collegiality. Remuneration always comes in many forms, not just in dollars: there is recognition, honor, gratitude, and respect. From these emotional supports, physician charity was once built and sustained. The natural desire to administer charitable healthcare was not effectively rekindled in the hearts of all American physicians. **The heart of one's happiness hides in the hottest heat of a hunt for the right to freely do that which one does well. (Ralzak)** For both, all American physicians and all American patients, true healthcare delivery happiness always was and always will be the honorable sweat of the brow labor of love that makes quality and accessible healthcare delivery happen with the right person, at the right time and in the right place.

Politics and the intense cathexis attached to personal and group alignment with economic-political "isms affecting the delivery of healthcare, when seen and appreciated only within the tunnel-visional confines of a nation-state, result in the eventual consideration of only myopic methodological metrics. The dangers in hiding behind concepts such as Federalism and Nationalism to pursue a personal political purpose also become painfully apparent. Now if Americans were so anxiously concerned about changing their healthcare delivery system, they must have taken pause and heeded some sage advice that was most often given by someone's dear mother; or did they not realize that when one might be digging oneself into a hole, the first thing to do is to stop digging and ask three questions: "Where am I?"
"How did I get here?"
"Where do I want to go?"
(Thanks again mom.)

Americans should have taken a "walk about" and a look about to see where they were in that self-dug hole and find or suddenly truly discover that they were in a financial crisis with not enough dollars available to pay for their future healthcare delivery needs if they were to be solely and totally dependent upon the amount of proposed future funding in the USA's governmental healthcare delivery systems -- Medicare, Medicaid and etc.. To make matters worse, technological progress supply side economics dictated an irresistibly alluring and ever-increasing demand for more and more of many newer drugs, tests and procedures. The USA dug itself deep into that hole by way of many years, more than half a century's worth, of shamefully poor fiscal planning along with counter-acting political policies that limited the physical mechanisms and modalities of healthcare delivery. However, American healthcare is unequivocally ranked #1 in the world for patient responsiveness, only if the patient knows the correct button to push for a response. Enormous confidence in American healthcare delivery continually drives global economic consumption to local American markets. Where else in the world can you benefit from extensive facial remodeling surgery just to simulate a smile on a poor child's face? America is a great nation in which to live, and Americans were at least proud that they had accomplished a super fine life style for themselves as they continued to age and expand their average longevity beyond the 80-year mark.

All Americans wanted to go forward and continue with the finest healthcare that Money could buy, but all Americans did not have the adequate funds for that particular purchase and wanted to spend a bit less for all the tons of paper work and third-party paper pushers that seemed to be increasingly involved in the healthcare delivery process. Several Americans did join their Sierra Club compadres and save some trees by making almost everything electronic, but there was still the overwhelming cost due to the absurd amount of cyber space administrators in various technical and hackable "clouds" of third party payer schemes. Transparency -- Americans should have wanted to know before being started on a treatment regimen that their course of treatment would be the most scientifically proven effective course to take. If there was some other regimen that did the job just as well and cost less, Americans should have been willing to take the cheaper and equally effective treatment. However, the erroneous concept of cost always equaling value in direct proportions was unfortunately habitually burned into their mindset. To clear any misdirection here, Americans should not have been willing to forgo a treatment just because it cost too much or would not meet some prejudicial committee's life-adjusted or quality-years criteria. That was not where Americans wanted to go from their ever deepening self-dug debt hole, and they should really have taken someone's sage dear motherly advice and immediately stopped digging themselves into that meaningless and increasingly expensive hole.

ICER (The Institute for Clinical and Economic Review, alias The Incremental Cost-Effectiveness Ratio) in the United States is a carbon copy of NICE (The National Institute for Comparative Effectiveness) in England. Both were boasting that they determine "Value" (value to the payer based on claims-made billing data compilation and not on true health improvement value to the consumer or for the provider; but oops -- this is never stated). Both governmental committees were amoral and unethical according to the existing American societal standards, but with a bit more of government-run propaganda or "engineering work" on altering societal norms and lowering societal expectations, those social standards could and would all so easily change:

The objective of this brainwashing "engineering work", more accurately put as political gaming or manipulative rue, is to bring about politically wise but popularly unacceptable change within a system, so that at the end of the effort, the people within the system, as well as those outside the system, feel somewhat weirdly satisfied and comfortable not only with the change but also with the politicians who brought about this change: A politically ideology-appointed "public group", (supposedly free from political tampering but with an obvious conflict of interest because of the pretentious politics of "appointment"), this "task force" establishes fine academic credentials as an acceptable authoritarian body capable of analyzing data and objectively determining a "best" course of action, (while holding true at all costs, to a false premise, that a cheaper way is always a better way). Public opinion regarding the change is sought through public hearings which are long and intensive with extensive public input, but all that noisy publicized input is really relegated to a sounding board which, from the very start, is never intended to be acted upon. The resultant "group-think" conclusion by "consensus" becomes a self-fulfilling prophecy that recommends legislative passage of overly onerous regulations detrimental to the general public's innate desires. Those horrid recommendations become the precise pre-arranged cue for the grand entrance of the original "appointer" politician, who then graciously and sympathetically seeks to lessen the public's burden, but not completely eliminate it. This psycho-political game is truly one of barter where the first entered bid for regulation is obviously inflated and ridiculous in order to obtain a compromise that will still favor the original political objective.

To re-spark public attention, some extreme "conservative" pundits of the opposite point of view went as far as to name-call entities such as ICER a "Death Panel" because ICER – or to name-call similar panels such as: a panel on "comparative effectiveness" (to evaluate "population group efficiencies" and "principles for allocation of medical interventions" in conjunction with a future "public option" government-run triage plan) or the then appointed "Independent Medical Advisory Committee" (IMAC). IMAC, by solely utilizing economic motives to establish norms for the quality and quantity of healthcare delivery, would have made mandatory, governmental enforceable determinations regarding allowable testing and treatment requirements that a "meaningful provider" might implement – a very salty slanted cookbook for administratively allowable medical practice payment regulation. IMAC's goal would then be to achieve an "adequate" number of "satisfactory" outcomes by implementing ethical and moral code formulas such as HRQOL (health related quality of life), QALY (quality adjusted life years), DALY (disability adjusted life years), and/or a type of UNOS (united network for organ sharing). All such acronyms represented **Healthcare Reform** point systems that could ration tests and treatments based on initial, alternative and total costs, the current and "productive" chronological age, economic and functional disability, and an actuarially calculated longevity for an individual. Thus a fundamentally phony prerequisite premise (equalization of age with physiological capability) and an invalid set of non-meaningful metrics would have been used to determine dire moral and ethical issues. A breast cancer in a young female may not have been worth treating because the cost of that treatment exceeded an administratively pre-determined fixed dollar amount or time limit "reasonably allotted" for limited increased longevity. Accordingly, some "panels" had advised that routine mammography testing for breast cancer in women less than 50 years of age was not worth the cost even though some statistically insignificant number of women were condemned to die for lack of early detection (thus the evolution of the "extremist" pundit's term "death panel"). According to the "talking heads", treatments indicated for pain and suffering such as hip and knee replacement surgeries would have also been rationed on the basis of age alone, or simply by creating the typical national healthcare delivery long waiting lines for surgical evaluation appointments as seen in other nations, followed by endlessly reshuffled priority lists for future surgical dates. (The Veterans Administration Health Care System got caught with their pants down after complications arose from this exact technique.) An environment could have and can be all too easily and functionally created whereby there is no practical way or manor to render the needed and/or desired healthcare delivery in a timely fashion. Caveat emptor!

Governmental optimal care (rationing) programs were too often based on the statistical efficacy of cold and uncaring societal group "average" lifetime survival statistics derived from a mixed combination of secondary prevention and tertiary prevention healthcare billing data. Perhaps this methodology was starting with a false premise from the "get go" for a specific individual patient who did not fit that "average" definition. (It would have been equally invalid to go in the other direction of extreme and base the odds on a Methuselah average age survival of 969 years.) Governmental control has too often led to the establishment of too many committees, an endlessly expansive bureaucracy that ultimately exerts an unwanted and unnecessarily obtrusive heavy hand to amorally manipulate migratory economic markets in the name of **Healthcare Reform**.

For example, many "Peer Reviewed" evidence-based scientific studies statistically proclaimed that Prostate Specific Antigen (PSA) testing past 60 years of age did not improve ultimate "average" survival – now before a great rush to judgment, think about what anyone's dear and beloved mother would certainly admonish, "Look to see and be prepared for where you wish to leap; you had better plan on what you are going to do when you get there before you make any attempt in moving in that direction". Therefore, take a different direction from "lies, more lies, and then statistics" and actually step back to examine as all the good and humanistic dear and loving mothers have taught their children – before moving in that direction, look outside the box for possible consequences resulting from what is being proclaimed here. No government agency wants to be credited with suddenly determining that one's ultimate "survival" in years is the goal of a healthcare delivery program, but they somehow all accept the concept as some unquestioned fact that has forever and a day been carved in stone. A more careful examination of that stone reveals that it is actually covered over in deep slippery-dirty wet mud or much more stinky malarkey that hides the more important concepts of quality of life, art of living and enjoyment of living. "Lifetime left" "survival" without healthcare delivery treatments after being diagnosed with prostate cancer at age 65 may actually be no better or worse that "lifetime left" "survival" with healthcare delivery treatments after being diagnosed with prostate cancer at age 65. But look closer at this Blarney -- what about all those years in between, perhaps 20-30 years between having made the potential diagnosis by secondary preventive screening and the eventual death? What about the interval enjoyment in living a healthy life? Nobody in their right mind would chose to lose their humanity, beastly or not, and suffer through painful cancerous metastasis to vital organs and painful pathological bone fractures for years and years until finally meeting up with their grim reaper, especially when all that miserable pain and suffering could have been greatly alleviated by immediate treatment after a PSA screening detection over the age of 60. Moreover, to quote any dear mother's wisdom, any "average" guess is, by definition, wrong 50% of the time; and 50% of the time the death might have been due to that painful metastatic cancer including collapsed and fractured vertebrae and other bones, and may have 50% of the time totally destroyed one's art and joy of living. Those amoral members of the U.S. Preventive Services Task Force, coyfully utilizing misdirection, recommended ceasing and desisting with the practice of routine PSA testing because that test does not define the "acuity" of prostate cancer. Just more Blarney to cover the malarkey -- if the disease was already in its metastatic phase, ultimate survival would not have been altered and further "expensive" therapy might be ill-advised for certain prostate cancer types. Of course, if there is no testing at all, those "over 65" men with early stage involvement, then curable disease will never be found; and by the way, the selectively cherry-picked political "Task Force" somehow never considered the bold factual statistical truth that mortality from prostate cancer has decreased 40% since the initiation of PSA testing.

The primary discussion point should have centered about the "joie de vivre" in good health versus dependent and painful survival until death by horribly painful apoptosis. Quite apparently, that is not what the "Task Force" was secretly tasked to do. So again, the real and certainly expected primary goal of secondary and tertiary healthcare delivery is to attain a state of health that permits one to be productive for oneself and for society, and also permits the enjoyment of the "art of living". When healthcare delivery fails to achieve that goal, then its efficacy should certainly be questioned. Government programs conveniently and continually fail to offer those proper meaningful metrics and parameters to evaluate Socrates's proverbial "examined" life that is worth living, a pleasurable life that much more expensive to continually cater to and, of course, continually more expensive to provide that degree of healthcare delivery necessary for the enjoyment or art of living. When publicized that a country such as England "enjoys" universal healthcare delivery, the dirty little secret is never let out that the poor in England for the most part are restricted to public-approved institutions, while the rich uniformly seek out more expensive privatized healthcare delivery that more adequately maintains their life style and pleasures, again essential for the art of living. That might be ok in a land where the masses voluntarily still worship a Queen, Royalty, and accept their place as Commoners, but that is not how it works here in the USA buddy.....

Determining what treatment does the best and gives the most satisfying and sustainable result, and paying a variable amount according to the quality of that actual end result obtained would be a possible logical and cost saving modality in a capitalistic society, but only when unanimous agreement can be rendered as to the definition of true health quality. If a healthcare delivery system were completely transparent, various providers could compete and list charges according to what the market would bear on an interstate basis. Such a national capitalistic-competitive migratory economic philosophy inspires entrepreneurial efforts to do things increasingly better and cheaper, but ICER was not interested in providing methodologies or mechanisms for such a proven productive migratory economic principle, the enterprising and wonderful capitalistic standard that historically enabled an American capitalistic society to rise to world predominance in less than half a century during the 1900's. The ICER ideologies ran far afield ahead of the current popular and rising progressive socialism. The ICER concept of value was determined by a statistical analysis of billing costs to the payer – cost per case, cost per hospitalization, and cost per "quality-adjusted" life year gained. ICER pre-determined that grandma does not statistically live out so many "quality adjusted life years" because she is all alone at home, even though she is independent; and, by the way, ICER would certainly not consider grandma to have a single "quality-adjusted" year left in her if she lived in some sort of long term care facility with multiple medical problems. Therefore, on a yearly basis, would it be morally proper for a physician to be mandated by a government's national triage system to carefully and didactically instruct grandma on precisely how to surely end her life by not taking her life sustaining medications or antibiotics -- a possible administratively mandated death-advisory task, unfortunately and unexpectedly thrust upon or federally mandated for physicians to perform in order to disguise its governmental migratory economic origin? There was already an established federal mandate for physicians to talk to patients about long term care plans in the face of medical complications.

Fee-for-service physicians argued, "If you should happen to receive one of ICER's clean low "value" ratings, you, by administrative decree, may not get the treatment that you need to stay alive – that's throwing out dear old grandma with the dirty bathwater. The ICER rhetoric is disgraceful. They boast of producing "tangible ratings" -- tangible in ICER-speak translates as perceptible, and perception, of course, is in the eye of the beholder. The horrific eyes of ICER are biased eyes; therefore, the American public must rely on their own good and dependable eyes to look about and see what is outside of that pre-dug healthcare delivery hole that the third party payers are so enthusiastically increasingly digging. That digging must immediately stop to enable one to clearly see exactly where Americans really want to go.

The corporate bar on the practice of Medicine was relatively simple to revoke, but why bother, that puny bar served as no great obstacle to go under or around and render non-functional. All future primary healthcare delivery, delivered by corporate-employed and salaried ancillary medical providers at some arbitrary imaginary forever fixed lower cost (which surely rises as the day is long) became a popular push and poll for political pundits. Migratory "laissez-faire" competitive economic principles again were ignored and avoided. Payments for episodes of inpatient care bundled into bigger bundles to a still lower total reimbursement resulted in only decreased total healthcare delivery and endless disputes between physicians and hospitals as to what percentage of the bundle payment each should be allotted. Each entity would eventually seek to do less and thus spend less work time while gaining leisure time for the lesser payments; that is a red hot potato rationing roast, not a red herring.

Pay for « Performance » (P-4-P), Pay for What ? -- What is "PHYSICIAN PERFORMANCE" ? In the new healthcare delivery world of migratory economics, in P-4-P programs, total through-put performance unfortunately became defined as output quantity divided by output cost. That is a simple and easily understandable formula which applies well to the making of gadgets and gismos, but becomes totally inappropriate when evaluating physician-delivered medical care. Way back in 1771, the father of mathematical economists, Pietro Verri, would have condemned employing and enforcing the aforementioned mathematical calculation as a direct violation, an unnecessary and inefficient implied taxation through an inept, redundant and equilibrium-destructive intermediary, a feckless administrative program run by feckless administrators.

Watch out for sneaky key words like "responsible" in front of traditional words like reform and healthcare delivery. When the greatest quantity at the cheapest cost comes out the winner, then patients and doctors come out the losers. Pay for performance (P-4-P) maximizes profit for the healthcare insurance industry while not significantly adding to medical quality, and often exists solely as an optimal cost reduction copy of the medical record that facilitates medical billing. That is an invalid raison d'être. The NEW administrative determination of physician "VALUE" became redefined as cost-effectiveness per specified monitored unit of prescribed and billed healthcare delivery service rendered, rather than the traditional trusted definition adhered to by patients who repeatedly and willingly laid down all their hard-earned dollars on assurances of quality, competence, and judgment to determine "VALUE". Those specific P-4-P monitored services did not reflect the quality of healthcare delivery rendered across the board and might have actually reduced total quality performance due to human nature's nasty mean economic equilibration trick of reducing emphasis in unmonitored areas to replace the increased cathexis placed on areas of mandated increased emphasis. Pay for performance and other such "quality" incentives must show true and meaningful quality improvements for patients and doctors and not rely on "optimal care" concepts and unproven economic profiling standards that pass unnecessary administrative costs (implicit economic expenses-taxes) on to the doctors and then onto the patients and general public in the form of taxes.

Economic motivations unduly tempted physicians to cherry-pick healthier and wealthier patients so that they could obtain the most rewarding profile and resultant higher pay; P-4-P report cards are too obviously an Un-Shuffled-Sort and always stacked that way for maximal efficiency, a system set-up for a uncaring but compliant physician to "beat the house": Patients are educated to get certain tests on the performance profile without understanding the more important nature and care that must be attended to for their total medical health. Because of the metrics set up by the P-4-P system, culturally diverse, poor, and medically complicated patients tend to profile out as noncompliant and give the good dedicated physicians yet diligently caring for them a bad P-4-P insurance bonus score. True quality of overall care is never measured; patient safety is often ignored. In the realm of irrational reality in functional human economics, good medical judgment, timeliness and accuracy in diagnosis tend to be downgraded as cookbook algorithm guidelines are more precisely adhered to for the sake of add-on bonus pay and lessened inappropriate penalties – a really mean unconscious beastly human psychological trick. Medical practice arrangements that shared computer billing systems were advantaged over individual competent and caring practices. The doctor who signed on to the Faustian agreement was auctioning his or her soul. Desire for wealth subsumed moral integrity. Such a devil's contract should simply not have been signed. Physicians should have just said no, stood their ground, bit the bullet and reaped the unfortunate financial consequences – morality and ethics should not have been for sale and so readily purchased from physicians. An initial grin and bear it attitude simply did not persist. Inappropriate **Healthcare Reform** could be and proved to be easily purchased for significantly less than Judah's thirty shekels.

The professional goal should be the best care that is possible, not the best for all after considering any unfortunate set of fixed insurance corporation-directed circumstances. The ideal should allow physicians the autonomy to make the best decisions for an individual patient's need and not be confined to the false premise of an absolute limited resource of funds, an "optimal care" concept that sacrifices quality to honor cost. Do not confuse increased medical quality to the patient with dollar value to the third-party bill payer. The eventual reporting and sharing of medical information should be for the advancement of medical quality and patient safety by providing data for valid research. Universal access, timely access directly to a doctor for a patient in need of healthcare, timely access to actual healthcare delivery, that truly meaningful timely access must be assured; not universal access to waiting lists where patients eventually die of old age from waiting or eventually become too ill to have a procedure performed. Information technology should add transparency to common, user-friendly, software that enables patient-authorized release and storage of all medical records through the internet. HIPPA requirements must be eased for the sake of transparency. Community healthcare delivery safety nets cannot be abandoned or replaced; they should be invigorated. If P-4-P programs are not patient oriented to improve safety, effectiveness, and true medical quality in patient care, then P-4-P simply becomes "pay for paperwork" – benefiting only insurance carriers with a reduction in cost with no benefit to patients or their caring physicians, and the potential to harm patients. If P-4-P continues to focus on cost reduction in medical claims, then further increasing depleted physician autonomy, whatever is left of it, will be detrimental to patients. When insurance-healthcare corporate firms direct healthcare delivery and de facto actually practice Medicine, P-4-P becomes reversed, turned around to spell out, "Perform -- for -- Pay", one of the oldest professions, but certainly not in the realm of good healthcare delivery. Physicians should have been forewarned. The cheapest care concept settles for what can just get the sick person by, for a passing grade of "C minus", and undermines physician authority. That is certainly not the A plus best that can be done for patients. If a student settled for a GPA of C minus in college, he or she might one day become President of the USA; but a pre-med student's transcript showing a C minus average would never have allowed that student to be accepted into any medical school in the United States. American healthcare delivery always strove for excellence from the brightest and the best. Physicians sold out to the migratory economic administrators of **Healthcare Reform** and degraded a desired excellence in healthcare delivery.

Mandated and unfunded health information technology, outright fee reductions, blending dollar limits on capitation, and yes, unproven and dangerous incentive metrics, not only biased but also inadequately and perversely compensated through various non-meaningful and medically unsound "Pay-for-Performance" (P-4-P) methodologies which considered only a marginal adequate benefit to a majority of population and did not correlate multiple disease entities in an individual patient -- all of these slick schemes and more were actually stings manipulated by legislative action, and all resulted in a decrease of services to high risk patients through a nebulous, indistinct and confusing grouping of modalities utilizing various mechanisms. The legal mumbo-jumbo or prestidigitation then seemed to magically evaporate into thin air any sort of a red herring concept known as rationing, but that old fishy stench hung on, still there for all to suffer and smell. A very few Americans yet remembered the often quoted inverse relationship between laws and justice, the ancient Roman words of Cicero.

Apart from the natural instinct inherent in Homo sapient human nature to cleverly outwit and then game any mandatory imposition put upon traditional routines that have habitually insured a comfortable livelihood, physicians, like cats, do not herd well and tend to readily see through pay-for-performance as really nothing more than Pay-for-Paperwork to reduce some program administrator's disturbing cost, a Payment-for-Perception of perceived cost-reduction and not a quality healthcare delivery improvement issue. Perception is defined as stark reality divided by one's hoped for and desired expectation. Where reality and expectation are of equal intensity, perception expresses a value of one. Where expectation exceeds reality, perception is diminished. The more unrealistic or unscientific be the hopefully expected cost-savings as compared to stark fiscal reality, the lesser becomes the final economic perception of its possible accomplishment --- but that is only when all is said and done; during the interim time, pundits praise the impossible as perfectly possible. The only possible benefit from P-4-P is a marginal cost reduction that is subject to the economic law of "diminishing repeated returns" popularized by economic liberalist and physiocrat Anne-Robert-Jacques Turgot, Baron de Laune in the 1700's. When additional units of labor are added to a fixed amount of capital, the entire productive process is eventually degraded to decreased production. The economic "principle of diminishing contentment" with repeated similar reward also applies to P-4-P. Economist Frank A. Fetter made clear that "One may have too much of a good thing" such as water on a hot day – each successive glass of water is appreciated less than the one before until a point is reached where a further drink it abhorred. The same can be said of candy or chocolate. Fetter coined this reversal in greedy desires of economic self-interest the "principle of diminishing gratification".

The fee-for-service model may not be the best or ever have been the most appropriate model for every single patient, but a mandated or incentive-paid avoidance of providing more services neither changed the model nor assured that a physician's job was done well under any model of healthcare delivery. They are billing data-driven population based practices that offer no improvement in the care of a specific individual patient while adding additional record-keeping expenses to an individual physician's medical practice. A bundled payment or a computerized "meaningful use" check–off form may hide or obscure a deficient service or an atypical cherry-picked patient population; and there are many more "wordsmithing" ways than one to skin any benchmark, no matter how high or low. Physicians not under the employment/payment umbrella of a hospital or institution complained to no avail concerning the inappropriateness and harshness of the Bundled Payment System: In thc bundle payment's system of defining value as equaling quality divided by cost, quality is redefined by specifically chosen theoretical and reportable metrics developed by the institution, payment sources and NIH item responses to variable question banks. Cost is specifically defined by CMS. PROMS, Patient Reported Outcome Measures, are risk-stratified to a relative value of complaints that might require re-auditing of the bundle payment system, while physician input of physical function, the classical test of valued outcomes, is put aside or completely ignored.

Cookbook Medicine continually suppresses then drowns superlative cognitive reasoning, and "Big Brother's" behind the shoulder presence in the examination and operating rooms cuts both ways as an imposition to the doctor-patient relationship. It is and was hubris to actually believe that a measurable metric of monitored increased pay would increase a dedicated professional's personal best. In the criminal justice system, such "rewards" would be considered illegal blackmail Money given as bribes to influence the judgment of a person or official who occupies a position of trust. An individual surgeon performs a pro-bono surgery with the exact same attention to detail as a personally paid-for or a third-party paid-for surgery. Nobody is ever completely equal to anybody else; each piece in the human puzzle is uniquely different; some surgeons are arguably better than other surgeons for what they do, but P-4-P does not and cannot alter the reality of natural talent or different levels of cognitive reasoning ability. No concert pianist would give a significantly better performance for a few extra bucks, so why expect any difference from a truly dedicated medical professional? P-4-P programs may save Money by increasing efficiency in assembly-line production and services, but not for direct healthcare delivery; in fact, P-4-P programs have been scientifically shown to reduce quality in medical care services.

One tragic example of quality reduction occurred when payment/treatment P-4-P was determined by checking and concentrating on "meaningful use" boxes in Dallas Texas. Diversion from the big picture could have resulted in a national calamity --a documented history of recent immigration from West Africa (and possible exposure to Ebola virus) was ignored by healthcare workers and an unfortunate Ebola-infected victim, T. E. Duncan, had been let into the United States in the Fall of 2014. Additionally, with the horse-head blinders of "meaningful use" firmly in place, he was initially sent home from a Dallas hospital only to require re-admission. The initial mistake was made, again, for allowing too much attention to be directed to gaining and gaming the same burdensome overly-distracting and individual quality-reducing P-4-P consequence. Why pay for no proven health benefit and the possible unintended consequence of poorer health and dangerous health outcomes?

Let's look at another example -- Medicare's Premier Demonstration project on P-4-P did not score participating hospitals with decreased death rates.[118] As opposed to billing-determined "meaningful use" criteria, only clinical "meaningful measures and metrics" can be justifiably measured, monitored, and then recorded as milestones. When some aspect of medical service is cut, then somewhere down the line there will most likely be a dear price to pay, and that price is most often not worth the initial cost savings for most clinically meaningful medical services. The same admonition can be registered for penalty versus reward in the self-reporting of non-meaningful measures regarding clinical processes and primary prevention as well as non-meaningful metrics for care coordination. The Physician Quality Reporting System (PQRS) jumped up to be in lock stop step with P-4-P and hoped to evaluate data reported via the internet. Fortunately, the price for reporting utilizing associated electronic equipment outweighed the benefit to the physician, and golden the rule of migratory economics triumphed with a multiple-year 70% non-reporting rate among private practicing physicians. More stringent Stage 2 program requirements demonstrated only worsening compliance data. 2014 Stage 2 attestation numbers for both eligible professionals (EPs) and hospitals revealed that only about 2% of EPs demonstrated Stage 2 capabilities and fewer than 17% of USA hospitals demonstrated Stage 2 capabilities.

Patient happiness, often engendered by lowered societal expectations, becomes a delusion used to rate and then scale pay reimbursement for healthcare outcomes. In an effort to please and assuage the patient, the didactic questioning of a medical history is replaced by a more naturally flowing or "Organic Conversation". The resultant intellectual stagnation brings out common human errors in perception, assumption and communication, which rise to dominate the medical examination. Administrators commonly fall into the psychological trap of actually believing that their push-pull propagandized patient-satisfaction surveys in some magical way directly reflect a true medical quality result from direct healthcare delivery; or that by embarrassing physicians, you can force them to increase the quality of their results. It is all too clever and all so easy and simple to be "the nice guy" physician and rapidly increase patient satisfaction while actually delivering a

---

[118] At baseline, the composite 30-day mortality was similar for Premier and non-Premier hospitals (12.33% and 12.40%, respectively; difference, −0.07 percentage points; 95% confidence interval [CI], −0.40 to 0.26). The rates of decline in mortality per quarter at the two types of hospitals were also similar (0.04% and 0.04%, respectively; difference, −0.01 percentage points; 95% CI, −0.02 to 0.01), and mortality remained similar after 6 years under the pay-for-performance system. The Long-Term Effect of Premier Pay for Performance on Patient Outcomes, Ashish K. Jha, M.D., M.P.H., Karen E. Joynt, M.D., M.P.H., E. John Orav, Ph.D., and Arnold M. Epstein, M.D., N Engl J Med 2012; 366:1606-1615 April DOI: 10.1056/NEJM sa1112351

faster turnover and poorer quality of healthcare delivery. Blinded healthcare delivery administrators also needed to beware of statistically significant results from scrupulously monitored and overly-staffed pilot demonstration healthcare delivery projects that were provided, and only could have been provided, with the aid of huge special interest "grants" to academic medical institutions. The inductive leap in applying their same controlled healthcare delivery techniques and outcome results to the general population with and especially without the accompanying special supportive "grant" fiscal supplements was most often fraught with disaster. It is quite interesting to note that these pilot projects have been and are rarely continued by the grantees once their grant Money has dried up. Health information technologies are great for billing purposes and convenient for rapid historical medical case review, but they in no way assure access to point-of-service medical care. A quick and easy migratory economic, a few cents spent on physicians providing patients with a disease and medication history burned into a wallet-sized CD proved to be much cheaper and did much better suffice.

Healthcare delivery proved not to be some a simple cookbook process that could be successfully applied in any type of environment. Coordinated care at a large institution with closed panel physicians that shared a common economic interest was much different from coordinating care in a rural or urban community through multiple Medical Homes and careful quality-driven case management. Both may have achieved improved results, but their methodologies had to be unique to their particular situation. Healthkeeper responsibility and trust had to be ideally extended to patients through an unfortunately fading away physician-patient relationship that was historically readily obtainable and ultimately sustainable.

Political programs that awarded a patient with a place on a waiting list and not a point-of-service healthcare delivery time-definite appointment with a practitioner or doctor -- well those programs certainly represent crisis points for any individual. When some bureaucrat set up a computerized program within an electronic medical record that had an error code to override the orally given advice from a trusted doctor and a computer-derived determination that denied the recipient patient's future medical needs on the basis of that initial crass error code rejection criteria – "beneficiary being too old or beneficiary requested care too expensive" – that type of politically sanctioned error code program presented a crisis for the individual too. If one had to wait weeks or months to get tests or treatments, there would arise a pickling crisis leading to delayed or denied medications or medical services rapidly becoming a critical matter and leading to the pickle in the crisis, the underserved patient. Sure, one certainly commonly expected and became accustomed to exasperating situations in life; one could safely wait for all the paperwork and nonsense that was usually more than sometimes necessary to register a car or get a driver's license at a government-run Division of Motor Vehicles; all that frustration didn't kill anyone. Waiting delays to get healthcare delivery or denied healthcare delivery could and occasionally did very well kill someone. Some few patients certainly justifiably feared that making one's healthcare delivery a bureaucratic issue with a government takeover of the healthcare delivery system would eventually lower the quality of healthcare delivery -- that would put everyone into a real crisis. With a healthcare system run by the government politicians, alias legislators, by way of their conflict-of-interest, alias politically-appointed "experts", and under the persuasive influence of their political campaign-contributors and K-street, alias multiple campaign-contributor special interest groups and their lobbyists, politically-motivated healthcare delivery decisions had to be expected as the most probable and predictable end result. Determinations of qualified eligibility or disqualifications for such things as drugs or treatments or early disease detection tests were also thrown into that conflict-of-interest political compost barrel. In such a system, waste, fraud, and abuse would naturally arise to the status of public enemy number one, and that common public enemy would go on to rob a certain percentage of individuals their hard-earned sequestered funds that could have been put towards medically needed healthcare. Quality is and was having a trusted healthcare practitioner see to and correctly oversee a patent getting the right and needed treatments, at the right time and at the right place. It might have seemed painfully obvious that rather than a computer, only a live and truly concerned healthcare practitioner could totally evaluate the medical-psycho-social milieu and then determine what which would be truly medically necessary for an individual; but then again, removed and unconcerned, politicians and heartless regulators of software programs could and did make such personal judgments. A personalized doctor-patient relationship protected an individual, but individual patients and patient groups seldom spoke up; they repeatedly failed to protect their right to obtain and preserve that type of sacrosanct relationship with any and all trusted healthcare practitioners. One size did not fit all, and when an isolated individual got stuck with a computerized medical care delivery system that only approved healthcare that would "on the average" be satisfactory for the vast majority of a population but not necessarily for that unique individual, well yes, that particular fellow American had a very personal healthcare delivery crisis. By the way, "average healthcare delivery" or such measurable metrics as "average intelligence" psychologically hide the intuitive truth that 50% of the cohort or population considered get or have below the average of whatever is being monitored.

Then again, dredging down more deeply into that slime-covered rotten dug-out pit of political motivation from an outside-the-box perspective, all this hoopla about physician performance may have been an unintentionally but quite cleverly contrived administrative smokescreen to hide true administrative socialistic intent. "Performance" may have been nothing more than a politically-correct proper-speak word for "Productivity". Speaking about the forbidden fruit topic of "enforced or enforcing human productivity" could have gotten very nasty very quickly. Physicians who yielded to P-4-P without a fight and saw more patient units per hour to better their scores necessarily cut back on the completeness of their medical examinations. A complete physical exam was at one time recommended once a year, then once every five years. As previously stated, the agreed time necessary for a complete history and physical exam is better than one hour. When "production" time allotted for the service was cut to ten minutes, then better than two thirds of the "performance" was also cut; items like: a thorough evaluation of retina and eye grounds, cranial sensory and reflex nerve testing, rectal exam, a skin search (especially under feet) for moles, hernia tests, strength and bone pain testing, balance and proprioception evaluation, range of motion testing etc.etc.etc.. A computerized history check-off sheet that was added to the official history and physical examination reflected uninformed and thusly inaccurate patient knee-jerk responses to a medical receptionist's queries and served to replace the once honored physician history portion of the physical exam. Wow, bet those things now absent in a physical exam rang a bell after reading, but the lowered expectations of the general public offered no rousing uproar – they, the American public along with their once beloved and trusted physicians, cooked themselves in the slowly heating pot of political Kickapoo Joy Juice just like in the dumb old frog boiling in the progressively heating water experiment. Yet, migratory ecolo-nomic of **Healthcare Reform** stumbled ever onward:

The third medical ecolo-nomic generation's (1990-2010) information storm hammered and flashed bolts of future shock into the medical community. Documentation, documentation, and documentation destroyed hills and valleys of evergreens that were made into paper, hastening environmentalist-sanctioned conversion of records into electronic records and billing forms. Older doctors looked to and depended on a computer-savvy set of younger doctors to mentor them through the "digital byte" storm. National standard organizations developed extensive sets of guidelines to be further documented during the examination and treatment of the patients. These guidelines were at first resisted; but as the older computer-phobic physicians retired from medical practice, the younger computer-oriented practitioners first found palm pilots, iPods and google pads which were all abandoned in a huge electronic garbage dump with the sudden appearance of yearly evolving myriads of technologically evolved "smart" cell phones with apps of every sort, as well as other innovative ways, for quick and easy use within the new doctors' allotted time slots, all to readily satisfy the electronic paperwork requirements. Those forests which had previously been destroyed just to furnish the paper could now look forward to a blissful future of reforestation. Paper charts and x-ray films, now transformed into electronic data, allowed those green conifer mountain forests to flourish once again by electronically rendering increased tunnel vision to the medical examinations. Environmental concern shifted to providing safe dumping areas for all the yearly discarded electronic devises. But **Healthcare Reform** had to get back on the trek, move on to that envisioned eventual common pathway, and forage onward on that bumpy switchback trail, the eventual road to future federal single payer universal healthcare delivery:

In 2009, the President Barak Obama administration introduced another presidential administration omnibus healthcare bill that initially included a government-run public option plan or a co-op option plan that would hopefully and most naturally morph into national universal single payer health insurance. The young, handsome and dynamic speaker tossed out his moving and powerful presidential pitch, but this curve-ball throw failed again to tempt the American batter to swing at an insider federal single payer plan. Relentless pounding political forces from the politically persuasive corporate insurance industry aided by an inept Congress rendered President Obama unable to effectively throw and deliver a single payer healthcare strike across the **Healthcare Reform** home plate. He just could not, at that precise moment in time, completely sell his federally run "Common Plan" migratory ecolo-nomic patterned concept, especially after the infamously withdrawn vote by Democratic Senator Lieberman of Connecticut in December of 2009. Furthermore, as previously elaborated, critical questions concerning his alternative fallback or backup plan, the Patient Protection Affordable Care Act (PPACA), yet remained.

Since any valid and legal federal tax bill must be passed first in the House of Representatives and not in the Senate, the Obama administration refused to cost out the ACA as a tax to the American public. The ACA law was first passed in the Senate then ratified by the house. Therefore and surprisingly to many, although insistently and publicly proclaimed not to be a federal tax by the Obama administration and the President, in 2012, the United States Supreme Court (SCOTUS, 5 yea and 4 nay) adjudicated that "the individual mandate" of the ACA, compelling every American Citizen to buy health insurance from a private or public insurer or else pay a penalty, essentially amounted to a legally levied federal tax that could be administrated by the Internal Revenue Service, and not an illegal legislative order issued under the justification of the "commerce clause". In the infamous case, *"National Federation of Independent Businesses versus Sebelius"*, the justices also upheld the right of the States to self-administer healthcare delivery programs, such as federal Medicaid, on a local-state basis.

In 2013, there still remained hope to affect change tempered by prudence, to find a truer version of migratory economic patterned **Healthcare Reform** similar to the not altogether forgotten "Common Plan", to enable national government-run healthcare as the climax of the progressivism saga. An optional federally funded provision in the ACA called for the establishment of "Healthcare Exchanges" in and/or by the States. A mandated insurance option in each State Healthcare Exchange called for a federally funded insurance entity for those citizens who could not fit into what private insurers had to offer. This portion of the mandate had the potential of acting as a foot-in-the-door for a future single payer federal plan. The fundamental overall mandate provided for universal individual participation in coverage, especially from the young and healthy, so that the aged and unhealthy could be adequately subsidized. Hope and Fear – Fear admonished that the young would ignore the mandate and thus crumble the exchanges. Hope, a nervous hope managed to so squirrelly seek to survive, but true enactment of that desired but "over lobbied to fail" federal single payer plan would just have to wait for another day.

To prevent excessive and overly expensive Emergency Room visits for basic healthcare delivery by "newly-insured" poverty-rated recipients, some states employed an additional **Healthcare Reform** modality that proved to be at least a partial solution. Adoption of a state-wide Basic Health Plan, such as the previously Republican-initiated "RomneyCare" in Massachusetts, hoped to reduce the churning of qualified recipients from Healthcare Exchange coverage to Medicaid assistance coverage and back again, as many recipients' incomes changed up and down in percent beyond and below the poverty level. The healthcare exchanges were designed to take mandated coverage premiums from the young and healthy, who typically consumed less care, so that there would be funds available to subsidize coverage for the poor, very young, chronically crippled and aged. The individual mandate was thusly designed to hopefully force these energetic young folks to participate. If they ignored the mandate, then, back to Fear, the exchanges might crumble; but again there was that strange audacity of hope that failure of the ACA could be a blessing that would inevitably lead to enactment of a national single payer health insurance. Questions dropped and fluttered about, up and down in the political winds, like the journey of so many multi-colored shedding leafs departing from their deciduous trees during the 2010 Fall season, a delightful "Indian Summer" in New England.

Had the universal healthcare delivery argument come full circle and blended into the mix once again? Exactly what was a true and just "right"; was the right to a level playing field for equal opportunity to compete to acquire goods vying with the right to share equally in distributions even if one chose not to compete at all? Was there such an entity as an endowed right to have happiness and healthcare and shelter and food, or rather was there the "constitutional" and "declaration of independence" right to "pursue happiness" through the right to work for one's healthcare and daily bread? And what about differences between Federalists versus States rights to administer either set of these purported or alleged **Healthcare Reform** rights? Was compulsory mandated federalist enforcement of healthcare cost payments, prescribed procedures and mandated limited benefits a fundamental loss of liberty and religious freedom or just another implicit tax? Would physicians be compelled to administer to patients in a government program by making such participation an enforced condition for renewal of their medical license? Would the same also hold true for hospital license renewal? Was or had healthcare delivery become a true human right or just another manipulative political tool? Had not Mankind historically donated "altruistic" healthcare delivery to win favor and political alliance both domestically and internationally ever since modern Mankind existed as a cave culture over 60,000 years ago? Why was there never a documented scientific study to show that government-funded healthcare delivery substantially improved the health of the poor? Would tunnel-visionary methodological nationalism continue to battle constitutional federalism in the wake of the ACA? Was the USA to ultimately have legislated unbridled federalism or constitutionally confined federalism in **Healthcare Reform**? How would the conflict between states' rights and federal rights ever be solved? Did not a civil war supposedly solve that issue over 150 years ago? If America's current dilemma politically evolved to become the nation-state's way versus the highway, then might America be embarking on a slippery slope to: Orwell's "_1984_"? Did society really save Money by not having routine healthcare delivery provided by hospital emergency rooms when one unmasked and considered the additional costs to prevent patients from frequently flying to emergency rooms, such as the costs of social workers, case managers, administrative overseers, 501(c) "Non-Profit" community health maintenance organizations and all the documented political time wasted or consumed by governmental employees and duplicative agencies in the process? So, when, how and where would or could all these hot peppered and politically salted arguments finally shake free or begrudgingly grind out? – Apparently not in the Congress of the USA.

To quote once again the acknowledged father-practitioner of modern Medicine, Hippocrates, "Diseases are not punishments ordained from Olympus." "The honorable duty of Mankind is, with dignity, to relieve suffering and keep the health." That was a centuries-old astute judgement based on the overall medical need of Mankind, not on any specific devised or written treatment regimen. Perhaps another judgement, wise or otherwise, based on the medical need of millions of Americans for **Healthcare Reform** was actually in the making.

The Supreme Court affirmed that federalist mandate to all Americans within the Obama Administration's ACA, a mandate to purchase private corporate health insurance or pay a federal tax penalty for not enrolling in federal or private state healthcare program. This affirmation judgement reignited current and traditional issues of how to actually provide reasonable and necessary healthcare delivery services to all citizens. "To do" wrestled with "how to do". Mahatma Gandhi had emphatically stated, "YOU must be the change you want to see in the world." People who live healthy lives consume fewer medical services than others, so might the federal government next mandate federal tax penalties for lack of exercise, an unhealthy diet, obesity, smoking and maybe more? Would such mandates be constitutionally valid or would The Supreme Court of The United States (SCOTUS) have to ultimately intervene once again?

The unraveling plot in the unread by Congress PPACA Act began to thicken. Clearly, anyone reading the written Affordable Care Act would have easily seen and understood that federal subsidies for certain qualifying U.S. citizens would be available "through an exchange established by the State." Nothing was written to this regard concerning an exchange established by the federal government. In May of 2012, the Internal Revenue Service interpreted the "State clause" to mean that the subsidies could also be offered to Health Care Exchanges established by the federal government, in addition to those established by the state governments. The infamous *"King versus Burwell"* lawsuit compelled the SCOTUS to intervene once again. Great concern arose over forcing SCOTUS once again to carefully re-read and re-interpret the not-read but supposedly written by Congress -- the unread ACA document; and then to rule on **Healthcare Reform.** SCOTUS faced the additional conundrum of acting as a clairvoyant oracle based on telepathy from the past – to ferret out what excuse for a rational cognitive human thought could have possibly existed in the collective mind of Congress at a previous point in time, that is to say, to determine the overall intent of an uninformed congressional vote on the infamous "read me later" congressional ACA document.

The SCOTUS verdict -- 6 yeas and 3 nays. Fearing that loss of tax credits "could well push a state's individual market into a death spiral,".....We must read the words in context".....Our duty, after all, is to construe statutes, not isolated provisions.".....Had Congress meant to limit tax credits to state exchanges, it likely would have done so in the definition of an 'applicable taxpayer' or in some other prominent manner.".....It would not have used such a winding path of connect-the-dots provisions about the amount of the credit." In summation, Chief Justice John G. Roberts Jr. adjudicated that "tax credits are available to individuals in states that have a federal exchange."

Dissenting, Justice Antonin Scalia commented that, "When judges take it upon themselves to "fix" a law — or to bless an executive "fix" — they diminish political accountability by encouraging Congress to be sloppy. And they bypass the political process established by the Constitution's separation of powers, arrogating to itself — and the executive — the power to amend legislation......This leads to bad laws, bad policy outcomes and fosters the cynical belief that "law is politics." In further dissent, he stated that the "quite absurd" SCOTUS decision would now "publish forever the discouraging truth that the Supreme Court of the United States favors some laws over others and is prepared to do whatever it takes to uphold and assist its favorites," and since the SCOTUS "rewrites the law to make tax credits available everywhere. We should start calling this law SCOTUScare."

In short, SCOTUS was called upon to do a major edit and re-write of a **Healthcare Reform** book-long, 1990-page legislative bill that was passed, but never edited or even once read by its supposed Congressional authors. Kudos to the court, they should have been paid double time and a half for their effort; and those bonus funds should have been deducted from Congressional pay checks for lack of due diligence. Exemplar of legality and precedent aside – well, as they say in New York City, shut up and "forgetaboutit". Time and circumstances of migratory economics move on, and evolutional adaptations inevitably continue. The ACA danced the side step to a not so creative "pass the buck to the next year" fiscal stability routine, and more than a few prominent procrastinated events yet whirled and pirouetted afoot to sunset in 2017. However, there would be neither chance nor opportunity for the Supreme Court to further wordsmith confusing wording in the ACA. SCOTUS judges could not once again mount up to ride their stallions to the rescue of a formerly progressive majority in Congress by rescinding more than a few ultimately important and transforming scheduled events on the coming action plan agenda such as Cadillac Plans, State Exchanges, Essential Benefits, and Reinsurance Bailout Programs. All of these items would be shortly and suddenly laid out on the federal fiscal butcher's chopping block. Money, Money, Money, it always was and will be about the Money – migratory ecolo-nomics driving **Healthcare Reform**.

2015 sang "Happy Golden Anniversary" to Medicare and Medicaid. Medicaid, originally a means tested program linked to public welfare, previously celebrated the Clinton Administrations 1996 Welfare Reform Act, officially the Personal Responsibility and Work Opportunity Reconciliation Act of 1996, which approved demonstration programs that immediately provided coverage to 2.2 million citizens not receiving public welfare. At conception, however, federal Medicaid covered only five services: physician payments, hospital inpatient payments not including mental health or tuberculosis, outpatient hospital payments, x-ray and/or laboratory testing payments, and adult skilled nursing facilities payments. Waivers for optional services were added by the states along with increasing amount, duration and scope of coverages. The state **Healthcare Reforms** continually lowered patient eligibility requirements while adding benefits in a shared-cost federally-matching system. Simple economics, increasing supply increases demand. For its fiftieth birthday, Medicaid celebrated number one status, the largest government healthcare program ever, and 69 million enrollees including coverage extended to over half of all long term care expenses and approximately half of all births in the USA. One out of every three California residents became covered by Medicaid and one out of every three USA citizens became covered by Medicaid or Medicare. Medicare, originally not a means tested program, celebrated the hope of reducing program expenditures by raising the cost of yearly premiums to those individual enrollees claiming more than $85,000 in annual income and to partnered couple enrollees claiming more than $170,000 in annual incomes. Nonetheless, projected future healthcare expenses for the USA were expected to consume 20% of the nation's economy.

Just as the historical Jim Crow Laws proved that poverty begets poverty, welfare of today begets welfare and diversity groups beget diversity groups with a generational lower standard of living for themselves. All chambers of political pundits express concern, but none offer truly workable solutions to alter the generational habituation. There are three obvious escape routes to offer healthy and able welfare recipients that have, can and will correct their unfortunate propagandized non-biological cognitive dissonance of resistance to change.

Number one is through higher education of and for academically qualifying individuals such as special or charter schools for the gifted and practical technical schools that permit satisfactory paying productive job opportunities in and out of the generational stagnant community for those less academically inclined. Number two is through entrepreneurial businesses started in the communities with the help of government grants that eventually expand the businesses in and beyond the niche welfare community level. Number three is, unfortunately, through some type of organized crime leadership that actually generationally suppresses and further disenfranchises others in the particular clustered welfare recipient group.

Remember that now ancient but formerly inspiring Presidential sentence, "If you like your Health Plan, you can keep it ….then…. if your insurance plan allows it"? Well perhaps one could temporarily keep that presidential proclamation, but not for long past Christmas 2016, as those words were set-forward to expire on January 1, 2017. At that time, an expensive list of the ACA's mandated benefits would come to realization for all insurance corporations desirous of continuing to sell their product. For example, employers with over 50 full time equivalent (FTE) workers would be unhappily mandated to offer insurance coverage. The new insurance product would naturally be more expensive and unfortunately too expensive for some people's pocket books. Also scheduled for 2017 was the elimination of the "high risk pool" set up for individuals with expensive-to-treat per-existing health conditions. All insurance buyers would have to share the cost to level out a dollar-green velvet playing field on the 2017 craps table. Working towards those ends, spikes in health plan premiums during 2015 were simply anticipatory precautions advised by every insurance corporation's actuary department. Bronze plans were up by 3.4% and Silver Plans were up by 5.8%, but they were only omens of double digit increases to come, especially for the aforementioned plans when their deductibles would be lowered to meet the new ACA standards. Then, the growing number of underinsured would be incentivized to create a sub-crisis of their own.

The Reinsurance Bailout Programs would wind down in 2017. Health insurance corporations would lose the ability to rely on the government and further American citizen taxation to cover specific reinsurance for "stop losses", thus ending the postponing an additional rate hike for the insured or group of insured. Additionally, individual claims amounting to from $45,000 to $250,000 per year would no longer be 100% covered by federal funds on New Year's Day 2017. Yes, the premium price naturally would increase; but future federal funding may not be kind enough to sufficiently cover those higher costs, thus permitting a migratory ecolo-nomic crisis in the healthcare marketplace. There would be rational abandonment, especially among the poor. One year more would not soften the blow. Come 2018, "Cadillac" health plans – worth greater than $10,200 per individual or $27,500 per family –would be subjected to a 40% tax and create even more unhappy people.

Back in 2006, the George Bush administration created Medicare Part D, an unfunded pharmacy benefit at that time which contained a coverage limit gap, a "Doughnut Hole" for an individual's total drug spending in a progressively variable range from about $2000 to $6000. It was felt that out-of-pocket purchases in these ranges would make people more aware and particularly careful about healthcare spending, thus avoiding the additional cost of "Insurance Hazzard". The ACA offered a federal subsidy rebate of $250 and a 50% discount on "brand name" drugs for seniors falling into that coverage gap and promised to totally eliminate the gap with very apparent unfunded federal subsidies by 2020.

That imaginary planned funding would come from cutbacks, a crackdown on supposedly excessive Medicare payments to Physicians and Hospitals. This planned assumption doggedly admitted that the ACA must increasingly depend on Medicare cuts to pay for the future planned subsidies. The congressional Business Office (CBO) predicted that Medicare funds will be cut to the tune of $153 Billion by 2025. Such a future scenario was quite unlikely to logically reason, as medical costs will continue to predictably rise in spite of future savings, at a time when expensive medical specialty services will be crowded out of ACA coverage. Rather than achieving a promise to cut deficits by one trillion dollars, the ACA actually hiked up deficits over the short term with no hope in sight for realistic and transparent future decreases over the long term.

The 25% or 30% or 40% or 44% (depending on the poll) of USA residents without insurance that previously provided the overburdened final straw on the Camel's back to originally pass the PPACA may very well return to the ranks of uninsured residents 5-10 years after the date of the **Healthcare Reform's** original passage. This very predictable resurgence of Medicine burden will spark its own new Money crisis if and when the tax payer funded federal subsidies dry up. Universal single payer federally funded and administered health insurance coverage must and will ultimately rise to its destined and proper place of prominence for Mankind. The USA's methodological nationalism, after over a century of procrastination hallmarked by governmental delays and obstructions, will finally join the "one world" global community of people acceptance and ultimately enact a federal single payer plan, which will once again provide for the evolution of a world-renowned dual standard of healthcare delivery.

MIGRATORY ECONOMIC FACTORS & PATTERNS EVOLVING MAN, MONEY & MEDICINE

PART EIGHT

GTO ERA ADAPTATIONS & THE ART OF LIVING
"DR. WATSON" & THE HEALTH SAFETY NET
THE ENTITLEMENT RIGHT TO WORK

The fifth overlapping migratory medical ecolo-nomic generation, from 2030 to 2050, will be a technology-driven "GTO" era of medical practice. The utilization of Nano-Histone Codes will hallmark the paradigm as a Healthcare Reform watershed event.

"I fear the day that technology will surpass our human interaction.
The world will have a generation of idiots." -- Albert Einstein

A patient-driven entitlement-right Universal Health migratory ecolo-nomic culture signet-sealed an authentication for the reestablishment of century-old ecosystem changes and various levels of academically and on-the-job trained ancillary healthcare providers. A myriad of licensed independent practice non-physician primary care medical services resurfaced as they once existed in the United States before the time of the Flexner Report, but now dynamically competing, highly trained and accredited. Additionally spurred on by exponentially increasing technological advances, the 100-year-old artificially created USA paradigm of allopathic, homeopathic and osteopathic physician exclusivity, which had resulted in insufficient numbers of physicians to care for reasonable medically necessary conditions, finally evolved into a genetic transformation of medical practice modalities and healthcare delivery systems/mechanisms/modalities to include a variety of healthkeepers, all working towards a common goal.

Major Healthcare Reform proposals nearly identical to those recommended by the 1923 Committee on the Cost of Medical Care (CCMC) again surfaced due to an economically unstable piecemeal federal-global system. The migratory medical ecolo-nomic landscape sparkled with electronic gadgetry utilized by a never-before experienced aged world community of computer-savvy elderly patients energetically seeking immediate access to mass optimal-care proven cost-effective diagnosis and treatment algorithms and technological mechanisms. However, admonitions and reproofs concerning newly-developed healthcare delivery catechisms continually sought the public eye, as they had been repeatedly viewed ever since the millennium of ancient times:

Aulus Cornelius Celsus, the leading physician of ancient Rome, warned that, "Before accepting any belief one ought to follow reason as a guide, for credulity without enquiry is a sure way to deceive oneself."
Then renaissance-wise Paracelsus added, "The art of Medicine cannot be inherited, nor can it be copied from books; it must be digested many times and many times spat out; one must always review it and knead it thoroughly, and one must be alert while learning it; one must not doze like peasants turning over pears in the sun."

Alfred Marshall's classic treatise, Principles of Economics, emphasized a second essential part to understanding the study of economics -- the study of "Man". In order to effectively accomplish his endowed economic right to the pursuit of happiness, primitive Man hunted and scavenged for survival, feasted and consumed by his sacred fire, and told-illustrated (often in poetic song) fantastic stories of his past and imagined future. His ancient primal nature was certainly not to be solely a creature of leisure and entitlement; if leisure and entitlement were his primary prime directives, he would have vanished in extinction from planet earth eons ago. Once a great warrior-hunter, Man now rules planet earth as a worker and artistic-technological adventurer. His primal basic need to "hunt-eat-tell and illustrate" is now replaced by his current need to "work-consume-portray and create". Economists constantly debated cost-effect economic acceptance versus societal appropriateness of switching relative or proportional percentages in leisure and entitlement time devoted to each of those three basic needs as they had evolved and will continue to evolve. Unbalancing socio-political economic norms invokes unanticipated consequences. Compromising one economic and primal need for the favor of another evokes an emotional response that overpowers migratory ecolo-nomic logic in political decision-making. Redistribution of wealth might seem to be accompanied in the political arena by a concomitant redistribution of leisure and entitlement, but the former is much more easily accomplished than the latter. A work versus leisure versus perform-create economic leisure-entitlement paradox may not be a paradox at all, but rather a basic and fundamental mechanism for Man's endowed pursuit of happiness, through which the "joie de vivre" and the "art of living" truly endear themselves as reasonable and accomplishable humanistic needs and desires.

The harsh basic beastly nature of primitive Man and his basic primitive economic of self-interest is simply sublimated in civilized society. The realization of primitive Man's heart of happiness happening in the hottest heat of his hungriest hunt and his primitive addictive intoxication to combat with his fellow Man can yet be experienced comfortably and be seen acceptingly sublimated in modern Man's sport and artistic activities. Societal rule and regulations curb migratory economic self-interest in return for the traded and economically bargained improved healthy survival for all of Mankind, and most especially for a healthy individual Man's enhanced opportunity to gain migratory economic success. While overcoming the perils, risks and violence of hunting for survival, the species of Man has also undergone a culling to selectively grant adaptive dynamic competitive advantage to those of the human race who could and would best economically procure and maintain a reproducible future generation. All life is short and culminated in a death that is certain, but feared only by that aforesaid species most commonly known as "Man" and none other. His independent cognitive reasoning also assigns him the horror of self-pity that is shared by no other life-form on planet earth. Man continually strives to allay, put aside and calm his primal fear of death and self-pity through various religious and societal means. Thus one can painfully and obviously observe a mental confusion that exists as a not-so-easy choice: the choice between fame and fortune or heroism and thus achieving sublimated immortality versus the choice to not risk the adventures of economic sublimated warfare nor fame, the choice to live a safer but unrecorded life and be forever forgotten in the unknown future of Man's existence. Depending on migratory economic circumstance, few versus many would believe to naturally sacrifice all, all for the sake of glory, which sometimes becomes cognitively but incoherently evaluated to be worth more than one Man's miraculous life. Under such circumstances, sake of migratory ecolo-nomic principal, religion or other habitual learned belief patterns then become more important and psychologically overriding than any fear of death.

Although sometimes greatly questioned with sincere introspection, Man is a somewhat sapient being, thus a "Homo sapiens" as his genus and species classification. As such, Man possesses a cognitive awareness, a realization of ephemeral mortality that no other living creature on planet earth can claim or appreciate. This high degree of contemplative intelligence leads Man to question a reason for his existence, a "raison d'être" or sole ultimate purpose. He unconsciously and sometimes consciously demands of himself, "Donne moi seulemont une raison d'être". Sadly, since he cannot simply, readily, and/or logically and convincingly answer even one part of that great universal question of "Why" for his existence, his natural built-in psycho-mental ego defense mechanisms generally offer him three or four possible solutions:

1. Choose to become eternally immortal through some spiritual sort of existences or through some unproven "scientific" prognostication.
2. Choose to be eternally remembered as a physical form of existence through enduring famous (and sometimes infamous) actions and accomplishments or simply through progeny.
3. Choose to be eternally insignificant and forgotten by simply and only seeking and enjoying the here-and-now pleasures and joys of limited mortality to the maximum of personal self-satisfaction.
4. Of course, permutations and/or combinations of the aforesaid three choices are also possible, and also the most probable.

Defense of personal property and territorial boundaries with deadly force stayed and maintained unquestioned rules or laws invented for the continual migratory economic survival of an individual clan of Man, and they are questionably advanced in modern societies to states of national and international migratory economic competition sometimes leading to frank warfare for defense of migratory economic principal. Total self-destruction logically remained an inconceivable concept, but for only a limited time in Man's ancient history. By splitting an atom in Enrico Fermi's "A-Bomb", Man has had the ability to instantly destroy his entire of planet ever since 1949. One might reasonably conclude that thereafter, the notion of war and the consequences of war would be seriously reevaluated and permanently curtailed; but this logical and well known unintended consequence of possible or inevitable total devastation has not stopped advancing Man's illogical concept of war, especially when advanced and fortified by unreasonable totalitarian habit or religious belief.

Furthermore, fear not or fear for more, for Man may yet expresses his primal primitive urges, instincts, and directives in spite of a morass of dependency in several of today's societies. Certain possible adverse migratory economic outliers and outcomes do need to be accounted for and understood. If the purpose of Man's invented migratory economic philosophy for peaceful co-existence with others of his kind and happy unquestioned acceptance of his relatively short lifespan amount to full acknowledgement of his universal insignificance and rejection of any thought or notion that he might be able to economically change anything beyond his immediate control, then enjoyment and migratory economic contentment within the "art of living" may require an a priori rejection of power, control, wealth, and social status. Such an economic rejection certainly provokes direct conflict with Man's basic bestial primitive nature, which also naturally selects for a strict and enforced-respected economic division of labor, status and wealth according to what he as an individual can most economically and efficiently accomplish for himself and/or provide for the sustainable success of his primitive tribe. Some may also argue that the nature of such an economic status rejection is not feasible or even remotely possible in today's celebrity driven, oriented and worshiped society. Celebrity was restricted to original production intellectuals in the ancient worlds, who by their thoughts and writings gained wealth, power, and a sense of immortality; today the American spectator society celebrates the actors and not the script. The wealth abandonment notion may also be based on historical migratory economic circumstances that may not be as relevant for the migratory economics of an evolved and evolving society where the migratory economic concepts of labor, work and **Healthcare Reform** have been drastically altered:

In the mid 1800's, John Stuart Mill admonished that labor was indeed a basic prerequisite for economic production in his *Principles of Political Economy*, but he also foresaw a future time in advanced technical production and social progress when the "Art of Getting On" would take a secondary role to the "Art of Living". The "need to work" and Herbert Spencer's economic "survival of the fittest" or "Social Darwinism" concepts may be or actually are extinct migratory economic concepts in Man's more modern yet still evolving industrialized societies where there is really no great daily struggle for economic subsistence. The historic necessary evil of an unemployed lower class just may, due to modern Man's ever-advancing technologically, just may evolve into a reasonable and necessary, good and wonderful opportunity for humanism and the "At of Living" to embrace and enjoy. Karl Marxian concepts of destitute workers being forced to revolt because they were unable to compete for basic human rights against the influence of industrial capitalists may all have to be put aside when a nation finally attains the ability to provide sustainable stability in feasible economic production with a less than a 14% work force, and/when at the same time that same nation provides adequate harmonious entitlements such as healthcare delivery to and for its non-working citizens. There has been an obvious decrease in the average hours worked per week by the masses of Man in industrialized societies, from over 100 hours in the 1700's, then 70 hours in the 1800's, next 40 hours in the 1900's, and to 30 hours or less in the budding 2000's.

Therefore, the obvious question certainly arises concerning primal drives and Man's willingness to abandon his instinctual "need" to work. An overabundance of leisure-consumption entitlement does not guarantee nor even result in contentment and happiness for Mankind. Man's instinctual need to hunt-work further evolves into a societal right-entitlement to be able to work, to be assured a job of some sort. Contentment in accordance with the "art of living" then arises when leisure-consumption time is consumed between "work versus portrayal-create". To accomplish this ideal, all citizens might be required to work a little less hard (politically termed less "smartly") and resultantly less productively for a relatively fewer number of hours per week, rather than require the severe decrease in the percentage of actual needed and vitally necessary workers to overtly manifest itself. Consider again the evolution of "Hunt-Eat-Tell and illustrate" to "Work-Consume-Portray and create" to possibly evolve further, and then draw a previously assumed "work–leisure-consumption–portray and create" paradox into an accepted, sustainable and stable accepted Alpha versus Beta migratory economic existence as commonly observed in wild wolves. The artificially derived conundrum of Man's differential appreciation of riches, freedom, and leisure may be solved by first admitting that during his entire short stay to play at the gaming table of life from his womb to his tomb, he is never totally equal to others of his species, neither in his natural abilities nor in his innate desires, with the dominance mixture of ability-desire factoring in as an independent migratory economic variable directed towards his economic or academic success to accomplish his personal and individualized chosen concept of the "art of living" and the "joie de vivre".

This resultant idealized "art of living" cannot possibly be enjoyed without an added consideration of another exquisitely important migratory economic factor: - - Man's adequate state of health and well-being. Virgil's "greatest wealth is health" understandably implies that health is also vitally necessary for the procurement of wealth. Work and leisure-consumption both look upon health, but again through emotionally and methodologically blinded rather than cognitively contemplative eyes. Without the exquisitely important ecolo-nomic of health, healthcare delivery, and migratory economic **Healthcare Reform** in proper balance, the remaining items on either essential priority for survival list, as well as Man's continued existence on planet earth, would be reduced to less than superfluous economic thought without action. What would Virgil say about Man's state of health today, where nowadays it may take near to all of one's wealth to just maintain one's health solely with direct healthcare delivery, and **healthcare's migratory medical ecolo-nomics seems to have become a purely political process with a mere suggestion of true health quality overtones**? Medical economic theory has certainly become encumbered by emotionally derived migratory socio-economic goals and visions. Just the thought of that unfortunate economic external consequence might have drawn strictly rigorous mathematical Vilfredo Pareto's ire and then frustrated his psyche enough to have him trip and fall over all his precision-perfect line and bar graph charts. After all, Pareto did admonish that the greed in self-interest and political profit-seeking can be either a constructive factor in production of economic goods or a destructive factor in the appropriation of goods produced by others e.g. (exempli gratia) the movie "Wall Street".

The documented historic capitalistic economic abundance of the USA has positively influenced and successfully driven other nations to also acquire economic wealth and influence. According to another father of economic theory, the English political economist David Ricardo, a nation's international influence is proportional to its economic worth, which can be designated by Ricardo's selected term, "capital". Thus, a nation's "capital" increases when total productivity exceeds total consumption, and vice versa. Consumption may be either productive, such as consumption by productive workers, or non-productive, such as consumption by non-workers or administrative workers. For a nation to retain and grow its true economic worth or "capital", taxation by its government can be offset by an increased economic productivity by its people or a diminished life style of the non-productive reflected as a decrease in unproductive and economically undesired consumption by all citizens. Therein lies the rub: A nation professing a dream of "liberty and justice for all" is formed by and for people who share a common economic dignity. The ideal economic policy of an imaginary utopian nation of free-willed people should optimally be driven to primarily satisfy that unifying communal economic dignity. There certainly is a duty on the part of any nation worth its salt to provide for the "humanistic and reasonably necessary" rights of the common Man so that a common citizen can live a free and healthful life that allows unimpaired equal economic opportunity that can lead to the ability to pursue happiness through "the art of living". Those "humanistic and reasonably necessary" economic rights include a citizen's right to work without harness or harassment, while enjoying an economically "adequate" wage and the concomitant quality of healthcare delivery that can allow such work or leisure-creativity to feasibly and sustainably continue.

As the future will surely dictate, there will neither be enough well-paying jobs that are actually essential nor even slightly needed in Man's advancing industrial-technological times. Nonetheless, the USA's current federally-directed mass mores both fear and despise the possible unequal social consequences of culling public education to cater to the best and brightest of American students, even though such stratification of educational practices are recognized and practiced globally by other successfully competing industrialized nations. Federal educational policy in the USA is simply another poorly thought out capitalistic marketable commodity to over-fund lower level and lower standard public educational institutions, and then direct them (with their over-funded sparkling new gymnasiums, baseball, soccer, and football fields) to teach to the level of the slowest learner in the individual class-level of subject-matter curriculum. The overabundance of socially-accepted basic and rote educational classes emphasizing simplified subject-matter in the USA secondary-school system (that simply increases the number or percentage and not the quality of graduates) is an inevitable politically-driven result, an unfortunate nearly criminal offering to the inadequately educated masses. Too many American teenagers look to college as place to learn to drink, rather than a place to learn to think. Enrollment into a graduate education program could occur in the USA directly after secondary-school with a limited pass rate national exam-accredited secondary-school diploma as is readily accomplished in the rest of the world; for instance, France offers a Baccalaureate, a national secondary-school (*lycée*) diploma. Graduate school pre-requisites can also be achieved quite efficiently and cost-effectively through the Internet without the overly-expensive cultural commodity "need" of formal enrollment in a specific and costly geographical-physical location (with an expensive stadium and football franchise). Continually taxing and increasing the funding to the migratory economic commodity of presently-designed public educational institutions without changing the "modus operandi" of their basic educational processes, and then expecting to produce a greater percentage of American leaders in ever-advancing science and industry is, well, here is a quote from one of the greatest thinkers of the 20th Century, Albert Einstein: "Insanity: doing the same thing over and over again and expecting a different result."

This pathetic systematic educational process in the USA has been "set in stride" by tenured academia that prefer the redundant repetitious catechistic "easy way out" rather than true entrepreneurial liberal art development. Didactic memorization becomes a standard for a degree and advancement rather than the immense creative expression of Man's imagination. A cookbook does not define the culinary expertise of a renown executive chef; a manual of directions cannot describe the achievements of an entrepreneurial technological genius. "The only thing interfering with my thinking is my education" – Albert Einstein

Ok, politics may be the theory and practice of influencing other people, but look what masochistic and self-hate consequence so often results from pushing some philosophical concept such as "higher education" for all without pre-planning and thoroughly examining those consequences of a political action: The USA's progressive "higher" educational system tends to de-emphasize the sciences and real-life vocational training and instead innovates or more truthfully manufactures useless college degree majors whose subject matter could only be destined to satisfy some non-existent and imaginary job market. The victims of this progressively liberal educational system are those "highly educated" American youths who remain stagnant in their opportunity for upward mobility and predominantly unemployed. They are victims of the progressive mushroom treatment – having been kept in the dark and fed a line of horse manure or bull dung.

American "higher educational systems" have taken one giant step further in prejudicially inhibiting a law-abiding citizen from recouping those disadvantages suffered under the tutelage of the aforementioned secondary-school programs and programming. The best American colleges and especially the finest and world-renowned American university graduate divisions offer unique college admission advantage to foreign educated students in deference to similarly or slightly less qualified American secondary-school graduates. Without an affirmative action program that preferentially selects for home-grown albeit slightly less prepared American students for admission to the USA's Top 20 Colleges and Universities, neither adequate nor sufficient numbers of trainable home-grown American citizens will end up locally ready, willing and available to take charge of future top-leading capital-generating corporations for the advancement of forefront technological or business entrepreneurial projects. The Gordian's knot to the conundrum reveals a migratory economic paradigm that evolved quite uniquely: Blindly marching onward into a valley of American cultural degradation, a pair of unusual, strange, and odd if not dumb and dumber bedfellows – liberal academic progressivism linked and shackled to capitalistic mass commodity sales, in the name of foreign cultural exchange and foreign academic diversity promulgation, was let to run amuck; yet that enormous debt was and is all paid from the resultant decreased savings accumulated by financially independent individuals among the USA taxpayers. The migratory economic of methodological nationalism in education ignores economic pluralism as one-sided intellectual stagnation holds back, condemns and decries a multiple perspective approach. Perhaps the USA educational dilemma is just another national border problem that a "don't fence me in" progressive political migratory economic agenda has blindly listed as taboo.

America will be forced to depend, as it has always depended, on an inexcusable and disgraceful fallback plan, a pitiable position that continually imports the majority of the USA's very top scientific intelligentsia. Individuals culled to become top honor students in foreign educational systems will continue to infiltrate the American medical establishment at all levels of healthcare delivery. This migratory economic paradigm directly influences **Healthcare Reform**: Foreign born or trained physicians will soon comprise 50% or more of all practicing physicians in the USA, and that percentage will continue to increase if no affirmative action is taken to evolve the migratory economic paradigm of American educational commoditization. Perhaps there is also an unintentional yet welcomed culling of herded American citizens to select for those who "leisure-portray-create" while legitimately unemployed and entitled to the benefits and rights of a humanistic life. Quite unfortunately, there is definitely some difficulty in properly distinguishing and isolating those particularly valued citizens in American society from other rather despicable and truly non-productive "leisure-entitlement only" fully able-to-work citizens and residents who purposely choose to feed solely from and upon the labor of others. A natural and not unexpected resentment by the productive and creative societal segments, be they working class or not, is directed toward those "entitlement only" individuals who are continually munching at the "public tax paid for" government-provided troughs. Although this nationalistic-capitalistic attitude cannot be overlooked, its political relevance and power is only slight and really ineffective. By stark comparison, the increasing political power brought to bear by the sheer numbers of those forever on entitlement programs in an equal-vote democracy cannot be overlooked or over emphasized; for that segment of society has become able to exert a most powerful if not overly powerful political economic policy influence. Several divergent coffers beg to be filled in the essential process of securing sustainable economic power for a nation. The delicate balance in determining a taxation percentage or amount is therefore a critical element for the continued economic growth of a nation. Too little taxation cannot maintain the mass psyche for "reasonable and necessary" public welfare and quality mass healthcare delivery. Extreme taxation to redistribute the wealth of a nation will first psychologically impair entrepreneurial migratory economic production and then stifle national production and decrease national productive consumption, ultimately leading to an overwhelming and rapidly inappropriate increased national unproductive consumption, unfortunately much more than the sustainable economic worth or health and well-being of a nation or its individual citizens can or will for long sustainably tolerate.....

Too much and undue attention to the correction of the aforementioned might risk leading one down the path to a shallow, uncaring and anti-social economic imperialism that would also destroy the renown American "art of living". Whenever opportunity knocks, a sustainable and successful migratory economic system must be resilient yet flexible enough to temporally stem any politico-economic storm and easily vacillate between a dedicated over-righteous, rigid conservative constitutionalism and a crude, rude-raging social-totalitarianism; yet ultimately the system must admit that all migratory economic positions are ultimately taken for the same exquisitely similar migratory economic reason. An ideal economic system best capable for providing for the "art of living" should balance true Alfred Marshall theorism with a Vilfredo Pareto mathematical resource-allocationism, and definitely not draw future migratory economic policy-making decisions from inappropriate past histories of migratory economic paradigms that may not be applicable in Mankind's advancing technological future. (First, remember from the future. -- Ralzak)

Remembering that the "wealth of nations rests in the confidence of their peoples" (Adam Smith), and realizing that a social-economic decadent society is an undisciplined society that has abandoned a "constitutional way of life", too many political pundit soothsayers predict Mankind's eventual doom, gloom and destruction. But, combining David Ricardo's deductivism with Adam Smith's inductive reasoning as a rudimentary course of migratory economic thought, it is possible to substantially stabilize and knead successively sustainable mixtures of Man's primitive drives folded with his economic desires into a desirable loaf of economically sustainable bread. Informed and understanding actuation of Man's selfish personal industrial interests in concert with his advanced societal humanistic interests in the "art of living" can make such a loaf baked to be not only palatable but certainly possible. Such a vital and critical migratory economic titration with compromise allows adequate sympathy for that delicate degree of national cultural health/wellness equality through appropriate **Healthcare Reform**. The accurate titration supports that critical balance which maintains the necessary spin of capitalism, prevents tipping over a national economy, stops decreasing a nation's economic worth, and maintains the health and well-being of a nation's peoples. However, there must be an enforced insistence on individual responsibility and disgust for politically oriented pundits who claim all ultimately unrewarding decisions and outright mistakes to be the errors or unintended consequences derived solely from those other than themselves.

Perhaps way back in 1705, Bernard Mandeville's book The Fable of the Bees, which told of private vices conflicting with public benefits (taxes), the supreme logic of Mother Nature adequately and logically explained this entire business of busy buzzy-buzzing clamor over politico-social controversies. Shortly thereafter, Jacques Turgot's *Reflections* told of three natural public economic divisions: procurers, developers and owners, in a society where the true wealth rested in the net taxable products of land and natural resources that were bartered and traded with little governmental involvement in a "laissez faire, laissez passer" economy. The concepts of taxation for "entitlement" and a humanitarian right to an "art of living" were non-existent. Five centuries later, governmental "big brotherism" aside, modern-day citizens, who apparently choose to wear horse-head blinders that blot out the total environmental experience, still steadfastly remain truly confounded that a limited budget generates a difficult balance. An individual's right to an entitlement becomes measured against a population group's right to an entitlement, and that already bedazzled public citizenry carefully watches, argues and ultimately gets stung by one of Mandeville's bees during and among the untidy and shaky balancing act between taxes and public benefits.

Per historical prime directive, economist Alfred Marshall's "Man" has also been emotionally compelled to blindly confuse and falsely overrate the importance of unique direct healthcare delivery economic commodities to the deference of unique indirect preventive measures. Fiscal planners had to reconsider the financial consequences of such an economic decision in light of other methods to more effectively attain True Health Quality. For instance, the logical evaluation of increased and increasing direct healthcare delivery expenditures, especially in the maternal environment, has always been conflicted within Man's natural behavioral migratory economic forces in both national and local fiscal planning for True Health Quality. Federalist demands versus states desires versus individual citizen "rights" and "authority" to control direct healthcare delivery have also repeatedly bedazzled a national and global audience and stifled the emergence of logical and timely migratory economic thought for **Healthcare Reform**. For example, medical-political economists applied a simple metric to economist Frederic Bastiat admonitions: Immediate birth outcomes are obviously seen, but their foreseeable future medical outcomes and additional societal expenditures are emotionally set aside by the human spirit and therefore not foreseen. The economic versus societal appropriateness of switching relative or proportional expenditure percentages between each of the evolved entities in direct and indirect expenses unbalances socio-political economic norms, invokes unanticipated consequences, and compromises one economic for the favor of another. That evoked emotion has in the past overpowered migratory economic logic in political decision making. Therefore, given the restraints of a limited budget, solely increasing funding for direct healthcare delivery processes in the maternal environment was not the proper migratory economic or True Health Quality outcome route to take, for simply increasing direct healthcare delivery processes may have been "much to do about nothing" when it came to substantially improving birth outcomes and overall True Health Quality outcomes for the USA. In no way was it or is it suggested that nothing further should or could be done to enhance technical and direct delivery processes; but rather an additional course had to be and must be also charted with guaranteed funding, utilizing experience and foresight, to insure that what best could be done within the bounds of the economy was in fact done, to most assuredly and most effectively improve and sustain future True Health Quality outcomes. Critical examination of the aforesaid pre direct healthcare delivery processes, such as smoking cessation, diabetes and obesity in the maternal environment as well as each and every other health and well-being environmental issue during a pregnancy had to be addressed, and in fact when are now commonly addressed save an overwhelming amount of future funding that would have gone to pay for the unfortunate ultimate lifetime of expenditures due to an overabundance of poor birth outcomes.

Federalism is the theory or advocacy of federal principles for dividing powers between member units and common institutions. In the United States, federalism is understood to be an evolving relationship between the federal and state governments. USA Federalism arose from progressive pundits' discontent with the Articles of Confederation, because they focused on constitutionally limiting the power, size and authority of the federal government. Modern Federalists continue to advocate for progressivism and **Healthcare Reform** arguments that revolve about constitutional versus progressive beliefs as well as state versus federal authority over healthcare delivery and medical practitioner/insurance corporation licensing.

Again, direct healthcare delivery continues to remain an obvious unique sellable service, a commodity whose migratory economic consequences have been and are, per historical prime directive, continually emotionally confused in fiscal planning. A commodity is delivered through commerce. As economist David Ricardo pointed out in his "Principles" (1817), "The end of all commerce is to increase production", a cyclic function. The result of increasing the funding for direct healthcare delivery becomes the need for more funding. The resolution of the migratory economic consequences for the "commerce" aspect of healthcare delivery in the USA, like federalism, has led to political pundit pandering, in which an unwillingly created group of philosophically opposing members find themselves bound together by covenant with a governing representative head.

Economic responsibility for healthcare is constitutionally divided between a central governing authority and constituent political units which both now face the added and further policy changing dimension of globalization. This migratory economic of globalization in **Healthcare Reform** is necessary not only for healthcare delivery but also for national defense and readiness for natural or technologically constructed global viral epidemics. Historic advances in progressivism in the USA have dynamically challenged a decentralized healthcare delivery system based on individual care to evolve into an integrated central governmental system by organizing not only the migratory economics but also the methodology of the healthcare delivery service rendered. Again, albeit important lessons that can be learned from reviewing historical perspectives may not be relevant in an ever-changing dynamic for future healthcare delivery planning. The evolution of this migratory ecolo-nomic healthcare delivery paradigm has had a rough and winding course over the past century. Federalist authority and perception of economic realities have risen and fallen in cultural importance, dynamically changing political adventure and often political misadventure. Final resolution can only come through compromise, and achieving that compromise becomes a new conundrum, while and when economic, political and religious forces continue to persist in the performance of open battle before the USA's aforementioned bedazzled public audience and now an added global audience.

Migratory medical ecolo-nomic forces of unresolved and unaccepted evolutionary constraints herd population masses akin to blindly leading unknowing sheep to slaughter, thus compelling the masses to totally allay themselves with divergent political-philosophical "isms". Single Sided Federalism battles against Institutional Federalism. Bail-out economic policies for corporations and non-enlightened concepts "too big to fail or jail" argue and conflict with supposedly natural monetarism or Milton Freedman–like, recession recovery and reversal economic and medical economic philosophies. Improperly termed Keynesian stimulus packages to curtail short-term migratory economic hoarding in the USA vie with free market reassembly and emergence of a more competitive rebirth or phoenix economic philosophy. Almost uniquely in the United States, there is overspending in times of surplus and deficit borrowing spending for on-going and new stimulus packages along with increased taxation in times of recession. Tax revenues are not a god-sent; those revenues are derived predominantly from a portion of the hard-earned capital generated by the productive members of a nation. True John Maynard Keyes followers would advocate for rainy day savings in times of plenty to accumulate a substantial surplus that could be then used to provide migratory economic stimulus packages to an economy in times of recession and hoarding. But alas, remember that Alfred Marshall's second part of economic theory allows for "Man", in his questionably reasoned decision making, to conveniently forgive, forget and overlook obvious logical facts that surely have unintended consequences. Remember that along that same line of thought in 1850, economist Frederic Bastiat had also warned that the human spirit more readily gives credence to that which is immediately seen in deference to that which is not immediately seen, but can be easily foreseen. Bastiat taught that "the bad economist pursues a small present good, which will be followed by a great evil to come, while the true economist pursues a great good to come, at the risk of a small present evil". Therefore, ill-conceived but humanly understandable from a perverse point of view, the diverse multi-level governances of Constitutional Federalism (the states) continually beg and whine for bread and wine from their supposedly limited-supplied or scarce fiscal resourced central Federal Government to pay for economically non-prioritized, redundant, and functionally uncapped state-run programs (such as **Healthcare Reform** -- Medicaid and ACA). Worse yet, both state and federal governmental agencies concomitantly continue to borrow and spend like drunken sailors, like there is and forever will be no tomorrow. Admonished by Bastiat, those short-sighted politically-motivated migratory economic courses inevitably lead to an unsustainable medical economic future in healthcare delivery for both the individual states and the nation.

There have been many conflicts of interest - economic, political and moral - intertwined in the development of a single payer national health insurance plan for the USA. Additionally, all have taken various sides on the healthcare delivery issue, and all have been subjected to wear tunnel-vision blinders imposed by the constraining forces of methodological nationalism. The administrative and judicial framework of the Nation-State can no longer be the unique and only relevant boundary for determining both the methodology and delivery systems necessary for high quality and cost-effective healthcare delivery maintenance. When all sides of the healthcare delivery debate are torn away or ripped from some of the subjugating blinders of "methodological nationalism" by a desperate need for global cooperation to fight international plague and disease, a truer understanding of the total scope in migratory economic relations to achieve policy goals become untangled, undistorted and appropriately balanced. Ultimate globalization of all aspects of healthcare delivery introduces a worldwide interdependence and strips away all those previously fixed-premised blinders. Constitutional principles of federalism will still play a most important role, but should now be viewed from a multi-level perspective of both analysis and governance on a world-wide stage.

As already described, there are basic "art of living" priorities for the sustained existence of a cognitive species, sometimes referred to as the "joie de vivre" priorities of "MAN". Not in any prescribed order of necessity for such happy and enjoyable survival, they are -- self, health, property, fellow Man, and God. Health is an ephemeral and politically perceived state of physical, mental, and societal well-being. The United States is ranked 27th in longevity among industrialized nations, and the popular media touts this unexamined statistic as a deficiency in the American healthcare delivery system. Actually, all first generation immigrant groups in the USA enjoy a greater longevity with documented poorer healthcare delivery availability than the average white male born in the USA. Healthcare delivery, therefore, is only one small contribution that can be made towards overall health and well-being, but the service or perhaps commodity of direct healthcare delivery has always been held in penultimate importance because the commodity of direct healthcare delivery can be readily envisioned as a clearly defined produced marketable item, a potential for-profit item of goods and services that greatly satisfy politically perceived wants and needs of both individuals and populations. In that respect, direct healthcare delivery is now a unique sellable migratory economic commodity for any modern industrial culture and it always has been of migratory economic importance, ever since Mankind existed as a primitive hunter-gatherer scavenger cave culture. The migratory economic knowledge with a sellable commodity of chants and herbs from a primitive tribe's Medicine Man was often bartered and traded to maintain peaceful relationships among other tribes of Man. The knowledge and the commodity of modern Medicine is a traded migratory economic today to gain favor from third world nations. In Man's modern industrialized society, direct healthcare delivery is not given gratis; it is a migratory economic commodity traded in various forms through purchases or taxation; and technologically advanced direct healthcare delivery can cost nearly all your wealth in order for you to maintain your health and well-being -- remember how Virgil described health and wealth. Today, Man is seemingly faced with a healthcare delivery conundrum. People are turned against each other as individuals and a society and constantly argue about "what to do" versus "how to do it". Healthcare delivery coverage vies with healthcare delivery access in every stratum of modern societies. The never-ending debate is always about political extremes of progressivism versus conservatism, where federal progressive reform in an evolving humanistic society is contrasted to fundamental and inalienable constitutional reforms. Federalism seems to be at war or at least warring with itself in each and every of the many obvious and sometimes secluded hills and valleys of "**Healthcare Reform**".

Looking at the USA through some historical perspective lenses aimed at the evolutionary healthcare delivery tree, privatization of medically-necessary direct healthcare delivery mutated apart from **Healthcare Reform** as a side evolutionary branch that eventually dried up, became brittle, and then broke off as a significant player for the masses on the national and global scene. Organized direct healthcare delivery or managed care was that part of a bough closer to the evolutionary trunk, yet able to carry nutrients from a vitalizing sap, which then blessed that system with a nimbleness to bend and withstand breakage. When the bough of organized direct healthcare delivery was severely bent, the system was less likely to break. That bough withstood evolutionary change, remodeled itself into a new trunk-shaped functional form and provided new channels for the osmotic flow of nutrients back to the main trunk of the evolutionary tree. In accordance with such an analogy, the trunk of the tree always was and always will be continuing to produce new and effective health advancements through governmentally controlled general public healthcare services, entrepreneurial private services, and various other healthcare delivery services, policies, and measures.

The part of tree trunk sap that initially explored and still seeks true **Healthcare Reform** is the USA's Public Health Service. The U.S. Public Health Service (PHS), so named in 1912, evolved from a former original species, the Federal Marine Hospital Service, a legacy to President John Adams' 1798 **Healthcare Reform** "Act for the Sick and Disabled Seamen". In 1902 the major health-related migratory economic emergency concern to public health was to immediately prevent diseases entering the USA by way of Ellis Island. A Public Health and Marine Hospital Service urgently dispatched examination and quarantine officers to sort out the immigrants as previously described. A few cases of Ebola in 2014 had the same impact on the public health system. The very first and penultimate important newly-named PHS mission was and is to contain communicable diseases: TB, Leprosy, Hookworm and Malaria led the original list that demanded an improved water supply along with sanitation and sewage disposal. The PHS role soon unobtrusively expanded into other vital fields such as the control of venereal disease; the PHS became the medical arm of scientific social safety assurance. Expansion of the PHS eventually led to the **Healthcare Reform** creation of the Centers for Disease Control and Prevention (CDC) and the National Institutes of Health (NIH). The Public Health Service quietly and quite secretly provided stability for a source of continual new growth atop that evolutionary healthcare delivery tree trunk. The public health service doctors and scientists were and are the secret service, the schutz schiessen of **Healthcare Reform**. They were and are the true, trusted, and unselfish national-defense healthkeepers of the nation. Immunization, antibiotic, and vitamin research was and is accomplished quietly and effectively. The rapid increase in Americans living to over 100 years of age in the 21st Century is the end result of PHS programs. The PHS administered continued advancements in public hygiene and safety, as well as reduction of environmental and personal injury accidents through public health measures and PHS research into societal health management of tobacco usage and AIDS. Migratory economic **Healthcare Reform** has allowed some needed branching of the PHS into a federal funding body, the United States Department of Health and Human Services (HHS). The future will soon realize and appreciate the original military origin of the PHS and see that all evolving migratory economic branches of that evolutionary healthcare delivery tree will need to report to and be a part of the United States Department of Homeland Security (DHS) network.

Yet sadly to remember once again, the World Health Organization (WHO) rates the USA 27th among industrialized countries in maintaining a satisfactory performance level of true health and longevity status for its residents. The WHO states that the USA is in need of **Healthcare Reform** to correct the problem. This unfortunate conclusion may be an inductive leap from a false premise. On a national or world stage, the true meaning of the term "Health" is that aforementioned combined state of physical, mental and social well-being. Longevity is one small part and is usually influenced by factors outside of the **Healthcare Reform** arena. The many and varied determinates of health can be broken down into metrics and monitored accordingly with Direct Healthcare Delivery being only one metric in the determinate of a nation's health and well-being. The relative importance of these metrics deserves exploration through available data sets. By doing such an analysis, one can readily develop milestones of meaningful and measurable monitored metrics and measures that can best and most cost-effectively enable a future filled with a sustainably enhanced true Health Quality and greater longevity for the USA.

There are some interesting data and statistics concerning the USA's immigrant population. As previously stated, regardless of nationality, race, or gender and with proven decreased access to established direct healthcare delivery systems, all immigrant groupings in the USA enjoy a greater longevity than the average USA–born white male. Therefore, disparities in true Health Quality are not all primarily the result of disparities in direct healthcare delivery access in the USA. There are many important metrics for true Health Quality that have lacked and truly deserve a greater scrutiny and a more appropriate funding. Survivorship or longevity consistently varies among geographical zip codes across the USA. Residential

Zip Codes within as short a distance as 10 miles from each other continually and consistently report near to 30 years' differences in longevity such as 61 years to 89 years in average survival. Residents living adjacent to commercial ports and busy freeways suffer twice the average incidence of lung disease and cancer. 16 ships burning bunker fuel pollute as much as one million cars. Violence, addiction, and substance abuse regularly and routinely murder American youth every single day. Poor nutritional and poor exercise choices have caused an epidemic of obesity, heart disease and diabetes. Air pollution and all types of smoking (direct first hand, indirect second hand, and third hand tobacco specific nitrous amines) consistently lead to prematurity, premature deaths, impaired lung development, asthma, chronic obstructive pulmonary disease, cancer, heart disease and chronic inflammatory disabilities. A conscious and unconscious mass self-poisoning from direct and indirect varieties of air pollution along with food supply pollution from industrialization have been ignored insidious decadences leading to a population exhibiting ill-health, shortened lifespan and de facto mass suicide, a population acting much like a mindless herd of Lemmings. It is no wonder that so many economists have overtly questioned the feasibly and sustained migratory economic stability of blatantly ignoring environmental hazards.

When considering economics as a social discipline, there are definable disparities of health effects among geographically disadvantaged racial, ethnic, and socio-economic communities resulting from industrial and diesel borne particulate matter that cannot be overlooked. The concentration of these health and environmental economic modalities and their impact in certain communities versus other cleaner communities exacerbates the seriousness of this issue and also raises socio-economic environmental justice concerns.

On the other hand, there are realistic and opposing economic concerns regarding the sustained survival of vital industries that do provide for the public good in terms of living convenience economics and mass employment economics that severely affect a state and nations gross domestic product. A fundamentally capitalistic democracy must carefully walk along a tightrope that delicately balances the social discipline of economics in the art of living and increased healthy quality of life for a populous of individuals against the economics necessary to maintain a nation's gross domestic product. The economic consequences of the admixture must be delicately titrated. Both, the sustainable economic survival of the business community and the health economics of that aforementioned populous of individuals, require that careful mixing-titering process for an accepted cultural balance of ingredients. Man's entire planet is suffering from the effects of unbalanced economic policy alignment; the citizens of every nation deserve to live in a healthier world that can maximally prolong their physical and mental longevity. The exciting and wondrous reunifying social discipline theme in interdisciplinary economics hopes to exquisitely balance that potentially pernicious walk along the precarious economic tightrope.

Direct Healthcare Delivery is, of course, a very important additional metric for measuring true Health Quality performance. Along with measuring and monitoring this metric should naturally follow "everyone's mothers" admonition that an ounce of prevention is worth a pound of cure. Myopic optimization of direct healthcare delivery has resulted in an ever-increasing economic slice cut from the USA's economy. That slice is enormous, 17.8% of GNP or $2.6 trillion - - $2,600,000,000,000.00. Vast amounts of hidden benefits in USA healthcare are exceedingly useful only if one lives long enough to reap them. Yes, living 80-year-old residents in the USA enjoy a future healthy and enjoyable longevity greater than 80 year olds living in any other industrialized society, but one first has to get there to reap that benefit. Foreign dignitaries and foreigners who cannot get enough adequate or specialized healthcare delivery in their countries of origin specifically seek out superior healthcare delivery in the USA, and all medically astute people unquestionably regard the USA's direct healthcare delivery as the "best in the world". Again, as a culturally-entrenched behavioral economic, the general USA public spends more dollars on non-essential uncovered medical treatments, surgeries and drugs than on the prescriptive medically necessary modality slice of the GNP.

Of total healthcare delivery, the metric "direct healthcare delivery fraction" contributing to national health and **Healthcare Reform** is certainly an important and major metric as it presently stands. However, continued justification for an unmonitored increasingly expensive budget item may be a misdirected migratory economic external whose yearly increased expenditure piece is a minor metric for improving true national health quality. Other-directed budget increases yield better national health quality results; and ignoring these other metrics coupled with a lack of monitoring begets undesired and unintended consequences. Justification for an ever-increasing direct healthcare delivery budget may be a misdirected external that deserves further scrutiny because environmental factors predominate as additional cost-effective quality improvement metrics for overall national health.

The Federal Government-imposed 1945 freeze on wages after WWII opened the migratory economic healthcare delivery door to corporate businesses by allowing employers a tax write-off for Money spent on emerging and expanding private healthcare delivery finance corporations, thus entrenching an entity known by the misnomer of "health insurance" rather than "medical debt expense insurance" or that previously and even more simply put term, "wealth insurance". Lack of individual health plan transparency and accountability became an unfortunate trend; performance and access data needed to be publicly released. Medicaid became even more difficult to regulate as enrollment steadily increased along with a politically-pandered ever-expanding list of available services.

2015 marked a 50th Anniversary for the migratory economic **Healthcare Reforms** of Medicaid and Medicare. President Lyndon Johnson had signed the legislation into the law of the land on July 30, 1965. Over the ensuing half-century, Medicaid, an income means-tested program, demonstrated a growth that outstripped Medicare and all original expectations. Medicaid is a voluntary State-Federal partnership administered by and with varied allowable benefits assigned by those states that were or are willing to set up the program. As a Medicaid policy-making entity, each state was and is most certainly accountable for possessing the wisdom to appreciate and understand the strengths and weaknesses in the processes as well as program benefit end results from continual data analyses and meta-analyses. Having done so, the states must and have incorporated experts with education, knowledge, training, vast clinical experience, and medical expertise to interpret conflicting results and foresee a myriad of unintended consequences that might be possible for every policy decision. For the Medicaid programs, this altruistic effort was often frustrating when presented with conflicting and incomplete evidence, and especially when the sometimes onerous task was accomplished in in the face of varied recipient expectations, the threat of lawsuits, and pandering political pressures such as legislative directives. Most importantly and fortunately, the states choosing to administer the program have had the fortitude and compassion to balance all the empirical medical findings on a finely titered scale with a current and evolving American ecology of cultural mores, ethics, and economics. While evaluating Medicaid medical policy "ecolo-nomics", the participating states adhered to dispensing a final policy prescription that always hopefully contained those aforementioned four fundamental virtuous ingredients: Justice, Autonomy, Non-Malfeasance, and Benevolence. In California, the Med-Cal program grew to cover more than one-third the total resident population and over one-half of all "children" under 21, while boasting to be the largest payer of mental health and long term care services. Nationally, Medicaid served to cover over 72 million residents and more than half of all USA births, thus incurring expenses eventually to exceed $600 Billion per year.

Laws are a product of continually changing political philosophies bolstered by a system of special interest lobbying. Insurance corporations are proven experts in accomplishing that task. The Federal McCarran-Ferguson Act voided interstate insurance corporate commerce and thereby exempted healthcare delivery insurance from anti-trust legislation. The particulars of the resultant federal law: 15 u.s.c. §§ 1011-1015, exempted the insurance industry from most federal regulation, including federal anti-trust laws, with boycott, coercion, and intimidation as exceptions. By stark contrast, most other federal laws do not apply to the sale of insurance, whether the states regulate in that area or not. "Acts of Congress" that do not expressly purport to regulate the "business of insurance" will not preempt state laws or regulations that regulate the "business of insurance." Collusion to increase individual corporate insurance members' profits quickly became an unintended or overlooked and unpredicted but inevitable migratory economic external for **Healthcare Reform**. That is why Americans could not buy healthcare delivery insurance across a state line in the early part of the 21st Century. Bipartisan support can and will easily reverse this inequity – eventually "K street" must yield to the public good.

Nonetheless, some clear path to improve the USA's national true Health Quality in an effective, sustainable, cost effective manner through true **Healthcare Reform** does exist. The most important and significant quality healthcare service plan that can be offered to all the people of any nation's society is early primary disease prevention. That having been said, one must be very careful to understand the intricacies of the term "prevention" because there are many often confusing nuances to that term, especially when enhanced and babbled in jibber-jabber by supposed migratory economic experts, prejudiced pundits with plentiful pockets of political pontification parlay points.

To simplify that meaningless morass and begin to explain: There are three levels of preventive healthcare delivery modalities for the practice of Medicine – primary prevention, secondary prevention and tertiary prevention.
1. Primary prevention is health promotion to avoid development of disease.
2. Secondary prevention is early disease detection to avoid disease progression and/or to accomplish a cure.
3. Tertiary prevention is an attempt to rid disease by restoring function and reducing morbidity within an established disease state. This level is unfortunately touted as direct healthcare delivery, a misnomer.

Preventive Medicine modalities can be directed to individuals, to groups or to the entire national or global population. Environmental disease prevention or accident prevention is a separate category that consists of governmental measures to include bans or prohibitions and fines.

Level one prevention, primary disease prevention, is an essential indirect healthcare delivery modality that is cost–effective for both a nation and an individual patient. All members of a nation's society should have ready access to primary disease prevention. One must be very clear of an exact definition here. Primary early disease prevention is distinctly different from secondary early disease detection. Primary early disease prevention is primarily the job of the nation's Public Health Service: the job of the Public Health Service is to prevent disease and pestilence, then manage or cure a society's diseases or pestilences. The job requires active or passive cooperation from the masses of a population.

Level two prevention, secondary early disease detection, is a healthcare delivery modality that may or may not be cost-effective for a nation according to how it is rationed. The cost of secondary early disease detection will continue to rise as newer technologies make it possible to detect more and more diseases. All members of a nation's society cannot afford to have its government pay for all state-of-the-art early disease detection because, unless rationed, new and developing early disease detection technologies for an entire national population will eventually bankrupt a nation. Secondary early disease detection is primarily the job of healthkeepers: The job of a healthkeeper is to detect, then manage or cure a patient's diseases. The job of a patient is to follow through with a treatment plan.

Level three prevention, tertiary disease prevention, is a direct healthcare delivery modality that is extremely costly and ultimately best primarily overseen by a primary care Medical Home run by primary care physicians, physician groups or medical corporations who are easily available to a select limited panel of individual enrolled patients 24/7/365. The healthcare delivery job is best accomplished by those who have the capacity to be willing and able to follow these patients through various specialized healthcare delivery programs and hospitalizations with many hands-on medical-surgical physician specialists and consultants, thus vastly improving the quality and medical outcome of the enrolled individual patient's healthcare delivery and overall health. The job requires a patient and a physician who are both willing and able to go along with the overall program.

The above defined Medical Home can be afforded by many, but not all members of a society. If a nation attempted to provide such an excellent service for all its residents bolstered by one-on-one hands-on caring for all, then inevitably that nation would also soon suffer bankruptcy. Modalities of care are obviously modified and tempered from the traditional because there obviously are not a sufficient number of licensed American physicians available or even in training to serve in such a capacity for all members of the American society, unfortunately translating to a desperate lack of primary care and especially sub specialty practicing American physicians. However, the global healthcare delivery and Healthcare Reform environment does predominate. For the Medical Home, an alternative that can be offered to improve the health of a society as a whole may be a Medical Orphanage run by a myriad of highly trained and competent ancillary healthcare providers under the auspices of a larger group health organization's direct supervision and responsibility, possibly along with privately licensed individual healthkeeper practitioners that can also interact with a federal single payer system.

Inevitably, after initiating various population-based healthcare delivery triage schemes and squeezing various categories of healthkeepers in "every which way including Sunday" to control costs, third party interests will still rapidly run out of financial juice; and patients will suffer the health consequences because the prospect of rationing healthcare delivery from a government-run public option triage system is a political hot potato, not a red herring; but the prospect is painfully obviously essential and inevitable. Essential and needed **Healthcare Reform** to single payer government financed healthcare should not be about paying a total coverage womb to tomb corporate insurance bill but rather about re-thinking the entire concept of monitoring and financing true health metrics and first prioritizing primary early disease prevention with real-life financial consequences for those residents who do not cooperate in the process.

However, if one is very young or very old, chronically sick or functionally disabled, or too poor to afford catastrophic healthcare coverage -- then there still is a big prejudicial selective access crisis and any single such person as an individual is right smack in the middle of the dysfunction. Even if one can afford healthcare delivery, healthcare delivery may eventually become politically unavailable to that person due to the politics of myopic optimization, until globalization breaks the imposed restraints of methodological nationalism in American public policies. The persistent politics of Presumptive Probable Deniability (PAD) concerning total health and true **Healthcare Reform** prevail from both sides of the political isle that separates those persistent and perennial pontificating political pundits. One last introductory thought to ponder --just because one does not take an interest in politics, doesn't mean that politics won't take an interest in that person -- and an ancient Greek, Pericles, profoundly proclaimed that admonition way back when, back in 430 BC.

There always have been and always will continue to be evolutionary political-economic trends that then develop into evolutionary processes. Besides shocking the nation with his theory of the leisure class, in the "Quarterly Journal of Economics", volume 12, 1898, Thorstein Veblen asked, "Why is Economics not an evolutionary science", since "evolutionary causality" determines economic paradigms. As always, culture drove migratory economics and migratory economics drove adaptive selection for healthcare delivery mechanisms in an ever-changing migratory medical-economic marketplace that results from an evolving migratory medical cultural ecology. That changing cultural ecology drives a paradigm of adaptive and then adapted migratory medical economics. Sparked by an evolutionary watershed event, evolving Morals beget Mores which beget Ethics which beget Cultural behavior pattern ecologies which beget Ephemeral Socio-economic Paradigms. The evolving migratory economics driving the **Healthcare Reform** process gradually expresses a defined phenotype over a period of about five years that generally lasts for about a generation to become the mutating genetic basis for further evolutionary paradigm speciation. From this churning of migratory economics in general comes the term "ecolo-nomics", a combination of ecology and economics, the mutating genetic basis for economic paradigm speciation. Then more specifically, "medical ecolo-nomics", the production, distribution, and consumption of wealth engendered by development, competition, and ultimate dominance of various healthcare delivery systems/mechanisms, combined with evolving human interactions, material resources, and consequent social/cultural mores. Following Thorstein Veblen's line of thought, these events can also be summarized as follows: Individual morals beget Cultural Mores. Cultural mores beget medical ethics. Medical ethics beget a medical ecology. A medical ecology begets medical economics. Medical economics beget new healthcare delivery systems/mechanisms of **Healthcare Reform** that are determined, regulated and reformed by the overall ephemeral culture and fiscal limitations of "medical ecolo-nomics".

One can also look at medical-ethical patterns and the migratory medical ecolo-nomics of **Healthcare Reform** from a philosophical point of view. Patterns of ethical action and migratory medical ethics can be envisioned to arise from the virtue of one's character (Aristotle) or from deep prerequisite moral obligation (Immanuel Kant). German sociologist Ferdinand Tonnies described two normal types of human association in his moral-sociological theories. One has an individual need set to be more significant than the societies – gesellschaft; the other has a social community set of needs more important than the individual need – gemeinschaft. From these distinctions, the concept of utilitarianism (John Stuart

Mill), or ethical action judged by the consequences of said action comes into play. The greatest good for the greatest number then becomes a migratory medical ethical pattern of **Healthcare Reform** and is so registered in the migratory medical ecolo-nomic of the day.

Technology marches on; but, of course, that proverbial heavy hand of government also has its own peculiar and disruptive way. Historically, for example, Casey Stengel would probably have said "It's déjà vu all over again when in 2008 CMS introduced the MS-DRG, the Medical Severity Diagnostic related group payment system for hospitals. The cost-savings DRG modifier idea was to compile Severity of Illness (SOI) scores into the DRG system and thereby increase or decrease payments to hospitals by retrospective review of hospital medical records. The key element for successful reimbursement was comprehensive, detailed, proven and accurate physician documentation. The déjà vu part dated back to the 1980's, when PRO's and PSRO's were established to review chart notes for appropriate Medicare payments and physicians were given detailed lectures on how to write long-hand notes in stylish cursive with certain catch phrases which would indicate to a Medicare reviewer a valid reason to justify a payment. But by mid-21st Century there was no cursive note writing; kids had stopped learning that art in school fifty years prior. Medical technological progress had also introduced the Electronic Medical Record (EMR) a long time in the past. Hospitals back then had responded with a one-two punch to establish a digital record since the "littera scripta manet" legality was ancient history. First, salaried IT personnel modified the hospital-owned EMRs to "ask" for and substantiate ancillary diagnoses and associated medical conditions with naturally expected comorbid complications (CC) or major complicating comorbid Conditions (MCC/CC) through a series of computerized check-off boxes designed to prove and document the increased severity of the claim to CMS. If all the appropriate boxes were not checked, then the treating physician could not enter the required note into the record. Second, the hospitals hired sub-contractors to review discharge summaries and then find reasons in the healthcare delivery for "expected" complications to override "never, never complications" so the hospital would not be "dinged" for an unexpected and unexplained complication. Then the MCC/CC would determine the MS-DRG. The cost of the mob of additional reviewers on both sides of the payment scheme somehow never got factored into any calculated consideration of this "cost-savings" migratory economic for **Healthcare Reform**.

Technological times of the mid-21st Century day were exquisitely removed from all those past **Healthcare Reform** modalities of practice. University of Pennsylvania students, walking up campus towards Wharton and fraternity row after a sporting event at the Penn "Palestra" passed by the historical site of an old ivy-covered campus edifice that once housed America's first general purpose mega-computer, over a thousand times faster than electro-mechanical machines -- this **Electronic Numerical Integrator And Computer** (ENIAC) with over 17,000 vacuum tubes once led the way to future solid-state computers that still could not begin to compete with the hand-held, not smart-phone, but "virtual cell phone" devices offering tons more RAM and increased operating speed buckled onto a Penn student's backpack belt, more computing power and storage than there ever was imagined to exist in an ENIAC edifice, an structured engineering marvel that would have had to reach into earth's atmosphere up beyond the clouds, thousands of times the physical structure of the ancient and now defunct building. Then, along came the new and improved "doctor" Watson…..

It would have been wonderful if there perhaps could have existed some magic bullet like the magic of artificial intelligence (AI) in a computerized algorithm that could perfectly solve all the mysteries of life, love and Medicine. And then one could have a bullet-clip filled with magic bullets that could be shot into the human body and cure all sorts of psychological miseries, diseases and ailments, all at once. But, alas, Man knew, knew all too well that such a miracle cure-all did not exist. So some deluded their thinking and reasoning with existing health information technology (HIT), hoping that an answer delivered through some sort of multiphase computerized algorithm would be crowned the savior for their healthcare delivery dilemma. The stimulus bill, to its very limited credit, recognized the need for research on improving HIT. However, HIT is and was a tool that should have been used to facilitate clinical care, not to create a cybernetic miracle that would revolutionize Medicine by reporting personal health data to an endless list of billing agencies. The government bought into the HIT magic bullet theory and then got waylaid and ambushed, snagged then entangled; the blundering government snagged itself with a political hook and entangling line and sinker. An individual, at least at first before being subjected to systematic lowering of expectations, could not hope to be satisfied with the average best for the maximum of the total population. Average meant better than some, but worse than others. The new and improved impersonal and non-humanistic computer programs were obviously prepared to have individual idiosyncrasies ignored and accept proportional rationing on the basis of cost to a HIT system as a new definition of medical quality. With that proper programming in mind, a HIT computer itself was de facto a "meaningful user" and could compute this new definition of medical quality as a function of cost-effectiveness. HIT then ruled as the final authority; HIT should have been allowed to give itself a big P-4-P dollar bonus, especially when puny public objections peaked at a level where the song of acquiescence refrain sounded like it is just "too easy not to try, if you never say hello, then you will never have to say good-by". Just "too easy" circumstances allowed the computer to be the point-of-service provider and function in place of a treating healthcare practitioner. One who sings too merrily and adherently that song of the Hobbit will eventually subject to the whip of the Orcs. Such a HIT provider with no humanistic programming had no compassion for the lives of Americans at the level of being individual human beings. Perhaps one of those imaginary or hyper-reactionary "Death Panels" actually existed somewhere in a cyberspace cloud.

Being that the concept of quality "results" had been replaced by the concept of quality "outcomes", many types of outcomes needed to be defined -- biomedical, socioeconomic, behavioral, and psychological – only to name a few. The true proof in the quality of a medical treatment pudding should have been the demonstration of improved health and life expectancy from enrollees in a particular health plan utilizing that treatment modality. Evidence, metered metric evidence, was necessary for a basis of analysis, so that particular type of evidence was, quite simply and cleverly, administratively created. The new prerequisite appropriateness or premise of the said evidence, however, seemed to be only briefly if at all considered, discussed or evaluated. The new guiding principle for all that jazz of "evidence" fell to a lowly illogic of imagined ultimate importance in demonstrating that the superficially selected data be outcome-based. Meaningfulness of the data was either ignored or abandoned. Rates or percentages of enrolled health plan members receiving mammography exams, pap tests, immunizations, colonoscopies, etc. served as bits of administratively selected data readily transformed into "medical evidence" to justify existing practice guidelines. When a practice guideline proved to continuously improve quality, "quality" as defined by such invalid aforementioned criteria, then that guideline achieved the award, certification or title of "standard". Nightly news broadcasts compared competing hospital/physician outcomes with competitive scores like baseball games. The public soon realized that this type of accountability might have been neither accurate nor meaningful. The standardization process was akin to taking a public opinion poll with a hidden agenda. The wording and presentation manner of the questions asked along with the gerrymandered rules of the game swayed the resulting calculated "outcome" results. Insignificant but popular medical problems were specifically chosen to entice process-making interest and acceptance by both the government and the general public. Finally, The Foundation for Accountability (FACCT) did (in fact) establish much more meaningful outcome measures, such as: health risk behaviors, major depression and treatment plan benefits. Accrediting agencies soon demanded this more meaningful type of data as part of their utilization review processes.

Physician and administrative analyst panels from both the Joint Commission on Accreditation of Hospitals and Outpatient facilities (JCAHO) and the California Medical Association (CMA) labored endlessly at fine tuning presentations concerning quality result/outcome issues. Both physician-oriented survey groups developed independent presentations that could be put in a can then carried and delivered to local hospital executive staffs by chosen physicians in the role of hospital surveyors. Surveyor training and hospital inspection-certification teams evolved into a too huge and heavy branch for the CMA to manage and the effort fiscally stressed the organization because that quality assurance activity was siphoning away time and Money from other needed CMA functions. In order to maintain clear and financially separate functionality, the CMA surveyor branch had long separated from the CMA. The medical association affiliate was thusly presented with a new availably for additional 501(c) grant Money, and then additionally staked with brand name recognition authority -- the Institute for Medical Quality (IMQ). The IMQ, separately budgeted and financed, continued to grow in size and influence. Universally respected by hospital administrators and staff, once the IMQ delivered its suggestion for specific quality improvement to a local hospital's executive staff, the local hospital administration quickly prepared and delivered near identical presentations to the entire physician and administrative hospital staff.

Much ado was made about naming a "goal" for quality. Milestones were more appropriate. "Utilization review" became "quality review", then "concurrent review". As Toyota captured the U.S. domestic market, Kaizen continuous improvement philosophies became incorporated into **Healthcare Reform.** "LEAN" 6-Sigma methodologies, originally developed at Motorola in 1986, soon followed, especially when Jack Welch demonstrated the advantages of "decreased downtime" to General Electric in 1995. Further improving a reporting system for medical quality, systemic thinking about processes that yielded results and learning in a non-blaming, non-judgmental atmosphere replaced "command and control" improvement programs. "Quality improvement" gave way to "continuous quality improvement". The concept of looking backwards to see what caused a problem changed into a concept of looking forward to improve performance and results. The processing names likewise changed. "Performance evaluation" became "performance improvement", then "continuous performance improvement". Mechanisms for improvement defined a time-line ordered array of steps, a Gnatt chart, like a catechism of progress milestones and a vocabulary to be recited by a physician on cue – "plan, design, measure (collect and monitor), analyze (assess), and improve" The quality process mimicked the economic W. Edwards Deming Cycle of plan-do-check-act (PDCA). Quality found itself redefined to equal the missing factor from results of work efforts divided by total costs. The basic concept from the business world of economics held merit -- everyone was to get involved, improve work processes, and then get better results. The quality assurance process became the reverse of "root cause analysis" for complications and errors. (Then what next, then what next, then what next versus why then, why then, why then?) The process of healthcare delivery became surgically dissected to determine the uniquely, most direct path to obtain the best possible "optimal quality" result. Any straying from the process path would be a reason for investigation to improve optimal quality. More efficient variations to achieve optimal quality were incorporated into newly formed pathways and bad or inefficient variations (former optimal quality results) quickly found themselves eliminated. Perhaps economic theories are just myths from the past, but the Lipsey and Lancaster 1956 welfare economic "theory of the second best" stood swinging a ready bat in the "on deck circle". The "team approach" stood ready to add and re-arrange various variables away from those formerly assumed to be optimal, thus giving rise to an optimal "next best". In more practical economics, the only valid time that any second optimal plan to arrive can get to be the best is like when the second mouse arrives to successfully remove the cheese from a mousetrap. It was astounding, time was fleeting, madness took its toll, the new "Rocky Horror" medical ecolo-nomic process worked well for the physicians and worked well for the patients in that era's time warp. A migratory ecolo-nomic **Healthcare Reform** "Win – Win"?

The concept of true and reasonable "medically necessary" care had yet to be established, and most probably never would, given a political environment ruled by lobbied financing and a simple majority vote of the masses. Patient designed and oriented criteria became the gold standard for evaluation of care in the third medical ecolo-nomic generation. The criteria fit in with the cost-effective information that third parties demanded. Statistically significant end result or outcome studies eventually predominated. Innumerable pamphlets of three dozen questions each were filled with patient evaluations of levels of patient contentment with life after medical encounters; this somewhat meaningless randomized data added to the total outcome data. Even the vague concept of "happiness" sought to be evaluated with supposedly evidence based criteria. The grading system rated and demonstrated how much a patient felt good about: the physicians, the facilities, the plan, the systems of care, the paramedical personnel, the cosmetic results of surgeries, the time required for return to work and social functions, and the cost worthiness for the entire encounter. At first blush, evaluations of "happiness" seemed the wrong course to pursue and a lot of hogwash; but on second-round look, contentment scoring unexpectedly served as an excellent teaching aid as to the current phase of universally lowered expectations. A healthkeeper patient did begin to grasp the concept of a healthcare dollar well spent -- an excellent learning approach to further effectively mold the public healthkeeper mindset. Patients and advocate groups could then better address the more important but troublesome concept of "medically necessary". Academic institutions and corporate think tanks such as Stanford University and the RAND Corporation pondered and issued political-enhanced "wordsmithing" reports in an effort to define what was and would be medically necessary. The final decision lay out of touch, like a potato too hot for any hand to carry.

This third medical ecolo-nomic generation was also truly the start of the information age. It became painfully obvious that doctor demographics and what doctors did could be critically and accurately analyzed for the very first time. Increased purchasing public (big business and the big brother government) scrutiny and selective cost-sensitive review validated doctor practices. Accountability was expected to, and indeed did, improve overall medical practice. The quality of healthcare delivery began improving even before outcomes were analyzed. Proven migratory economic theory had many times demonstrated that any large business enterprise, once exposed to an external review process, suddenly self-improved when made aware of the covert investigation by corresponding corporate raiders. The big corporate medical businesses proved to be no different.

Over ten million Americans sought healthcare delivery abroad in 2012 and 2013. The most highly desired physicians for their medical tourism were physicians trained in the United States who then relocated their private surgical practices to foreign soil like New Zealand or Taiwan. American Medical Centers followed: Harvard to India, Mayo Clinic to the Mideast, Johns Hopkins to Asia, and Texas Christian Health to Mexico. The list of most popular hospitals for Americans included the Wockhardt Hospital in India, the Parkway Health Chain in Singapore, and the Bumrungrad Hospital in Thailand. Dermatology and Plastic Surgery centers all about the Caribbean included scuba, golf, tennis, and sailing excursions for patients perfectly packed into waiting room lanai bars. "Perceived value equaled quality divided by price."[119] Shirts still ruled the world, as some venture capitalists made it big and others lost their shirts in a giant Money pool.

---

[119] Deloitte and Touche LLP, New Roles, New Responsibilities for Health, 1995, p.111

In 1999 alone, half a billion dollars was invested in healthkeeper.coms, and most of them were not even on line. In 2010, that amount of high-roller capital became plankton for investment venture whales. Four publicly traded insurance corporations covered nearly half of all Americans with private insurance – WellPoint Inc., Aetna Inc., Cigna Corp, and United Health Group. KFHP and Sutter took the HKO lead in California. Megamergers blossomed after 2015, while all types of insurance corporations desperately lobbied the Federal Government in fear of an evolving government-run single payer plan **Healthcare Reform** in some future reality.

Health Net of Woodland Hills, California's fourth-largest healthcare insurer, sold out to Centene Corporation of Ohio for $6.8-Billion, allowing Centene to acquire a total of six million members and boast to be the largest Medicaid insurer in the USA. Scheduled to close escrow in 2016, Aetna funds found their way deposited into a $34.1-Billion account to purchase Humana. But the real biggie deal of the year went to Anthem's purchasing of Cigna for $54.2-Billion, thus allowing Anthem the glory of standing for the gold medal prize, number one in the USA with a record high number -- 53 million enrollees.

Population healthcare defined outcomes, outcomes used to measure a pre-determined percent of "success oriented goals" achieved within a constant accepted control risk; and this type of population healthcare delivery became the new gold-standard. With emphasis placed on patient education and self-care at home, physicians, who once promised their patients that they would do "everything medically possible", altered that promise to render a new-age message, a concept quite difficult for the individual patient to swallow -- to do the necessary and correct procedures to achieve a "timely best and cost effective result". The "correct" treatment did not always translate as the "right" or "best" treatment in the general patient mindset. Patients were not always socially-oriented administrative-progressive thinkers, especially when directly faced with health preservation fears concerning themselves or loved ones. At the same time, they did not as a group politically commit to advocate for, "Preserving the physician's role in placing the patient's medical needs as a priority over economics". The meaning and memory of the first half of the 20th Century medical ecolo-nomic price differentials were lost as migratory medical economics continued to inexorably intertwine with politics. The general public rarely denied that some (albeit unknown and unexplored) sort of a healthcare delivery crisis continually existed in America. The USA eloquently existed as a great and diverse society, which was and is, admittedly, also not totally perfect, albeit "perfect" defined as the enemy of good and superb. **Healthcare Reform** was necessary, but not considering and not taking into account specific measures to avoid the many potential unwanted albeit unintended consequences of political actions could easily make things even worse than they were. One should be very careful with needed **Healthcare Reform** and not leap in false faith to totally demolish an established functioning healthcare delivery system in a hopeless pursuit, a dream, just a dream for an idyllic degree of perfect perfection which was and always will be practically unattainable – back to that continually trying to "get what you want" song by the "Stones" and ultimately getting what is of need.

The retail medical clinic model of medical care was alive and well and growing at an exponential rate throughout the United States. Customers (formerly known as patients) shopped in stores while they waited for their appointments and spent an average of over twenty bucks before they ever got to see a Physician Assistant or a Nurse Practitioner or have that $50 five-minute consultation/chat with some physician located somewhere else, hopefully on planet earth. With that sort of healthcare delivery model-mechanism merchandizing, the super-store's total cost for the medical care delivered was not reduced below a break-even price, but still effectively sold as a loss leader by some comprehensive one stop discount enterprise or nationally expanding drugstore chain. Restaurants had been doing something similar for years. Restaurant customers are now well conditioned to arrive and be handed a beeper at a busy or pretend-to-be busy restaurant – while supposedly waiting for a prepared table, the customer sits at the bar and has a few "happy hour" drinks and perhaps some discounted hors oeuvres that would not have been ordered at all had the customer been seated immediately after arrival.

Patients were coyly conditioned to be pre-shopping customers -- Walgreen's was in town and CVS Pharmacy was in every town. And patients better be good and patients better not pout, because when Wall Mart Healthcare came slaying into town to compete with Target, the prices sure went down. The allotted telemedicine third party payer price for rendering healthcare delivery went below what the private medical practice business of a primary care physician or healthcare practitioner could bear. Live "chats" with a doctor from some misty and vague cloud on the Internet were also much cheaper than seeing some fee-for-service physicians face-to-face – but were they better?

Primary care physicians, physicians who were ultimately committed and dedicated to a fundamental patient-doctor relationship for better disease management, did not stand alone to bear this possibly unjust but assuredly growing societal burden. Cognitive abilities acceptable for direct primary healthcare delivery had definitely been downgraded in societal worth and the product prescription was near to all that the average patient remembered from an encounter. Optometrists had been selling eyeglasses for years as a method of defraying inequitable payments for their fine individualized refractive expertise. Podiatrists traditionally offered footbaths, pedicures, and all types of commercial arches to offset the small margin of profit made from their examination and diagnosis billings. It was almost as bad as a child getting a sugar-free lollypop at a dentist's office. Diagnostic acumen and cognitive expertise remained very expensive to develop and also quite time consuming to acquire and maintain, but difficult to bill out as a valid cost in the medical arena (as opposed to the legal arena). Yes, on the other hand, legislative lobbyists and lawyers simply charged by the hour. There was no chance of legislative effort to have one's routine legal bills government-regulated according to outcome measures, and no one objected to the non-contract cost of the newest annual model i-Phone at $800 when it cost just $50 for Apple to produce the product in China.

Too many emergency rooms had already closed, and too many hospitals were threatening to close because there was little or no profit margin left for the actual healthcare delivery of life-threatening medically necessary conditions. Hospitals began looking to horizontal and vertical integration models so that they could compete with other types of business enterprises and sell other medically related services horizontally and then delve into other vertical business ventures such as various non-medical provider services and commercial markets like fast food sales and boutique shopping experiences. Every big business firm seemed to want to be a one-stop-shop – for everything that a customer could possibly buy while being held captive (i.e. while waiting) for the essential service that brought the customer into the establishment in the first place. The original purpose of the visit then could not help from being diluted and downgraded in importance. **Healthcare Reform** should never have been sacrificed to the purveyors of bait and switch cost-containment migratory economics.

Taking a step back and looking at whether to be or not to be developing an acknowledged socialistic "public plan" or "common plan" was really a weighing decision on the American collective psyche because of a collective moral ambiguity concerning the re-distribution of any wealth and power, including healthcare services through the migratory economics of **Healthcare Reform**: Was the USA still basically a free capitalistic society that honored personal liberty, or had the majority of its citizenry joined their millennials and converted their philosophical values to a totally socialistic morality? Could this trend be reversed or was it a "fate accompli" that had to play itself out over a generation or two? Was the American dream still a dream of fearless equal opportunity for an equal best shot chance for any individual to be highly rewarded through the hard work of productivity, or was it changed to a divided fear mongering society advocating strict and fearful equal consumption for all regardless of individual productivity? Was the equalization of "opportunity" to become wealthy and successful being replaced by a philosophy which instead favored government regulation to mandate attained wealth redistribution to produce "equalization" of incomes and outcomes? Left wing big-government administrative progressivists walked with a saintly air about themselves, but they consistently diverted their path or ran from any interviewer who would obstruct their socialistic "divide the classes and conquer all" political path and dare to ask a few hated and feared basic questions such as:

"Do you still covert your personal possessions – then why do you still possess them?"

"Is abandonment of all "over-average amounts" of personal property a vital and necessary prerequisite to live in harmony with other human beings?"

"Cannot you truly love others without becoming some sort of saint by giving away to the state all that you shall ever work to possess beyond what others possess?"

A total amount of personal individual wealth can last at most one short lifetime, usually only a quarter or less of that lifetime, so why the sudden socialistic rush to immediately re-distribute that hard-earned briefly-possessed personal wealth? Social welfare doesn't trickle, but flows and gushes down from capitalism on an "as needed" basis; if more is truly needed for valid migratory economic reasons, then the capitalistic migratory economic system should and would gradually adjust to seek a workable harmonious equilibrium -- why was there a sudden social need for a flood of wealth re-distribution? (Remember the impending dollar crisis due to excessive governmental borrowing with resultant over-indebtedness.) If the wealth of an average American is more than the wealth of an average citizen of a foreign nation, should not that average progressive-socialist American then re-distribute his/her wealth and personal possessions on a global basis to be completely equal with others? Is the material might of the USA, as determined by its capacity for economic production by and for its peoples in relation to peoples of other nations, a significant, honored and prized national goal; or should that national personal possession of wealth and power be completely re-distributed equally among other less productive, less wealthy, less powerful or in progressive-speak "less fortunate" nations to the extent that the USA would then become a "nation among nations", an equal material might player on a level global playing field? If wealth and power is not hoped or planned to be redistributed to that extent, then just where does the divide and conquer progressive socialist scratch the calloused earth on the political playing field and draw the proverbial line.....

and would the exact placement of that line drawn in the shifting sands of time be an individual decision, a democratic majority decision or a governmental-progressivist administrative consensus decision?

Stratification of natural physical talent prevents the majority of people from becoming professional athletes. Continual dedicated athletic practice does not change that reality for the majority. Only a few can make it to the top. Equally hard work and sacrifice to produce and attain the highest strata on the capitalistic layer cake is also not achievable for the majority. At the top, there is only room for a few. Nonetheless, an able and healthy individual is expected to work to produce and achieve the highest cake layer possible for that particular person's ability. Those able bodied individuals should not forever be non-productive recipients, governmental dependents who for oncoming generations continually wallow in entitlement welfare. Man should not solely and continually gobble away at a capitalistic cake and then expect to have that sweet and easy nourishment available forever. Man may forever want and wish, but Man cannot continually just have endless cake and expect to eat it too. Consumption cannot exceed production for very long.

Political pundits so often misquoted an imagined exact amount of uninsured residents in the USA that their words came to be most often ignored, but nonetheless, a significantly great and unacceptable number of citizens and residents in the United States still survived with no insurance or inadequate insurance coverage to completely pay for or adequately attain their necessary healthcare delivery follow-up obligations after initial stabilization of their acute medical ailments in emergency rooms, as provided for by President Reagan administration's EMTALA. Moreover, America's make-shift or rag-tag safety-net of community clinics were continually overburdened and under-funded; the safety-net clinics just could not take up any more – there was left no slack. County Hospitals and county-funded facilities were also filled beyond capacity. All these vital and essential medical clinic types remained scattered across the USA in a courageous attempt to provide some semblance of a healthcare safety net and offerings of primary care medical homes for that truly vulnerable segment of well-meaning and deserving poor people in the American population. These honored complex networks served as the last resort for a growing number of uninsured patients, and these clinics faced continual increasing financial challenges while they dauntlessly strove to fulfill an honorable mission that offered underserved communities a spectrum of clinical services. And still, there existed a crowd-out of medical care that went aimlessly into American streets in both rural and urban areas in every single one of the USA's states, without exception. There was no central legislative action to simply bolster and adequately fund these proven institutions for trusted and sustainable direct healthcare delivery. Why, for heaven's sake, were these God-sent safety net institutions publicly and politically ignored as valid and cost-effective healthcare delivery mechanisms that could be organized for uninsured Americans on a national basis which would, by vital necessity, include interstate national licensing and interstate unobstructed commerce for these clinics and all healthkeeper practitioners?

Americans repeatedly failed to politically organize and openly confront the distinct and known problems inherent in a government-financed healthcare delivery system: The cost would be great and would naturally be greater and greater as time went on. That reality had to be faced and accepted by all Americans as a necessary evil for the necessary attainment of a contemporary paradigm accepted as morally "good". There was no need to lie or to hide this truth in blurred statistics or to sugar coat this issue; all Americans would eventually have to accept that reality; but of course, such a rational and logical approach would not at all be politically brilliant or expedient. The additional demographics of patients served in any government-financed plan revealed that they, because of cherry-picking, lack of specialized care and frank refusal of healthcare service, would always be sicker, more multiply-disease ridden and unfortunately more often chronically disabled. These patients, such as Medicaid recipients, would not be a cherry-picked population pool like a pool of healthier active workers (unlikely to have an excessive amount of chronic diseases and absolutely not requiring dialysis or organ transplants) assigned to a corporate health plan HKO. Also, the potential for excessive use and disuse of benefits directly accountable to the customary practices of patients in the increased enrollment sector of any government-financed plan would be exceedingly greater than in a private pay process. There would naturally have to be strict ongoing audit and investigation activities to reduce this expected increase in fraud and abuse. The constant shadow of big-brother government would have to be omnipresent and generally accepted for the sustainable survival of such a healthcare delivery plan. Health Insurance Plans and needed healthkeepers would necessarily have to be assigned to the public, not chosen by the public. Too many Americans cowardly refused to buck up, face these realities, then learn and plan ahead with evolving healthcare delivery systems/mechanisms to adequately handle their inevitable migratory economic consequences.

The idea of free market competition with a government-financed plan competing against private healthcare delivery plans amounted to a "nail-down" version of the old "bait and switch" sales marketing technique (you can't buy the precise item or move that nailed-down item off the shelf). There could not have been and can never be a truly level playing field for competition with private plans when the government is directly involved. Demographics are destiny (August Comte), and the demographics of government-financed plans cannot and will not allow such things as equal bargaining or fair competition with private plans. With necessary-for-survival preferential laws, statutes, and subsides favoring any government-run plan that offers open enrollment to the general public, the issue of eventual crowd-out would become an enormous concern for private insurers. The insurance corporations knew this all too well. At first, naïve Americans expected some ground rules to be put in place, some assurance that would not suddenly collapse the many institutions of private healthcare delivery, but not such laws as a Supreme Court approved federal tax in the form of a mandate for compulsorily private health insurance coverage and federally financed Healthcare Exchanges. On the other hand, private insurance corporations yet feared that without that mandatory universal coverage clause, the potential gradual erosion from private systems to cheaper but not necessarily better quality government-run plans over the course of a generation would still be quite too substantial for their fiscal sustainability. The insurance corporations were willing to gamble on a too big to fail government payoff, a bail-out; they all knew quite well that total enforcement of a mandate through a taxation process would be impossible when such a great percentage of American residents neither filed nor paid federal taxes.

All forms of healthcare delivery models continue to be dynamically evolving processes in the unique American medical ecolo-nomic **Healthcare Reform** evolution. New models and systems are ever-emerging to challenge static and non-adapting methods of caring for all American residents. The rest of the industrialized world looked and still looks to the USA with mixed expectations. Americans should be filled with hope for an improved and ever-improving healthcare delivery system/mechanism. Individual and group practicing physicians along with all American patients continue to play an innovating and transforming role, with a vision to deliver an accessible and affordable Quality of Medicine in all aspects of **Healthcare Reform** to all the peoples residing in planet earth's greatest country, the USA. But knowing and hoping is not the same as doing....

Everyone knew intuitively and could easily understand and comprehend that exercise, clean environmental living and a healthy diet, when combined with a healthcare delivery system that offered immunizations and maternal health programs, were the very best and possibly the only scientifically proven measures that could actually prevent the origin of disease and promote a healthy longevity. American citizens already had these immunization and maternal health systems in place and could partake of those American healthcare delivery benefits for all at any time that they pleased. However, that is not how Americans choose or chose to behave or to have their duly elected representatives legislate priorities. Rather than walk or pedal a bicycle to work, Americans drive their cars to relative sedentary jobs, only to return home and assume a couch potato silhouette as they watch a mesmerizing television screen and consume quantities of alcohol and salty chips to metabolically elevate their sugar levels, blood pressures and body weight to unsafe ranges. The American culture accepts, enjoys and actively promotes the excessive consumption of fast foods, preservatives, fats and sweets; and then the general citizenry suffers with poor healthcare outcomes from poor primary disease prevention programs and increasing rates of diabetes, obesity, and heart disease. One might ask if the American Dairy Association, with their mass media campaign for milk, cereal, bread and butter for breakfast, is the responsible culprit for the rising number of heart by-pass surgeries. To the hamburger counter question, "Would you like to super-size that?" -- The majority in that paradigm of American culture unfortunately responded with an overwhelming positive, "YES". Modalities of the three consumption evils -- salts, sugars and fats – unfortunately the food stuff that is exquisitely filling to the tummy, really tastes great and is relatively cheap and addictive – are continually promoted for consumption to the American public by governmental agencies because again, the migratory economics of health and **Healthcare Reform** are inexorably intertwined with politics, and politics is always the victim of lobbied interests. Since repeated statistical studies show that kids preferentially pick out unhealthy food choices at government-funded school lunches, then why not just take the bad stuff completely off the menu? What is logically simple is often politically impossible.

During the signing of the National Cancer Act of 1971, President Nixon announced the beginning of a federally funded "war on cancer". In spite of an apparently well-planned three-pronged trident approach (research, drug therapies and medical-surgical treatments), it seems that the feds became bewildered as to exactly where to start this well-funded war to eradicate the genesis of all types of cancer. Perhaps they should have considered another quote from good old doc Hippocrates, "Let food be thy Medicine and Medicine be thy food".

Since most Americans did and do not exercise regularly, their bones lose their mineral content and become osteoporotic at an earlier age than bones should, and then all too many aged Americans present to emergency rooms with vertebral fractures and extremity fractures from relatively minor falls. The over 60-year-old American sense of body balance, proprioception, is out of alignment, and a small stumble or trip often ends up as a serious hip fracture or fatal skull fracture. Americans experience more pathos and invest a greater cathexis in cosmetic surgery than they do in cancer surgery. Have Americans lost their logos, and what does this say about the popular American cultural ethos?

Americans passively accept a horrible air pollution problem in their port cities, from marine vessels that burn bunker fuel, which contains 27,000 ppm sulfur; they smoke cigarettes during pregnancy; and then Americans complain about their healthcare delivery system having poor outcome statistics regarding infant mortality and prematurity. Multiple analyses by the South Coast Air Quality Management district concluded that over 700 premature deaths could have been prevented every year in the South Coast Basin alone if the existing marine vessel controls in an already approved State Implementation Plan were actually implemented. Diesel exhaust is a putrid stench that exudes from ships, railroads and freeways to contaminate the air that all Americans breathe. City-dwellers allow the unfiltered exhaust from cargo trucks to spread the swill contained in those fumes inland, to pollute cities with small tar and smoke particles mixed with chemicals that poison American bodies in various ways. Those fumes insidiously spread disease, disability and death. Being closer to freeways, resident inner city populations are proportionately effected to a greater extent, leading to cultural and economic disparities in cancer rates, respiratory disease and heart disease rates, as well as a clear cut case of social injustice. Living closer than 500 feet from a freeway is an especially bad prognostic indicator, but there is really no place to run -- 50% of all Californians live within one mile of a freeway. Non-thinking knucklehead administrative city planners built grammar and elementary schools in close proximity to railroads and oil refineries; they chronically allowed American children to be transported on unfiltered, filthy, fuming and disgusting diesel burning school busses. The parents of these unfortunately victimized children talk and argue about absenteeism, school infirmities and child access to healthcare delivery at their parent-teacher association meetings, but they repeatedly fail to change the obviously unacceptable state of affairs. Appeals to the administrative hierarchy typically fail to resolve the problem for the victimized children. An apparently universally unconcerned or impotent administrative school board hierarchy is crippled by antiquated horse-head blinder methodological imperatives and practices.

There is a saying of multiple origins that some people call a proverb: "Treat the earth well: it was not given to you by your parents, it was loaned to you by your children. *We do not Inherit* the earth from our ancestors; *we Borrow* it from our children and grandchildren." Mother Nature's weapons that wreak havoc to our planet are molten earth, fire, wind and water. With these tools, She creates floods, droughts, tournedos, hurricanes, earthquakes, tsunamis and erupting volcanos. Historical and future unpredictable "natural" environmental-economic crisis or eruptions -- from such natural sources at Mother Nature's command -- always have and will continue to wage war upon Mother Nature's opposing green environmental contingent. The industrial-economic structures built and managed by and for the pleasure and benefit of Mankind wage a similar war. There is great political controversy within this topic as to what extent, if any, future climate change is now influenced by Man. However, putting aside all the political arguments pro and con concerning the degree that human efforts may contribute to long term global warming after the present population of Man is dead and gone, there is absolutely no rebuttal to the fact that humans, Man of today's world, are irrationally, insanely, slowly, but quite efficiently and effectively poisoning themselves in this generation, right now while the present human populations are, albeit temporarily, still alive and kicking. As for the human race, Mankind has to reconsider what possible insidious deadly course may have unintentionally been chosen to run; and this re-evaluation must be done in a timely manner -- before there is no longer any healthy human race to run on any course. The immediate pressing and undisputed problem is that pollution of planet earth's air, food and water supply affects all Mankind – for richer or for poorer.

Here on planet earth, the human race, Man is the alien species. Mankind is the alien species because Man alone is an independent cognitive thinker, therefore rationally responsible for the unintended environmental-economic consequences of altering the purity of his everyday living space, his healthful lifespan and the immediate purity of planet earth. Man's pollution also affects his eventual sustainable industrial economic stability. To paraphrase Charles Dickens,..... It is now the best of times, it is now the worst of times, it is now the age of wisdom, it is now the age of foolishness, it is now the epoch of belief, it is now the epoch of incredulity, it is now the season of Light, it is now the season of Darkness, it is now the Spring of hope, it is now the Winter of despair.

Preservation of health (a tale on one pan of a hanging balancing scale) and expanding industrial technologies (a tale on the opposing pan of a hanging balancing scale) are important interdisciplinary issues, but they too often find themselves in hot single-minded contention and competition. There are well–documented lists of tragic economic consequences resulting from such conflicts. Their combined wasteful economic costs in terms of dollars as well as their wasted listings of hampered human essentials, the essentials of health and wellbeing for Man's civilized lives, are both too often lost in the industrial dust and human decay resulting from and resting on economic industrialization battlefields. Arising from that interdisciplinary economic war and warring, the most essential evolved human pleasure, the joy and art of living must never be overlooked in the tale of the two sciences – the economic-technological tales of industrialization and the preservation of the immediate healthy environment.

Again yes, for richer or poorer, all Mankind must eventually suffer the consequences of polluted food, air and water. However, living conditions and simple geographical propinquity to sources of pollution awaken the reality of economic social disparity. Disparities from those resultant economic burdens call out, shouting for environmental justice. Several of the obvious health hazards have already been documented. Mercury in the water supply and foods results in heavy metal toxicity and mental health complications. Lead blood levels that result in decreased IQ are mostly found in the impoverished people that live near areas emitting noxious lead. Short run economic opportunities should not selectively and immediately disparage any racial or ethnic group in the social sector or eventually any grouping of Man whatsoever for that matter.

Mankind must have a vision of cleaner air and water, but interdisciplinary economic policy is desperately needed to make and sustain medically necessary compromises, priceless compromises and improvements for the evolved higher enjoyment and improved health naturally expected and now culturally demanded for Man's everyday live. Only then can we take pride in having established a sustainable healthier and happier longevity for Mankind – the beastly human alien species.

Ok, think about this: Each and every day, three times as many Californians die prematurely from the toxic effects of particulate air pollution.......Three Times -- Three times more die each day than those who die in fatal traffic accidents -- and that adds up to over 9000 Californians dying each and every year to come with no end in sight:
Air pollution is a pestilence, a pestilence that plagues Man, plagues Mankind from his womb to his tomb, so obvious action must be taken. Environmental protection can and in many instances does lead to economic growth. All the cost-benefits may not be readily achievable, but the economic cost-effectiveness for a healthy life, for Man to enjoy the art of living, is and should be so overwhelmingly and painfully obvious. A simple solution -- Protecting the environment gives Mankind a longer life span and safeguards his future generations.

Putting some known and experienced events into local USA perspective:
The entire Western World of Man was all so excited and concerned about the globally publicized oil spill from one solitary oil rig in the Gulf of Mexico some years ago --- 9000 tons of hydrocarbon pollutants spilled into the sea each day resulting in a filthy scum on the ocean waves and beaches that killed wild life and affected the local economy of states like Florida and Louisiana.

So, just think about this fact — California alone spills 9000 tons of hydrocarbon pollutants into the air weekly, weekly spilling, each and every week -- and there is no one single leaky oil pipe to cover up with mud and cork. Think about dead people, not dead fish. You can replace a pipe, but you cannot replace a human life. Delving into the mortality statistics of major cities in China reveals an extreme geographically-related increase in the loss of human life and wellbeing due to the toxic effects of pollution, especially for those living within cities or near to highly industrialized areas.

Typically, the demand side of the interdisciplinary policy-benefit equation really does not demand enough of the wonderful benefits that can and will be supplied to the people affected. Perhaps past interdisciplinary economic policies have been acting in silos, not fully communicating with other programs, lacking an integration of data and policies, and not reaching out sufficiently to the beneficiaries of the various programs. Future interdisciplinary economic policy must provide a well-integrated strategy to correct those misconceptions and to attain health-based air/water quality standards. The absolute need for such standards and compromise must be made totally transparent so that all peoples of every nation can accurately and intelligently evaluate the risks and consequences related to both sides of the interdisciplinary economic equation.

Yes, the entire world shares a common vision of clean air and environmental justice, and now, right now, interdisciplinary economic policy is desperately needed and wanted to implement a healthier lifespan for all Mankind. A civil society also demands interdisciplinary economic integration to correct ostensible societal disparities in a healthy living environment. Perhaps a famous and timely quote may help to awaken humane interdisciplinary economic reasoning: "Of all of the forms of inequality, injustice in health is the most shocking and the most inhumane" --- Martin Luther King, Jr.

Today, the fundamental migratory economic need and the innate compulsive human desire for a "work ethic" demand economically productive jobs to balance income disparities. These primal urges that encourage industrialization have to be fairly weighed against the health and longevity need for pollution control of Man's biomass. **Healthcare Reform** is not so simple: Money -- Iron and steel production alone in China are responsible for 40,000 jobs as well as for over 40,000 health ailments due to the associated pollution. The environment of pollution is a world environment that includes the direct effects on health/Medicine as well as the indirect health effects caused by decreased essential and necessary for survival food production and production of pollution-tainted foods that expensively sicken but do not reduce the growing biomass of Man.

There are enormous evolutionary environmental terrors far beyond Mankind's control or influence. The magma at the core of planet earth rotates every 12 to 25 thousand years on an irregular basis. At that time, the magnetic poles switch from north to south over approximately 300 to 500 years. Solar storms viciously attack Man's earth and severely destabilize the environment. Mankind most certainly does live in the age of the great ice melt. The ongoing rising sea levels and depletion of river beds lead to loss of forested lands and associated oxygen production with an associated rise in carbon dioxide, which results in depletion of the earth's high atmosphere ozone level with eventual and inevitable global warming. The pollution caused by Man's industrialization must at least fractionally add to this climate change, but the actual extent is hotly but politico-scientifically debated and not yet totally resolved for veritable mass social consumption/acceptance even today.

Mankind deserves to know when the air we breathe is dangerous, so that Man can protect himself. Parents have a right to know about the quality of air their children breathe. The air that Man breathes is worth fighting for; Mankind's children deserve nothing less. Ground-level ozone pollution, also known as smog, poses a major health risk to millions of people throughout the world. Ozone smog triggers asthma attacks, sends people to the hospital and even shortens lives. Newer evidence warns that ozone worsens heart disease and increases the risk of low birth weight in newborns. Ozone can be deadly, shortening the lives of thousands each year at levels currently labeled "safe." That research shows that Man has been living with too-weak limits for years, and suffering the consequences. That ongoing situation must change. Ozone or "smog" standards have been reviewed – and found to be too weak. Strengthening the official limits for ground-level ozone pollution is critical to protect the health and art of living for humans that are presently alive.

Yes, there is absolutely no doubt that Man has irresponsibly created a carbon footprint into the atmosphere and crusty surface of his earth. But of what lasting significance is that footprint to the recoverability of planet earth after and when exposed to eons of eroding winds of time? Or, in the infinite is the slightest of all changes yet significant? In that light, Man should act as a pragmatic economist; philosophical thought -- leave to Ralzak. Therefore, it becomes foolhardy and a truly waste of time to debate the political argument; but an argument for which there can be absolutely no debate or rebuttal is this fact -- the obvious immediate damage to the health and wellbeing of Man, provoked and engendered by his forsaken fellow Man, is all caused by Man's irrational pollution of his very own environment right here and now.

Moreover, the immediate deleterious living and fiscally disabling health effects of industrial pollution are an absolutely intuitive "given" in any **Healthcare Reform** calculus equation and worth consideration as a totally separate and unique economic entity. Solar, wind, hydropower and volcanic power plants are innovations that help to decrease pollution, but they alone cannot overcome the massive effect of industrialization or an unexpected melt-down in a Man-made nuclear power plant.

Mankind cannot afford to forget:

1957 – Windscale fire in the UK;
1979 – Three Mile Island in the USA;
1986 -- Chernobyl in the USSR; and
2014 -- Fukushima nuclear power plant in Japan.

Unfortunate examples such as the 1984 Indian gas tragedy at Bhopal and the painfully obvious filthy Rhine pollution blatantly stare in the face of Man.

According to economist Paul Samuelson, the ultimate goal of the general science of economics is to improve the living conditions of people in everyday life. The social costs and strained living conditions directly associated with industrial pollution are generally not paid nor psychologically borne by the polluting industry. That too often hidden or disguised economic "externality" is then conveniently overlooked. Even the Chicago School, as expressed by Milton Friedman, insists that business has a social responsibility to "use its resources and engage in activities……..without deception or fraud". When seriously considered in the economic calculations, that social cost "externality" due to pollution becomes a technically negative economic predictor, a significant factor that changes all the previous economic calculations. The new calculations then too often painfully and ostensibly stand out as examples of frank market failure.

Today, there is a tightrope, a high wire tightrope that must be walked by all Mankind. While walking along this perilous high wire, Mankind carries a long balancing pole weighted by industrialization at one end and the environment, physical and human, at the other. Sustainable industrial development goes hand in hand with effective waste management to decrease pollution. **Healthcare Reform** mechanisms for interdisciplinary balance include establishing a common ground for goals among varied industrial and environmental interests. To realize this tedious and tenuous economic balance, there must be mechanisms for reliable data collection and honest economic forecasting from both sides of the argument. There is no enigma that cannot be solved/decoded by Man. There is already a paradigm shift in the way economists view their craft. There must be innovative and sustained humanistic independent cognitive reasoned processes for globalization of all interests. Private business industry development must immediately exercise their dutiful societal-social responsibilities to meet the cultural ethics of the 21st Century. Economic hegemony in the development of third world nations must be avoided and curtailed on a global scale. The secret to human implementation of the long balancing pole lies in interdisciplinary economic compromise at an optimum level of informed social acceptance. With true entrepreneurial spirit, there is a definite role for governments to intervene, to remove regional imbalances and to build state-supported agricultural, transportation and mechanical infrastructure with proven green environmental and eco-design pre-planned sustainably viable economic concepts. But the science of migratory economics and its many economists also have a dire duty calling: To this end, interdisciplinary economic studies must start with valid data sets from economic indicator instruments on both sides of the economic spectrum. There is presently a fearfully urgent call for this sort of interdisciplinary economic evaluation before irreversible damage is done to the environment of Man's planet earth and ultimately his future health and wellbeing. Industrialization and its by-products fester throughout the world of Mankind at an ever-increasing rate, with a seven-fold industrial acceleration in just the past ten years. A weighty and sacrosanct onus to find the ideal socio-economic balance is placed directly upon immediate and future **Healthcare Reform**.

Automobile seat belts save more lives than cardiac surgery, but police ticketing records prove that Americans are reluctant to wear the life-saving belts; yet Americans have no problem consenting to a much higher degree of risk with cardiac surgery. The horrid habits of smoking and tobacco – there should be no need to discuss those practices; but some of the things Americans talked about every day did tend to be confusing and mixed up in defined and accepted medical terminology: The greater American society maintained an "endowed right" to be healthy enough to be free and able to pursue the American ideal of happiness. Therefore, Americans confused "health insurance" with "health maintenance", and then confused both of those terms with "health measures" to insure with greater certainty a lifestyle blessed with freedom from pain and suffering. This concept of an "endowed right" to freely act and attain a productive life at any age range was certainly ingrained into the ecology of American cultural mores and medical ethics. American physicians perform more hip and knee replacement surgeries at a rate and actual number higher than anywhere else in the world, and thereby do more to free the American elderly population from the stressful burden of depressing constant and persistent pain. Remember that octogenarians living in the USA have a longer and more fulfilling life expectancy than octogenarians living anywhere else in the world – but the American population first has to survive long enough to get there.

Even after the passage of Medicare and Medicaid, physicians avidly supported charity programs to keep hospitals running. During the third medical ecolo-nomic generation (1990-2010) relationships between physicians and hospitals changed. Physicians, who had formerly donated their Money and their allotted time to help struggling private hospitals, saw those same hospitals sell out to for-profit HKOs. Personal physician trust, participation in fund raising activities, and donated Money were all lost and replaced with ill feelings of abandonment and anger generated about wasted past contributions. Physicians and hospital administrators changed their meetings from breakfast tables to arbitration tables, and spiteful lawsuits became the new topic of conversations concerning Medicine.

Physician charity shifted to be expressed through various medical group and specialty practice group organization projects rather than through individual physician contributions. HKOs competed to have the best press and media coverage for their free immunization programs. Immunization programs became especially popular charitable functions because immunization programs could be written off the plan's taxes as Money losers, economic loss leaders for the HKOs. The cost of the drugs and services were never adequately reimbursed in the first place, so that plan-covered immunizations actually cost out of pocket Money for the health plan. Under those circumstances, making immunizations a charitable event provided for both, a tax write-off and fulfillment of mandated community service activities for a tax-exempt status. Dollars, dollars – big dollar check-presentation ceremonies served as photographic propaganda opportunities on the evening television press reports, and "Kodak moments" in press releases reinforced the derived charitable spin. Cultural diversity programs were likewise spun as charitable undertakings in media advertisements for the health plans.

HKOs openly advertised for culturally diverse physicians, and the acceptance of Medicaid patients into the plans became publicly proclaimed, openly boasted but privately suppressed. Succumbing to the financial pressures of decreased reimbursements, individual physicians tightened their belts and their budgets; they uniformly donated less Money in every direction, and both the charity organization donations and the professional society membership dues totals failed to meet their needed budgetary quota. Physician participation in all types of medical societies and organizations dipped to an all-time low -- a seemingly low abyss, even after many medical organizations lowered their dues rates. There seemed to be a paradigm of decreased desire to contribute to any type of charity or political organization. Physicians simply gave up pro-bono care, charitable pretense and costly gestures as a group, a group that unfortunately felt no longer honored by society.

Who then remained to care for the less fortunate in society? Government rebates and tax credits for basic healthcare delivery or catastrophic healthcare costs assured neither access nor quality. Nothing could or ever did adequately replace a charitable physician-patient relationship. During the first half of the 20th Century, County Hospitals and University Hospitals thrived, totally dependent upon the charity of volunteer physician faculties. A third medical ecolo-nomic generation (1990-2010) study performed at the University of Washington concluded that, "Increasing nonclinical workload demands and higher patient loads are a substantial threat to the recruitment and retention of volunteer faculty."[120] Physicians had previously signed, sealed and delivered concessions with contractual arrangements, which included guidelines for rationed treatment alterations. Having accepted the mandated rationing of care, many doctors felt guilt in passing that edict down to the individual patient. That doctor guilt was significantly lessened by ego defense transference of individual physician autonomy to HKO physician-group autonomy.

All Americans generally agreed that **Healthcare Reform** was necessary within the USA healthcare delivery system because so many things cost too much and apparently yielded little or no benefit according to the majority of media propaganda. Americans acknowledged the unnecessary contributing costs due to defensive medical practices, yet duly elected USA legislators scoffed at any substantial effort or attempt at legislating effective tort reform. They wept and cried to correct financial waste in the USA healthcare system, but those same recidivistic legislators failed to define the precise and exact layers of healthcare

---

[120] "Volunteer Physician Faculty and the Changing Face of Medicine", WJM, V.174 4-2001, p.242

financing that had to be reformed or eliminated. The financing of all that Americans demanded as a cultural ecology conflicted with a denial of financing for what Americans ethically deserved. In the planning for less expensive healthcare delivery systems/mechanisms, legislative migratory economic decisions were driven by an ever changing set of cultural mores and ethics that the American medical ecology demanded, and that was just part of the conundrum within the many pieces of migratory medical ecolo-nomics. USA legislators vacillated in willingness to plan for and sequester advance financing for unexpected health accidents such as environmental trauma and possible pestilence both at home and abroad. Yet there was a substantial majority willingness to devote predictably expected large sums of dollars to endlessly manage the unbearable ailments of the chronically sick and disabled uninsured and underinsured. Some openly questioned the concept of being morally bound to finance not only the nation's Medicine but also the rest of Man's world of Medicine, and in so doing cost the Money coffers of the USA to suffer dearly. Americans searched the traditional benevolence of their hearts; and as loyal citizens, many Americans agreed that they should pay for some portion of that huge cost as well as the continually increasing cost of evolving technologies, made even more expensive by the increased medical need of America's continually aging society. There was a wish for a magical solution, but there existed no great and terrible giant above the clouds hoarding a magical goose that laid golden eggs nor any vast sea-green presidential-pictured woodland-wonderland fruit from forested magnificent Money trees.

Systems of healthcare financing in the USA cost a lot, much too much; and there were additional multitudes of administrative expenditures, financing arrangements and legislative priorities that had to be curbed or eliminated in **Healthcare Reform** to make healthcare delivery for all less expensive; but Americans had to move cautiously and carefully when tampering with the point-of-service end of the USA's fragile healthcare delivery equation. There were so many political pontiff promises, more promises, and then forgotten statistics. There were arguments concerning the immediate need for **Healthcare Reform** versus gradual change in coverage or services/mechanisms. Every one-sided stakeholder secretly thought about "what's in it for me" (WIIFM) and "what is not in it for me". Were Americans simply playing a game of cost or consequences? When an omnibus reform package without significant tort reform and without the assurance of independent private contracting was projected to cost more than the present USA system, then some Americans inquired as to the purpose of reform if nothing other than to socialize 18 to 20 percent of the USA's economy, to the point where over a generation of time the USA's government would eventually exhaust the practical collection and use of "other peoples' Money" (taxes) and be forced to severely ration American lives by legislative decree.

Yes, the total cost of the overly administered third party run American healthcare delivery system was not adequately financed by existing "Wealth Assurance" alias "Health Insurance" mechanisms, and there surely still existed 30 million or so American "residents" that completely lacked any "Wealth Assurance" whatsoever. So, how was that particular sector of the American population to be tended to or accounted for – or was tending and accounting a real practical problem or just a political problem? There was something out there called The American Health Safety Net, but since that concept could not be comprehended by knucklehead governmental administrative solution-finders, why even bother to think about it to begin with? By the way, why not at least consider what an average American mother might have to say? That "two cents worth" of advice might bring back a million bucks in return.....Another basic thought that one's dear loving mother surely must have imbedded in her progeny's pea brain at least a dozen times – before you go about to repair, change or fix something: 1. Be sure it is really broken. 2. Be sure to understand how, why and who broke it in the first place so that you can make the fix better and prevent it from being broken again.

Logically (but alas not politically) the question must have been asked – How, where and when had the 30 million or so uninsured citizens and residents in so many communities of the United States been obtaining their healthcare delivery from an existing system that was suffering, broken and urgently needed to be fixed, changed or abandoned by **Healthcare Reform?** Does a "fix" mean a migratory economic "fix" or an access "fix"? "Fixing" "coverage" really does not satisfy either of the two aforementioned "fixes". Where did the apparently unavailable funding for "wealth assurance" suddenly come from to pay for emergency stabilization at a county or private hospital à la EMTALA or at a too poor to pay follow up patient visit at a Federally Qualified Health Center (FQHC), a County Clinic, a free clinic, a rural clinic, or a mental help clinic? Where will those essential and needed funds come from in the future? Will **Healthcare Reform** substitute something else for their future? Of course there are truly dozens of possible migratory economic resources that have been and will be tapped, and many clinics run under the aegis of thin margins from continuing grant funding; but wherein lies the essential great economic deep-pocket? "Texas"? – No, the word was, is and will always be "Taxes". The answer to how, where and when demands at least a brief look at a vital and well-functioning complex web of healthcare delivery brought about by previous **Healthcare Reform**. This dedicated health maintenance web for the 30 million uninsured had developed and evolved at local community levels and was most often referred to as America's great and wonderful "Health Safety Net".

Healthcare practitioners, public health programs and private charities loosely affiliated to continually spin, weave and knit these ever-evolving vital health safety nets in order to satisfy unmet medically necessary community needs, especially for the poor, vulnerable, and uninsured. Albeit that the general economy, political policy and local budget priorities do tend to economically alter and vary the level and volume of healthcare delivery via the safety nets; nonetheless the basic scope of evolutionary changes in this safety net system did and does fundamentally directly respond to an evolving level of reasonable patient healthcare delivery needs. These needs have historically been met by dedicated healthcare delivery practitioners either directly contracted, legally mandated, or by their plethora of charitable intents. In general, the "Safety Net Clinics" can boast with openness and pride, for they have provided a dignified high standard of medical outcomes from healthcare delivered with unwavering compassion, deep commitment and understanding of the wants and circumstances of disparity in diverse and underserved communities as well as to the unsheltered and homeless. These crucial and culturally appropriate healthcare delivery services have been and continue to evolve with continuous local safety net **Healthcare Reform**.

Known deficiencies in healthcare delivery, such as overburdened and rushed practitioners, lack of care coordination and follow-up after initial stabilization, and lack of patient knowledge and initiative for self-care have been directly addressed in the safety net system. Each medical school in California runs and supervises at least four medical student safety net clinics. The concept of the patient-centered "Medical Home" has been successfully introduced into the Safety Net, thereby increasing preventive care and integrating mental health and specialty services. Non-physician-centric "care coordination", especially for the socially and psychologically complex patient, via social workers and medical case workers has proven to be an essential element for the well-being of the public at large by reducing emergency room visits and improving the safety net populations' health. Treatment algorithms for chronic care in the safety net system tap into existing community services to coordinate clinical information systems with the intent of developing informed and activated self-management proactive patients to develop further innovative strategies for best practices in the safety net healthcare delivery system. Medical outreach to the homeless and telemedicine consulting are examples of internal **Healthcare Reform** via the safety net clinics. A new trust and personal attachment to the safety net clinic has rendered and most likely will increasingly render happier and healthier uninsured patients.

So, with all this healthcare delivery system's functionality in place and running at top speed, did any member of the United States federal legislature perchance remember his or her dear loving mother's advice – before you go about to repair, change or fix something via **Healthcare Reform:**

1. Be sure it is really broken.

2. Be sure to understand how, why and who broke in the first place so that you can make it better and prevent it from being broken again. Sadly, and unfortunately, it is doubtful that any members of the legislature that voted-in an unread piece of legislation – the PPACA – had any knowledge of or even cared to investigate the great and wonderful American Health Safety Net system of healthcare delivery. The number one thing that the safety net system truly needs for a sustainable fix is actually quite simple – it's Money, honey.

That said, it would have been ever so very easy to say, "Let's fix what is broken and build upon what works", but first American citizens and legislators alike had to agree on what exactly was broken and exactly what did not work in the past. This type of catchy-phrase rhetoric may have led one to assume that fundamental deficiencies and inefficient duplicative organizational systems, "funding and administrative issues" were on the table to be fixed, but that vitally needed bargaining table had not been set, and the dinner menu with transparent prices included had not been printed for public display, so last minute adjustments could again and did again substitute an entirely new set of menu selections and prices. Barriers to healthcare delivery such as interstate insurance sales and tort entanglements are what should have been on the menu to be removed, but those very practical and doable solutions amounted to no more than just namby-pamby pantiwaister wimpish wishes in the wailing winds, not any thoughtfully planned or guaranteed future reality. Beguiling rhetoric did not reveal that the secret "single" payer in a government-issued "public or common plan" triage system was more than one person; in painfully obvious reality, that mysterious governmental "single payer" was and will be really the more than 100 million people that regularly (and on time) paid, pay and will pay their very substantial USA taxes. (Note that nearly half of the people residing in the USA pay no direct federal income tax each April 15.) Most of the politically corrected verbiage that was redundantly bantered about needed a further critical translation down to a common sincere, honest and true "wordsmithing" that was easily understandable by all, followed by a sincere moral commitment to try to do for thy neighbor what thy neighbor cannot reasonably do for himself or herself.

Phony network provider lists exuded a nasty odor from the get-go; but there may also have been an obscured and much more insidious plan for their existence. After documenting the certified enrolling, the admitting of literally thousands of mandated-beneficiaries into ACA approved health plans, health insurance plans that obviously were grossly lacking in sufficient physician numbers to deliver anywhere near the medically necessary and assumedly expected healthcare delivery, one might somehow get the bright idea bulb going off in one's brain that an unfortunate but perhaps not unforeseen problem might possibly exist in the structural anatomy of those fraudulent plans. At first the enormous discrepancy in the physician-patient ratio would not manifest itself, but after about five years of progressively increasing problems with delivering sustainably adequate healthcare, the disturbing unbalance in the phony provider lists could/would no longer be adequately hidden, swept under some carpet or successfully ignored.

At this critical and chaotic point in time, two solutions might jump up to present themselves: The first would be to discredit and disband the obviously dishonest health insurance scheme. Thousands of patients would be suddenly totally lacking medical services and roaming the streets in organized discontent. The second would be to provide that sorely lacking medically-necessary healthcare delivery to the picketing horde of thousands via limited or non-licensed medical practitioners. Now, under the mantel of subduing the increasing stress from all that cleverly created chaos, which of the two solutions would one imagine to be the most likely to prevail?

As a remotely possible unexpected side benefit, the malpractice tort reform issue would be partially solved. With no expensive medical license for a physician practitioner to lose (at a cost of over half a million dollars incurred from form a decade or more of higher educational studies and apprenticeships for physicians) and no deep-pocket malpractice insurance coverage to bank on, the limited or non-licensed practitioners of new and improved primary care cookbook Medicine would not qualify as appropriate lucrative financial targets for various entities to sue. Even lawyers can't get blood out of a rock.

Finally, the unveiled goal: Americans would all be required to do more with less: The Accountable Care Act (ACA) was merely an unsecured and wobbling steppingstone that allowed Americans to be re-directed on the way to the stabilized structure of federal single payer National Socialized Healthcare, which would come with approvals and denials dictated by big government bureaucrats, mandated patient and physician participation and offerings of decreased services and decreased reimbursement from an increased variety of providers and practitioners. There would be decreased payments to providers of all types; there will be less of everything to go around, but everything in health care delivery that would be left over would be shared equally. Health plan insurance corporations would lose their autonomy and be governed and treated as a public utility. Akin to the insidious economic of ACA **Healthcare Reform** -- the entire new migratory economic delivery market would be dictated by governmental fiat. Americans would all be equal in opportunity for a basic level of healthcare delivery, and Americans would all enjoy less overall healthcare delivery while being treated by a decreasing percentage pool of American-trained physicians. The basic methodology of healthcare delivery would be poisoned and almost destroyed; but then uprooted, re-vegetated and regrown with genetically-altered new-age architecture. A healthcare delivery Phoenix remained dormant, yet sleeping soundly; but that bird will be destined to rise, spread its wings, and soar from the ruins of the old and decaying ACA migratory economic in **Healthcare Reform**.

Who was or will be ultimately be in control?..... As part of the daily buzz, free passes for reserved seats begged everyone to watch the grand spectacle – A gladiator elimination contest to the death in a grand coliseum. The future bloody battle between the feds versus the insurance corporations pretty much would relegate physicians and patients to the status of spectators in the bleachers. Claude Castonguay, one of the founding fathers, if not the architect, of the Canadian Healthcare System, stated: "We thought that we could resolve the system's problems by rationing services or injection of massive amounts of Money into it.......but now.....we are proposing to give a greater role to the private sector so that people can have freedom of choice." The clock was ticking in the USA, already past time to find new architectural designs to build a basic system of healthcare delivery through the migratory economics of **Healthcare Reform** that would function anew, almost but not quite past time for searching into the future with a different outlook and honoring the past with a new set of emphasis on old and yet functional archaic modalities/systems/mechanisms.

With only 20 million or so, depending on your favorite push-pull poll, American resident lives uninsured, the medical ecolo-nomic mutation to single national payer **Healthcare Reform** would not really consist of a leap or even a long step to administratively muster beyond the ACA. After all, the United States government has been the traditional single party payer of Medicare, Medicaid, Indian Health Services, Armed Services, Veteran Healthcare Services, Prison Healthcare, many state, municipal and all federal employee healthcare services, including services to the three administrative bodies in Washington, DC, and not to forget additionally many carved out services such as Child Health Services, entities such as Federally

Qualified Health Center (FQHC) services as well as domestic healthcare defense services.

Americans had to start with an investigation of their foundations and then build a case upon those immutable tenant corner-stones. Para-medical personnel and the introduction of waves of foreign trained physicians with general licenses to practice Medicine and deliver healthcare interstate, throughout 50 states and all USA territories, would soon be set to drive down costs by introducing and inducing true and valid national competition into healthcare delivery. Free and unhampered entrance into subsidized medical education for all hid just around the vapor path of an internet cloud. Innovative technological development with accompanying creative destruction will always be near impossible to completely halt, but future genetic-mediated preventions and cures will also bring down costs by eliminating the need for many expensive manual-directed procedures.

Corporate medical practice through long though out algorithms for group disease management already had been replaced by a dramatically improved system. There happened to be a new physician on the block that carried no black "doctors' bag" but generated treatment algorithms in a nanosecond. His name was -- "Doctor Watson" -- a DeepQA IBM supercomputer originally developed by David Ferucci. Doctor Watson had an artificial intelligence close to a Homo sapiens' cognitive reasoning ability, and could understand and answer questions posed as ordinary humans naturally speak and query. More than just replacing the help desk or telephone advise nurse at some health plan or hospital, Dr. Watson was able to take and record patient histories, correlate symptoms and objective findings, review the pertinent medical literature and ogles of patient charts, order appropriate tests, arrive at a most likely diagnosis and advise additional cost-effective treatment alternatives. CVS Health formed a partnership with IBM to utilize the "cognitive computing" IBM POWER7 Dr. Watson in a healthcare delivery cyberspace cloud to "better" manage chronic diseases, predict failing or deteriorating health, foresee any potential health crisis, and reduce emergency room admissions. IBM Supercomputer, "Watson, MD" could do and will do what is necessary to effortlessly push "House, MD" right out of his extraordinary "medical disease detective" job. But wait, if Mankind is still alive and kicking in fair health, there is more to come……

"In the year 2025" a giant medical milestone, a technological watershed event exponentially expands the availability and the use of Artificial Intelligence (AI). Dr. Watson will give birth to a technological offspring, a fantastic child super-super computer with 10 times parent DR. W's mother-board's I.Q.; and the AI creator, the human society, will readily accept the new baby AI's godlike healthcare delivery advice administered from on high, from the infinite knowledge storage clouds of the Virtual Internet, from the highest heavens to the lowly earth, quickly passing through the vast darkened Nebulas of aged Internet cloud systems in cyberspace. AI, Artificial Intelligence might someday threaten to rule the earth through this Virtual Internet, but enough with that science fiction stuff for now.....

A **Healthcare Reform** pendulum had not yet completely swung across the pit of healthcare delivery mechanisms and modalities; that weighted bar was yet still in early motion, eventually swinging from TV's Dr. Marcus Welby to the U.S. Spaceship Enterprise's Lieutenant Commander Leonard H. McCoy, Bones, MD: The now ancient yet classic American doctor had maintained an image of a kindly and charitable gentleman, making a house call carrying a hand-held "black doctors bag". That historical physician carried every bit of necessary pharmacy and medical technology in that little old "black doctors' bag". However, there was not much of either to lug around. About the year 1900, a leach in that hand-held black bag often served the primary role in a doctor's treatment modality preference list. **The holding of the patient's hand in the hand of the physician was of sacrosanct importance.** One hundred years later, the hand-held smartphone of the 21st Century doctor diagnosed disease states through a variety of macro and microscopic monitoring systems. With the patient's hand held in one of the physician's hands and a smart-probe in the physician's other hand, determinations of full-color three-dimensional heart function could be recorded in Katmandu and instantaneously interpreted by a super specialist in New Delhi. **The holding of the patient's hand in the hand of the physician continued to be of sacrosanct importance.** Startreck's Bones-MD would eventually carry a hand-held "Tricorder" an attractively attached scanner in a smart-looking case on his waist-belt. The Tricorder's sensor scanned a patient's medical aura, an aura that would reveal all sorts of pathology. The "Tricorder" then recorded the pathological data and analyzed that data for necessary changes to correct any pathological formations in the patient's patho-physiological aura. **The holding of the patient's hand in the hand of the physician yet continued be of sacrosanct importance. Bones regularly held his patient's hand in his own free hand** during the process and often found it very necessary to reassure those about him of his primary mission as a practicing physician to treat and cure disease states -- with frequent reinforcing exclamations such as, "Dammit Jim, I'm a Doctor, Not a Database." As clever or smart as they may be, **Dr. Watson and his super-smart progeny might have no hands**, but in the future **androids will have hands**. So that aforementioned pendulum or weighted bar was perhaps more likely a weighted bob at the end of string, a plumb bob directed to the center of the earth swung from a string line suspended from an on high in the sky hook, a foretelling and a remembering, quietly marking a continual circle in time, evolving while restating philosophical directives for all physicians from the past and for all the physicians that will ever be. Not to any dedicated physician's surprise, that simple message went along and goes along with what was once said by a 30-year-old Man, an ancient physician healthkeeper from the Island Kos, circa 430 BC; "Diseases are not punishments ordained from Olympus. The honorable duty of Mankind is, with dignity, to relieve suffering and keep the health." **Dr. Watson "et alii" will require that essentially important blue tooth module, the additional sacrosanct importance of an android physician's hand to hold a patient's hand.**

Way back in 1965, one of the co-founders of INTEL, Gorgon Moore, predicted that an exponential growth in technology would double memory capacity and computerized computational speed about every two years. That prediction was updated in 2010 to about every three years going forward from 2013. The fuse for a mobile wireless information and biomedical explosion had long been lit and is presently igniting the combustibles. Watch out for the glass-shattering sonic boom. Sleeping Beauty's wicked witch will be able to look into her "mirror-mirror on the wall" and instantaneously be diagnosed and advised corrective measures to improve her health and wellbeing as well as her complexion. The general-use stethoscope has already been replaced by a **hand-held** ultrasound unit run by a smartphone application. Various tablets, jail-broken just short of a brick, were rapidly readied for transmissions from neuro chips that can be inserted into the brain, chips that can allow paraplegics to walk, chips that will soon be old-hat when the nano-technology ultimately takes over. Sub-cutaneous implanted miniaturized chips will store all of Man's life encounters until that nano-technology produces little engines which will drive themselves anywhere in the human body to detect and correct any type of health or biochemical imbalance. Virtual medical examination visits or encounters with hands-free Dr. Watson AI or his future hands-on and more intelligent look-alikes will not be an end-all at all. One in five patients might still require actual hands-on practitioner healthcare beyond that simple yet **sacrosanct human hand-holding assurance**, but that will not be the source of dynamic competitive advantage in the healthcare industry. There will be a lot more expensive technology for Doctor Watson to compete with in the future and these new technological devices will not have to converse with Dr. Watson, their technological functions will be personalized to the individual patient.

Yes, there will be an endless flood, an inundating deluge of consumer products available for health and wellness that will flood then drown the medical ecolonomic landscape. Artificial retina smart phones will be available in an individualized contact lens; mobile robotics will produce an individualized TV's "million dollar Man" from a crippled human; individual genome analysis will allow production of individualized drugs; individualized stem cell banks will be able to target individualized cancer stem cells for permanent eradication; individual organ cloning will be enhanced with individual 3-dimensional organ printing; and individualized medical treatments will cure the "worried well" before their disease processes can be manifested. On the environmental front, over-dependence on fossil fuels will be curtailed, first with additives and paint-on pollution-absorbing compounds, and then end with disruptive technological advances that will finally mandate all polluting industrialization systems and agencies previously too big to fail to in fact fail and go to jail. But wait, the recidivistic and redundant use of the word "individualized" in the preceding horridly long run-on sentence was for dramatic effect; two or three migratory economic factors evolving **Healthcare Reform** seem to have slipped from true and accurate migratory economic accountability here:

1. Curing the masses of assumedly walking well and providing technological advancements for common-use may be a noble pursuit, but where and when to find those greenback dollars falling from the sky to pay their enormous bill is up for more than dispute or civil debate.

2. The migratory economic paradigm of "doing the best for the most number with the unfortunate sacrifice of the individualized individual" must have been drastically evolved if not totally rescinded to allow for future research and cost-advantaged timely commercial production with profitable sales of the ephemeral "top of the line" yet certainly technologically advanced medical devices.

3. The predicted participatory effort of the fast-food and entertainment-minded (Remember "bread and circus") American populace to take on a personalized preventive Medicine ethic is certainly desired and indeed hoped and prayed for, but that migratory economic paradigm evolving **Healthcare Reform** may not so readily come to fruition when placed in direct competition with altered public values and expectations influenced by capitalistic-driven addictive marketable commodities.

To ultimately better expose and explore the true healthcare linkage of Man with himself, his Money and his Medicine, all Americans will advance onto and into an era of AI-directed globalization in healthcare delivery. The cooperative efforts of medical practitioners from various countries and nations working together and collectively practicing the art of Medicine as fellow healthkeepers will be the ultimate solution. Globalization of healthcare delivery will most assuredly severe and brake all the inappropriate ties and constraints historically imposed by methodological nationalism. The Ebola virus epidemic was not a mere wake-up call to migratory economics in **Healthcare Reform**. The Ebola virus epidemic was a civil defense siren that sounded a wake-up call all around the globe. It is truly a global world that modern Man lives and plays in. Economist John Maynard Keynes once stated, "In the end we are all dead", so perhaps all of the previous political infighting concerning the migratory economics in **Healthcare Reform** was really "much ado about nothing". A decadent society did not, does not and will not promote health and wellbeing. A decadent society promotes neither the "art of living" nor migratory economic sustainability. Bread and Circus, the decadence of the Roman Empire, directly translates in the USA as an unfortunate migratory economic paradigm -- national nutritional policies and passive mass entertainment commodities for the uncaring and unconcerned passive observer that promote obesity, diabetes, hypertension, heart disease, osteoporosis, dementia, pollution of the air and food supply, violence, secularism, promiscuity and decreased fertility. This migratory economic paradigm cannot sustain itself; within 200 short years, the USA's population genetics will be 90% replaced by repopulated peoples. All the present-living USA peoples should look to treat those future diverse peoples, future citizens of the USA, as honored and invited guests; and acting as proper hosts, at least work a bit around the old homeland to tidy up the place, to offer them, the newcomers, a clean and healthy future to live in the United States of America.

Perhaps in partial response to those burning questions and statistics, the USA Institute for Health Improvement (IHI) set forth a three-point National Quality Strategy....
"Better Care": IMPROVE the overall quality by making healthcare more patient-centered, reliable, accessible, and safe.
"Healthy People/Healthy Communities": IMPROVE the health of the U.S. population with proven interventions to address behavioral, social and environmental determinants of health in addition to delivering higher-quality healthcare delivery.
"Affordable Care": IMPROVE by reducing the cost of quality healthcare for individuals, families, employers, and government.

Given, that Man, his Money and his Medicine utilize an evolving set of morals to interpret and label with absolute eternally proclaimed pronouncements of "good or evil", and given, that logically looking from afar at the "big picture", morals merely denote and connote a temporary culturally accepted standard adhered to by an ephemeral contemporary society for an even more temporary period of time. Then it can be therefore reasoned that all of this "improvement" or **Healthcare Reform** had to conform and adjust to a current set of mores and customs that prevail as well as to the direct forces of continual change in specified special interest groups: the specific **"concerns"** of patients, practitioners, big business and federal government:

Patient concerns had evolved: The culture of American Medicine had evolved well beyond the point of patients unwilling to accept depersonalized and non-physician care. Most of the public masses were quite willing to accept unquestioning belief in Internet healthcare algorithms without bothering to research or enquire any further. American made "Apps" were readily available on cell phones to consult a "DOCTOR". When the poorly thought out 1996 Clinton Administration HIPPA requirements seemed violated, apps were developed in China and Germany for sale in the USA. Immediate access trumped quality care in their reasoning processes. There was of course continual concern, however, as to what amount of healthcare delivery could be considered basic care and exactly what amount had been politically termed "Cadillac" healthcare. The increased percentage of aged in the population were also quite concerned about what degree, that is to say, what **scope, amount, and duration** degree their entitled healthcare delivery insurance payments extended into long term and end of life healthcare delivery, a consistent stormy cost which continually rained down upon them; and eventually that pouring rain soaked up all their life-long savings.

More efficient healthcare delivery systems/mechanisms had evolved, from individual impersonal department store counter-service Medicine to mass concert hall evaluation and management systems to care for the two most expensive healthcare delivery items of the 21st Century -- chronic disease ailments and Aged American Disability and Depression (AADD). Furthering the efficiency and expediency of these aforementioned evolved diagnostic and treatment regimens, systems and mechanisms lowered the cost of care but not necessarily the quality of healthcare delivered. "Transparency", an interesting word, but what a growing percentage of patients wanted and deserved. "Transparency" proves to be the ability to know the immediate cost, implicit costs and varied outcomes derived from a particular healthcare delivery service administered from a number of mutually competing vendors and providers. That select minority of the populace is merely begging for the very reasonable right to make an informed decision before some product, commodity or service on their computer sales wish list or preliminary check-out basket actually is moved to the cart in anticipation of a paid purchase. Yes, some patients really wanted the ability to shop and compare prices so that they could get the biggest bang for their buck on an item per item basis, but the overwhelming majority of patients most likely and unfortunately continued to chronically suffer from the horrid moral hazard of loss of personal responsibility attributable to supposedly "free" insurance coverage and would not really care one lick about "transparency". The carriers and politicos, of course, would also be quite content with the anti-transparent reluctance to allow their never viewed secret spread sheets open to public scrutiny. In brief, without too much effort in the direction of aggressive bargaining, patients ultimately would trade a bit of choice and quality for cost containment. To paraphrase an old, buried but forever revered Philadelphian, Ben Franklin, "Those who trade choice or quality for cost get neither".

Physician concerns persisted: Once upon a time there were five readily recognized and questionably respected professions, or perhaps only four respected if "the oldest profession" is not to be considered: Military, Clergy, Law and Medicine. The profession of Medicine evolved away from being physician-patient centric. An established three-way medical service payment policy always remained contrary to the tenets of the Hippocratic Oath. As medical entitlement programs increased, the concept of physicians donating pro-bono or charity healthcare delivery for the unfortunate sector of the public decreased; more dollars into entitlement programs resulted in less physician dollars into pro-bono activities and frank charity. Allocation of doctor time necessarily followed because the practice of Medicine became federally adjudicated a trade and could no longer be legally called a true profession. Physicians no longer independently set, monitored, and enforced standards. The practice of a profession is a public sanctioned and public accountable privilege; what the public giveth the public may taketh away and unintentionally be deprived of the benefit forever in so doing. Yes, for about 100 years, physicians remained as a select group with special training not easily or commonly obtained, and some yet were dedicated to a life-long practice during which they used their skills for the benefit of the public before self, fulfilling a crucial need for the public more competently that the public could do for itself. The average physician, now unquestionably an employee enacting a known set of employee grievances, had first been told to increase productivity by working "smarter"; but when the crucial point of accumulated straws on a camel's back became so painfully obvious, physicians began to ask, "Just how much "smarter" can you get"? Aggravated name-calling conflicts concerning executive political alliances and progressive manifesto actions on the part of medical societies and associations such as the American Medical Association (AMA) divided the house of Medicine. A nearly extinct dinosaur grouping of private fee-for-service physicians found themselves continually at odds with institutionalized salaried practitioners. Private concierge Medicine practices vied with algorithmically derived medical homes sponsored by corporate medical insurance establishments. The classical image of physician autonomy shrank in importance then blurred its form and vanished from consideration in a new and yet evolving cost-effective business world of medical practice. A concomitant new ideal, a concept of leisure time and the art of living pervaded the physician practitioner routines and resulted in a limitation of medical practice hours with a concomitant lowered expectancy for income, power, and wealth to pass on to future physician generations – beginning insidiously during internship and residency and extending to limited visionary horizons and a limited cathexis for dedication to life-long medical practice. In this new age, medical students severely limited their investment of mental and emotional energy to a life-long marriage with a profession of medical practice. The new young doctor uniformly advocated for universal-governmental single payer healthcare delivery "JOBS" with regular weekly daytime punch clock log in and log out paid hours, hopefully on a "permanent part-time" basis. There was little to no concern about who would be there to care for patients who presented themselves on nights and weekends with urgent but non-emergent medical problems. That coverage solution, not completely solved at national physician union negotiating tables, encouraged the importation of an increasing percentage of foreign-trained physicians.

Physician leadership roles in this age of medical practice evolved into prominent types -- the physician practice manager-leader versus the physician business-industry-leader. Just having a MD behind one's name in this day and age did not in any way imply or signify that the named individual cared a lick for the welfare or plight of other fellow physicians as originally professed by Hippocrates, nor did the "MD" title offer sufficient credential and privilege evidence that one was knowledgeable or competent enough to administer any current treatment methodologies; or in fact that such and individual had ever in a lifetime actually independently treated one single patient for anything. For most new physician-CEOs, the MD was just an interim stepping-stone degree attained before finally enrolling in some geographical or Internet-based business school to attain an MBA/PhD and many degrees beyond.

Ancillary healthcare delivery extenders also had concerns: As naturally to be expected, the void left by physician non-participation in primary medical healthcare delivery had to be filled and in fact was filled by ancillary healthcare delivery "extenders". At first, these extenders were driven, produced and certified by physician-organized programs; but as their need dramatically increased, apprenticeships sprung up as did the Biblical lawyers, "like weeds after a storm". That need extended far beyond any training barrier and far beyond a history and physical exam. Flu shots could be best obtained where they were most commonly administered -- at the local supermarket. Optometrists had for some time been legally certified to do laser eye surgery in some states. Nurse Practitioners (NP) regularly performed right heart catheterizations in hospitals and ran independent birthing and medical treatment centers not affiliated with physicians or hospitals. Physician Assistants (PA) not only opened and closed complicated surgical operations but also independently operated during a significant portion of the surgical procedure and followed through with inpatient and out of hospital post-operative patient care, all done without the direct aid of the operating surgeon. Without mandatory direct consultation from a sleeping specialist, specialty-trained PA's were routinely sent to the Emergency Room at night to evaluate and manage surgical patients after an Emergency Room physician called for a specific surgical specialty consultation. PAs and NPs discovered the legal ability to prescribe unlimited drugs and totally independent administering or performing surgical procedures hid just around the corner. In certain sectors of medical practice, expertise had gone beyond the level of the practicing physician. For instance, a hospital-based clinical pharmacist routinely revoked and re-wrote physician drug orders, and the same was often true for physician prescriptions to physical therapists; so there was only at most a very weak argument preventing those "ancillary healthcare delivery extenders" from becoming "licensed independent practitioners" (LIPs). The Medical social worker and the Medical Case Management specialist were better equipped and adept than physicians when it came down to primary preventive care and preventing patients from too frequently returning to the Emergency Room. Patient evaluation score cards rating their healthcare experience usually ranked extenders significantly higher than the very few physicians that they encountered.

So what would a group of average patients from the overwhelming masses rather have serve them, an old and dying Dinosaur physician or a newly welcomed space alien Licensed Individual Practitioner (LIP) and/or an emerging non-licensed medical practitioner assistant's assistant? The new choice to lay down one's betting Money was between tired and retired remnants of fee-for–service versus the emerging vivacious general medical extender practitioners and their new-found assistants. The progressive devaluation of a physician's cognitive ability and a near complete devaluation of a physician's stored intellectual knowledge already had proved previous and especially future expensive medical education to be a very poor investment. The intellectual medical knowledge and algorithms contained within computer cookbooks already provided value-added cost-effective recipes to alleviate or possibly cure nearly any set of symptoms. The emerging ethic of equal work for equal pay regardless of prerequisite qualifications was also already placing generalist physicians' salaries far below the dollar level of many specialized physician assistants and nurse practitioners. In any case, the ultimate survival of the "art of Medicine" became limited and available to only a few pay-as-you-go patients through new distinct healthcare delivery pathways, and that ancient art of Medicine was practiced only at limited and/or exempted geographical locations. Certain exempt and quite fiscally sustainable specialty surgical practices at specialized national institutions outside the public healthcare delivery system and often outside the USA already offered cash-only surgery. These unique higher quality specialty practices surely not only survived, but also lived long and continued to prosper due to the persistence of a significantly large select group of direct-pay patient consumers. Especially with the globalization of medical practice, financially rewarding medical practice outlier systems sustained survival for specific individual doctors who also offered and practiced the continuance of that sacrosanct doctor–patient relationship and the "art of Medicine" in a worldwide fee-for–service environment.

Then there still was the matter of **third party and/or/versus government concerns**: All the "single payer" arguments really boiled down to these opposing political commentaries: The stated purpose of a "public plan" is to offer uninsured citizens a mechanism to be insured by cutting the costs of health insurance, decreasing their dollar enrollment rates and increasing popular enrollment. However, if the government maintained a truly a level playing field to compete with services and incentives offered by private plans, then those same private plans could simply compete among themselves and there would be no point to having a "public plan" offered by the government. If, on the other hand, the government offered incentives (other peoples' tax dollars) that gave the "public plan" an unfair dynamic competitive advantage over the private plan competitors, then the "public plan" would naturally and gradually gain enrollees to the point of dominance and eventually replace the existing private healthcare insurance market. Quoting Mark McClellan, a director for Medicare during the President Bush administration, "You can't have it both ways. Either the government plan can substantially lower costs by exerting power that other plans don't have; or, if you go the other way, and you don't give the public plan any special advantages, and you make sure it doesn't get too big -- in that case, it's not going to be any less costly -- So, what's the point?"

In simply three words, the concerns of all the third parties really boiled down to a bunch of dead American presidents on new aquamarine greenbacks – United

States Dollars. Private corporative interests vied with the Federal Government as a healthcare delivery institution because the private middleman got rich and stayed rich. Corporations only sought to be assigned to or aligned with the governmental programs for a potential huge cut of the action. The rationed-adjustable humanistic "spread" in the gamble became delegated to a betting of-and-on the odds, not the quality of the healthcare delivery.

As an additional reminder of unsustainable governmental promises, here is a forgotten governmental promise from a long past half-century, at the precise time when the Medicare legislation was originally enacted:
"Nothing in this title shall be construed to authorize any federal officer to exercise any supervision or control over the practice of Medicine or the manner in which medical services are provided or over the selection, tenure, or compensation of any officer or employee of any institution, agency, or person providing health services....."
Not so amazing and astounding to anyone, the healthcare insurance industry had long ago quickly and completely ground that migratory economic -- that exactly quoted physician-comforting fantasy admonition -- ground it into dust and then scattered the remains to the eternal winds of time.

National single payer healthcare delivery, once attained, will not be America's final medical ecolo-nomically adaptive **Healthcare Reform** solution to a sustainable quality and accessibility of medical care -- Evolution never stops. After Y2K, the total amount of human knowledge doubled. The unveiling of the magic of chromatin explained a **21st Century scientific watershed event -- the breaking of the histone code.** Cloning of human tissues began in Italy way back in 2001. The expected human life span, prolonged by public health measures in the governmental sector and genetic engineering in the drug industry produced an elderly American population that doubled during the years 2000 to 2050.[121] Aged American Depression and Disability (AADD) along with chronic disease became the number one healthcare delivery concern. People lived healthier and longer lives, but then witnessed their health rapidly decompensate over a few months before death. The total USA population eventually increased in an acceptable linear fashion with a continued decrease American citizen fertility compensated by increased immigration, which was not really significant when compared to concomitant exponential increases in world population, due to uncontrolled birth rates continually accelerating the biomass of population -- limited contraception combined with overall better healthcare, health and longevity, especially during

---

[121] U.S. Bureau of the Census, "We the American Elderly", U.S.Gov.Print.Office, D.C., 1993

the population productive years of life.

Does "Man's" moral and ethical obligation per Hippocrates, "to cure pain and suffering and keep the health" rest on the basis of religion? "The world is my representation"; 18th Century aristocratic philosopher Arthur Schopenhauer contended that a basic dissatisfaction ingrained in "Man", an endless will that caused pain and suffering, continually drove Man to seek satisfaction for his existence, found best through the "transcendental ideology" of aesthetic contemplation and atheism that can ultimately lead to a form of human compassion. The anti-religious son of a Lutheran pastor, Friedrich Nietzsche, a dedicated disciple of 19th Century German political and social thought, admonished that the continuance of Western Culture ultimately depended on Man's ability to transcend the hurt and decadence engendered by fundamental amoral abandonment of faith that so easily leads to a meaningless existence. Nietzsche feared that the political tools of politically subversive organized religions would not suffice to stem this overwhelming tide, and a "Superman/Uberman or Übermensch" may or may not arise to aid ordinary Man's emergence into his "Eternal Return" and ultimately justify his existence. Man's rise to action would be urgently needed before the unstoppable advancing of time, ending in complete and total societal implosion. Man must feel the pain in time to be on time to react by fleeing and freeing himself from the imminent disaster. Joseph Schumpeter's designated-named "Italian Adam Smith", criminologist and economist Cesare Beccaria taught that in human nature, "the proximate and efficient cause of action is the flight from pain: the final cause of action is the love of pleasure, Man rests in good times and acts when in pain." But the determination of just how much hurt and pain might be necessary to reach the exact tilting point or final piled straw tolerated on a proverbial camel's back "for Man to react" is complicated and certainly difficult to accurately calculate, as Nietzsche had admonished.

The loss of nuclear family values and politically advocated generalized secularism such as, "It takes a village to raise a child" led to a further loss of religious faith within the American society, and a further decreased fertility rate. That American population fertility rate had been already lowered further by the politically encouraged free use of "government-paid" birth control modalities from an age level of beginning adolescence and the unfortunate routine casual use of abortion, often as a routine birth control modality mechanism that often was employed beyond 24 weeks of a healthy pregnancy. California Health and Safety Code Section 123460-123468 states that abortion is unauthorized if performed on a viable fetus where continuation of the pregnancy poses no risk to life or health of the pregnant woman. Add to this the Latin sentence, "Leges Sine Moribus Vanae", which translates -- laws without morals are in vain or useless. Now question why there was relatively little public outcry after the many sanctioned inter-uterine injections of lethal substances such as potassium chloride into otherwise unproven to be abnormal and thereby possibly normal late term fetuses so that a late in trimester electively aborted "stillbirth", a non-viable fetus, could be assured with consistency in a fetal ultrasound test five minutes later. This unfortunately quasi-legal maternal medical practice custom, haven arisen from a moral acceptance of what would have historically been considered frank and amoral malpractice, removed financial and malpractice liability from hospitals and physicians. They would have been otherwise faced and pressured with denying healthcare delivery to an unwanted live newborn baby in acute medical need of resuscitation and intensive care after a late term elective abortion. Was that poorly informed and unadvertised scheme connived through some sort of secret progressive administrative collaborative intrigue or plot that allowed an immoral "Death Panel" action to occur, or is it really that difficult to determine when the sanctity of a human life actually begins?

A prediction: They had all judged amiss, for they had forgotten the power and glory of the continually churning diverse ingredients in the uniquely American crucible. Those diverse genetics produced, are producing and will continue to produce a different kind of "Ubermen" for the American future, and that strictly American cultural product will definitely and defiantly react to the predicted societal pain and transcend all societal hurt and abandonment admonished by the aforesaid philosophers and politically actuated decisions of old.

An organized High-Teck healthcare delivery system with Nano-Technology in the second half of the 21st Century quickly came to be termed a "GTO", (not a homologated Ferrari touring sport car -- Gran Turismo Omologato -- or a sixties tri-carb muscle car by Pontiac), but a "Genetic Transformation Organization". Nano-markers circulating about the human body alerted various interest groups as well as the individual via holographic voice and image transmissions. [122]

---

[122]

HOLOGRAPHIC INTERNET TRANSMISSION :

KatieJane#3@holo.net

How is my great grandpapa papa doing? -- I love you, and thanks so much for the "snow rocket", the 36-volt lithium, slick slider (SS) air-propelled snowboard that you designed and produced with your personal portable 3-D printer -- what a great Christmas present!

Me?....

I'm once again spending the Christmas holidays up in North Lake Tahoe with granny K1 -- your Tech-Gen daughter Katie, the "pioneer woman". She is really great with me. She certainly never had any of those thoughts that "lay buried, unspoken, for many years in the minds of American women", but she is now such a "prude". (I think that was your generation's word -- or possibly your mom's?) I can't believe that granny K1 pioneered women's enrollment at NMMI, a previously all-male military college, or that she ever surfed the diamond runs on a snowboard. Is it true that she landed a role in a childhood production of "Little Abner" just because she was the only girl that could act while holding a live pig? Because now, she just keeps harping on me about the dangers of my new SS power air-glider board. I just love my new SS. Mom (K2) and dad are hesitant to jump on and try a "sweep". Check out the holo-clip of me making some nasty moves over Diamond Peak on my SS at the end of this transmission! It is sooo great to be a Nano Generation girl!!!

Lake Tahoe is just so addicting beautiful -- crisp, sparkling, and clear to the bottom. No more of that green sludge any more -- Genetically Engineered (GE) Nano gobblers gobbled up all those terrible nitrates and phosphates and then fell tumbling to the bottom of the lake, where the sticky backsides of the Nano gobblers glued themselves onto MTBE precipitate from old California gasoline that had been coating and contaminating the lake-bottom. A subsidiary of the GE nano-company easily scooped up the non-water-miscible precipitate of fat-backed Nano gobblers and shipped tons upon tons of all those little nasties way out to Kansas. Those fat-backs now fertilize GE king kernel corn -- the genetically-altered variety with GE tiny leaf pores that promote exuberant plant growth in a minimal moisture environment.... Nuff bout that stuff....

OK – The answers to your two sharply provocative questions that only my great grandpapa papa is allowed to ask –

"What's new with my sweetie K3's life?", and "How about my sweetie K3's love life?"

Answer #1:

Same old, same old; SOS, DDSS. Why doesn't anything around here seem to change? Time is fleeting; time is my enemy; and I need a new one of those things you like used to call a "job". Why so? "Jobs" are just creative distractions-diversions, created to keep Man's evolved society occupied and out of trouble. Historically, work and "jobs" became more important along with expanding humanism, during a time of secularization and loss of interest in devout religious practices. In the 19th Century, everyone labored, but only about 9% to 14% of the population enjoyed true, scripted "job" employment. (So very few could complain, "That's not my job".) In the 20th Century, "jobs" were created for about 90% of the population, most of whom thought that they were doing something that was somehow vitally necessary for a productive society. "Job" creativity evolved. Superfluous, intermediary small business owners suddenly found themselves unable to do their own office management and office dusting. Ultra small businesses reinvented middle management and labor stratified itself once again. The office manager took on assistants; the office duster and the office floor sweeper belonged to separate unions, etc. In the second half of the 21st Century only 9% to 14% of "jobs" are really necessary, but this time everybody is acutely aware of the social and statistical significance of those "jobs".

Guaranteed employment ended after the first half of the 21st Century. An employee today has to continually show and prove that she/he is increasing the "value" of the business (multiple definitions of that word "value" still dynamically compete for relevance). If not, then the function of the employee is without merit and the "job" is terminated. Strangely enough, a new "job" is then immediately created.

435

What am I going to do that can contribute to some increased "value", and how am I going to go about it? How about a stint at healthkeeping? You told me that healthkeeping used to be the rage, an inspiring and challenging art and science of medical practice and healthcare delivery; but nostalgic reverence is one thing that has certainly changed.

Whose fault was it? Who had the incipient bright idea? Who was to blame, or who was to credit? Who cares? 1973 may have been the start of it all with the defining of recombinant DNA. Or perhaps I can go back farther in contemporary measurable distance of time and blame/credit Watson and especially the genius of Crick for igniting a technological campfire with a spark from the twisting of a double helix. That genetic hotspot got out of control about the Y2K, when the entire human genome was finally mapped. That campfire overflowed its campgrounds to become a wildfire in the forest of enquiry. A scientific inferno rampaged the countryside; the technological DNA research forest set ablaze and all too soon lost containment. Medical cryptographers a generation later broke the histone code and unveiled the magic of chromatin. Medical ecolo-nomics intensified the conflagration with additional fuel. Healthkeepers developed Genetic Transformation Organizations (GTOs). Drug companies flourished by providing the proper proteins and peptides to alter and/or simulate the action of human, animal, plant, and not yet invented genomes. Healthkeeper engineers continually redefined the concept of applied genetics, as with the development of independent organ cloning. That DNA technology forest fire paradigm eventually burned Nano markers and Nano transmitters under electron microscopes.

Now here sit I with my Nano Generation (NG) left to deal with all the unforeseen and some unintended consequences. I can't and won't keep a gig that lasts more than five years. I don't desire the continued repetitive work, and the work really doesn't need me. My NG has a globally uniform negative growth rate, and is constantly surrounded and inhibited by nagging old and ancient living people. The 20th Century ephemeral concept of retirement has long since melted away. A good number of these oldsters actually started out as pre-historic late Baby Boomers, but most of those constantly complaining about our major healthcare delivery concern -- Aged American Disability and Depression (AADD) -- are from that ancient (and confused) Generation "X". The Generation Xers brilliantly survived the "Dot-com Renaissance". Why have they refused to get any of the new nano-implants to monitor their health? Such continued arrogance intensifies that X-Generation gap! You, great grandpapa papa, are from an even older generation – you lie of course and pretend to be as young as a late Baby Boomer (you are actually my very favorite pre-Boomer, of course), but you at least have a nano-implantable six-language translator-transceiver with a voice and remote activated defibrillator. You can order your favorite chiffon cake in any language, anywhere in the world. (Big deal -- you can order, "Chiffon cake", but you still can't eat any chiffon cake unless your loving little darling K3 bakes, with great granny nonna's secret recipe!) Do the Generation Xers feel cheated in that they were promised a tapestry of Baby Boomer retirement benefits and then had those cash reserves and unjustified "entitlements" pulled away from under their feet as they blindly stood on their multiple imaginary benefit and pension rugs?

Then there is back to me, myself, and I – I'm a young adult post mid-21st Century, one of the early Nano Generation babies. I'm really battling the old "Technological Generation" of "Renaissance-Y" power that controls and refuses to get out of my "job" market. Those old guys and especially those little old lady "share-a-job" coffee clutches of Tech Gen gals (like dear granny K1) will probably stay employed long enough to tick off my great grandchildren. I have already obtained three post-graduate degrees through Holo-net studies, but many other Nano-Geners have done the same. All that effort amounted to not much in one-upmanship for us over those Terrible-Techies. I'm now contemplating Wharton's dynamic competitive strategies for more effectual long term planning. The healthkeepers tell me that I will live well past the now traditional 120-year mark, but I don't trust them, so I decided to become one myself, one of those Physician-Healthkeeper-Facilitators (PHFs). I do trust you and your life-long example of medical practice, great grandpapa papa; and I also truly feel that deep, inner "propensity to serve" emotion, which you have found to be so personally rewarding throughout your life.

Mobility is no problem. Nobody actually owns a home anymore. Nobody saves for retirement -- there is no retirement! There is no famine or lack of shelter for anyone in America. Higher education and all sorts of research opportunities are universally available and free to all on the Holographic Internet. Everyone has a communicator, and more and more people are opting for the implantable variety. "Urban Legend" persists, and there was a false fright last year that a sterility gene was linked to a communicator implant. Gen Xer paranoia?

Society is seamless, and I can slip in anywhere. I have only to test the waters and see if I can adequately market myself. I checked out "healthkeeper.com" on the Holo-Net and found that I needed only two more Internet courses to qualify for an entrance exam entitled "Physician-Healthkeeper-Facilitator-Apprenticeship, the PHFA exam". (I can't fathom how you tolerated a geographically stagnant "medical school" in Philadelphia for four years to get your "MD" degree and then did an indentured servitude intern stint there in Philly before qualifying for an independent license to practice healthkeeping.) I am taking the PHFA-required courses now with a few friends in a study group. I prefer small private learning groups over those massive government-run higher education centers -- you know, those "free" public Holo-Net educational clinic centers that have replaced what used to be the infamous California state college and university systems. Pink Floyd never foresaw that dark educational brick in the wall!

Once I pass the PHFA exam, I can apprentice in some Nano-medical or Nano-surgical specialty for two years, and then qualify for a Physician-Healthkeeper-Facilitator, the PHF examination. After I pass the PHF exam, I can practice as a PHF for five years. At that point, and at every subsequent five-year point to follow, I will be required to take a re-certification exam. Should I unfortunately not score high enough on the initial exam, but still score above the norm, I could work as a Physician Assistant and qualify to retake the PHF exam in one year. Most likely, after one or possibly two five-year gigs as a PHF, I would move on to some other personally rewarding and mentally fulfilling field of endeavor.

Nanotechnology really took over after 2025. Nano toys -- the building of all types of computers from the molecular level are the "Gilbert Erector Sets" or "Legos" of my Nano Generation. Personalized health monitoring nano-implants are the fad. Nano-microsonic devices control the common cold by making viruses so drunk with "nano-rock music" that the little viral varmints forget how to cross cell membranes – and then merrily, merrily, merrily dance themselves to death. Great granny nonna told me that our nano-scientists must have researched the dance idea from your ΣN college fraternity parties, when you two were "dating". I understand that "dating" was a chivalrous remnant, a historical cultural-sexual separation concept that existed when men yet yearned for "feminine approval" and women still sought "masculine security" in pre-marital exclusivity relationships. You know, that just doesn't happen anymore. Maybe I'm old fashioned, but I must admit that I do personally seek out those emotions from my parents.

Yes, Sir Francis Bacon finally got his 17th Century wish. We now have a system of healthcare delivery rules and regulations to outwit human intelligence and reason. Since the historical unacceptable high cost of healthcare delivery logically resulted from third party corporations profiting in a labor-intense techno-driven industry, cheaper labor and industrial automation accomplished equilibrium of cost, access, and quality. Now, Physician-Healthkeeper-Facilitators are needed and utilized for diagnostic and treatment revisions in less than nine percent of healthcare disease states. The PHFs like to call themselves "healers", but nobody else does. Genetic Engineered programs have changed medical treatments and just about eliminated surgical "cut and sew" indications. Most all of the elective surgical procedures performed in the 20th Century are no longer necessary, sanctioned or warranted. Ralzak's functional

MRI interview is now an every-day occurrence, with totally portable monitoring via a downloadable app to boot.

The basic aggressiveness of the human race can be easily altered with established genetic transformation magic, but that GE prestidigitation is officially illegal. Such Alteration Technology (AT) remains as our second great social controversy. Simply ignoring the existence of AT best solves most of our troublesome social controversies. Therefore, physical trauma still persists and remains the most lucrative aspect of healthkeeping for a PHF. Trauma healthcare delivery demands immediate attention and immediate availability from a PHF. (Stat work also pays extra bucks.) The funding comes from the Federal Homeland Safety and Defense (FHSD) budget. 99% of all healthkeeper profits, however, are from nanotechnology sales.

What about our first great social controversy? Its political-technical fallout worries us every day. This number one controversy is more than troublesome, and just can't be ignored. The "Star Trek" fad ended long ago, and a century-old "Battlestar Galactica" is the new political football. In addition to Avatars, which constantly record and instantly recall all my life's activity, we have the technology to make Independent Artificial Intelligence (IAI) -- computers that think, analyze, and "keep on learning" -- computers that are smarter than we are, computers that can independently out-think and out-reason us, computers that don't need us -- should we continue to advance or even use this known and possibly unmanageable technology? Should we embark on much more dangerous evolutionary courses than those debated during the human cloning controversy of the 20th Century? Ours is not an industrial revolution where we are afraid of losing our "jobs" -- hell; we don't even care much about our "jobs" anyway. We are really afraid of losing our species. At this point, there is no controversy about cloning super-humans -- at least they would evolve from our human genes. IAI development is like encouraging a takeover of planet earth by a dark, evil empire with no Luke Skywalker to save us. The unintended consequence may be that there will be no time to worry about the fleeting of time, if time's passage becomes, for us, no more.

Your second question -- "How about my sweetie K3's love life?" -- How about what love life?

I'm just a lonely little dandelion flower, totally lost and ignored in a great expansive meadow, in full bloom, and about to suddenly wilt, go to seed and be forever blown away. Yeah, knew you wouldn't even budge to buy that scenario! --- Actually, I've had my eye on this cute and intelligent guy who conveniently has been one of my H-Net study partners for the past year. He is also applying for the PHFA exam next month. Granny K1 is constantly over-stuffing him with food every time he turns around, and she refers to him as the "hottie". And yes, great grandpapa papa, you have indoctrinated me well -- he is also a "responsible" person. I'm still in the stalking stage of our relationship, but my snare-trap is set with a hair trigger. What he perhaps doesn't know is that he has already stepped well into the catchment area of my encircling snare-ring. Quoting from granny K1's childhood theater line, "Thar be no runnin' fo' em', come Sadie Hawkins Day!"

By the way, his father graduated from the last remaining "medical school" in America, which oddly enough was also the first medical school in America. You know, at the same university at which you and great granny nonna met when you were both a "sweeter" seventeen. Well, my sweet Bo's father set up an "Ivy League Consortium" of surgical practitioners that work on a cash basis and have their offices and surgical facilities in New Delhi, India. They also have cash-on-demand care contracts with several American companies and international corporate co-ops.

Great grandpapa papa, I know how you relish and delight in telling tall tales about haphazard human anthropology; but I am really uncomfortable with human history. Even when I search back, beyond "the

Continuing technological discoveries coupled with social adaptations and population migrations created an unstoppable force, a concomitant new longevity and better quality of completely new-age genetically modified health preservation delivery arose to become readily available for all the people on planet earth. Even greater challenges will surely be continually created to continually modify the social ecology and economic mores of future healthcare delivery modalities -- for MEDICAL ECOLO-NOMICS, by American HEALTHKEEPERS in the future 22nd Century, to determine and express quality and accessibility through progressive migratory economic evolutionary **Healthcare Reform.**

Rush-hour big city freeway traffic demonstrated an evolved complacency of lowered expectations among the masses of people on their stop-and-go way to and from their daily work. Traditional healthcare access freeways have also been consistently stymied with huge traffic jams. Administrative historical solution created Pre-Pay express lanes that moved much more quickly, but at the time-wise opportunity expense of those complacent smug individuals with lowered expectations, the greater masses of people unwilling to pay any extra cost for access to their needed healthcare delivery. The overwhelming majority of healthkeeper-seekers remained incredibly satisfied or perhaps mesmerized, creeping along at a snail's pace in a randomly selected but no-extra-cost traffic lane, patiently waiting for the highway to come to some foreseeable end. Then the long wait ended. Futuristic **Healthcare Reform** dispensed of that wasted time and effort by magically eliminating the need for all that traffic. Continued discoveries of evolving disruptive technological advancements forced that entire highway system concept into extinction.

The futuristic transportation and exploration concept of the ancient winding **Via Appia**, Western Civilization's first road, was never envisioned as a construct that would come to an eventual end. That cobblestone road, built from Rome to Brindisi, serviced a gateway to the Adriatic, next on, on to the Mediterranean Sea, then onward to better link one culture with another, and finally on to better expose and explore the true link of Man with Mankind. Likewise, the road to universal

---

summer of the Roman year 699", I sense myself becoming a forgotten and hopelessly disoriented human in an unbelievably awesome universe. Is my phobia of history a future shock, or is the total human species story just too short or an evolutionary accident about to supernova? My beloved great grandpapa papa, please tell me, what ever did happen to dear prehistoric Ardi? Was he really a naive, happy, and adventure-less Hobbit, or was he more like me?

XXX OOO -- Katie -- K3 Your loving, third generation, "Calamity Jane"
PS -- How about my SS holo-clip? Please, pretty please, don't transmit the clip back to granny K1! Let's keep my adventures our secret—kiss, kiss. ------ **Holographic Download Completed**

single payer healthcare delivery for the United States does not end at a designated national or international border. That road is also a future gateway. Americans now live and forevermore will live in an era of active, elbow to elbow dynamic global competition. The often tedious and frustrating construction of that USA healthcare delivery road was, is and increasingly will be a definite part of medical ecolo-nomic evolution played on an expanding and culture-linking world-wide stage. The globalization era for highest quality healthcare delivery and migratory economic **Healthcare Reform** has long since arrived and will not depart after America has enjoyed and then surpassed its GTO era. That bumpy winding medical ecolo-nomic road, with all its testy trials and tribulations, mastered then won an evolutionary contest of endurance. The USA road will transform into a newly engineered future super healthcare delivery highway, the **Via of Healthcare Reform,** a transportation marvel that will not only merely service an expanding gateway to all the seas, oceans and land masses of this world, but also a fiscally sustainable superhighway that will eventually service worlds to come, and a multi-lane freeway that will economically assure all its many lanes remain open and running 24/7 – to replace yesterday's regrets with anticipation for tomorrow -- to continuously create new and wonderful frontiers, opportunities for all American healthkeepers, for all varieties of healthcare delivery providers and healthcare delivery recipients -- to happily explore and enjoy their one and only chance for a precious ephemeral but exquisitely marvelous human life and for experiencing a humanistic art of living. The illumination serving that new road of **Healthcare Reform** will be a beacon for freedom and opportunity that will continue to make the USA the greatest nation on planet earth, an inspirational and charismatic leader for the rest of the world to follow and emulate for generations to come.

--30—

THE EXACT NUMBER

OF

AUTOPSIES PERFORMED

BY

LEONARDO DA VINCI

BEFORE TERMINATED

BY A

PAPAL BULL

TO

CEASE AND DESIST

441

ADDENDUM _____

This American medical ecological and economic history, a saga of Man, Money and Medicine or "textbook" of sorts, blossomed primarily for the benefit of my many dear students. I have taught and lectured on the subject of migratory medical ecolo-nomics for many years and have too often found myself digressing "off on a tangent", describing particularly interesting moments of historical trivia. This obviously over-opinionated book is an attempt to bring some overall order to my lecture series and deliver to my students the essentials of the course curriculum (this also allows me an excuse to continue to be verbose and freely lecture on interesting sidelights to the actual historical events).

Now, some small tasty bits of advice just for my students:

Other readers of this book need burden their tired orbits no further to the pain of physical strain from eyeballs jumping across what might seem to be a haphazard set of reasoning ocular saccades up and down these pages. I thank you sincerely for the opportunity and pleasure you have afforded me by your reading, and I will forever wonder and muse if you were adequately amused, maddened or just confused.

For those other of you, my dear students who have struggled through this text as a class requirement, the party is not quite over. My lecture courses in migratory medical ecolo-nomics (Man, Money and Medicine) also requires that you, my dear students, give an individual seminar as part (really just about all) of your final grade. That great fun and interesting adventure is the wonderful and exciting challenge that still lies ahead. Therefore, I am compelled to now advise you concerning what I consider to be the necessary mechanics for a good presentation:

First and foremost, don't worry, be happy! Your presentation seminar is a celebration, not a crucifixion. Please, please, please don't speak with a Wimpy-whiny-crying voice -- you were not spanked or punished; my course was an elective choice, and you could have at any time dropped it from your curriculum. So please don't let a cry-baby voice torture me and your fellow students during your seminar presentation. Strange but true -- Perception, perception, perception. How you say things is truly more important than what you actually say! A smile increases face value. When you smile, yes, just like in the good old song, everyone in the seminar smiles with you.

When you get tired of smiling, consciously push your lazy-crazy facial cheeks way back and smile some more. Smile until it hurts, then keep on smiling even if and when it really, really hurts. Enthusiastically, look directly at your audience and don't roll your eyes – non-verbal communication always out-shouts/trumps whatever harmonic your vocal cords happen to be expressing. Don't ever let your audience catch you primping at your clothes or standing in the forbidden crossed-arms to shoulders position. The words that actually come out of your mouth should be spoken in a non-threatening and in an anticipatory excited tone.

What ever happened to dear old ancient Ardi, the once supposed hominoid "missing link"? Don't let that happen to you! Prove that you are more than a simple ape, more than just a hominoid and more than just a member of a "cave bear clan". Do all that is necessary to show, tell and prove your unique sapient complexity and independent 60-thousand-year-old cognitive reasoning -- flaunt your humanity:
Be a biped; get up on your own two feet.
Be an inventor; use complex computer tools in discovered and novel ways.
Be master of the sacred firelight; project Power Point and videos on the wall.
Be a speaker of symbolic thought; present your creative, interpretive seminar with artful body language as well as spoken language linked to persuasive and imaginative illustrations, graphs and charts.

Anthropologists cannot resist acting as or pretending to be futurists. We all start life no smarter than the first Cro-Magnon did. We entered the technological age without a lick of improvement in human physiology or intellectual brain function. We live in the time of the greatest ice melt. Don't get caught napping, because in just a few missing eye-blinks you might get swept away by a turbulent torrent in a flash flood!

Act energetic, even if you are dog-tired, exhausted from pulling an all-nighter in preparation for your seminar. If you walk around with your head down, your misdirected and mumbled words of wisdom will not be believed. You are giving a live presentation, so act alive, not dead or dying. Come alive; stay alive. Don't act like Punxsutawney Phil predicting a bad winter! Respect and enjoy the honor and privilege of having a captive audience. A line drawn from your chin along the bottom of your jaw should always be parallel with the floor.

Carved in Pavonazzo marble and located at the far end of the portico of "Santa Maria in Cosmedin", *La Bocca della Verità* displays a huge Man's face and wide opened mouth. Myth has it that if the truth is not spoken while one's hand is placed in the aforementioned mouth, then the hand cannot be withdrawn. You must convince your audience that you have one hand placed in that ancient mouth. If you keep your head up and speak with enthusiastic authority, you will be believable even if what you are saying makes no sense at all -- just say it with conviction!

I will have totally and unquestionably failed as your teacher in presenting my course, "Man, Money and Medicine", to you if you do not by now realize that perception, not fact, had the major influence in altering the political dynamics of healthcare delivery through the migratory economics of **Healthcare Reform** during the 20th and 21st Centuries. Please, pretty please, remember these following things in order of decreasing importance when making your verbal presentation:
First – vocal intonation, then -- posture and body language, next -- facial expression, and finally -- the least important 10% of your overall perception (and what you stayed up practicing all night) is the actual language. But by all means do practice, practice, practice – for only perfect practice makes a perfect presentation.

You and only you, vivacious, live, in the limelight and on-stage, can get my seminar course credit – So......

Try to look good. Avoid distracting clothing and jewelry. Freshly pressed ordinary pants and/or dresses combined with well-combed hair (if you still have some) are all you really need. Suits still rule the world! Intuitive sign language is essential. When using your hands for expression, keep them at shoulder height so that the audience will concentrate on your face. When in doubt about what to do with one free hand, place it in a pant pocket or jacket pocket (J.F.K. style). If standing in front of a classroom, the needed personal space for a seminar is about ten feet. Perhaps you may have thought about totally avoiding your stand-alone personal appearance at the seminar by hiding in the background and playing a movie. A charismatic and well-trained actor scripted in Quick Time video may make a better presentation, but that gig will not get you any of my course credit.

Arrive well ahead of time and try to sound enthusiastic and exciting. The passive voice promotes a perception of objectivity and truth, but the rhyme dulls the senses. Don't use it -- don't put your audience to sleep. (Remember how sleepy you felt reading my text!) Think of your seminar presentation as your penultimate sales pitch. The best grade is given to the presentation that sells for the highest price. A good salesperson has first to sell herself or himself (alas it is sooo boring to be politically correct). A video or live substitute presenter does not sell you to the seminar audience. You just went through a whole lot of work to get this seminar together and you owe it first and foremost to your own nasty self to sell it -- the fruit of your labor -- for the highest price possible.

Develop within yourself a fire of determination to keep on trying. Make it absolutely impossible for you "not to try and let the world go sailing by". (He/she who sings the song of the Hobbit is doomed to dance to the dirge of Tolkien's Orc.)

The beauty of your seminar presentation lies not in its logical conclusion, but rather in its orderly, rational and serene process that can only yield to a painfully obvious natural conclusion while opening visionary doors for further investigation. It is the process that makes the good cheese. It is not where you get to, but rather how you get there that counts. In the simple words of the Three Stooges, "wherever you go, there you are". Semper ubi sub ubi. There are, alias, also the contrasting immortal words of Dirty Harry, "ya gotta know ya lima tations". However, there are some few and inspiring techniques that are quite helpful and can be easily and effectively mastered by all my students with just a bit of that old perfect practice:

THERE ONCE WERE NINE MUSES.....

1. Win over your audience! Don't be too professorial because nobody cares about an egghead; don't put on airs and become an annoying, arrogant, impertinent snot. Remember that they, the seminar students, are **your** audience; treat them with loving care as you would with any of your prized possessions. Remove tension and anxiety between you and your audience by revealing a personal flaw. Everyone cannot be a successful comedian, but anyone can utilize a simple opening line such as, "I'm afraid that this will be more of a learning experience for me than you." Such an implanted suggestion or thought will put your audience at ease and gain you sympathy at the same time. Perception, perception, perception, yes, and now add a little perfect practice. Having won over the audience, psychological transference makes you into a contemporary

harmless friend. Your words then, and only then, also become at once accepted, interesting and thought provoking.

2. Putting evidence versus eminence aside, let us not forget the law of parsimoney, otherwise referred to as Oakham's Razor, where selection of a theory containing fewer assomptions usually wins, so in simpler termis, KISS! -- Keep It Simple Stupid! Be sure to prepare: slides with simple background colors like blue and simple script colors like yellow, white and an occasional startling red with one-liner animations, seven-second max on video inserts, and mostly three (up to seven) lines of type max per slide. Talk, point, then cover, and you won't have to run to take cover! Allow your audience to view only brief glimpses of a screen, blackboard, mounted paper pad, or whatever teaching aid you might employ. You are quickly and insidiously training them to look and concentrate predominately on only you, just you and you alone.

3. Don't let your inanimate slides or demos upstage you! It is difficult to follow a dog and pony act. Compelling, attention grabbing slides or demos may not always be in your best interest. Keep the spotlight on yourself at all times and don't allow your audience to consider looking at anything else. Your slides are there to help you and only you. They are not there for the audience to independently read and contemplate. If you want the audience to think about some printed matter, then give them a printout after you are finished with the presentation. Tell them in advance to turn off and put away all electronic and manual pens, pencils, portables, phones and pads. Let them know in advance that copies of your original musical score will be available at the end of your gig. All your charts and graphs should demonstrate an immediate point. If a more detailed analysis of a chart is necessary, then the main chart should be broken down into several smaller ones to demonstrate those finer points. If the audience perceives a need to examine any slide with more than a glance, then too much time is being spent away from the most important subject, which happens to be you. You are the presenter and the presentation merged and morphed into one live body.

4. Serenade the individual while singing to your audience! Draw eye contact from individuals in the seminar audience with your own direct eye contact while you speak. Switch to a different individual in a different section of the seminar room with each new thought or concept. Keep jumping around in a random manner while being sure to cover all

446

corners and sections of the room. Keep each and every individual in your audience continually guessing in anticipation as to when your eye contact will return their way. Enjoy playing this on-going game of eye contact with your seminar audience, and constantly rate your own effectiveness as you are giving your presentation. This game is a bit more difficult than walking and chewing gum, but once you start to play, you will rapidly become a totally addicted player. If you are fortunate enough to further present your paper to an audience larger than my student seminar, then serenade specific groups or sections in that audience as your eyes enthusiastically jump about an auditorium with each new point. Beam your eye contact to every section. Nobody likes to be left out, and each section will secretly yearn to compete with the remaining sections for the return of your glance.

5. Don't heckle the heckler! The tricky tactic of returning a disparaging remark is reserved for a very few name-recognized professionals. Nobody likes a jerk and everybody has sympathy for the underdog. Even though it is not logical, neutrality equates with credibility. Again, perception is king, and the easier tricky tactic is to make the heckler the obnoxious bad guy jerk and you the poor innocent victim. You will then gain power through general audience empathy, if not sympathy for victims' rights!

6. Tell 'em, tell 'em, and then tell 'em again! State what you are about to say. Say it. State what you just said. Just let everything flow in a logical order, and do not be afraid of being redundant. The goal, purpose or objective of your presentation must always and continuously remain crystal clear and concise in the actively engaging mindset of your magically attentive audience. Remember always that you are the magician doing the mesmerizing. If your audience can remember one new thing that you said one month later, then your presentation was excellent. If your audience can remember three new things that you said one month later, then your presentation was outstandingly superb. It sometimes helps to organize your presentation with a central outline of three or four points that you can refer back to by way of a repeating slide or something fancy like the "Prezi" software program.

7. Location, location, location! When seated at the large conference table in my classroom for group rebuttal, your personal space measures about three feet. Please do not ever sit next to your old professor. He does like

your presence, but he is actually there to help you and act as a facilitator in the process. If you sit next to him, you may lose the attention of the students at the other end of the table. If you sit apart from him, then you and he can more successfully stare down extraneous conversations and keep all attention pointed at the star performer for the day -- and, of course, that person is you and only you.

8. Make a true friend! Keep your audience as your friend after the presentation is finished. Thank everyone for the pleasure of their company during your presentation. Be empathetic. Offer your future time for added questions or discussion. If you are sincere and respectful, true empathy will be graciously returned to you in so many multiple fold. That is an important part of the great blessing bestowed upon a successful teacher.

9. Be yourself! This last and final point is the most important of all. My ultimate purpose in teaching this course is to give you a framework to independently think and reason freely so that you can determine for yourself the pros and the cons, ecological and economic, pertaining to future migratory economics of organized healthcare delivery systems and **Healthcare Reform** – what Man has done and is likely to do with his Money for Medicine. This stated purpose is especially important to me because I see and relish you, my dear students, as the creators of our American future. I do not want your seminar presentation to be a parroting back of my own particular views and prejudices. I expect you to arrive at your own individual conclusions. Don't pull your punches. If you have a radically different point of view, feel free to express it; and be prepared to defend a strong rebuttal. You cannot have possibly taken any part of my course without immediately realizing that there are very few things in life that I enjoy more than a good, sound, factual, and heated argument.

Don't be scared away or put down by the ostensibly false pontifical aura of this professor. Please, fearlessly push forward and pursue your opposing points of view contrary to his expressed opinions; he is constructed of crocodile-thick skin and is an ardent disciple of Socrates. When he starts getting off, way off on some historical event, please be kind, because his prejudices most likely arise from the fact that this old man has most probably been there and actually done that. He values questions way more than ephemeral answers. He views political progress as an oxymoron resulting from migratory ecolo-nomic forces. Those who are kind refer to him as idiosyncratic; those who are unkind seek a sterner vocabulary. When listening to his lectures or reading one of his books, prepare yourself to laugh, cry, shout and swear, sometimes all at once. He believes that, as first stated by Leonardo, it is a poor apprentice that cannot surpass his (or her) master. When openly affronted or confronted by vehemently expressed opposing philosophies, he loves to experience a secret inner joy and sense of pleasure put forth by their exciting challenges, and is thus gratefully inspired to delve deeper into the opposing psyche by throwing down his own gauntlet. Briefly put, he just loves to argue. But above all else, he truly, truly admires each and every one of his dear students (especially those ardent debaters, those with whom he ostensibly picks on during and outside of seminar class and those with whom he vociferously disagrees with the most).

Switching my writer's tone back now to the more personal, sincere and honest first person, I take great personal pride in developing independently thinking students; I am forever so deeply honored and humbly privileged for being blessed with this unique teaching opportunity during my lifetime: a chance to help accomplish part of an amazing developmental spirit in youthful and eager American minds for the glorious future of our beloved USA. So go guys, go on, get to it and do it better and better each time again and again. You guys,…..you guys,……...you, ….. you make me feel so proud!

A generations-old traveling fellowship to England, France, Switzerland and Italy inspired Dr. DiLibero into investigate migratory medical ecolo-nomic mechanisms – Mans manipulation of Money for Medicine. Extensive personal experience with worldwide systems plus national and international lectures on varied migratory ecolo-nomic healthcare topics formed the basis for this book. As an educator, three years in a row USC's emergency medicine residency program awarded him "best teacher of the year". He rendered services to the Los Angeles County in-home indigent care program while a resident physician, then further served the healthcare needs of the underserved by becoming Director and CEO of the South Los Angeles Collaborative - Health Care Safety Net, which led to his appointment as Medical Director for Cope Health Solution MSO, and his overseeing of 23 safety-net community clinics in Los Angeles County, coordinating their programs with USC County Hospital through the LA County Board of Supervisors. He has served and held office for several State, Federal and private healthcare posts:
Orthopaedic Staff Surgeon -- VA Northern California Health Care System
Senior Medical Consultant – California Medicaid (Medi-Cal)
DHCS –Dept. Health Care Services, California Benefit Division Branch Chief
CMB -- California Medical Board, Examination Commissioner
EMS -- Emergency Medical Servises Commission, LA County
IMQ-JCAHO -- Hospital Surveyor -- California Medical Association (CMA)
HSA -- Health Service Agency, Kaiser Hospital Los Angeles Representative
KFHP -- Hawaii Kaiser -- Orthopaedic physician recruitment chair – 1983
AAOS -- American Academy of Orthopaedic Surgeons, fellow
AAOS – National lobbyist, California trauma representative, and book editor
AAOS -- EMS representative to the DOT for Paramedic National Standards
LACMA -- delegate to the CMA & CMA delegate to the AMA
COA & CMA -- Occupational Health and Workers' Compensation Committees
DWC -- California Workers' Compensation Examination, Lecture/Instructor
SAEM -- Society for Academic Emergency Medicine, Assoc. Prof. USC 1972 – 2000
STOREP – Association for the History of Political Economics
CEO – SLAC-HCSN -- South LA Collaborative – HealthCare Safety Net
CEO – PVC Secret Software
CEO – LAFMC-TPA – The Los Angeles Foundation for Medical Care
Board of Directors – M.E.D.I.C.S. – Emergency Disaster Mobile Response, CA
Board of Directors – COA -- California Orthopaedic Association
Board of Directors – SEPA -- State Employed Physicians Assiciation
Board of Directors – UAPD -- Union of American Physicians and Dentists
President -- IAMA – Italian American Medical Association, Los Angeles
President -- USC Orthopaedic Alumni Association
President -- Beverly Hills PRO-PSRO
President --LACMA LA metropolitan district 2002-2005
President -- Los Angeles County Medical Association (LACMA #135) -- 2006
BOOKS:
MEDICAL ECOLO-NOMICS, 2001, TXu   981-118
HEALTHKEEPERS, 2002, TXu   1-054-120
THE BUSINESS OF MEDICINE, 2007, 978-0-9815969-3-8
THE QUALITY OF MEDICINE, 2008, 978-0-9815969-4-5
ORGANIZED HEALTHCARE DELIVERY, 2009, 978-0-9815969-5-2